The Surprising Reality of Human Existence

New Research Insights into Mysteries of Life, Death and Ultimate Meaning

EUGENE BELL-GAM

THINKERS
HOUSE

First published in Great Britain in 2022 by
Thinkers House, London, England

A catalogue record of this publication is available at the British Library

ISBN Paperback: 978-1-8384765-1-9

Cover design from an illustration by Gerd Altmann

TABLE OF CONTENTS

SECTION B: ABOUT LIFE & DEATH

Dedication

To my dear wife Sylvia and family
For your unstinting love, support and patience
over the more than a decade it has taken to complete this work.

Preface

Two of the most profound events one can witness are a new-born baby inhaling its first breath, and a dying person exhaling their last breath as they depart this mortal domain. However, it remains a complete mystery just how consciousness arises at the dawn of life or how it ceases at death. Not only are we still in the dark about the essence of life, new research is revealing that states of 'living' and 'non-living' are not as clearly defined as we thought.

Panpsychists have long argued that the entire universe (animate and inanimate) throbs with intangible consciousness that stems from a fundamental mind. According to this view, nothing ever truly 'dies'; constituent matter is merely reorganised in new formats and the flow of universal consciousness continues unabated. Hence, techno-futurists and transhumanists are seriously researching concepts like 'mind uploading' in the hope of extending existence beyond our biological lifespan. But is human immortality a feasible idea? If so, in what form and where does all this leave long-held ideas about a soul?

In this book, I show in lay terms how information from scientific research is opening the door to a new understanding of life and death as complementary transitions of virtual realities that arise from highly complex metaprogramming by an unknown superintelligence. I also review the growing evidence in astrophysics that everything we perceive exists within a sophisticated cosmic bubble that can only be fully comprehended by an *external* observer – a development that is radically changing traditional definitions of God.

Remarkable advances in medical science since the middle of the 20th century have dramatically increased life expectancy. Unlike past generations, we now enjoy levels of longevity that have made it possible to live in 'denial' of death: when the inevitable occurs, we express surprise and consternation.

However, persistent global vulnerability to diseases like Ebola and COVID-19, and growing fears that a human-induced sixth extinction event may well be underway, are forcing us to confront the reality of our fragile and uncertain existence. Traumatised by human inability to control our own fate, many have been plunged into dark despair and are questioning the value of life. But surveys show that, despite disenchantment with organised religion, the new existential crisis is actually *reviving* personal spirituality: more people have been searching online for ways to connect with a supernatural God for solace and relief. This work offers a fresh perspective on these contradictions that I hope will contribute to strategies for coping with bereavement, grief, and increasing angst about life.

American historian and philosopher William J. Durant quipped in 1965 that *"Education is a progressive discovery of our own ignorance."* Indeed, intellectually honest scholars of all shades accept that we still know next to nothing for certain; plenty of room exists for new ideas. Humanity urgently needs critical thinking on the true meaning of life beyond the illusory vanities that dominate our brief, mortal existence.

Digital technologies and social media have changed the way information is garnered, accessed and disseminated. In recognition of this trend, references in the e-book version of this work are, wherever possible, hyperlinked to online material. The numerous cited sources are again listed at the end, so print versions also offer scope for further exploration of topics. Verbatim quotations are shown in italics (words already italicised in source material are underlined for emphasis). I hope the layout and organisation will allow for seamless reading. Welcome to my knowledge odyssey!

Middlesex, England, July 2022

Introduction

"I have no doubt that in reality the future will be vastly more surprising than anything I can imagine. Now my own suspicion is that the Universe is not only queerer than we suppose, but queerer than we can suppose."
J. B. S. Haldane, scientist, in *Possible Worlds and Other Papers* (1927)

Apocalyptic game-changer

Pandemics have always been[1a] a catalyst for dramatic shifts in worldviews and huge social transformations. Yale University historian Frank M. Snowden's acclaimed 2019 book *Epidemics and Society: From the Black Death to the Present* described the wide-ranging changes ushered in by past global outbreaks. However, as sociologist Peter Rose discussed in a July 2020 review,[1b] even Snowden's timely work did not foresee the extraordinary upheavals and scale of death that would be wreaked by a new coronavirus (SARS-CoV-2) which spread rapidly across the world in early 2020. The World Health Organization (WHO) named the associated disease 'COVID-19' and declared[2] the outbreak a global pandemic on 11 March 2020.

A piece of biological code

COVID-19 has reminded us of the precariousness of human existence and exposed the depth of our ignorance of life mechanisms at fundamental level. Public figures and media outlets initially mislabelled SARS-CoV-2 as a bacteria-like 'organism' or 'microbe'. However, the virus is actually a protein-encased fragment of *the same* nucleobase sequences that encode genes for life. Most people are aware that we all have unique genetic information stored in a DNA (deoxyribonucleic acid) database within each cell nucleus. But, until recently, few outside the biological sciences had heard of the RNA (ribonucleic acid) transcripts[3a] from genes that actually drive life[3b].

1

Indeed, until exciting news about fast-tracked mRNA vaccines[4a] to combat COVID-19 started circulating[4b] in mass media, the general public was blissfully unaware that each of the estimated 100 trillion diverse cells[5] which make up our bodies is an extremely busy nanofactory that functions continuously to keep us alive. The mRNA (*messenger RNA*) transcripts cells copy naturally from DNA carry 3-letter codons that specify which amino acids a myriad of nano-actors should use to manufacture *thousands* of molecular protein machines for various biological functions. Synthetic mRNA seeks to induce protein production artificially for boosted immune protection.

Viruses are viewed by some scientists as 'non-living' because they can only survive and replicate in a living cell. The astonishing thing is how these bits of otherwise inert biological code manage to infiltrate and disrupt cellular hosts in much the same way 'Trojan horse' computer viruses are programmed to sneak into digital devices to spy on users or just wreak havoc. SARS-CoV-2, in particular, is unlike any pathogen (infectious agent) that medical scientists have encountered in modern times. A study[6a] by a multidisciplinary team at Icahn School of Medicine, Mount Sinai, New York, found[6b] that, after breaching cells, the virus somehow manages to mute the defence process that activates our immune system. Normally, a viral intrusion instantly triggers transcription of genes in DNA into mRNA coded strips for speedy production of interferons – versatile protein sentinels that raise the alarm so uninfected cells can take precautions. However, the extraordinary stealth of SARS-CoV-2, combined with a period of dormancy[7] in asymptomatic seemingly healthy carriers, makes early detection[8] of infection and isolation of patients almost impossible.[9] Hence, authorities were forced to implement expensive rolling tests and enforce unprecedented 'social distancing' plus quarantine 'lockdowns' of entire populations until they acquire so-called 'herd immunity'.[10a,b]

Tsunami of grief

Tragically, due to the high risk of SARS-CoV-2 infection, relatives and friends were also denied the opportunity to visit suffering patients or interact with corpses of victims. Inability to be with[11] stricken loved ones in hospitals and care homes as they pass away; suspension[12] of the funeral rites that humans have cultivated over thousands of years; and enforced post-burial isolation[13] have created what psychiatrist Yalda Safai described[14] as *"prolonged grief disorder".*

Psychologists Yusen Zhai and Xue Du from Pennsylvania State University also warned in a July 2020 journal article[15] of serious *secondary* impacts of pandemic-related loss and grief, including[16] socio-economic, physical and mental health issues for individuals and communities. According to a 'bereavement multiplier' indicator published[17] the same month by a team of American and Canadian sociologists, each death from COVID-19 in the USA impacts[18] approximately nine close kin; a desperate situation that the authors forecast is primed to unleash[19] a 'tsunami of grief'.

In recognition of the huge toll of sudden and unexpected bereavement within communities, a collaboration of American professionals in social work and palliative medicine has issued practice guidelines[20] to assist care providers dealing with affected families. Mental health specialists are also actively exploring[21] possible benefits[22] of spirituality and religiosity as part of coping strategies.[23]

However, it's becoming clear that something other than traditional approaches will be needed to overcome the continuing and spreading psychological stresses. Such is the fallout from this still-mutating coronavirus that meaning and purpose in life may never return for millions of anguished sufferers without a radical change in the way we view personhood[24] and life-death transitions.

3

Reassessing values

The COVID-19 pandemic is also forcing us to reassess what we really value in life. Almost overnight, our relentless pursuit of material wealth to feed an ever-growing global consumerist economy has been superseded by fear of possibly fatal infection by an invisible agent. Like the notorious highway robbers who terrorised road travellers in parts of Europe with 'Your money or your life' stick-ups from the 17th to 19th centuries, the virus has challenged[25] authorities and citizens everywhere to make agonising choices between 'economy first' business-as-usual responses that risk higher infection and death rates, or 'people first' quarantine lockdowns that may reduce transmission rates and fatalities but also cause lasting economic and societal damage. Such has been the sense of anxiety and dread that, according to a March 2020 report[26] in *The Guardian*, former British Prime Minister Gordon Brown called for a temporary form of unified global government with executive powers to tackle the crisis.

As 2021 dawned, it became clear that, despite the scramble to vaccinate populations, the new disease is likely here to stay[27]; lifestyle changes induced by the threat may become permanent. Researchers around the world are frantically modelling[28] possible future impacts, but there are so many unknowns that it's hard to make projections which policymakers can rely on for mitigation planning. We have truly entered a post-everything era in which virtually nothing[29] can be predicted with any certainty.

Nevertheless, some commentators espy a silver lining amidst all the havoc and angst. In an uplifting and thought-provoking article[30], Canadian anthropologist and cognitive scientist Samuel Veissière listed five positive behavioural developments that are already evident in societies across the world.

We are, Veissière noted, no longer inattentive to what matters; global cooperation is spreading on an unprecedented scale; our sense of altruism has expanded beyond relatives and nationalities; humans have been forced to drastically scale back the frantic pace of modern living; and we are finding new meaning as we reconnect with loved ones and the most vulnerable in our communities. He reflected: *"In remembering that our lives are intrinsically connected, and in taking note of the fragility of the world we took for granted, we are also reminded of how precious we are to one another."*

Norman Lewis, an innovation and technology consultant in the UK, also expressed confidence in an April 2020 essay[31] that the unique gift of human intelligence, which has ensured our survival for millennia, will help us develop new thinking to overcome the traumatic experiences of COVID-19. Lewis wrote stirringly:

"The pandemic has shown that existing knowledge is never enough to deal with the unexpected and the unknown. The expertise we have today, the knowledge we have accumulated and preserved in books, journals and libraries, as well as the technologies we have at our fingertips, can only take us so far. [....]

"Covid-19 must be a turning point. Inspiring a new generation to take up the struggle would preserve one of humanity's greatest legacies — it would breathe new life into the quest for knowledge, ensuring this will be preserved and furthered for generations to come. Above all else, it would reaffirm the authority of human reason and its foundational role in the problem-solving we will need in the future."

The big question then, as the 21st century continues to unfold with great uncertainty, is the extent to which we can continue to have secular confidence that humans have capacity to fully decipher the information programming behind life and shape our own destiny.

What can we know?

Throughout history, every culture has found it necessary to invoke the supernatural to explain our inability to influence fate or control the passage of time. Traditional religious accounts of a spiritual afterlife reflect our refusal to accept the transient and arbitrary nature of life, and finality of death. Although belief in a personal God has declined in Western societies since the 20th century, death denial has persisted: surely, there must be something more to our complex existence?

As far as we know, we're the only extant species that's capable of higher-level cognition. For some mysterious reason, we alone have the capacity to indulge in introspection and contemplation of life, as well as to discuss and create historical records of ideas and findings that successive generations can digest and build on. According to neuroscientists, we appear to be mentally tuned to 'thirst for knowledge'.[32] It's now known that human brains come equipped[33] with a basic, foundational algorithm for the sophisticated mental computations that give us[34] unique intelligence. Thus, we're able to investigate and reach conclusions about the universe and earthly biosphere that sustains us – even though we're part and parcel of the same environment.

However, as influential philosopher of science Sir Karl Popper argued[35] in 1959, we can never have absolute certainty about anything: what we observe in the natural world is liable to change over time, so all we can do is to keep re-evaluating our knowledge base as new evidence comes to light. Significantly, despite the immense amount of information that has emerged about our natural world since the 19th century, we still lack answers to what science writer Gregg Easterbrook called[36] 'really, really big questions' in 2011. Physics, which investigates the origin of matter and natural laws, is riddled with unsolved problems and seems to have hit a dead-end.[37]

Theorists have discovered that at least[38] 26 dimensionless and universal physical constants of unknown origin needed to be in place for *anything at all* to come into existence. The universe is evidently fine-tuned to accommodate life of equally unclear origin. The source of consciousness and highly specific, [39a] fundamentally restricted[39b] biological coding remains very much an enduring mystery[40].

Intriguingly, findings are showing[41] that nothing may 'exist' in the sense we use to describe things in everyday life. Indications are that the physical world we perceive (including our mortal bodies) arises from an invisible quantum dimension by means of[42] abstract mathematics that we've barely begun to comprehend. Can we ever attain full knowledge of this deeper reality? Science has allowed fleeting peeks behind the veil, but so far the true meaning of it all continues to elude us.

Colin McGinn, a philosophy of mind specialist, discussed the limits of human understanding in a 1994 article.[43a] McGinn argued[43b] that we will never be able to resolve existential questions unless we somehow manage to achieve what he termed *"cognitive transcendence"* to a much higher intelligence level. Nevertheless, Australian colleague David Chalmers expressed[44a] new optimism[44b] twenty years later that increasing convergence on answers within mathematics and the natural sciences gives hope that we may yet achieve major breakthroughs; superhuman transformations may not be required. Whatever lies ahead in our knowledge odyssey, the truth about our existence is sure to differ greatly from current assumptions as J. B. S. Haldane memorably commented in 1927.

How can we tell what is real?

To a layperson, questioning the reality of our 'flesh and blood' existence might seem odd and foolish. Are our senses and emotions not enough to distinguish reality from unreality? However, philosophers have been debating this topic for thousands of years.

7

Issues arising offer a fascinating insight into the roots of current speculation that everything we perceive may be just a simulated reality projected from the edge of the universe. For some scholars, only objects, events and phenomena that are physically observable or measurable are considered 'real'. Materialists, in particular, contend that true reality arises solely from detectable matter and energy: they reject any claims of 'unnatural' or 'supernatural' experiences. But the 20th century discovery that the matter which gives us 'stuff' is actually a strange association of invisible subatomic particles with unpredictable properties has made it difficult to define reality *purely* in physical terms[45]. Also, can we credibly say mental constructs like thoughts and mathematics are 'unreal' simply because they lack material form?

Problem of thoughts

French philosopher René Descartes (1596 - 1650) famously declared that *Cogito ergo sum* (Latin for 'I think, therefore I am'). He reasoned that the very fact we have enough awareness to indulge in cognitive doubt about our existence proves we're real beings with functioning minds. The trouble is, our personal thoughts are inaccessible by others – these highly subjective inner mind processes lack the universality we ascribe to objective reality. As 16th century English playwright William Shakespeare observed: *"There's no art to find the mind's construction in the face"* (Macbeth 1:4, 15).

Descartes also noted that we can only speak for our own minds since we don't have insight into the thinking of other people and can't even say if other minds exist or there's only one, shared universal mind that we all tune into. This view goes back to ancient Greek tutor Gorgias (c. 485 – 380 BCE) who argued that universal consensus on knowledge and reality might be impossible, as we can't be sure of anything other than our own perceptions.

A modern variation of the Gorgias-Descartes solipsistic argument is that we see and interpret the world through *different* 'reality tunnels'; a phrase coined by American psychologist Timothy Leary who is notorious for extensive research and promotion of psychedelic drugs in the 1960s and 1970s. Of course, humans are prone to illusions, hallucinations, and delusions. But all societies have developed a 'consensus reality' on what is rational and legitimate.

Despite these difficulties, it's undeniable that ideas forged in minds past and present are the inspirations for inventions and technologies that have enabled humans to build advanced societies. Thus, even though only an individual is privy to their thoughts, it's reasonable to argue that these inner human products are just as 'real' as the outward manifestations everyone can see and experience.

Problem of abstractions

Another issue is the status of descriptive properties (shapes, colours, sizes, quantities etc.) and other factors like geometric figures and numbers. These concepts, collectively labelled 'universals', are neither 'things' nor 'phenomena' in the accepted sense. Nevertheless, they are very much part of the mental tools we use to make sense of the world. Some metaphysicians even argue that universals are independent objects with self-identity. However, others deny that universals 'exist' as such – they say these entities are just nominal symbols without the concrete particulars associated with physical forms. But there's agreement that numbers may be 'abstract objects'.

Ancient Greek philosopher Plato (c. 427 – 347 BCE), in particular, strongly believed universals are perfect, unchanging, eternal and essential 'forms' that exist objectively *outside* human mnds. However, despite this 'realism', we only perceive universals as abstractions that help inform our thoughts and enterprises.

9

According to Plato, everything we behold in our physical world is an imperfect copy of such timeless forms[46a] or *ideals* in an invisible realm – just as prisoners chained in a dark cave from birth would only ever experience the projected shadows of out-of-sight objects. In other words, we inhabit a false reality. This early proposal is uncannily similar to modern scientific arguments[46b] for a holographic universe inhabited by simulated beings.

Plato's pupil Aristotle (c. 384 – 322 BCE) agreed that universals are real entities, but he counter-argued that they co-exist *inside* our world with the things they describe. He reasoned that we only perceive matter meaningfully when it acquires substantial form – another prescient idea that was adopted nearly 2,300 years later by quantum physicists struggling to explain[46c] how material things manifest 'magically' from numerical matrices in an invisible realm.

Nonetheless, medieval friar William of Ockham – the 14th century English theophilosopher famous for the principle of simplicity now known as 'Occam's razor' – disagreed with both Plato and Aristotle that universals have substance and independent existence. Ockham insisted that all the problems[47] associated with imagined location of these symbolic perceptions in other realms can be solved by simply accepting that they stem from the mind of a transcendent God. But he cautioned that such matters can't be resolved by human inquiry and must be left to blind faith.

All in the mind?

In the early 1700s, Irish theophilosopher Bishop George Berkeley took things further with a treatise[48] that claimed everything we perceive (whether physical objects, phenomena or universals) is an illusion *constructed* by the mind. Unsurprisingly, contemporaries dismissed the radical proposal because it was so disquieting and contrary to everyday intuition.

However, by the 19th and early 20th centuries, Berkeley's so-called 'idealism' had become the mainstream position within Western philosophy. Some idealists argue that conscious reality is the product of individual minds. Others believe there's just a singular, universal, pre-existing mind. Interestingly, several Eastern philosophies share the view that consciousness stems from an immaterial mind or spirit which likely spans multiple planes or dimensions.

The case for a fully mind-projected reality received unexpected scientific support in the mid-1920s when theoretical physicists Niels Bohr and Werner Heisenberg showed[49] it was the best explanation for the weird relationships between light and subatomic matter that quantum mechanics (QM) had revealed.[50] Albert Einstein had helped[51] to develop the new physics, but he was so stunned by the profound significance for our understanding of 'being' and 'existence' that he refused[52a] to accept[52b] such a nebulous view of reality. Einstein argued[53] for the rest of his life that the 'Copenhagen interpretation' championed by Bohr and Heisenberg was incomplete because, as he famously put it in a letter to colleague Max Born in 1926: *"I am, at all events, convinced that He [God] does not play dice."*

Einstein's incredulity is understandable. How could human minds be 'projecting' the everyday reality we observe? He scoffed[54] this was like saying the moon only exists when we look at and asked[55] sarcastically if the mind of a humble mouse can also create physical reality. But, bizarre as it sounds, this tenet of QM has been validated[56] in several experiments and successfully applied[57] in groundbreaking technology.

The problem for 'realists' like Einstein is that science is a 'nuts and bolts' naturalistic tool developed by humans to study things that can be physically detected; it can't investigate immaterial minds.

11

If, indeed, we project our own reality, then the question arises whether visualisations and experiences are ongoing brain productions in real time from the quantum matrix[58]; a transmitted broadcast from elsewhere; or a downloaded copy from a pre-existing reality. But exactly how is this happening, and who or what is orchestrating our perceptions? What happens to these 'movies' of rich life experiences when we die? Do they just vanish into nothingness, or are they stored in another dimension for reruns in our world or some other domain?

New perspectives

Continued confusion about the meaning and implications of the fundamental phenomena behind our reality – which still defies description[59] in any language other than sophisticated mathematics – has made it difficult for scientists and philosophers to agree on the precise nature of our existence, and just where to draw the boundary between living and non-living. American astrophysicist Adam Becker fretted[60] about the lack of progress in his 2018 book *What Is Real?* He questioned in a related interview[61] why, 100 years after theorists revealed the stunning events occurring at invisible quantum level (a feat he described as *"the most successful theory in all of science"*), physicists still lack[62] a rational explanation in terms of our visible world and everyday experiences.

Physicists have established[63] that virtual matter particles flit in and out of existence in random quantum fluctuations, but no one knows how this puzzling activity interacts with 'mind' to produce our reality and conscious experience. The possibility of extra hidden dimensions (up to eleven[64a] have been proposed[64b]), and an ever-inflating multiverse of endless universes with different laws, has deepened[65] the mystery. Andrei Linde suggested[66] at the 2007 meeting of the American Association for the Advancement of Science that our observable universe could be just a tiny part of a cosmic *"eternal feast where all possible dishes are served"*.

After a century of discord and failure, some scholars are concluding[67] that only metaphysical explanations may be possible. This admission radically alters traditional scientific thinking on what might lie beyond our mortal plane. Indeed, as cosmologist and astrobiologist Paul Davies observed in a 2003 commentary[68], a multiverse interpretation of reality means countless copies of humans could be existing at the same time (or in some unrecognisable 'afterlife' form) within multiple simulated worlds created at the whim of a non-human superintelligence. Davies pointed out in a related essay[69] that these extraordinary ideas are essentially the same as religious narratives that have been around for millennia. He wrote:

"Far from doing away with a transcendent Creator, the multiverse theory actually injects that very concept at almost every level of its logical structure. Gods and worlds, creators and creatures, lie embedded in each other, forming an infinite regress in unbounded space."

James Gleick explained in an enlightening review[70] of Becker's book that scientists, being human, can't avoid *"straying into a no-man's-land between philosophy and religion"* when they try to make sense of the weird occurrences in the quantum realm. However, regardless of worldview, the convergence of ideas on the nature of things is creating room for new understanding that brings fresh meaning to life; helps to reduce fear of death; and provides a plausible outlook for coping with grief at the sudden loss of loved ones.

It's now clear that everything – from the fabric of our universe to life processes in biological bodies – is founded on sets of very specific information that evolve according to natural laws of unknown origin; all within mathematical constraints. In subsequent chapters, I present the remarkable evidence that's emerging within science and mathematics for an 'unnatural' universe, and show why support is growing for the idea that it's all a gigantic holographic projection[71] simulated from without.

13

Of course, it's reasonable to ask why any advanced intelligence capable of generating such a wondrous creation would permit the immense suffering and evil we regularly witness and experience alongside delightful gifts of joy, love, friendship, music, laughter, art and much more. I discuss some philosophical and theological answers to this troubling paradox which lies at the centre of our existential puzzle.

SECTION A

About Existence

1. Out of Nothing

Now the earth was formless and empty, darkness was over the surface of the
deep, and the Spirit of God was hovering over the waters.
And God said, "Let there be light," and there was light.

Genesis 1:2-3

What is light?

The mysterious phenomena at subatomic level that Einstein found so troubling were discovered purely by accident. The nature of light, and the mechanisms that give us visual perception, had long been controversial and hotly debated. Ancient Greek philosopher Empedocles (c. 494 - 434 BCE) saw human eyes as special 'lanterns' powered by[72] a mysterious 'fire' that streamed light *outwards* to illuminate the things we see – a concept now called 'extramission'. But we can't see in the dark, so this 'fire in the eyes' explanation was obviously flawed. Plato then suggested[73] that vision involves three streams of light – one from the eyes, another from the thing being observed, and a third from a luminous body (sun, moon or an artificial source like a candle).

However, Democritus (c. 460 - c. 370 BCE) – famous for the earliest known atomic description of matter – was unconvinced. He believed all human senses arise from streams of *external* atoms received and shaped by the soul inside a living body. Accordingly, Democritus proposed that vision comes from thin layers of atoms or *eidola* that 'slough off' objects and 'waft' through the air to our eyes – an opposing concept now known as 'intromission'. The dispute laid the ground for 2,500 years of arguments[74] about light: is it a form of energy (like heat), or a material thing composed of physical atoms?

Aristotle was the first to speculate that visual perception might be arising from mental images constructed from incoming *information* by what he called the 'soul'; not from physical *eidola* copies of objects as suggested by Democritus. In Book II of his classic[75] *De Anima* (Latin for 'On The Soul') written c. 350 BCE, Aristotle concluded[76] that human vision is enabled by light that's *transmitted* to our eyes through intervening media like air and water. This view was confirmed over 1,300 years later when medieval Arab scholar Ibn al-Haytham (known in the West as Alhazen) published results from several experiments on light in his pioneering *Book of Optics*.

Wave perturbation or matter particle?

The next significant contribution came from René Descartes in *Traité du monde et de la lumière* (Treatise on the World and on Light) published between 1629-1633. Descartes asserted that light was an *emission* from luminous bodies that travels instantaneously as a 'wave impulse' across tiny 'corpuscles of matter' in intervening media. He summarised these views in *La dioptrique* (Optics); a 1637 essay that also outlined a new law of refraction. However, French priest and scientist Pierre Gassendi argued that light was an actual *physical stream* of matter corpuscles (particles); not the emergent wave perturbation across bulk media described by Descartes.

Three decades later, Sir Isaac Newton published results of experiments with prisms that showed[77] what we perceive as 'white' light is actually a composite of different colours. He argued in a 1672 presentation to the Royal Society that light could not possibly travel as waves because it does not bend around obstacles like sound (it gets reflected, refracted or absorbed). He expanded these arguments in his 1704 book *Opticks*. Newton's immense reputation ensured that the particle view of light prevailed for another 100 years until the early 19th century.

The controversy resurfaced in 1801 when British scientist Thomas Young displayed[78] strange light interference patterns at a Royal Society meeting. Young argued that the phenomenon was better explained by a *wave* concept of light (like overlapping sounds) than Newton's *particle* theory. He also suggested the colour streams observed by Newton were caused by different wavelengths of light; not independent streams of matter. However, despite the compelling evidence, Young's interpretation was rejected[79] for 15 years until French civil engineer and physicist Augustin-Jean Fresnel presented conclusive evidence at the *Académie des Sciences* in Paris that wave theory was the only possible explanation for both diffraction and interference light patterns.

In 1845, Michael Faraday, a self-taught English researcher and innovator, discovered that light and electromagnetism are related. Faraday also speculated that light might even propagate mysteriously in a vacuum *without* the need for any physical medium; an attribute that implies light existed in some domain *before* the universe (as we observe it) came into being. But contemporaries were sceptical[80a] – perhaps because Faraday lacked a formal education in science and was known[80b] to have strong religious convictions. However, sure enough, 20 years later Scottish physicist James Clerk Maxwell deduced[81] from mathematical equations that light, electricity, and magnetism are all different manifestations of *the same* mystical phenomenon. This remarkable finding was confirmed when German physicist Heinrich Hertz revealed[82] in the 1880s that electromagnetic waves and light travel at *exactly* the same speed and can traverse thin air; laying the foundation for radio and wireless communications.

By the end of the 19th century, there was general agreement that light propagates as waves and the matter was regarded as settled. But nature was harbouring even bigger surprises that would upset core assumptions in classical physics.

Light and the quantum realm

Max Planck, another German physicist, had been busy investigating why the colour of a heated object changes from red to orange and then blue as its temperature rises – a phenomenon known in physics as 'black body radiation'. In October 1900, Planck derived[83] a formula that described this baffling thermal spectacle. To his surprise, the mathematics suggested that energy actually consists of small, separate, indivisible quantities or packets that he called 'quanta' (from the Latin word for 'amount'). This is what gave heat emissions such discrete colouring at different temperature levels.

Planck's work was a major turning point. If, as thought, heat and light propagate in waves, then energy emissions should appear as a continuous, blurred spectrum; not sharply distinct colours. But, at this early stage, Planck did not[84] see the discovery as anything revolutionary; he assumed an explanation would emerge within existing laws of physics. However, it soon became clear that this idea of energy in individual 'chunks' was a new rule of nature that suggests whatever sustains our world at fundamental, out-of-sight level exists as 'bits' that are very different from the holistic shape and form we perceive and associate with everyday things.

In 1905, Einstein (then just 26 years old) applied Planck's remarkable finding to another puzzle: why some materials discharge small amounts of electricity when exposed to light (the photoelectric effect). Einstein showed[85] that the phenomenon can be explained by representing light as particle-like quanta[86] which dislodge electrons from materials on impact. However, the physics community was unimpressed; the dogma of light as waves was too well-established. Nevertheless, Einstein ploughed on with his idea and boldly predicted[87] in 1909 that *"the next stage in the development of theoretical physics will bring us a theory of light that can be understood as a kind of fusion of the wave and [matter particle] theories of light."*

19

Einstein's work on photoelectrics eventually earned him the 1921 Nobel Prize in Physics. Despite this triumph, colleagues were still reluctant to accept that light could exist as both wave and particles. Even Planck, who originated the idea of energy quanta, viewed Einstein's new depiction of light as a mere mathematical tool for describing the enigmatic relationship observed between invisible electromagnetic radiation and visible matter.

But things were about to change. In 1923, American physicist Arthur H. Compton showed[88] that, when light from X-rays and gamma-rays is projected on materials, it scatters in *all directions* and with *less energy* (like colliding billiard balls). The finding vindicated[89] Einstein's description of light: such a distinctive scattering pattern indicated the rays were impacting as streams of discrete particles; not as waves which would have spread out evenly (like water disturbed by a pebble).

Within a year of Compton's demonstration, French physicist Louis de Broglie extended[90] the wave-particle theory to electrons and confidently predicted that a similar duality would surface in *all* matter, regardless of form. Amazingly, this seemingly unlikely proposition was confirmed three years later in separate experiments led by[91a] George Paget Thomson at University of Aberdeen in Scotland, and[91b] Clinton Davisson at Bell Laboratories in New York, USA.

Double-slit magic

Researchers experimenting with updated versions of Thomas Young's 1803 light interference apparatus provided the first hints that de Broglie's predictions on matter duality had merit. In basic set-ups of the iconic double-slit experiment[92], two closely-spaced parallel slits in an opaque barrier are used to split the beam from a steady light source for observation on a screen at the back.

The projected pattern of alternating bright and dark bands fading out on either side (diffraction effect) shows the light is propagating as rippling waves. However, physicists using improved equipment in the mid-1920s made a remarkable discovery – the band images have a strange 'grainy' texture; an indication that the light is *also* impacting the screen as discrete particles. How could this be?

To add to the mystery, shooting individual light photons at intervals in a straight line through *one slit* at a time gives rise to sharp images of the slit (rather than fading wave bands). But, shooting the same photons at the same intervals through *both slits* concurrently causes the alternating bands to reappear – even though the particles have travelled singly with no opportunity for mutual interference. These intriguing results suggest[93] a solitary light particle can go through two slits *at the same time* and 'interfere with itself' to yield a tell-tale wave pattern; an astounding and counter-intuitive scenario *unless* the particle is somehow transforming into a wave in mid-flight.

Stranger still, when experimenters placed detecting devices at the slits, they found that each photon then passed through one or other slit – *not* both slits as would happen with waves. Also, detection caused wave interference patterns to be replaced by clear outlines of the slits – another indication the light was impacting as particles. Thus, it appears the mere act of 'observation' or 'measurement' at slits causes arriving light waves to 'collapse' into discrete particles that then go on to form the outline images we would normally expect (like cast shadows).

These mysterious outcomes were recognised as examples of wave superposition. Just as multiple waves moving across physical media like air and water overlap each other to form a single new wave, quantum wave-particles can exist in *multiple overlapping states* and be in *several positions* at the same time. This was a truly profound finding[94].

21

Double-slit results with light photons have been reproduced with other particles like electrons[95a] and even with composite atoms and complex molecules[95b]; an indication that superposition is a fundamental aspect of nature. However, there's still no satisfactory explanation[96] for this bizarre property at quantum level.

A '2-in-1' solution

Einstein welcomed all the exciting developments, but he still lacked a full mathematical explanation for the strange behaviour of light. Then, in 1924, Indian physicist Satyendra Nath Bose authored a short article[97] that resolved the issue. Bose realised that, although light quanta are distinct bits, they would be identical at the same frequency and look *inseparable* to a privileged observer. This brilliant insight was the first indication that light might exist as both wave and particle *at the same time*; not just interchangeably.

Einstein immediately recognised the significance of this approach and collaborated with Bose to develop a new field of 'quantum statistics'. They derived new mathematical equations that allowed Einstein to predict reverse conditions under which atoms would start to display wave-like quantum behaviour; a unique state of matter now called the *Bose–Einstein Condensate* (BEC).

From mathematics to being

The notion that light and matter exist as both wave and particle was firmly established by the mid 1920s. However, no one could explain how the underlying mathematics 'magically' produces our everyday reality. As Dick Teresi observed in a 1997 review[98] of *The Fire Within The Eye* (a historical sketch of light by American physicist David Park), the whole issue is so confusingly mind-bending that it can only be grasped by meshing philosophy and science.

A numbers game

In 1925, German theoretical physicist Werner Heisenberg (in collaboration with Max Born and Pascual Jordan) proposed[99] a new description of subatomic matter particles in terms of abstract mathematical *probability*; rather than the definite features and fixed or calculated location of things we observe in our physical world. This 'matrix mechanics' reflected Heisenberg's flexible philosophical approach[100] to science. He agreed with Danish colleague Niels Bohr that it's impossible for humans to observe or detect a quantum entity in holistic form (wave *and* particle at the same time); they argued that we're limited to perceiving things in one state or the other, but not both – a constraint now known as the 'uncertainty principle'.

Intriguingly, despite being counter-intuitive, matrix mechanics helped to explain the 'fingerprint' radiation that gives atoms and molecules unique identity: their observed spectral lines could be arising from 'quantum jumps' of particles within a matrix of energy levels. However, many physicists found the use of *variable* number coefficients to represent all we perceive unsettling because of[101] the uncertainty this introduces into science, and the uncomfortable questions it raises about our reality. The implication is that nothing 'exists' until intangible wave-particles 'hovering' somewhere in an unobservable quantum matrix are mysteriously 'resolved' by unclear processes into observable or detectable substances.

Sceptics, led by Einstein, preferred the 'wave mechanics' published[102] in 1926 by Erwin Schrödinger which used traditional Newtonian principles (how an object responds when force is applied) to describe the likely initial state and position of an entity lurking in the quantum realm. Schrödinger's mathematical 'wave function' allowed him to derive an equation for tracking the evolution of wave-particles over time into stationary quantum states – similar to familiar standing waves in observable media like air and water.

Enduring uncertainty

However, Max Born soon quashed the hopes of traditional physicists that old, classical principles could solve quantum mysteries. Born showed[103] the same year that even a wave function harbours huge statistical uncertainty about the whereabouts of *anything* that's still in an unresolved quantum state. He proposed an alternative solution to Schrödinger's equation that linked[104] the *probability* of a particle's manifestation in a particular position at any given point in time to the square of its mathematical wave function.

Born also introduced new concepts of probability amplitudes and dynamic wave packets that, as he explained[105] in his 1954 Nobel Prize acceptance lecture, finally confirmed *nothing* can be known for certain about the essence of things at quantum level. Heisenberg's claim that our universe is fundamentally unpredictable was, it turned out, a cardinal rule of nature.

The strangeness of our reality was reaffirmed in two reviews[106a,b] of competing theories presented to the Royal Society in early 1927 by English theoretical physicist Paul Dirac. He developed a unified theoretical framework (QFT) and linked the new physics to electromagnetism for the first time in a concept he called 'quantum electrodynamics' (QED).

In 1928, Dirac also made the startling discovery[107] that *two different* states of atomic matter can be deduced from quantum equations: one with familiar electrons (negative electric charge), and the other with strange antielectrons (positive electric charge). Dirac wondered *"why Nature should have chosen this particular model for the electron instead of being satisfied with the point-charge"* and speculated in a 1930 follow-up article[108] that the hypothetical antielectron could be a novel type of proton awaiting discovery.

In 1933, American physicist Carl D. Anderson experimentally detected the particle Dirac had predicted mathematically. Anderson showed that[109] this was, indeed, an exotic *positively-charged* electron or 'positron'. It was the first indication that mysterious 'antimatter' might exist in some out-of-sight dimension.

Subsequently, it emerged that any 'antiparticles' and normal matter particles coming into contact will instantly destroy each other and revert to light photons. Intriguingly, photons uniquely incorporate *both* particle states but have no mass. American theoretical physicist and Nobel laureate Richard P. Feynman suggested[110] in 1949 that time might flow *backwards* in a world of positrons, instead of the irreversible forward flow we experience. Thus, it appears the physical universe (including humans) only exists in its current form[111a] because some mysterious agency has prevented[111b] the intrusion of antimatter into our everyday reality.

Dirac's visionary work laid the foundation for development[112] of the elaborate Standard Model of particles and fundamental forces which physicists now use to describe everything that exists. But a long list of unsolved issues continues to defy explanation in terms of the physical phenomena we're able to observe or detect.

Unlikely human enablers

The most controversial aspect of quantum theory is the claim that *no physical reality* exists at fundamental level; there are only wave-particles suspended in an indefinite state of quantum superposition. According to the Copenhagen interpretation that emerged in the 1920s (named after pioneering physicists led by Niels Bohr at the University of Copenhagen in Denmark), these 'ghostly' entities remain in limbo until they are 'prompted' to manifest as real particles in our world by an agency that, somehow, 'collapses' their wave function by the mere act of observation or measurement.

What agency?

However, it's still unclear whether a conscious mind is needed for the essential intervention that produces matter particles from the underlying mathematics. Although Copenhagen originators didn't specify the nature or status of required 'observers' or 'measurers', it was accepted that, to exert any influence, any such agent had to be *outside* quantum systems. But how could this be happening and where do humans fit in this scheme of things? These questions lie at the heart of the so-called measurement problem in physics.

John Von Neumann, a Hungarian-American mathematician and distinguished scientist, examined the problem at length in *The Mathematical Foundations of Quantum Mechanics* (1932). Neumann projected the *entire* universe (humans included) as a giant initial wave function and argued that only a *non-physical* mind, endowed with *externally generated* consciousness, qualifies as a plausible agency for converting mathematical probabilities in the quantum realm into physical reality. This interpretation implies that humans are integral[113] to the world we perceive; nothing would exist – at least, not our everyday experiences – if there were no minds that could 'make sense' of the universe.

However, humans are very much part and parcel of nature – we're a conglomeration of zillions of atoms that exist in unresolved quantum superposition. So, how could we have any role in creating the very physical reality we're involved in? Moreover, evolutionary history based on the fossil record indicates our Homo genus did not appear until around 2.3 million years ago within a timeline for existence that goes back 4.5 *billion* years. What, then, is the source of 'mind' for manifested reality before the earliest humans appeared? Has this mysterious entity always co-existed with wave-particles behind the quantum veil?

26

Even if we accept the panpsychist view[114] that mind and consciousness permeate the entire universe, this still tells us nothing about the processes and pathways through which our reality is constructed and deconstructed. In any case, we can't tell if other organisms experience a different reality (or even multiple realities unique to each species). As an ancient biblical philosopher mused, *"Who knows if the human spirit rises upward and if the spirit of the animal goes down into the earth?"* (Ecclesiastes 3:21, NIV).

A gift from nowhere

These considerations (and more) launched a long-running dispute between 'realists' like Einstein and Schrödinger, and 'instrumentalists' like Bohr and Heisenberg. Matters came to a head at the Fifth Solvay Conference held at Brussels in October 1927. Realists contended that quantum mechanics (QM) as formulated was incomplete because the world we perceive can't possibly be founded on statistical probabilities and uncertain states of matter particles. Instrumentalists advocated a pragmatic approach based on the *efficacy* of the theory: if it works and produces practical results, they argued, scientists should simply accept it as a gift from nature and move on without worrying about metaphysical or religious implications.

After days of spirited discussions, during which an exasperated Bohr reportedly[115a] told Einstein to *"stop telling God what to do"* in response[115b] to the latter's insistence that *"God does not play dice"*, the instrumentalists won the debate. However, Einstein and Schrödinger didn't give up the fight – they believed adopting an essentially philosophical interpretation[116] of causality for quantum manifestation (as opposed to the fully-testable, physical explanations hitherto recognised as 'science') was a misguided move that could end up undermining the entire practice of naturalistic research.

Relative perceptions

Special Relativity

Earlier in 1905 – later hailed as his *Annus mirabilis* (Latin for 'Miracle year') – a young Einstein had published three[117] scientific papers in addition to his breakthrough proposal on photoelectrics that cemented his reputation as a visionary physicist. Two papers outlined new principles of Special Relativity that provided further insight into the peculiarities of light. Einstein predicted mathematically that:

1. The *laws of physics* are the same everywhere for observers in inertial frames of reference (i.e., in stable motion relative to each other). The same laws of light and gravity apply here on earth as in every corner of the universe, however distant.

2. The *speed of light* in a vacuum (free space with no matter) is constant. It remains the same for all observers regardless of their relative motion or that of the light source.

These concepts, later validated by experimental observations, may appear simple enough. However, they emphasise that light exerts a profound influence on the way we perceive space and time.

Einstein calculated that the faster an object moves, the more mass it acquires. He showed that[118] *energy* and *matter* are different aspects of the same thing and can be transformed into each other: a relationship expressed in the famous equation $E=mc^2$, where E is energy, m is mass and c is the speed of light. This mysterious equivalency means no object[119a] in our physical domain can ever[119b] reach or exceed the speed of light (a feat termed *superluminality*), because it would then acquire infinite mass. In other words, the boundary of our observable universe is strictly defined by light.

Einstein's derivations also indicated that perception of time depends on one's location and state of motion – it can slow down or speed up dramatically depending on the *relative* velocity of a moving body (like our planet) to an unmoving observer located elsewhere. Speed, of course, is the rate at which an object on the move covers distance over time: we see objects sited at vast distances (like stars) because of the immense speed of emitted light travelling back to us over deep time. Thus, for the speed of the light we're observing to appear *the same* over *all time* and from *all locations* however remote and differently sited, either our perception of cosmic distance, or time passage, or both must be false. Indeed, a million years on earth may be just a millisecond for an observer residing 'at rest' in distant space.

Strange as it sounds, this weird time dilation has been detected in several practical settings. Clocks on spaceships run slightly slower than similar clocks on earth – a team of European physicists and mathematicians demonstrated[120a] in 2015 that it was impossible[120b] to build an ideal clock that will maintain consistent or 'proper time' while under huge acceleration. In 2016, US space agency NASA announced a year-long study[121a] that showed an astronaut had aged more slowly[121b] than their twin partner on earth. These findings raise intriguing questions about the 'real' length of our biological lives, and the factors governing our earth-bound mortality.

Relativity theory suggests that if it ever became possible to achieve faster-than-light quantum teleportation of humans in some form to the ultimate source where time stands still, we might gain immortality and live forever. However, while some remarkable successes have been achieved in teleporting particles[122] (including some gaseous atoms[123a,b]), there's no indication we'll be able to transcend our light-imposed existential dimensions anytime soon[124]. Extensive (and continuing) validation of Einstein's predictions provides further evidence that the reality we observe is firmly constrained by natural rules rooted in physics and mathematics.

Cosmologists now recognise time as a fourth dimension that more fully defines the complex manifold we exist in – they use holistic 4-D space-time models to locate and observe things in the universe, instead of the 3-D geometry we apply in everyday life. Interestingly though, a 2018 study found that[125a] rules and limitations of relativity may not[125b] apply to entities in the hidden quantum realm.

Soviet scientist S. G. Suvorov explained the background and motivation for Einstein's stunning discoveries in a 1979 review[126]:

> *"Einstein gave great importance to generalizing the results of experiments and the part played by theory, in which nature is regarded as an integral whole; for Einstein, all the variable parameters used in a theory are interconnected and interdependent; this also applies to space and time, which lose their substantiality and, thus, absoluteness."*

Spookiness and blurriness

Convinced that everything in nature is connected and can be explained rationally, Einstein continued to search for a way to show that the Copenhagen interpretation of quantum theory was incorrect. After moving to the USA in 1933, he and colleagues Boris Podolsky and Nathan Rosen at The Institute for Advanced Study in Princeton, New Jersey designed a classic thought experiment that's now known as the *Einstein-Podolsky-Rosen paradox* (EPR).

To explain the puzzle of light's odd '2-in-1' wave-particle behaviour, S. N. Bose had proposed a solution[127] in 1924 that treated photons as individual particles *but* with identical features that made them inseparable. Einstein and Bose jointly pioneered *interdependent* particle systems or ensembles that could only be meaningfully described in terms of collective statistics. Bohr and Heisenberg then added notions of complementarity and uncertainty that made it impossible to ascribe physical properties to any *single* particle.

In a 1935 article[128], Einstein, Podolsky and Rosen imagined a pair of such interacting particles with inseparable, complementary identities. Accordingly, these particles should remain inextricably linked even if they fly away from each other and end up at the earth's North and South Pole respectively. Quantum theory suggests that tinkering with a particle at one end would affect its partner at the other end *instantaneously* and vice-versa; regardless of distance apart or time elapsed since they separated.

The EPR theorists argued that there were only two plausible explanations for such an extraordinary 'entangled' phenomenon (famously dubbed[129] *"spooky action at a distance"* by Einstein). Either (1) faster-than-light exchange of information was occurring across huge distances in violation of Special Relativity rules and the Principle of Locality, or (2) particles are endowed with 'hidden variables' that allow detection of 'non-local' signals *without* any physical interaction or intervening medium. They concluded that, if physicists agree the first scenario is impossible, then *"the description of reality as given by a wave function is not complete"* – a crucial component of nature must exist that's so deeply-embedded, it had continued to elude the brightest of researchers. The argument appeared watertight and, despite a vigorous reply[130] from Bohr claiming it contained *"an essential ambiguity"*, physicists remained stumped for decades[131] thereafter.

Schrödinger's blurred cat

Delighted at the EPR development, Erwin Schrödinger published two technical discussions in 1935[132a] and 1936[132b] to further highlight what he called *"unavoidable"* but *"repugnant"* implications of particle entanglement when a conscious mind is introduced into quantum theory. He also authored a new thought experiment in German that illustrated[133] his objections in lay terms.

31

Schrödinger invited readers to imagine a cat locked in a steel box along with an out-of-reach device consisting of a Geiger counter, a bit of radioactive substance, and a flask of poison. The setup is such that the substance may or may not decay. But if just one atom decays, this is detected by the counter which then activates a mechanism to release poison from the flask and kill the cat. In other words, the cat's fate becomes 'entangled' with the uncertain quantum state and 'behaviour' of the lethal substance's atoms.

Schrödinger pointed out that the Bohr-Heisenberg view implies that the cat remains a 'blurred reality' of being alive and dead at the same time until the box is opened and checked. Expressed in terms of quantum physics, the cat would exist as a 'mixed or smeared out' wave function of living *and* dead superposed states until an agency 'collapses' the system into certainty by observation or measurement. Schrödinger scoffed that such a position of *verschränkung* (German for 'entanglement') is beyond ridiculous. The cat must be either alive or dead at all times; it can't be both.

The cat paradox is a classic illustration of inherent problems[134] with any Copenhagen-like reliance on an unspecified agency *outside* a quantum system to produce the reality we observe in our physical world. How and when exactly do mathematical 'probabilities' — supposedly spread-out in some invisible domain — become transformed into the subatomic particles of matter that then congregate into things we perceive and experience? Indeed, do any such abstractions exist? How did the observers or measurers needed to bring about these mysterious transformations arise? If these essential enablers (with or without conscious minds) were brought into being by other observers in higher existential shells (secondary, tertiary etc.), doesn't this invoke infinite regress that leads right back to philosophical and theological arguments for a first cause or 'unmoved mover' like a theistic God?

Help from friends

Eugene Wigner, another eminent Hungarian-American theoretical physicist and mathematician, shared[135] the view of long-time colleague John Von Neumann that a separate, conscious mind is an essential component of quantum theory. But this philosophical mind-body duality is difficult to apply[136a,b] in physical scientific settings. In particular, it raises metaphysical questions that go back to 17th century French philosopher René Descartes: do humans have individual minds with 'parcels' of consciousness, or is it a universally-shared phenomenon?

Wigner discussed these thorny issues in a famous 1961 article[137a]. Drawing on Schrödinger's cat paradox, he outlined[137b] a scenario where a physicist friend is inside a closed laboratory experimenting on an atom suspended in uncertain quantum superposition – like a flipped coin kept spinning in some out-of-sight dimension. The friend has a device that can be applied to instantly resolve the state of the atom (heads or tails?) for physical observation. Wigner noted that, from his point of view as an observer *outside* the lab, the friend is 'entangled' with the experiment and the *entire setup* will remain clouded in uncertainty until he (Wigner) enters the room for an appraisal. Meanwhile, of course, the friend might have resolved the atom's state and noted the result.

The tricky question, then, is just when does the atom's quantum state 'collapse' into certainty? Is it when the friend makes a conscious measurement, or does everything (particle system and experimenter) remain in quantum limbo until Wigner enters the lab and applies his own consciousness to ascertain the position? In our everyday reality, the answer is obvious. However, the perpetual state of uncertainty in the hidden quantum realm, and human inability to directly witness quantum-to-physical transitions, leaves physicists reliant on mere statistical probabilities suggested by complex mathematics.

According to quantum theory, *both* Wigner and his friend can legitimately present different narratives about when, and how, the invisible atom became physically observable. Clearly, once the 'measuring' device is applied in the lab, the friend could not remain superposed between 'knowing' and 'not knowing'; the atom's state would be confirmed *before* Wigner became aware about the outcome. He therefore concluded that reality for human observers 'takes shape' when the requisite information enters each person's *subjective* consciousness – we don't share other minds. Only an ultimate observer with *universal* consciousness would be instantly aware of all events in space and time, or have relevant advance knowledge.

Wigner also pointed out that, while the friend's initial intervention would 'collapse' the atom's mathematical wave-function and force it into our physical world for observation, the *underlying information* might remain hidden in the quantum realm and continue to generate further abstract wave-functions. Thus, another observer may conduct similar measurements but come to completely different conclusions about the atom's state.

More complex versions of Wigner's thought experiment (with multiple observers instead of the original two) have provided strong support for his startling prediction of contradictory realities in concurrent or alternative spheres of existence. In 2018, Swiss theoretical physicists Renato Renner and Daniela Frauchiger explored[138a] a variation in which they (Renner and Frauchiger) act as external observers of two colleagues (friends A and B) locked in separate boxes. Friend A tosses a coin and sends an encoded quantum message to Friend B who decodes it and learns the coin's resting state. Meanwhile, Renner and Frauchiger use similar quantum theory to perform independent calculations that predict the outcome. Surprisingly, the external observers reach inconsistent[138b] conclusions that don't[138c] always agree on the result when they access A and B.

34

The Renner-Frauchiger report shocked fellow physicists[138d]; not least because science works on the assumption that all researchers will arrive at the same objective results for experiments if the foundational premise is sound. Understandably, it was perplexing to contemplate that quantum theory – a proven description of out-of-sight matter particles which underlies many useful[139] technologies – may not be applicable to the large, composite objects in our everyday world; especially in scenarios that involve human minds.

Something was clearly amiss, but things got even stranger. In February 2020, a European collaboration led by Markus Hennrich from Stockholm University in Sweden published an ingenious study[140a] that used laser apparatus to indirectly monitor[140b] the evolving quantum state of a strontium ion trapped in an electrical field. Process tomography allowed the group to reconstruct snapshot measurements taken over just *a millionth of a second*. The stunning results showed that[140c], indeed, atoms are linked to several quantum superpositions and the act of measurement only 'collapses' one. What, they wondered, happens to all the other 'ghostly' states?

In August 2020, another group centred at Griffith University in Australia reported[141a] the outcome of a novel 'proof-of-principle experiment' that tested the metaphysics behind weird conclusions emerging from various 'Wigner's friend' scenarios. The work revealed an underlying theorem which, as Caslav Brukner from the Vienna Center for Quantum Science and Technology explained in a related commentary[141b], *"can be interpreted to imply that in quantum physics, observers are indeed entitled to their own facts."*

Findings from these intriguing exercises have profound implications that go beyond the 'absurdity' of quantum entanglement that Einstein and Schrödinger had sought to demonstrate. They (1) suggest that mind and consciousness are central to the processes that 'conjure up' our reality; (2) strengthen the argument that these phenomena exist *outside* our body and are independent of the physical systems they generate from intangible quantum states; (3) provide a scientific basis for the idea that we 'create our own reality' through individual consciousness; and (4) raise the possibility of *alternative* realities being perceived by different observers concurrently or sequentially.

Although the realist camp had succeeded in reviving debate about the meaning of weird quantum events for our observable world, developments in the mid-20th century shattered hopes for a 'natural' explanation that meets our intuitive expectations.

Is there hidden knowledge?

Unorthodox American physicist David Bohm shared the EPR conclusion that nature must be hiding 'elements of reality'. However, unlike Einstein, he regarded seemingly absurd occurrences of quantum particle entanglement and non-local 'action at a distance'[142] as serious possibilities that could finally help to show that out-of-sight wave-particles may, after all, have tangible, physical features.

In 1952, Bohm came up with a proposition that did not involve 'ghostly' quantum superposition or mysterious application of minds to 'collapse' wave functions. He suggested[143] that quantum particles are real, physical entities *but* must have built-in 'guiding waves' and 'hidden variables'. According to Bohm, the missing information is the exact *position* and *momentum* of a particle at any one time; vectors that would allow us to assign it a definite location in space – just as we regularly visualise everyday large objects. He explained that the crucial values remain elusive because trying to measure them disturbs the particle's pilot wave; thus triggering an instant change in space coordinates that ensures the whole system remains invisible. Of course, Heisenberg's uncertainty principle predicted it's impossible for humans to obtain complementary values for quantum entities.

Between worlds

Bohm's proposal is now called the de Broglie-Bohm theory[144] as it, essentially, reprises the 1927 concept of matter waves pioneered by Louis de Broglie. Bohm accepted that particle 'pilot waves' are abstract, mathematical constructs in 'non-local' dimensions that we may never detect physically. But he argued that[145] his combined description, at least, assigned some reality to matter at quantum level. In 1957, he proposed an experiment[146] using the new approach that he asserted could yield *"the first clear empirical proof that the aspects of the quantum theory discussed by Einstein, Rosen, and Podolsky represent real properties of matter."* Thus, in the context of[147] the double-slit experiment, a matter particle only travels through *one* slit (as would a normal object); but its invisible pilot wave travels through *both* slits to produce the wave interference observed on a background screen. Bohm's concept implies pilot waves act like hidden 'radio antennas' engaged in constant processing of signals from a giant, universal wave function in the quantum realm that never collapses. Hence, all particles manifesting in our physical world are able to maintain 'non-local' faster-than-light entanglement with each other; no communication or intervening media is needed. In other words, *everything, everywhere* is mysteriously connected across space and time.

This astonishing conclusion led Bohm to join neuroscientist Karl Pribram's pioneering research[148a] into quantum holography; a collaboration that yielded[148b] a new holonomic model of brain-generated consciousness. While not outwardly religious, Bohm was (like Einstein) deeply spiritual and believed in[149] the power of meditative thought. In his 1980 book *Wholeness and the Implicate Order*, he argued for[150] a holistic *"enfolding-unfolding universe and consciousness"* in which our reality is just an 'explicate' order of temporary forms materialising from a fundamental all-subsuming 'implicate' order – a model strikingly similar to ancient Greek philosophical proposals.

Bohm's ideas were developed further in a long-term collaboration with quantum physicist Basil Hiley at Birbeck College, University of London. Their research culminated in another classic book titled *The Undivided Universe* which was published posthumously in 1993. Bohm and Hiley used complex algebra to construct[151] a rigorous mathematical framework that applied[152] quantum theory in support of a holistic 'implicate-explicate' hypothesis of the invisible, entangled processes across domains that yield manifestations we detect in our everyday, physical world.

However, Bohm's realist alternative to the comparatively 'surreal' Copenhagen interpretation struggled to gain mainstream acceptance – especially after a 1992 so-called ESSW critique[153] (acronym coined from the names of its four authors) claimed it produced equally surrealistic particle behaviour in double-slit experiments. Finally, in 2011, an international team of physicists led by Aephraim Steinberg from the University of Toronto in Canada showed that[154a], indeed, it's possible to plot a photon's trajectory through double-slit apparatus using *precise* measurement of position and *approximation* of momentum; a finding that provided[154b] indirect experimental support for Bohm's idea of hidden but integral particle pilot waves. Four years later, another group (including Steinberg and Howard Wiseman from Australia's Griffith University) published[155] a follow-up study that found the surrealism reported by the ESSW team stemmed from fundamental misunderstanding of the *non-local* 'other-worldly' nature of pilot waves; although Bohm also depicts these as ever-present components of matter particles in our *local* observable universe.

Ubiquitous correlations

If Bohm is right, the quantum realm from which everything springs will always remains shrouded behind a mathematical veil: humans can never fully understand the processes by which wave-particles become (and retain) the substantial forms we perceive.

As Steinberg remarked in a 2016 overview[156a] of his group's new rebuttal of the ESSW case against Bohmian pilot waves:

"The universe seems to like talking to itself faster than the speed of light. I could understand a universe where nothing can go faster than light, but a universe where the internal workings operate faster than light, and yet we're forbidden from ever making use of that at the macroscopic level — it's very hard to understand."

Indeed. The 220-year-old double-slit experiment is still the most striking illustration of our continued confusion about light's role at fundamental quantum level. Back in 1965, renowned American theoretical physicist and Nobel laureate Richard Feynman called[156b] double-slit revelations *"a phenomenon which is impossible, absolutely impossible, to explain in any classical way, and which has in it the heart of quantum mechanics. In reality, it contains the only mystery."* Feynman was hardly exaggerating; Bohm is not the only physicist to resort to an explanation of quantum weirdness that involves 'unnatural' entities from some transcendental domain beyond our observable world.

But speculative clues have emerged. In 2001, theorists devised[157a] a quantum information framework that showed[157b] how correlations might arise between entangled particles in the quantum realm and observable particles in our classical realm. American physicist Wojciech H. Zurek, one of the originators of this hypothetical 'quantum discord' mixed state of things, suggested[157c] two years later that it might be a key enabling stage in the undetected pathway which 'brings things' into being – somewhat like the inconspicuous daemon processes that operate continuously in the background of physical computer systems to facilitate easy use of 'surface' application software. Zurek's proposal is interesting but, alas, quantum discord is impossibly difficult[158] to quantify for direct testing because the required algorithms are far too long for practical computing.

Nevertheless, in 2011, a Brazilian team reported[159a] that an experiment with a two-qubit system of chloroform molecules had allowed[159b] fleeting detection of correlations between particles in a quantum-classical mixed state at room temperature. It remains to be seen whether the extraordinary result can be leveraged for deeper investigation into the fundamental processes that produce our physical reality.

Reality check

Bohm's approach to weird quantum features (especially non-locality of particle pilot waves) intrigued Northern Irish physicist John S. Bell. When Einstein, Podolsky and Rosen speculated in their EPR critique that particles must have 'hidden variables' waiting to be discovered, they meant *local* features that can be detected in our physical world; not mysterious pilot waves in non-local dimensions. In fact, objections by some physicists like John von Neumann were interpreted as adamant denial[160a] that quantum mechanics is even compatible[160b] with the concept of hidden variables in *any* domain.

Bell inequalities

In 1964, Bell published a detailed analysis[161a] of all the contentious issues raised by the EPR paradox. He showed[161b] that 'spooky' entanglement at a distance is inevitable within quantum mechanics, and that 'hidden variables' were highly unlikely to be local attributes. In other words, as Bohm had surmised, 'other-worldly' non-locality of hidden variables is a vital ingredient for quantum theory to work properly. Bell supported his conclusions with a remarkable mathematical theorem that proved there was a limit to the extent of correlation that could exist between *locally* entangled particles. Quantum mechanics does not support any such limitation; rather, unlike exclusively local proposals, it perfectly fits the scenario of *unrestricted* non-local entanglement indicated by calculations.

In a follow-up 1966 paper[162], Bell strongly criticised sceptics who had dismissed Bohm's work without in-depth studies. He also showed that hidden variables are *strictly contextual:* they apply to quantum particle systems *but not* to large observers or measuring devices – a crucial factor that might help to explain why, despite human 'entanglement' with quantum entities, we don't experience any of the weirdness that exists at out-of-sight microscopic level. Such a specific, targeted constraint raises the possibility that we may exist at a different level of reality from our constituent matter particles.

The strange 'quantum contextuality' identified by Bell was proven separately[163a] in 1967 by Simon Kochen and Ernst Specker and has since been reconfirmed in simpler mathematical proofs; including one in 1990[163b] by N. David Mermin who famously called[163c] the Copenhagen interpretation a *"Shut up and calculate!"* evasion, and another in 1991[163d] by Asher Peres who pioneered[163e] explanations of EPR particle entanglement in terms of information theory.

All the so-called Bell inequalities[164] laid the foundation for the first practical investigations into deeper quantum mysteries. As Andrew Whitaker from Queen's University Belfast noted in a 1998 review[165], *"Bell's work led to the possibility of exploring seemingly philosophical questions, such as the nature of reality, directly through experiments."*

Breakthroughs

Nearly 20 years after Bell shocked the physics world with his unequivocal theorem, French physicist Alain Aspect and two colleagues at the University of Paris validated[166a] his findings in a series of experiments. Recent experiments with tighter parameters have proved beyond doubt[166b] that entangled particles can definitely interact in an inexplicably fast way beyond the speed of light.

Still, dissenters clung to the possibility that some local agency *within* our observable world could be intruding to 'fix' experimental outcomes. However, in 2017, an international team of cosmologists and quantum physicists led by Anton Zeilinger at the University of Vienna announced[167a] results from a novel study that reaffirmed[167b] Bell's constraints on local information exchanges. The group used light that emanated from Milky Way stars *over 600 years ago* to generate random measurements of correlations between photons travelling in *current real-time* between buildings. Incredibly, they still detected[167c] unrestricted correlations – an indication of non-local entanglement that must have arisen *before* anything came into existence.

That same year, another international study co-ordinated by Italian physicists Rosario Lo Franco and Fabio Sciarrino confirmed[168] that light photons can be entangled *even while* superposed in wave-particle states. Then, in 2018, a team led by Mika Sillanpää at Aalto University in Finland announced[169a] successful quantum entanglement of two aluminium drumheads about the width of a human hair; an astonishing feat that showed[169b] it's possible to generate and detect entanglement in everyday objects.

The complementary Bell–Kochen–Specker derivation on quantum contextuality, which places vital restrictions on hidden variables with regard to observers and measuring devices within our local physical world, was also validated experimentally[170a] in 2009 by a team of European physicists led by Christian Roos and Rainer Blatt from the Austrian Academy of Sciences. The landmark achievement strengthened[170b] arguments for a holistic quantum-classical universe that hangs 'between worlds'.

The matter is now considered beyond dispute by most mainstream physicists: no realist conjectures based solely on observable phenomena in our physical world can explain the peculiar nature of things at quantum level.

American mathematical physicist Henry P. Stapp elegantly summed up the challenge posed by Bell's work in a 1975 review[171]:

"Science can be pragmatic or fundamentalistic. The aim of pragmatic science is to make predictions about what will be observed in different situations. The aim of fundamentalistic science is to understand the fundamental nature of things. [...] The basic problem in fundamentalistic science is to find a unified model of reality that is consistent with relativistic quantum theory. Bell's theorem imposes a severe condition on models of reality, for it demands [that] an adequate model account simultaneously for the observed causal structure on the statistical level and the noncausal structure on the individual event level. An adequate model of reality must, moreover, provide for a unified understanding of all of Nature."

The problem is, no one has been able to devise a purely naturalistic *"adequate model of reality"* that reconciles our everyday experiences with the weird behaviour of quantum entities. Ironically, the supposedly 'absurd' contradictions of quantum theory that realists like Einstein and Schrödinger sought to highlight have instead helped to cement it. The inescapable evidence is that light and matter particle entanglement and non-locality are, indeed, fundamental aspects of nature. Traditional dogmas of observable or measurable cause-and-effect, and associated physical realism[172], fall apart at the interface of our material world with the quantum realm.

Lee Smolin's 2007 exchange[173] with Jeremy Bernstein in *The New York Review* showed that even a compromise 'between worlds' proposal like de Broglie-Bohm particle pilot waves remains highly contentious: in 2016, an international group led by Martin Ringbauer from the University of Queensland in Australia published[174a] fresh experimental results that the authors claimed show such models are far from sufficient[174b] to fully explain quantum phenomena.

So, where next for physicists? Will they have to settle for the pragmatic *"Shut up and calculate!"* approach that N. David Mermin derided in 1989?

Holographic fingerprints

In 2014, Anton Zeilinger and co-researchers in Austria announced[175a] they had found a way to 'split' entangled infrared photons and pass one half of each pair through a model cat (homage to Schrödinger's cat). Amazingly, they were able to recreate[175b] the *exact image* of the cat with just the split halves that had never interacted[175c] with the object. The editorial introduction in *Nature* hailed the development:

> *"As well as demonstrating a fascinating aspect of fundamental physics, this observation can be of practical relevance for a wide range of imaging applications since it allows the use of a detector in a different wavelength range than the one illuminating the object."*

It was already well-established[176] that it should, in principle, be possible to use entangled photons for remote extraction of information from an object 'at a distance' for holographic 3-D reconstruction. But the Zeilinger lab effort was the first known demonstration of this seemingly impossible feat – the application of light that has *never touched* an object to create a perfect copy. The achievement is hugely significant.

Normal holograms are recordings[177a] of light fields created by superimposed light from a split laser beam: one half (*illumination* beam) is passed through, or bounced off, the target object, while the other half (*reference* beam) is directed straight onto the recording medium where the split halves recombine[177b] to form an interference pattern that can be diffracted later to render stunning virtual 3-D copies of the imaged object. The ingenious procedure was first outlined[177c] in 1948 by Hungarian-British physicist Dennis Gabor.

In 2016, physicists at the University of Warsaw in Poland reported[178a] another spectacular achievement: the first ever hologram of an *unknown*, single light particle (photon) reproduced *from nothing* but detected quantum wavefronts. The researchers explained the importance of their astounding result in a press release[178b]:

> *"Our experiment is one of the first allowing us to directly observe one of the fundamental parameters of photon's wave function -- its phase -- bringing us a step closer to understanding what the wave function really is. [....]It's likely that real applications of quantum holography won't appear for a few decades yet, but if there's one thing we can be sure of it's that they will be surprising."*

Just three years later in May 2019, a European collaboration coordinated by Fabrizio Carbone from École Polytechnique Fédérale de Lausanne (EPFL) Switzerland published[179] an ambitious proposal for *"Holographic imaging of electromagnetic fields via electron-light quantum interference"*; an idea that would have been dismissed as fantasy just a few years earlier. The researchers described their concept thus: *"Unlike conventional holography, where signal and reference are spatially separated and then recombined to interfere, our method relies on electromagnetic fields to split an electron wave function in a quantum coherent superposition of different energy states."* A decade earlier, an American team at Stanford University had shown[180a] it might be possible to use atomic-level microscopy to construct *"holograms comprised of individually manipulated molecules"* for storage of[180b] huge amounts of data in electron waves.

Evidently, quantum holography is no longer the esoteric research topic that Pribram and Bohm bravely pioneered in the 1990s. In February 2021, a team at the University of Glasgow in Scotland led by Hugo Defienne and Daniele Faccio announced[181a] successful reconstruction of an object from information imprinted on a *single* remote photon.

45

Another group from Spanish and German institutions has also outlined[181b] a revolutionary method *"for recording a hologram of single photons without detecting the photons themselves, and importantly, with no need to use a well-characterized companion reference photon."* Defienne discussed some exciting potential applications of such seemingly 'magical' techniques in a companion essay[181c]: *"Soon this quantum holographic approach could be used to unravel biological structures and mechanisms inside cells that had never been observed before."* Suddenly, Pribram-Bohm proposals on holonomic brain functions don't seem so improbable.

Unsurprisingly, these new scientific insights are raising even deeper philosophical questions about the reality we perceive. Quantum holography takes the fascinating reproduction of objects with, essentially, *nothing* but light to a whole new level. Not only is *no interaction* required between the enabling light and objects of interest, the entanglement of photons (light particles) across space and time means our universe (along with its entire contents) could be[182] a holographic reconstruction that was pre-programmed *eons ago* by an external, superhuman observer.

However, the precise position and role of humans in this mysterious scheme of things remains unknown; there isn't even consensus on the extent to which science should interact[183] with metaphysics to search for answers.

Multiple worlds, Parallel lives

In 1957, Hugh Everett III, a 27-year-old PhD student at Princeton University, proposed another radical alternative to the Copenhagen-inspired idea that mind-initiated events somehow force physical matter to 'materialise' from invisible wave functions. According to quantum theory, the mathematical matrix underlying everything houses innumerable probabilities. Everett approached the problem by exploring the ultimate fate of multiple, possible quantum scenarios that *never manifest* in our observable world.

Reality menus

Schrödinger's cat paradox and Wigner's later friend scenarios show that, as humans are themselves the product of matter particles, we're inevitably 'entangled' at all times with the quantum realm. Everett argued[184] this interactive existence means every measurement or observation we make will 'blend' us with superposed particle states and trigger *our own* wave function to split into the myriad of existential possibilities predicted by quantum statistics. He suggested that, in this context, 'measurement' means every act of *choosing* from the range of options that life constantly presents – *not* mysterious 'collapsing' of wave functions. Once we make a decision regarding a set of possibilities, we're stuck with our choice as we can't go back in time to undo things.

According to Everett, the several life options that we *don't* choose continue to exist independently as multiple products of the original quantum wave function – along with 'split' versions of ourselves. He explained that the particular outcome we experience after making a choice is just a 'relative state' of reality that joins others in our 'memory card' to yield a particular branch of history. The inescapable conclusion, said Everett, is that we have doppelgänger split copies creating *parallel realities* somewhere (he didn't specify exactly where) with completely different and unique[185] historical narratives and futures. Thus, *all* possible quantum outcomes do manifest in an ever-branching tree of reality, but our perception of 'now' depends on which splinter of 'self' we represent and which position in the system we happen to find ourselves after making everyday choices.

Everett first outlined this extraordinary hypothesis in a draft paper[186] presented to his PhD advisor John A. Wheeler in 1956. The work included a mathematical derivation that extended Schrödinger's equation for tracking wave-particles to the *entire universe* over all time.

47

Like Bohm, Everett's starting assumption was that everything which could ever exist stems from a *perpetual* universal wave function: all possibilities materialise from a single, gigantic, foundational superposition. However, while Wheeler was impressed[187] with Everett's originality, he failed to persuade Niels Bohr's group that the idea had merit. Copenhagen pioneers were already grappling with the unsettling implications of Bohm's hidden variables, so they were wary of another 'other worldly' proposal that blended composite macro-objects (humans and measuring devices) with quantum micro-entities (particle wave functions). Nearly 40 years earlier, Bohr had devised a principle for separating visible classical from invisible quantum entities in physics. But the issue is still unresolved[188].

Eventually, Everett had to settle for a watered-down publication that omitted controversial reality 'splits'. The experience left him[189] disillusioned with academia and he quit theoretical physics work.

Many worlds

Everett's formulation of multiple realities, alternative histories and branching futures remained dormant until 1970 when theoretical physicist Bryce S. DeWitt (an initial sceptic) reinterpreted[190a] and popularised[190b] the concept as the *Many-Worlds Interpretation* (MWI). DeWitt reasserted Everett's notion of a non-collapsible universal wave function – thus avoiding the measurement controversy and need for 'collapsing' action by conscious minds to create reality. But Everett had only described continual splitting and branching of an *observer's* quantum state, while DeWitt concluded[191] that this implies there are many other *unseen worlds*, all existing *in parallel* at the *same space and time*, and all with the same physical laws. This expansive view means the innumerable split copies of humans envisaged by Everett exist *simultaneously* within other worlds. The question then arises[192]: do our doppelgängers have our exact lifespan or do some die earlier, later, or live eternally?

Interacting domains?

In 2014, Australian physicists Howard Wiseman and Michael Hall, and German mathematician Dirk-André Decker (WHD), jointly published[193a] an even more radical version of MWI. The trio agreed Everett-DeWitt 'worlds' are huge in number, but argued[193b] there must be a fixed limit because these are not hypothetical but *real classical worlds* which exist in parallel and interact continually. They suggested that *"all quantum phenomena arise from a universal force of repulsion that prevents worlds from having identical physical configurations"*; there's no need to reference a *"mysterious quantum wave function"*.

According to WHD, humans inhabit this interrelated set of *"many-interacting-worlds"* and have to perform constant observation exercises to determine which world we inhabit. Wiseman explained this bizarre idea in an accompanying, non-technical essay[193c]:

> *"Probability only enters the theory because an observer, made up of particles in a certain world, does not know for sure which world she is in, out of the set of all worlds. Hence she will assign equal probability to every member of that set which is compatible with her experiences (which are very coarse-grained, because she is a macroscopic collection of particles). After performing an experiment she can learn more about which world she is in, and thereby rule out a whole host of worlds that she previously thought she might be in."*

Wiseman asserted that their proposal closely mirrors how quantum mechanics operates in our world, and therefore offers *"the exciting possibility that it might be possible to test for the existence of these other worlds."* He concluded: *"For us at least there is nothing inherently implausible in the idea, and for fans of science fiction it makes those plots involving communication between parallel worlds not quite so far-fetched after all."*

However, in his 2018 book *Beyond Weird* (a review[194a] of the history and current state of quantum theory), former *Nature* editor and author Philip Ball criticised all many-worlds interpretations as 'illogical' and 'incoherent'. He commented in an adapted excerpt[194b]:

"The MWI — if taken seriously — is unthinkable. Its implications undermine a scientific description of the world far more seriously than do those of any of its rivals. The MWI tells you not to trust empiricism at all: Rather than imposing the observer on the scene, it destroys any credible account of what an observer can possibly be. [....] We needn't fear a scientific idea that changes our view of macroscopic reality. But an idea that, when we pursue it seriously, makes that view inchoate and unspeakable doesn't fulfill the function of science."

One inference that Ball found particularly troubling is that humans exist in *perpetual* superposition along with innumerable quantum copies in remote domains. The notion, he pointed out, has serious implications for personal identity: where does the real 'I' reside within such a fluctuating reality? Also, where does this leave the long-held view that *subjective* consciousness is an essential ingredient of quantum theory? As he argued: *"Consciousness relies on experience, and experience is not an instantaneous property: It takes time, not least because the brain's neurons themselves take a few milliseconds to fire. You can't "locate" consciousness in a universe that is frantically splitting countless times every nanosecond, any more than you can fit a summer into a day."*

Many minds

In 1988, American philosophers David Albert and Barry Loewer attempted to overcome the MWI personhood dilemma by reinterpreting[195a] 'many worlds' as the 'many minds' of an observer. According to this Many-Minds (MM) approach, when we choose an option, we resolve[195b] to one mind (or quantum mental state) and all other possibilities vanish into inaccessible domains.

Hence, it's impossible for humans to 'go back in time' and undo everyday decisions and consequences (although we can, of course, make amends). Albert and Loewer also reasoned that our minds can't be the same as biological brains because quantum theory tells us the latter are aggregates of superposed matter particles. They argued: *"the way we conceive of mental states, beliefs, memories etc., it simply makes no sense to speak of such states of a mind as being in a superposition."* But this implies minds exist independently *outside* physical bodies and can continue in perpetuity like 'souls' – a highly controversial notion in science. Furthermore, mind-body separation in this context conjures up the spectre of 'mindless hulks'; human bodies with brains that may or may not still host a mind having (literally) lost *all* available mental states to the quantum abyss in some split-second of indecision.

In 1996, British philosopher of science Michael Lockwood recast[196a] Many-Minds as 'many perspectives' or points of view rather than separate metaphysical minds. He viewed 'minds' as mere *representations* of a superposed brain that's constantly entangled with the environment. Accordingly, he proposed[196b] that mental states (representing all possible quantum outcomes) remain 'hosted' *within* a human observer until one is selected and the others split off into copies in parallel realities. Lockwood argued that this embeds optional mind states in individuals at all times and makes accidental 'mindless hulks' unlikely – an approach fellow philosopher and metaphysician David Papineau found[197a] plausible; albeit with the reservation[197b] that it makes more sense to formulate the concept as *biological* 'teleosemantics' which doesn't involve[197c] mystical mind states inside or outside our physical bodies.

However, after a detailed analysis of associated issues, Cambridge University mathematician and information scientist Matthew Donald concluded[198a] in 1997 that separate, *non-physical* minds are, indeed, the fundamental blocks of our reality and cannot be dispensed with – just as Bishop Berkeley proposed[198b] in the early 1700s.

51

Donald pointed out that the many-minds worldview has profound *ethical* implications for the way we exercise our gift of free will that go beyond scientific and philosophic debates. He wrote[198c]:

"As far as the basis for rational decisions is concerned, the question is whether or not, if we accept a many-minds theory, it makes any difference to how we make decisions. Here, despite Papineau's 1995 and 1996 arguments that it should make no difference, I do retain a suspicion that, if one does take many-minds theory seriously, then it does make a difference. I think myself that it makes one think more carefully about all the possible outcomes of an action. If all futures happen, then one cannot get away with anything any more. A lucky escape in this world is merely confirmation that many other worlds are unpleasant. Perhaps if we accept many-minds then it ought to lead us to be more "rational"; to take seriously, for example, the very large negative utilities that we might attach to some very unlikely events. Whether this is a good thing or not depends on how we draw the line between being careful and being neurotic; how we manage to accept the reality of risk without being overwhelmed by it."

Nonetheless, the troublesome issue of split personal identities persists in both 'many worlds' and 'many minds' models of quantum realities. There's no way to tell which of the proposed host of minds represents the real 'I' *before* a decision, or which one (if any) will continue to be associated with the state an individual assumes *after* a decision prompts splitting into fresh quantum copies. Furthermore, as Philip Ball discussed in his 2018 critique[199], it's impossible to formulate a rational hypothesis with predicted outcomes that can be scientifically tested. Thus, like the famous Schrödinger's cat, MWI and MM interpretations of quantum theory spawn new dilemmas that vividly illustrate the difficulties theorists encounter when they try to apply the physics that govern unobservable microscopic entities to observable macroscopic phenomena in our everyday world.

Branching multiverse

Thirty years after DeWitt reformulated Everett's universal wave function as the MWI, Oxford University physicist David Deutsch revived[200a] and expanded[200b] the idea. However, unlike MWI in which multiple worlds have *the same* laws of physics, Deutsch advocated a multiverse of infinite universes with *completely different* laws, physical constants and varying conditions. He argued[200c] in 2001 that this was the inevitable outcome of any quantum theory explanation *"in terms of the simultaneous existence of parallel universes or histories."* Furthermore, declared Deutsch, universes in a multiverse remain largely apart for all time. He explained the basis for this assertion in a *Philosophy Now* interview[201]:

"Within one of these groups, which we call a parallel universe, the particles all can interact with each other, even though they barely interact with particles in other universes. They interact in much the same way as the ones in our seen universe interact with each other. That is the justification for calling them universes. The justification for calling them parallel is that they hardly interact with each other, like parallel lines that do not cross."

According to a 2001 *New Scientist* report[202], Deutsch chided contemporaries for *"hiding"* from the mind-blowing implications of quantum theory and dismissed the Copenhagen interpretation as *"gibberish"*. He declared: *"Quantum theory leaves no doubt that other universes exist in exactly the same sense that the single universe that we see exists. This is not a matter of interpretation. It is a logical consequence."* As Matthew Donald had urged[203] in 1997, Deutsch advised those troubled by the thought of doppelgänger copies existing in parallel, inaccessible worlds to adopt a philosophical outlook: *"By making good choices, doing the right thing, we thicken the stack of universes in which versions of us live reasonable lives. When you succeed, all the copies of you who made the same decision succeed too. What you do for the better increases the portion of the multiverse where good things happen."*

53

The idea of infinite universes has ancient roots. As science writer Tom Siegfried discussed in a brief 2019 historical sketch[204], the proposal has always been controversial. He compared current incredulity to Austrian physicist and philosopher Ernst Mach's denial in the late 19th century that atoms existed – on the seemingly reasonable grounds that no one had ever seen one. However, in addition to problems of invisibility, contemporary multiverse critics argue that it's an unwelcome distraction that leads nowhere.

In 2011, renowned South African theoretical physicist and mathematician George Ellis authored a scathing critique[205a] in *Scientific American* (reprinted in 2014[205b]). He commented:

> *"What is new is the assertion that the multiverse is a scientific theory, with all that implies about being mathematically rigorous and experimentally testable. I am skeptical about this claim. I do not believe the existence of those other universes has been proved—or ever could be. Proponents of the multiverse, as well as greatly enlarging our conception of physical reality, are implicitly redefining what is meant by 'science'."*

Ellis restated these objections in a *Nature* commentary[205c] co-authored with British astronomer and astrophysicist Joseph Ivor Silk. They warned: *"As we see it, theoretical physics risks becoming a no-man's-land between mathematics, physics and philosophy that does not truly meet the requirements of any."* Interestingly, even religious scientists are divided on the idea of a multiverse. Some, like renowned[206a] University of Alberta physicist Don Page, view the concept as confirmation of God's omnipotence. Others denounce it[206b] as attempts by atheists to undermine the case for an intelligently-designed reality: an unlimited number of universes, with all possible sets of properties and conditions, greatly increases the statistical chance that a 'life-friendly' cosmic bubble like our universe could emerge *without* the otherwise baffling 'fine-tuning' that points to a superintelligent designer.

Quantum immortality: Cheating death

Another bizarre implication of many-worlds (MWI) and many-minds (MM) proposals is the theoretical possibility that an individual might constantly defy death by splitting off into a 'survivor' quantum copy in some new reality every time a life-threatening situation arises. This tantalising prospect of 'quantum immortality' was first broached by British mathematical scientist Euan Squires in his 1986 book *The Mystery of the Quantum World*. But it was Swedish-American physicist and cosmologist Max Tegmark who stirred wide debate in 1997 with a provocative 'quantum suicide' thought experiment[207a].

Tegmark imagined[207b] a scientist in the boxed, superposed position of Schrödinger's famous cat; *but* with full control over a 'quantum roulette' routine that has uncertain outcomes of life or death. According to the Copenhagen interpretation, each time the trigger of a 'quantum gun' directed at the head of the scientist is pulled, a conscious observer opening the box will instantly initiate a wave function 'collapse' and perceive the subject as either dead or alive. However, since MWI rests on a universal wave function that *never* collapses, it becomes possible for an adept individual to smoothly transition to a new, branched quantum copy in the event of death. Of course, this 'reincarnation' would exist within some other-world reality that's inaccessible to a present-world observer; they will only see a dead body in the box if the scientist has been unlucky enough to 'catch a bullet'.

In a 2000 commentary[208] titled *What is it like to be Schrödinger's cat*, British philosopher of science Peter J. Lewis highlighted quantum suicide as a perfect illustration of the problems with MWI. He noted that, despite the high risk of death, MWI and MM appear to suggest it would be perfectly rational to join the cat in the box with confidence that one will survive (albeit in some other reality).

However, in a 2003 response[209a] to Lewis, David Papineau denied that MWI and MM had a *"counter-intuitive death-defying implication."* He argued that Lewis was misguided in his assertions and cautioned[209b]: *"It is certainly true that the many minds interpretation of quantum mechanics violates many of our most basic assumptions about reality. But it does not go so far as to urge us to risk death with abandon."*

Quantum hell

American metaphysician David Lewis (renowned[210a] for his insistence[210b] that other worlds exist and are as real as the one we inhabit) raised another terrifying prospect in a 2001 lecture[211a]: what if we attain quantum immortality but our successive copies are incrementally degraded with every 'reincarnation' until life becomes unbearable? This would represent an eternity of ever-worsening 'quantum hell'. Turkish philosopher István Aranyosi analysed[211b] the daunting probability in 2012 but reached the reassuring conclusion that such an outcome is unlikely.

Controversial scenarios like quantum immortality continue to stimulate lively discussion about the chances of a multiverse in which *anything* is possible, however contrary to intuition and common sense. As Tegmark commented drily in his 1997 seminal presentation:

"Many physicists would undoubtedly rejoice if an omniscient genie appeared at their death bed, and as a reward for life-long curiosity granted them the answer to a physics question of their choice. But would they be as happy if the genie forbade them from telling anybody else? Perhaps the greatest irony of quantum mechanics is that if the MWI is correct, then the situation is quite analogous if once you feel ready to die, you repeatedly attempt quantum suicide: you will experimentally convince yourself that the MWI is correct, but you can never convince anyone else!"

No-tricks manifestation

Since the discovery that pre-20th century classical physics (which governs the properties and behaviour of large, everyday objects) can't be applied to small, out-of-sight building-blocks of matter (particles, atoms and molecules), physicists have depicted a 'quantum world' that's quite distinct from the 'classical world' we're able to observe. However, mainstream descriptions of particle transitions between these two domains involve metaphysical concepts like 'minds' or 'hidden variables' that are difficult to investigate scientifically.

Quantum decoherence

In 1970, H. Dieter Zeh, a theoretical physicist at the University of Heidelberg in Germany, published a seminal paper[212a] that dispensed with the need to provide separate descriptions of large, observable objects and small, unobservable quantum entities. Physicists describe wave-particle superpositions as *coherent* states – a mathematical term adopted from constantly overlapping waves in bulk media like air or water. According to quantum theory, out-of-sight coherent states consist of *information* only and stay as such until some event brings forth the incoherent *physical* states we perceive and experience.

Zeh interpreted[212b] particle transitions between invisible coherent states and visible incoherent states in terms of *irreversible loss of information* or 'decoherence', rather than inexplicable wave function 'collapse'. He pointed out that microscopic quantum systems do not exist in isolation but are demonstrably *entangled* with macroscopic systems and the environment; a state of affairs that suggests wave-particles are subject to the same fundamental thermodynamics that drive interactions throughout the universe. Just as large objects and systems lose energy through friction or dissipation until things reach a state of thermal equilibrium, Zeh argued that natural decoherence compels small entities like particles and atoms to gradually lose the quantum information that keeps them hidden.

57

Like Bohm and Everett, Zeh envisaged a perpetual, underlying universal wave function that governs *all* entities – whether in an observable everyday state or unobservable quantum state. Crucially, his emphasis on *information*, instead of physical properties, allows physicists to describe matter particles as *permanent* mathematical wave constructs in a single world; thus removing the need for mysterious 'measurements' that (supposedly) force particles to materialise from a hidden realm. According to Zeh, all that happens is that gradual information loss steadily reduces *wavelengths* of particles until they lose weird quantum properties and coalesce into physical entities we're able to observe.

A quarter of a century after he first outlined his ideas on decoherence, Zeh presented a full theory[213a] in non-technical terms. He criticised[213b] the way conventional physics separates microscopic particle states from macroscopic composite objects and commented:

> *"While elementary particles are described by means of wave functions (that is, superpositions of different positions or other properties), the moon seems always to be at a definite place, and a cat is either dead or alive. A general superposition principle would even allow superpositions of a cat and a dog ... They would have to define a 'new animal' [...]. In the Copenhagen interpretation, this difference is attributed to a strict conceptual separation between the microscopic and the macroscopic world. However, where is the border line that distinguishes an n-particle state of quantum mechanics from an N-particle state that is classical? Where, precisely, does the superposition principle break down?"*

Zeh affirmed his view that a holistic interpretation is the only way to resolve anomalies and contradictions in quantum theory. He worked tirelessly with co-researcher Erich Joos at Heidelberg University to promote[213c] decoherence as a plausible and consistent quantum-based description of *all* physical reality within *one* world.

In 1999, Joos authored a brief introduction[214a] to the concept that included a frank discussion of its chief weaknesses – inability to explain the fate of multiple unselected quantum probabilities, or the enduring problem of exactly *how* we apply consciousness to perceive things. He concluded[214b]: *"We should not be surprised, however, if it finally turned out that we do not know enough about consciousness and its relation to the physical world to solve the quantum mystery."* Nevertheless, in a 2003 essay[214c] Joos defended decoherence as a useful approach to nature; although he recognised that a *"strong psychological barrier"* has to be overcome before our *"classically biased mind"* can accept that the world we perceive is only apparent and entirely quantum based.

Indeed, the thought that our mortal frames are ultimately composed of matter wave-bits derived from intangible mathematics is unnerving to say the least. But for Serbian-British physicist Vlatko Vedral, decoherence is a natural explanation for all types of physical manifestation in a universe where quantum information provides the fundamental building blocks of reality. Vedral argued[215a] in his book *Decoding Reality* (2010) that the concept, at least, offers a self-explanatory approach to the question of origin. As he explained in an interview[215b]:

"The common answer is that there <u>was</u> some kind of original creator of this information. The trouble is that this answer doesn't really solve anything because as a physicist I'd also like to understand this being itself. I'd like to explain the origin of God. And then you encounter the same infinite regression. For a scientist, "Why is there a universe? Well, because something even more complicated created it the way it is" isn't an explanation. We want a better answer than that. You can argue that science will never get there, that it's an open-ended enterprise. Maybe this is faith. [....] Being negative by saying that it looks too complicated has always been refuted by scientists. That's why I believe there is hope for us to understand more and more."

Decoherence has been adopted and developed by several other theorists; notably Polish-American physicist Wojciech Zurek who coined[216a] the term 'einselection' in 2001 for associated environment-induced[216b] loss of information. Zurek introduced[217a] the notion of 'Quantum Darwinism' to describe[217b] how the environment 'selects' from several available quantum states to give us the physical reality we perceive. Certainly, Zeh's 'one realm' idea has taken root[218a] as the most pragmatic[218b] and cohesive[218c] description of the universe. But it's still far from[218d] a full explanation of quantum oddities.

Spontaneous manifestation

In 1985, Italian physicist Giancarlo Ghirardi and colleagues Alberto Rimini and Tullio Weber (GRW) at the University of Trieste introduced[219a] a new 'one world' model that describes an almost magical process of microscopic-macroscopic particle transition. Unlike the *gradual* loss of quantum information suggested in decoherence, GRW resurrects[219b] the Copenhagen notion of wave function collapse or reduction into particle states as a *spontaneous* process governed entirely by natural laws. Swiss philosopher Roman Frigg (an academic with a background in theoretical physics) assessed[219c] this 'objective' approach to quantum mechanics (QM) in a 2009 compendium:

"The leading idea of the theory is to eradicate observers from the picture and view state reduction as a process that occurs as a consequence of the basic laws of nature. [....] A system governed by GRW theory evolves according to the Schrödinger equation all the time except when a state reduction, a so-called hit, occurs (hits are also referred to as 'hittings', 'perturbations', 'spontaneous localisations', 'collapses',and 'jumps'). A crucial assumption of the theory is that hits occur at the level of the micro constituents of a system (in the above example at the level of the atoms that make up the marble). The crucial question then is: when do hits occur and what exactly happens when they occur?"

Perhaps because of the 'crucial questions' typified in Frigg's assessment, GRW has not attracted the level of support physicists have accorded Zeh's decoherence; environment-induced particle transitions are seen as a more plausible scenario. Erich Joos complained[220] in 1987 that the rival GRW proposal *"does not ... allow one to deduce classical states (particle trajectories) without invoking additional principles."* English mathematical physicist and philosopher of science Sir Roger Penrose has persistently argued for *gravity-induced* spontaneous quantum state reduction (see his submissions in 1996[221a], 1998[221b] and 2014[221c] among others). However, detecting gravitational effects at minuscule quantum level is an uphill task[222a] – physicists are still debating[222b] whether gravity even applies to individual particles, atoms and molecules of matter (it clearly doesn't apply to light because photons have no mass).

Ghirardi acknowledged in an encyclopaedic overview[223] that the type of 'collapse' into physical reality suggested by GRW is extremely difficult to detect or reproduce experimentally. But he counter-argued that it's not completely inconceivable and, unlike decoherence, shows how particle wave functions might collapse *without* conscious observers. He wrote:

"Quantum mechanics, with its revolutionary implications, has posed innumerable problems to philosophers of science. In particular, it has suggested reconsidering basic concepts such as the existence of a world that is, at least to some extent, independent of the observer, the possibility of getting reliable and objective knowledge about it, and the possibility of taking (under appropriate circumstances) certain properties to be objectively possessed by physical systems.

"[....] We are making here specific reference to the central problem of the theory, usually referred to as the measurement problem, or, with a more appropriate term, as the macro-objectification problem."

More incompatibilities

Sceptics of 'one world' proposals like decoherence and GRW are adamant that huge issues remain unresolved. As Princeton University theoretical physicist Stephen L. Adler commented[224a] in a 2003 article[224b], *"If we insist on having only one world existing within the standard arena of states and operators in Hilbert space, we must instead discard one or more of the assumptions.... by injecting new physics."* British physicist and Nobel laureate Sir Anthony J. Leggett also concluded that the inference of 'other-worldly' particle non-locality is unavoidable in quantum theory. Leggett argued[225] in a 2008 article: *"Unless we are willing to sacrifice one or more other intuitively plausible notions such as that of the conventional 'arrow of time', it appears impossible, in either context, to maintain the classical notion of realism."*

Two decades earlier in 1985, Leggett teamed up with American physicist Anupam Garg to formulate[226a] a mathematical Bell-type crossover barrier between the microscopic quantum realm and the macroscopic classical realm we experience. Starting from two simple assumptions – 1) a macroscopic object is always in one state/position at a time; it can't exist in a superposition, and 2) a macroscopic object's state/position can be determined without disturbing its inherent nature or subsequent behaviour – they derived a test for 'macro-realism' (the Leggett-Garg rule) that they predicted[226b] would be failed by all genuine quantum entities.

Several experiments have since validated[227a] the Leggett-Garg rule. One remarkable study reported[227b] in 2014 by a team at the University of Bonn in Germany found that even a relatively 'massive' caesium atom could not pass the test because it exhibits[227c] mysterious quantum superposition (manifests in more than one location at a time). These developments have dealt a blow to realist hopes for theoretical unification of the quantum and classical worlds.

Pseudo-particle simulations

The Leggett-Garg hurdle has forced theorists to search for new models of microscopic-macroscopic relationships. Since the mid-1970s, biophysicists struggling to decipher the structure and functions of sophisticated protein macromolecules have used[228] so-called 'coarse-grained' computer simulations that attempt to mimic out-of-sight molecular activity. In 2007, Johannes Kofler from the University of Vienna and Časlav Brukner from the Austrian Academy of Sciences proposed[229a] a similar approach to the conundrum of quantum particle transitions to everyday objects. As they explained[229b]:

> *"Conceptually different from the decoherence program, we present a novel theoretical approach to macroscopic realism and classical physics within quantum theory. It focuses on the limits of observability of quantum effects of macroscopic objects, i.e., on the required precision of our measurement apparatuses such that quantum phenomena can still be observed."*

A year later, Kofler and Brukner applied[230a] the ambitious concept to explain[230b] why we do not experience Leggett-Garg type difficulties with everyday large objects that are, after all, composites of unobservable wave-particles in uncertain locations. But they acknowledged that some quantum states are unlikely to manifest in nature *"because of their high computational complexity."*

Coarse-grained quantum simulations have been embraced by a desperate physics community. Still, as a team led by Christoph Simon from the University of Calgary in Canada showed[231a] in 2011, the efficacy of such models diminishes[231b] rapidly with increased size of systems due to[231c] formidable difficulties in making precise quantum measurements at macro level. Thus, even this virtual approach is subject to severe constraints that prevent us from gaining practical insights into the nature of particle transitions.

Bridging the gap

The search for a navigable bridge[232a] between hidden microscopic and visible macroscopic states of matter is keenly followed by information scientists researching[232b] the feasibility of quantum computers. Unlike the two-state 'bits' (binary digits) that encode data in ordinary computers, 'qubits' (theoretical units of quantum information) exist in superposed states and non-local entanglement with countless others – thus offering scope for *unlimited* encoding of data. However, decoherence renders qubits inherently unstable: the slightest interaction with our local world environment leads to[232c] rapid loss of quantum properties that confer infinite capacity.

Is the goal of reconciled domains that optimists like Vlatko Vedral hope for[233] achievable? Complete success could, in theory, put humans on a path to unprecedented knowledge for manipulation of physical reality at fundamental level. In a biblical sense, this will be akin to 'eating from the tree of life' and becoming 'like God' (Genesis 3:22). Of course, the 'elephant in the room' is still consciousness – its precise relationship[234] to the reality we perceive is perhaps the biggest mystery posed by quantum physics.

What you see is what you get

Although decoherence suggests transition of unobservable wave-particles to observable objects is irreversible, studies show[235a] reversibility is possible[235b] in a world where time flows *backwards*.[235c] But, whether we accept a 'one world' or 'many worlds' explanation, *how* and *why* humans exist as both 'observable entities' and 'conscious observers' remains as mysterious as the out-of-sight phenomena we're striving to understand. Early 20th century quantum theory pioneers chose to shrug their shoulders and adopt a 'Shut up and calculate' attitude. Now, their 21st century successors are advocating an even more pragmatic 'What you see is what you get' approach.

Probabilities and personal belief

Predictions of real-world trends are usually based on statistical sampling or measurement of observed patterns of *historical data*. In the 18th century, English statistician and theologian Thomas Bayes came up with a mathematical theorem that allowed[236a] the probability of some event or trend to be quantified in terms of a person's *rational belief* or *reasonable expectation*. This Bayesian 'doctrine of chances' was published[236b] posthumously by the Royal Society of London in 1763. A decade later, renowned French mathematician Pierre-Simon Laplace developed the concept into a practical tool for updating statistical inferences whenever new evidence comes to light.

As science historian Sharon Bertsch McGrayne recounted in her 2012 book *The Theory That Would Not Die*, the subjective Bayes-Laplace derivation was scorned as 'unscientific' in the 20th century and all but abandoned[237]. However, since the early 2000s, a group of physicists and philosophers have revived Bayesian probability to emphasise the role of a conscious observer in quantum theory.

In 2002, American physicists Carlton Caves and Christopher Fuchs, in collaboration with German mathematician Rüdiger Schack (CFS trio), published[238a] a pioneering proposal that used Bayesian individuality to resolve the myriad of probabilities posed by undetermined quantum states. They wrote:

"We argue that the distinction between classical and quantum probabilities lies not in their definition, but in the nature of the information they encode. In the classical world, maximal information about a physical system is <u>complete</u> in the sense of providing definite answers for all possible questions that can be asked of the system. In the quantum world, maximal information is <u>not</u> <u>complete</u> and <u>cannot be completed</u>."

65

CFR cited[238b] the 1935 argument of Einstein, Podolsky and Rosen (EPR) that quantum states cannot be *"real states of affairs"* since they only represent *partial* knowledge of entangled systems at any one time. Hence, the trio contended, it can be legitimately assumed that *"quantum states are states of knowledge"* and consequently *"all the probabilities derived from a quantum state, even a pure quantum state, depend on a state of knowledge; they are subjective or Bayesian probabilities."*

Fuchs introduced[239] the abbreviated term 'QBism' in 2010 for this *subjective* 'Quantum Bayesianism' view of reality that rests on personal belief or 'states of knowledge', as opposed to universal consensus arrived at by *objective* agreement on facts or states of affairs. In 2014, he co-authored an updated[240a] version with Schack and Cornell University physicist N. David Mermin that stressed[240b]:

"Unlike Copenhagen, QBism explicitly takes the "subjective" or "judgmental" or "personalist" view of probability, which, though common among contemporary statisticians and economists, is still rare among physicists: probabilities are assigned to an event by an agent and are particular to that agent. The agent's probability assignments express her own personal degrees of belief about the event."

In other words, reality is an entirely personalised construction from optional quantum probabilities that may or may not accord with the views of others. Unsurprisingly, as Mermin acknowledged in a 2012 commentary[241], contemporaries are highly sceptical about such a relativist interpretation; they fear it risks undermining objective science and the consensus reality that has glued societies together for thousands of years. Nevertheless, Fuchs and Schack boldly reasserted[242a] in another 2014 paper[242b] that *"In QBism (or quantum Bayesianism) a quantum state does not represent an element of physical reality but an agent's personal probability assignments [...] QBism's agent-centered worldview can be seen as a development of ideas expressed in Schrödinger's essay 'Nature and the Greeks'."*

However, in a 2015 critique[243a], American theoretical physicist and science historian Michael Nauenberg refuted the argument that *"apparent"* non-locality of particles justifies highly-personal QBism. He complained the proposal *"effectively denies that the outcome of experiments are described by permanent records, independently of the views of any particular observer or so-called "agent.""* Fuchs, Mermin and Schack replied[243b] that attempts to square clearly inherent non-locality of particles with objective interpretations of reality are responsible for *"broad and irreconcilable disagreement even after 90 years ... of widespread confusion"* in quantum physics. They explained why the matter can't be divorced from wider philosophical considerations:

> *"QBism is not about the validity of quantum mechanics, but about how to understand the basic concepts that appear in the theory: states, probabilities, measurements, and outcomes. [...] QBism is a genuinely novel way of thinking about the function of science. It raises subtle questions about the nature of science, the nature of human experience, and the relation of scientists to each other and to the world they are attempting to understand."*

The concept has added yet another layer of discord to the already contentious debate about the meaning of quantum phenomena. Still, Fuchs again defended the CFS view of reality in a 2015 *Quanta* interview[244]; although he admitted it raises new questions that are just as difficult and uncomfortable as those it seeks to answer.

Whose reality is it anyway?

Apart from Einstein's famous enquiry whether other animals have conscious capacity to create physical reality, no one has established a testable basis for human mind-matter interactions. Even German physicist-philosopher Gustav Fechner's 19th century psychophysical laws, which attempt to track[245a] and quantify mental response to sensory stimuli, do not suggest[245b] any direct processing links between the organic brain and its inorganic environment.

67

Tunnelling revelations

There's now growing speculation that consciousness may be linked to[246] another mysterious phenomenon known as 'quantum tunnelling' – the ability of wave-particles like electrons to traverse physical or energy barriers *effortlessly* and *instantaneously*; regardless of mass or distance. The fascinating behaviour was discussed in, at least, one 1928 report[247a] while quantum physics was still emerging. But the full implications only became apparent in 1962 when American electronics engineer Thomas Hartman deduced[247b] from calculations that particle tunnelling time might actually be *zero* (no detectable delay); a startling and controversial proposal that threatens to overturn the long-standing speed limit for everything in nature set by Einstein's special relativity. Bizarrely, indications are that[247c] the thicker or higher the barrier, the faster the tunnelling proceeds.

Experimental results obtained in the early 1990s by German physicist Günter Nimtz and co-researcher Achim Enders suggest[248a] that particle time travel is indeed[248b] superluminal (faster-than-light). But how could this be happening? Nimtz published a review[248c] in 2011 that described tunnelling entities as 'virtual particles' which exhibit 'non-local' signalling. This implies that *all* particles (matter or electromagnetic) can 'pop up' *anywhere* in our universe at will, whether or not there's quantum entanglement with 'partners'. However, the notion that superluminality and non-locality might be manifesting *even within* the reality we observe is hotly disputed.

Physicists agree[249] that a particle has to be in wave-form to achieve such miraculous barrier-tunnelling. Accordingly, Ghanaian-American engineer and scientist Herbert Winful argued consistently in 2002[250a], 2003[250b], and 2006[250c] that it's an error to assign a speed or velocity value since waves 'propagate' and don't have capacity for superluminal mechanical travel in the sense used by Newton and

68

Einstein. Winful attributed[250d] the near-zero barrier traversing time observed in some experiments to *"a lifetime of stored energy or stored probability escaping through both ends of the barrier"*.

Winful's stance appeared vindicated when a team from the Max Planck Institute for Nuclear Physics in Germany announced[251a] in 2017 that they had used an ingenious technique to measure[251b] particle tunnelling time at between 80 to 180 attoseconds (reckoned as 1×10^{-18} or one *quintillionth* or a *billionth of a billionth* of a second). However, Nimtz and Horst Aichmann (another long-time co-researcher) counter-argued[251c] that virtual particles don't spend 'physical time' inside a barrier that can be measured – a complication Paul Davies alluded to[251d] in a 2004 contribution.

The case for zero-time particle tunnelling received a major boost from a new measurement[252a] of just 1.8 attoseconds reported[252b] by an international collaboration in 2019. Another study led by Aephraim Steinberg at the University of Toronto in Canada highlighted[253a] the complexities of time measurements at quantum level. Steinberg noted[253b] in July 2020 that it seems as though a particle *"appears on the far side without ever crossing the middle"* of a barrier. These developments have prompted[253c] reluctant admission that particle tunnelling may, after all, be superluminal; albeit with the caveat[253d] that this still doesn't imply superluminal *signalling* because (unlike entangled partners) it's unlikely that single particles can transmit information across barriers in, literally, no time whatsoever.

However, Nicolas Gisin, a physicist and quantum information pioneer at the University of Geneva, pointed out[254a] in a 2005 contribution on the 100th anniversary of Einstein's 'miraculous year' that the notion of non-local signalling actually goes back to 17th century classical physics. Gisin quoted[254b] Sir Isaac Newton's equally troubled reaction to the seemingly *instantaneous* effect of gravity across cosmic space and time:

"That Gravity should be innate, inherent and essential to Matter, so that one Body may act upon another at a Distance thro a Vacuum, without the mediation of anything else, by and through which their Action and Force may be conveyed from one to another, is to me so great an Absurdity, that I believe no Man who has in philosophical Matters a competent Faculty of thinking, can ever fall into it. Gravity must be caused by an Agent acting constantly according to certain Laws, but whether this Agent be material or immaterial, I have left to the Consideration of my Readers."

In 2012, Gisin and a group of international colleagues proved mathematically[255a] that, if we rule out the notion that particles can communicate at faster-than-light speeds, the only other[255b] explanation for their quantum entanglement is that each bit of the universe is, somehow, instantly connectable to bits elsewhere. The co-researchers concluded in their report:

"If we want to keep no-signalling, it shows that quantum non-locality must necessarily relate discontinuously parts of the universe that are arbitrarily distant. This gives further weight to the idea that quantum correlations somehow arise from outside spacetime, in the sense that no story in space and time can describe how they occur."

A deeper reality

Interestingly, as Dennis Gabor showed in 1948, every bit of a holographic projection[256] is interconnected and holds *the same* amount of information as the whole since each bit represents light scattered from *every point* on the recorded 3-D object or scene. Hence, even if a hologram is severed or disrupted into tiny pieces, the whole projection can still be seen in each piece – as long as it contains the interference pattern of the original light waves that were superimposed to produce the recording. In addition to this extraordinary universality, the level of detail and amount of information captured at microscopic level makes holograms ideal for speedy and efficient storage, retrieval, and processing of large amounts of information – the perfect tool for archiving infinite data from quantum information processing at scales required for recording and projecting a vast enterprise like our universe.

The possibility that we're virtual products of a deeper, unknown reality is now a serious consideration in physics. As Princeton University astrophysicist and computer scientist Piet Hut asserted in a brief 2000 essay[257a], the ultimate message of quantum mechanics is that there are no 'things' in reality; only unexplained 'actions'. He compared the reluctance of realist colleagues to accept this state of affairs to their tendency to hold on to familiar computer languages. Hut remarked: *"Similarly, our understanding of the material world, including the very notion of what matter and existence is, is likely to keep changing radically over the next few hundred years. In what direction, we have no idea."*

But is scientific insistence on empirical evidence sustainable? French theoretical physicist and philosopher of science Bernard d'Espagnat summed up the dilemma of physical science researchers in a 2009 article[257b]:

'I believe that some of our most engrained notions about space and causality should be reconsidered. Anyone who takes quantum mechanics seriously will have reached the same conclusion. What quantum mechanics tells us, I believe, is surprising to say the least. It tells us that the basic components of objects – the particles, electrons, quarks etc. – cannot be thought of as "self-existent". The reality that they, and hence all objects, are components of is merely "empirical reality". This reality is something that, while not a purely mind-made construct as radical idealism would have it, can be but the picture our mind forces us to form of ... Of what? The only answer I am able to provide is that underlying this empirical reality is a mysterious, non-conceptualisable "ultimate reality", not embedded in space and (presumably) not in time either."

71

Indeed. Accepting that we can only ever conceive quantum correlations and universal non-locality in mathematical terms has profound implications for human understanding of the nature and causality of our existence. Anton Zeilinger (erstwhile President of the Austrian Academy of Sciences) expressed hope in a 2016 essay[257c] that *"an understanding is possible via the notion of information"*, but suggested we need *"a new deep analysis of space-time"* to make progress. He concluded: *"The hope is that in the end we will have new physics analogous to Einstein's new physics in the two theories of relativity."* However, renowned Canadian physicist William G. Unruh advised in a 2017 discussion paper[257d] that *"it is best not to think of quantum mechanics as non-local, but rather that it is non-realistic."*

From moment to moment

What, then, are laypersons to make of quantum mysteries? Are we really immersed in an aether-like sea of consciousness that wave-particles traverse spontaneously to create the world we perceive? Despite disagreements among physicists and philosophers about the nature of light and matter *after* manifestation in our physical world, there's general consensus that everything springs from superposed abstractions computed in some unobservable domain that remain entangled with the things we do observe. Moreover, evidence is emerging that quantum effects are the foundation for life itself. As German nanoscientist Frank Trixler wrote[258] in a 2013 review: *"physical and chemical processes which are crucial in theories about the origin and evolution of life can be traced directly back to the effects of quantum tunnelling."*

Intriguingly, it now appears that even the *unpredictability* of fortunes and events experienced in everyday life is rooted in the essence of things in the quantum realm. In 2012, a Canadian-Swiss collaborative research group published[259a] compelling experimental data that we can't predict accurate outcomes at quantum level; regardless how much information we have beforehand.

72

The unsettling implication is that our uncertain 'moment to moment' existence stems from fundamental algorithms in nature. In a subtle allusion to Einstein's insistence that 'God does not play dice', co-researcher Renato Renner from the Institute for Theoretical Physics (ETH) in Zurich quipped[259b]: *"In other words, not only does God 'play dice,' but his dice are fair."*

The finding of inherent uncertainty is indirectly supported by another study reported[260a] in 2015 by a group of European mathematicians and computer scientists. The interdisciplinary team found that, at quantum level, it's quite impossible to determine the spectral gap of matter – the energy needed to 'excite' an electron to a high-enough level for interactions. Their theoretical calculations also indicated that adding just *one* particle to a large object of any size could dramatically change its properties. This means even 100 percent information on the microscopic properties of a substance at a particular point in time is not enough to predict its macroscopic behaviour a single attosecond later.

Report co-author Michael Wolf from Technical University of Munich in Germany commented[260b]:

"We knew about the possibility of problems that are undecidable in principle since the works of Turing and Gödel in the 1930s. So far, however, this only concerned the very abstract corners of theoretical computer science and mathematical logic. No one had seriously contemplated this as a possibility right in the heart of theoretical physics before. But our results change this picture.

"From a more philosophical perspective, they also challenge the reductionists' point of view, as the insurmountable difficulty lies precisely in the derivation of macroscopic properties from a microscopic description."

Epistemic implications

Over 140 years before the advent of quantum physics, German philosopher Immanuel Kant tackled the relationship between mind constructs and physical experience. In his classic treatise[261a] *Critique of Pure Reason* (1781), Kant separated[261b] knowable 'phenomena' from unknowable 'noumena' and 'things-in-themselves' that may have independent existence. He pointedly cautioned against assumptions that we have the capacity to define or perceive total reality.

The quantum conundrum has laid bare the limits of our ability to acquire reliable knowledge about *anything*. We're unable to see past the mathematical veil drawn over causality at fundamental level. If, as several proposals suggest, our reality is a *subjective* selection from multiple quantum probabilities, it's hardly surprising that we've evolved such diverse (or even disparate) worldviews. The challenge is to explain to those claiming cultural, religious or moral supremacy that our differences are an inherent feature of the universe; no one has access to (or can even conceive) ultimate truth.

The inference that we're, essentially, virtual constructs ought to influence how we conduct our worldly affairs – especially how we treat other living beings (including non-humans). It should also induce reflection on the possible fate of our information 'states of being' when the quanta of light that illuminates our mortal sojourn is extinguished. Ancient philosophers did not have access to insights from quantum mechanics, but they had the rationality and intuition to understand that the many unknowns in nature are enough reason to live and die with humility. As a biblical sage observed:

> *"Surely the fate of human beings is like that of the animals; the same fate waits them both: As one dies, so does the other. All have the same breath; man has no advantage over the animal. Everything is meaningless. All go to the same place; all come from dust, and to dust all return."*
(Ecclesiates 3:19-20, NIV)

74

2. Out of Nowhere

When you read or hear anything about the birth of the universe, someone is making it up. We are in the realm of philosophy. Only God knows what happened at the very beginning (and so far he/she hasn't let on).
Leon Lederman, physicist, in *The God Particle* (1993) chap. 1[262]

A cosmos with no pre-history

Quantum theory describes the emergence of tiny, building blocks of matter from wave-particles that appear to fluctuate in and out of an unobservable realm. Scientific hypotheses on the origin of huge, observable cosmic structures are just as fascinating.

Until the early 20th century, religious creation myths were the dominant narratives on origination of the universe; the boundaries of which were thought to be defined by our Milky Way galaxy[263a] which hosts *billions* of stars. Einstein's relativity theories[263b], and vastly improved equipment that allowed observation of distant celestial phenomena, gave scientists unprecedented insights into cosmic mysteries. It soon became clear that the universe encompasses[263c] *countless* galaxies with *trillions* of stars, and might even be infinite.

A dynamic cosmos

Einstein's calculations suggested the universe was a flexible environment in which things and events are observed differently, depending on one's location and velocity. But this was inconsistent with the fixed, unchanging model he and other early 20th century astronomers supported. Einstein therefore derived solutions to his general relativity equations using a contrived 'cosmological constant' – a hypothetical unknown force that kept the universe static.

75

However, Russian physicist and mathematician Alexander Friedmann showed[264a] between 1922 and 1924 that Einstein's equations could be solved *without* a cosmological constant. This suggested[264b], for the first time, that the universe has capacity to *expand* or *contract* and, thus, may have a structure that's flat, spherical, open or closed. Subsequently, Georges Lemaître, a Belgian priest who was also an astrophysicist and cosmologist, claimed in a 1927 French article (reprinted[264c] by an English journal in 1931) that he had derived results that confirmed our universe was actually *expanding*. Lemaître even provided an estimated value for the rate of expansion.

Einstein initially dismissed Lemaître's findings. As with the weird physics of tiny particles at quantum level, he could not bring himself to accept the implications of his own brilliant work on gigantic objects at cosmological level. But confirmatory observations by astronomers soon forced him to accept[265] that the universe was, indeed, expanding – overturning yet another dogma in physics.

Big Bang: A creation event?

Buoyed by Einstein's endorsement of a non-static universe, Lemaître boldly speculated[266a] in 1931 that *"If we go back in the course of time we must find fewer and fewer quanta, until we find all the energy of the universe packed in a few or even in a unique quantum."* It was, he suggested[266b], the explosion of this tightly compressed 'primeval atom' that hurled matter and energy in all directions and kick-started space and time. He explained:

> *"If the world has begun with a single quantum, the notions of space and time would altogether fail to have any meaning at the beginning; they would only begin to have a sensible meaning when the original quantum had been divided into a sufficient number of quanta. If this suggestion is correct, the beginning of the world happened a little before the beginning of space and time."*

Lemaître also asserted that the homogeneous universe which emerged from this unique event has continued to expand at an *accelerating* rate. This hypothesis was quite revolutionary[266c], but it was supported by American astronomer Edwin Hubble's factual observation that the universe is definitely expanding at great speed. Nevertheless, contemporaries were sceptical because of Lemaître's deep Catholic faith: his description of a universe emerging instantaneously *ex nihilo* (Latin for 'out of nothing') was seen as an attempt to foster belief[266d] in divine creation on 'A day without yesterday'. But he denied any such bias and countered: *"As far as I can see, such a theory remains entirely outside any metaphysical or religious question. It leaves the materialist free to deny any transcendental Being ... For the believer, it removes any attempt at familiarity with God."*

Lemaître is now acknowledged[267a] as the pioneer of modern theoretical cosmology. However, mainstream resistance to his 'Big Bang' hypothesis persisted for decades – the term was actually a derisive description coined[267b] in 1949 by English astronomer Sir Fred Hoyle who strongly opposed[267c] what he saw as 'back door' importation of theology into science. Prior to Einstein's acceptance of Lemaître's findings in 1931, he had privately considered[268a] an alternative 'steady-state' universe that had no beginning, has always existed, and will always exist. The concept was independently revived[268b] and reworked[268c] in separate 1948 papers by Hoyle and colleagues Hermann Bondi and Thomas Gold. They proposed that ongoing expansion might be fuelled by creation of matter from *empty* space. But it was unclear[268d] how this could be happening.

The matter was settled when left-over radiation predicted by Lemaître – a *cosmic microwave background* (CMB) – was detected[269a] in 1965. Stunning extra-galactic events observed[269b] in 1998 confirmed another key Big Bang prediction: expansion of the universe *is* rapidly accelerating.

A fine-tuned cosmos

Cosmologists date[270a] Big Bang at nearly 14 billion years ago. This unique event is thought to have occurred *outside* known physical laws and constraints in a tiny fraction of a second at faster-than-light speeds. However, in the 1970s, it dawned on scientists that the ordered, life-supporting universe that we inhabit would not exist if it was spawned exactly as imagined. Among other issues, a violent explosion of that magnitude would not yield the uniformly isotropic distribution of matter and flat landscape we observe in *all* directions. Until recently, these key anomalies known as the Horizon[270b] and Flatness[270c] problems could only be explained in terms of 'fine-tuned' initial factors arranged by some unknown agency.

Anthropic Principle

In 1973, Australian theoretical physicist Brandon Carter argued[271a] that fine-tuning of the nascent universe was a *natural* pre-condition for eventual emergence of intelligent observers like humans. As South African mathematician and cosmologist George Ellis related in a 2011 review[271b], Carter's 'anthropic principle' introduced the controversial idea of *purposive* 'observers of nature' (already integral to quantum theory) into large-scale cosmology. The theme was adopted and expanded in *The Anthropic Cosmological Principle* (1986); a historical review of similar proposals by cosmologists John D. Barrow and Frank J. Tipler. The authors argued[272a] that the appearance and survival of intelligent, information-processing, carbon-based life is a predetermined[272b] outcome of a meta-programmed universe. Tipler asserted in a later 2003 article[272c] that *"the quantum mechanical principle of unitarity"* is actually a form of teleology which *"requires intelligent life to survive to the end of time."* The extraordinary and profound implications continue to stir widespread debate[272d].

Inflating our bubble

In 1979, American theoretical physicist Alan Guth hit upon a more 'scientific' way to explain the universe's uniformity and flatness anomalies and reconcile Lemaître's Big Bang with our life-friendly habitat (a problem Paul Davies dubbed[273a] 'The Goldilocks Enigma'). As outlined in a paper eventually published[273b] in January 1981, Guth proposed that the universe could have started as a quantum 'point' bubble with a self-contained scalar energy field in a false vacuum state (somewhat similar to Einstein's mysterious cosmological constant). It was, he speculated, this primordial entity that *inflated* rapidly and exponentially to an initial size as particles in wave-form tunnelled into a true vacuum – loosely comparable to instantaneous pumping-up of a tiny, infinitely dense balloon. Such a dramatic event would have caused[273c] the founding bubble to heat up rapidly and supercool; thus accumulating huge potential energy for subsequent gradual expansion into the universe we observe.

Researchers at the European particle physics facility CERN later coined[274a] the term 'inflaton' for quanta in the 'birthing' energy field that became the first particles of matter. However, as Guth admitted: *"Unfortunately, the scenario seems to lead to some unacceptable consequences, so modifications must be sought."* One problem is explaining how the supercooling phase ended, and the bubble managed to reheat to stupendously high energies needed for formation of observable matter from fundamental particles. Another is total 'blankness' on the *origin* of the proposed inflaton energy field and, indeed, absence of any firm evidence that it ever existed.

In October 1981, Russian-American theoretical physicist Andrei Linde (then at the Lebedev Physical Institute in Moscow) showed that[274b] initial expansion could have been enabled by a 'slow rolling' inflaton energy field, rather than abrupt wave-particle tunnelling (American contemporaries Paul Steinhardt and Andreas Albrecht submitted[274c] a similar proposal three months later).

79

But, although the idea resolved 'cold-to-hot' reheating mysteries in the early universe, it resurrected inexplicable fine-tuning since it implies pre-matter quantum inflatons *already had* optimum energy and mass to spawn the entire universe.

Another startling implication soon dawned on inflation pioneers: it's possible that similar 'birthing' events *have continued* elsewhere in the unobservable universe. In 1983, Steinhardt hypothesised[275a] how such 'eternal inflation' might be occurring and Ukrainian-American colleague Alexander Vilenkin introduced[275b] a version of quantum tunnelling that showed *all* inflation models lead to a multiverse of never-ending bubble universes. Linde eventually consolidated[275c] these incredible ideas in a 1986 proposal for an *"Eternally existing self-reproducing chaotic inflationary universe."*

While some physicists enthusiastically embraced the idea of a limitless multiverse as the solution[276a] to fine-tuning problems, others worried that this approach creates an entirely new dilemma: how can you even begin to map and quantify an *eternal* cosmic structure of infinite proportions? The insurmountable difficulties led Paul Steinhardt to doubt the entire concept. As he protested[276b] to *Quanta* in 2014: *"Our universe has a simple, natural structure. The multiverse idea is baroque, unnatural, untestable and, in the end, dangerous to science and society."*

Endless reincarnation

In the 1960s, a team of Princeton University theorists researching cosmic microwave radiation from Big Bang had considered[277a] another type of eternal model: a *closed* universe which expands and contracts over hot and cold epochs. Steinhardt teamed up with American colleagues Justin Khoury and Burt Ovrut in the early 2000s to conduct research with South African physicist Neil Turok on a similar[277b] 'ekpyrotic' universe that slowly contracts *almost* into a singularity before 'bouncing back' in a fresh cycle[277c] of expansion.

Steinhardt later collaborated with German physicist and cosmologist Anna Ijjas to develop a refined version[277d] of a cyclical model that can be tested indirectly. To the bemusement of erstwhile Inflation co-theorists, Steinhardt abandoned[278a] the idea altogether and became one of its strongest critics[278b].

The concept of an eternally reincarnating universe has since won some converts[278c]. Interestingly, as Brazilian cosmologists Mario Novello and Santiago Perez-Bergliaffa observed in a 2008 review[278d], similar models of the universe feature in many ancient religions and philosophies (Babylonian, Egyptian, Greek, Indian, Mayan and Aztec among others).

However, among several unresolved matters, it's unclear exactly how thermodynamic entropy (tendency of energy and matter to *disperse* rather than aggregate), and the mysterious force driving accelerating expansion (Einstein's cosmological constant), can be overcome in a *contracting* universe before it's 'bounced' into a reversal and gets 'born again'[279a]. There's also the issue of time: would inhabitants of a deflating world experience 'backward flow' of events? In 2014, British physicist Julian Barbour and Canadian colleagues Tim Koslowski and Flavio Mercati showed that[279b], in theory, time can indeed flow in two directions from a Janus-like starting point to create[279c] *different* futures from *the same* past.

Whatever the mechanisms and sequences, any reversal that ends[280a] in a so-called[280b] 'Big Crunch' would extinguish life on earth as we know it. Our observable horizon is limited by the speed of light, so signals from a collapse that started at the edge of the universe would have travelled many light-years before detection – leaving us little time to adapt (assuming we've advanced enough to make survival even possible).

Unsurprisingly, Big Bang, as modified by the Inflation model, remains[281a] the favoured origin explanation among mainstream physicists – despite[281b] the uncomfortable multiverse implication. As Princeton University astrophysicist J. Richard Gott explained[281c] in a 2017 essay:

> *"It seems pretty clear that once you get inflation started, it is hard to stop it. Inflation should go on forever, creating a multiverse that will continue to spawn bubble universes eternally. Although we can't see these other bubble universes, we have theoretical reasons to believe that they exist, because inflation seems to imply that our Universe is not a one-time event. But perhaps the best evidence for inflation in the early Universe is the fact that we see a low-grade version of inflation starting in the Universe now: the current accelerated expansion of the Universe."*

How did it all start?

Modern scientific narratives on origination of our universe have revived millennia-old arguments about ultimate causation. Regardless of worldview, it's hard to argue convincingly that the ordered cosmos we behold (and its underlying mathematical matrix) evolved without any primordial agency and for absolutely no reason. Proposals that everything stems from random 'uncaused' events quickly run into a dead-end of infinite regress[282a] that offers no plausible[282b] answers.

Unmoved mover

Aristotle blended[283a] physics and metaphysics in an early description of a non-physical 'unmoved' or 'prime' mover that set everything in the physical universe into motion. The concept was adopted nearly 1,000 years later by medieval theophilosopher St. Thomas Aquinas (c. 1225–1274) in a 'necessary being' proof[283b] for the existence of God. Such 'first cause' propositions are now known as the Cosmological Argument[283c].

Genesis controversy

In 1987, Arvind Borde, a mathematician and cosmologist at Tufts University in Massachusetts, teamed up[284a] with colleague Alexander Vilenkin to investigate whether it can be proven mathematically that time, as we experience it, had a definable starting point. Remarkably, Borde and Vilenkin succeeded in devising a theorem with Alan Guth (eventually published[284b] in 2003) that showed even an ever-inflating multiverse must have had a *definite beginning*. In other words, physicists can't avoid a Genesis-like origination event. As the trio (dubbed BGV) put it, *"inflationary models require physics other than inflation to describe the past boundary of the inflating region of spacetime."*

However, in 2004, cosmologist Sean M. Carroll (a prominent atheism advocate) and graduate researcher Jennifer Chen at the University of Chicago issued a challenge to the BGV conclusion. They contended that[285a], when all aspects of quantum mechanics are considered holistically, *"spontaneous eternal inflation can provide a natural explanation for the thermodynamic arrow of time"*, and *"inflation occurs asymptotically both forwards and backwards in time, implying a universe that is (statistically) time-symmetric on ultra-large scales."* Essentially, Carroll and Chen depicted the universe as a de Sitter construct completely governed by natural laws that 'ping pongs' between being flat and rapid expansion to any number of symmetries or dimensions. In this scenario, they argued, it becomes meaningless to contemplate any 'beginning' for the universe since time is eternally 'bounced' from forward to backward modes between entropy boundaries.

Vilenkin countered in a 2013 response[285b] that the Carroll-Chen 'time-symmetric' model for the universe (and similar proposals) still can't evade the mathematically-derived BGV origination paradigm because, whether inflation of our bubble is seen as an event in the distant past or indeterminate future, the phenomenon *must have started* from an infinitely dense singularity.

The point was reasserted in a review[285c] Vilenkin co-authored with Audrey Mithani – they showed that *all* 'birthing' models for the universe (eternally inflating, cyclic, or hibernating 'seed') need a starting point in time. According to Vilenkin, the reason for continued controversy over BGV theorem is not because it lacks scientific merit. He explained in a 2012 Tufts University interview[285d]:

"For many physicists, the beginning of the universe is uncomfortable, because it suggests that something must have caused the beginning, that there should be some cause outside the universe. In fact, we now have models where that's not necessary—the universe spontaneously appears, quantum mechanically.

"In quantum physics, events do not necessarily have a cause, just some probability. As such, there is some probability for the universe to pop out of "nothing." You can find the relative probability for it to be this size or that size and have various properties, but there will not be a particular cause for any of it, just probabilities.

"I say "nothing" in quotations because the nothing that we were referring to here is the absence of matter, space and time. That is as close to nothing as you can get, but what is still required here is the laws of physics. So the laws of physics should still be there, and they are definitely not nothing."

So, how did it all begin? Vilenkin admitted frankly:

"I cannot really claim that I understand the beginning of the universe. We have a picture which kind of makes sense, which I think is an achievement. Because, if you think about it, you say, "OK, what happened before the Big Bang, before inflation?" It seems you can keep asking these questions and the answer is impossible."

More holographic clues

In a 2007 essay[286a], Paul Davies chided colleagues for continuing to dodge the *"inconvenient truth"* of a fine-tuned universe. He wrote:

> *"The root cause of all the difficulty can be traced to the fact that both religion and science appeal to some agency outside the universe to explain its lawlike order. [.....] I propose instead that the laws are more like computer software: programs being run on the great cosmic computer. They emerge with the universe at the big bang and are inherent in it, not stamped on it from without like a maker's mark."*

Indeed, there's now general consensus[286b] that foundational matter did not 'explode' outward into *existing* cosmic space. Rather, *space-time itself* emerged from a primordial vacuum and continues to propagate like a ball's surface with self-contained energy. According to physicists, matter for gigantic galaxies (and all they contain) is being mysteriously generated by quantum fluctuations of virtual particles along the way. In this scenario, there's no centre; all points of the universe that are now rapidly receding from each other were once part of the founding singularity. Astronomers calculate that the observable horizon stretches for about 46.5 billion light-years in all directions. But it's impossible to say for sure if the universe has a 'boundary' or if it's an infinite structure.

In an earlier commentary[286c], Davies stressed his opposition to the idea of a boundless multiverse fuelled by endless inflation:

> *"Taking the multiverse theory at face value, therefore, means accepting that virtual worlds are more numerous than "real" ones. There is no reason to expect our world – the one in which you are reading this right now – to be real as opposed to a simulation. And the simulated inhabitants of a virtual world stand in the same relationship to the simulating system as human beings stand in relation to the traditional Creator."*

85

But what if we're really *"simulated inhabitants of a virtual world"*? Several alternatives to an eternally-inflating multiverse propose a finite outcome not that long after quantum fluctuation produced the 'founding egg' – a *holographic bubble* that eventually evolved internal observers like humans. Theoretical physicists Arshad Momen and Rakibur Rahman suggested[287a] in 2011 that such a model might explain why we perceive the observable universe in three spatial dimensions (3-D); it helps to create the illusion of physical reality. A Canadian team centred at the University of Waterloo in Ontario wondered[287b] in 2014 whether the singularity that spawned everything is hidden behind a holographic 'causal horizon' *outside* the universe.

Notably, celebrated English mathematician and cosmologist Stephen Hawking's final hypothesis[288a] on origin, co-authored with Belgian colleague Thomas Hertog in 2018, used the hologram model to formulate[288b] an 'exit strategy' from eternal inflation that could produce a universe which is *"finite and reasonably smooth."* Hawking and Hertog observed:

"The holographic form has led to a fruitful and promising application of holographic techniques to early universe cosmology. No field theories have been identified that correspond to top-down models of realistic cosmologies where inflation transitions to a decelerating phase. However we find that many of the known AdS/CFT duals are ideally suited to study eternal inflation from a holographic viewpoint."

Missing cosmic chunks

There are other indications that our reality is a virtual projection from beyond our observable horizon that's programmed to self-propagate according to meta-information hidden in extra dimensions. As Paul Dirac accidentally[289a] discovered in 1928, each of the matter particles which make up everyday objects has an antimatter partner that has remained[289b] stubbornly elusive despite decades of research.

Now, physicists and astronomers are wondering[289c] if these mysterious 'absentees' hold the key to other anomalies detected in our universe.

Dark matter

Stars in spiral galaxies move in fairly stable orbits around a central bulgy mass. According to Newton's principle of universal gravitation and Einstein's geometric update within general relativity, the *farther* away an orbiting star is from the centre of its galaxy the *lower* should be its acceleration and speed.

In 1922, Dutch astronomer Jacobus Kapteyn deduced[290a] from observational data that stars in our Milky Way were moving at much faster speeds than expected from their orbital radius. A decade later, Kapteyn's compatriot Jan Oort made a similar inference[290b] from discrepancies in the computed mass[290c] of visible stars. These puzzling results were confirmed[290d] in 1933 by Swiss astronomer Fritz Zwicky while studying the Coma cluster of galaxies.

Clearly, the gravitational pull of visible matter in galaxies of that size was insufficient to keep them 'clumped together' at observed high orbiting speeds. The startling and unavoidable conclusion[291] was that a huge quantity of existing but *invisible* cosmic mass must be providing extra gravitational 'glue'; otherwise galaxies would, literally, fly apart. However, the mystery of the so-called 'dark matter' was more or less 'shelved' for another 40 years.

Then, in the early 1970s, American astronomer Vera Rubin and colleague Kent Ford at Carnegie Institution of Washington made a new discovery. They found that[292a], not only were regions of the Andromeda galaxy rotating too fast for their observed mass, most stars were actually orbiting at roughly the *same speed* regardless of their distance from the galaxy's centre. The unexpected finding upset crucial assumptions[292b] in astrophysics and forced cosmologists[292c] to address the old issue of missing cosmic mass.

Apart from galaxy rotation anomalies, another indication of hidden background matter has emerged. As a consequence of his redefinition of gravity in terms of space-time curvature, Einstein predicted[293] that the gravitational field of stars in galaxies would 'bend' light emitted from even more distant cosmic objects like quasars and cause a magnified, multiple-image appearance that's proportional to their mass. Image distortion from what's now known as gravitational lensing was detected[294a] in 1979, and a team at the Sloan Digital Sky Survey (SDSS) in New Mexico, USA reported[294b] the first confirmed cosmic magnification observation in 2005. Additionally, precise SDSS data analysis revealed[294c] far greater lensing effects than could be attributed to the visible cosmic matter; a discrepancy that confirmed[294d] extra mass was lurking somewhere.

Although it's been dubbed[295a] 'dark matter' because it doesn't emit, reflect or absorb any electromagnetic radiation (including light), physicists acknowledge that the missing mass may be completely transparent[295b] or even exist in some dimension outside our 4-D reality. However, no one knows what it consists of – hypothetical particles like axions[295c] and WIMPs[295d] have been suggested, but there have been no confirmed detections. Following a disappointing 2013 attempt[296a] at LUX in South Dakota, USA (the world's most advanced facility for investigation of dark matter), Richard Gaitskell from Brown University, Rhode Island admitted[296b]:

"We saw nothing. We do not have a single dark matter candidate event. We have entered the new millennium and yet we still have no idea what 95% of the universe is made of. Our level of ignorance is quite staggering, and it's one of the largest challenges we have right now."

Nevertheless, after reviewing all available data and analyses at a 2014 symposium in Los Angeles, 190 scientists from around the world reaffirmed[296c] the existence of out-of-sight dark matter.

The invisible mass is thought to surround[297a] visible galaxies in halo-like spheres. However, it's unclear if these halos interact in ways other than gravity with ordinary, baryonic matter that's composed of recognised particles in our universe. American physicist and astronomer James Bullock proposed[297b] in 2015 that dark matter may only 'self-interact' in a parallel, invisible sector. But, just a year later, a statistical analysis of 36 'mini-spiral' galaxies by Italian astrophysicist Paolo Salucci and co-researcher Ekaterina Karukes uncovered[297c] striking correlations between dark matter halos and the cosmic mass they enclose – a significant insight that suggests hidden interactions may be taking place. Salucci remarked[297d] in a press release:

"From our observations, the phenomenon, and thus the necessity, is incredibly obvious. At the same time, this can be a starting point for exploring this new kind of physics. Even in the largest spiral galaxies we find effects similar to the ones we observed [....]. These 36 items are the tip of the iceberg of a phenomenon that we will probably find everywhere and that will help us discover what we cannot yet see."

Intriguingly, a collaboration of cosmologists and particle physicists at Durham University in England also reported[298a] in 2014 that a computer simulation, which assumed regular interactions between particles of 'cold' dark matter and light photons, surprisingly resolved[298b] the long-standing problem of far less observed satellite galaxies around our Milky Way than predicted by formation models. The result indicates that the mysterious features of nature deduced mathematically at minuscule quantum level also apply at mega-cosmic levels. As lead study author Celine Boehm explained: *"By tuning the strength of the scattering of particles, we change the number of small galaxies, which lets us learn more about the physics of dark matter and how it might interact with other particles in the Universe. This is an example of how a cosmological measurement, in this case the number of galaxies orbiting the Milky Way, is affected by the microscopic scales of particle physics."*

Variable gravity?

Continued failure to physically detect dark matter (directly or indirectly) has prompted some physicists to consider other ideas. The most popular alternative uses modified laws of gravity to dispense with the need for extra clumping to hold galaxies together in cosmological models. Proponents contend we don't know enough about gravity to predict (as Einstein did) that the weak levels we observe at relatively small scales in our solar system also apply at much larger intergalactic scales.

In 1983, Israeli astrophysicist Mordehai Milgrom pioneered a *Modified Newtonian Dynamics* (MOND) model in three seminal papers that argued, 1) it's possible gravity is stronger[299a] than predicted at large distances from the centre of galaxies; 2) adjusted gravity allows velocities of stars in galaxies to be reconciled[299b] with their actual, observed masses; and 3) new derived values eliminate the need[299c] to assume large amounts of hidden mass must exist in galaxy systems.

Milgrom's idea has slowly gained credence among initially sceptical colleagues. Advocates argue that, among other things, it explains[300a] the small-scale structure and curious distribution of ordinary matter within galaxies like our Milky Way much better than dark matter models. However, as it was conceived as an adjunct rather than a full cosmology theory, it doesn't account for the formation[300b] and large-scale clustering[300c] of galaxies along with inter-galactic buffer zones. Furthermore, early MOND models only proposed adjustments to Newton's old law of gravity and did not address Einstein's geometric model based on general relativity. Milgrom teamed up with Jacob Bekenstein to tackle[301a] these deficiencies in 1984 and the latter attempted a solo remedy[301b] in 2004. Still, critics are adamant[301c] that MOND actually *highlights* the need for a good deal of the dark matter it's supposed to discount.

American astronomer Stacy McGaugh, an early convert, has authored several papers[302a,b,c] in support of MOND; although he conceded[302d] in 2014 that the theory says little about formation of large-scale cosmic structures and has *"critical outstanding issues"* (challenges also acknowledged in a historical review[302e] by Robert Sanders). Interestingly, a comprehensive analysis[303a] of 153 galaxies co-authored in 2016 by McGaugh with fellow astronomer Federico Lelli and physicist James Schombert revealed a pattern that showed[303b] the rotation of a disk galaxy conforms to a previously unknown universal law which governs its *visible* matter; regardless[303c] of any surrounding dark matter.

Nonetheless, a team of US-based astrophysicists studying[304a] the massive 'bullet cluster' (two colliding galaxy clusters) had further weakened the case for MOND when they reported[304b] direct measurements of associated gravitational lensing in 2004. The results not only matched Einstein's relativistic space-time predictions, it showed[304c] Newtonian gravity *could* apply at larger galactic scales – a result that favoured dark matter theory. However, Canadian astronomer Jon Moffat, a prominent MOND proponent, denied the findings invalidated alternatives like his vector-based Modified Gravity (MOG) model[305a]. Moffat and colleague Joel Brownstein issued a rival report[305b] in 2007 that showed how MOG could also explain[305c] the bullet cluster observations. Czech-Australian astrophysicist Pavel Kroupa complained[305d] in 2016 that *"dogma"* is holding back more widespread research into MOND.

Information as matter

Amidst the proliferation of ideas, perhaps the most significant for our understanding of the reality we're immersed in is that missing dark matter may represent *computed information* that underlies our observable universe.

The idea that information might actually be a *physical* entity goes back to theoretical physicist Rolf Landauer's calculation in a 1961 IBM paper[306a] that even a single binary digit (bit) of data contains a fixed amount of heat energy which dissipates as entropy when computers process information. Hence, Landauer reasoned, the irreversible erasure or merging of a bit's logical state, which occurs constantly during computing manipulations, must also represent an irreversible emission of its heat content – an equivalence that implies information is essentially physical in nature.

Landauer's proposition launched a long-running controversy with numerous papers taking a 'for' or 'against' position. His IBM colleague Charles Bennett defended the basic concept in a 2003 review[306b]. Although reversible computing in which no information is erased and no heat is released is theoretically possible, Landauer's principle imposes a *practical* limit that can only be exceeded if other physical costs are incurred. As quantum information theorists Joan Vaccaro and Stephen Barnett acknowledged in a 2011 analysis[306c], the sort of physical costs required to evade Landauer's principle can't be absorbed within current or foreseeable technological constraints.

The first experimental verification of Landauer's principle was announced[307a] in 2012 by a team from German and French institutions led by Eric Lutz. They wrote: *"This result demonstrates the intimate link between information theory and thermodynamics. It further highlights the ultimate physical limit of irreversible computation."* The huge significance of the astonishing achievement with just a one-bit *"single colloidal particle trapped in a modulated double-well potential"* was made clearer in a 2015 follow-up assessment[307b] by the French trio from University of Lyon: they noted *"the probability that the system returns to its initial state under a time-reversed procedure."* Unsurprisingly, the issue is still contentious; accepting that indestructible information is equivalent to physical heat leads to some extraordinary conclusions.

92

In 2016, physicists at the University of Perugia in Italy published[308a] a computational measurement they claimed[308b] showed Landauer's information processing limit can be exceeded *"provided the operation is slow enough and frictional phenomena are properly addressed."* Thus, they declared, *"no fundamental energy limit need be associated with irreversible logic computation in general and physical irreversibility is not necessarily implied."* However, this assertion was challenged the same year by an innovative quantum test with three qubits reported[308c] by a Brazilian group led by Lucas Céleri from The Federal University of Goiás – the results strongly indicated that *"an operation that changes the information content of the system must necessarily generate heat in the reservoir, exactly as predicted by Landauer's principle."*

A further demonstration of Landauer's principle on a broader scale was achieved in 2018 by Chinese researchers led by Mang Feng at the Academy of Sciences in Wuhan. Feng's group showed experimentally[309a] that the principle applies at *all levels* in nature – even in a pure quantum system. They wrote: *"Our experimental investigation substantiates an intimate link between information thermodynamics and quantum candidate systems for information processing."* As Massimiliano Esposito from the University of Luxembourg observed in a related commentary[309b], the finding confirms that processing information *always* produces physical heat; even at the ultimate, fundamental level at which anything is known to exist (including within biological cells).

Living things are involved in a constant interchange of heat with their environment, so a reinterpretation of life in terms of *information exchanges* over forward-flowing time has profound implications. Should humans gain God-like ability for *reversible computing* and consequential *time-reversal,* we could (theoretically) eliminate biological ageing and achieve true immortality. But, how feasible is this mind-blowing proposition?

93

THE SURPRISING REALITY OF HUMAN EXISTENCE

Regardless of chances of success, American electrical and computer engineer Michael Frank argued in a 2017 article[310a,b] that humans have to aim for reversible computing if we are to progress:

"Physical time-evolution can itself be viewed as simply being a computation that takes the "old state" of the universe, and computes the "new state" from it, in place, in a one-to-one fashion; and no new uncertainty is introduced during this process, if you hypothetically knew the exact laws of physics and followed the evolution exactly. All of the entropy that appears to exist in the universe can be considered to be simply an illusion that is only suffered by limited beings such as ourselves because we lack such an omniscient perspective. For this reason, it seems quite likely that reversible computing <u>can never be proven to be impossible</u>, since this would require proving that the omniscient perspective couldn't exist, even hypothetically, which would be an odd thing to try to prove, given that physicists assume the existence of such a perspective all the time."

Physicist Melvin Vopson at University of Portsmouth in England took things further in a 2019 paper[311a] that combined Landauer's principle with Einstein's relativity in mathematical arguments for a *mass-energy-information* (MEI) equivalence. According to Vopson, information bits are not just units of potential physical energy, but are fundamental 'building blocks' of our universe with *"finite and quantifiable mass"* that can be determined by experiment. He concluded: *"In fact, one could argue that information is a distinct form of matter, or the 5th state, along the other four observable solid, liquid, gas, and plasma states of matter."*

Vopson further suggested that dark matter might very well be *information* mass. As he explained in a 2020 lay overview[311b]: *"M.P. Gough published an article[311c] in 2008 in which he worked out ... the number of bits of information that the visible universe would contain to make up all the missing dark matter. It appears that my estimates of information bit content of the universe are very close to his estimates."*

94

If Vopson's new MEI equivalence principle is confirmed experimentally, it will establish that elusive dark matter is, indeed, a form of hidden information. However, this will still leave scientists a long way from a comprehensive account of the structure and components of our universe. Astrophysicists calculate[311d] that ordinary matter makes up only about 4 percent of the universe. Dark matter accounts for another 26 percent. This leaves a whopping balance of *70 percent* of critical matter density in the early universe (as indicated by Inflation theory) still unaccounted for.

Dark energy

Scientists have been stunned by observational confirmations[312a] since the mid-1990s that expansion of the universe is definitely *accelerating*. How could this be happening, when everything known about the pulling and bounding power of gravity indicates otherwise?

As with dark matter, the inescapable inference is that yet another invisible component is pushing galaxies rapidly apart against the force of gravity. Furthermore, it must have powerful 'gravity repulsion' to avoid being sucked into rotating galaxies. Physicists speculate that this unknown factor, labelled[312b] 'dark energy', must be distributed evenly throughout space-time and likely accounts for the undetected 70 percent of the universe.

While invoking dark energy helps scientists to reconcile the large-scale structure of the universe, it adds to the already arduous task confronting investigators of dark matter. There's no clear explanation[312c] of exactly *what* dark energy is or *how* it operates at either quantum or cosmic levels. The whole concept is highly speculative and still lacks a practicable and testable experimental framework. As the Dark Energy Task Force (DETF) assembled to develop a research programme for the US Department of Energy, NASA and NSF reported[312d] in 2006:

"Dark energy appears to be the dominant component of the physical Universe, yet there is no persuasive theoretical explanation for its existence or magnitude. The acceleration of the Universe is, along with dark matter, the observed phenomenon that most directly demonstrates that our theories of fundamental particles and gravity are either incorrect or incomplete. Most experts believe that nothing short of a revolution in our understanding of fundamental physics will be required to achieve a full understanding of the cosmic acceleration."

Some physicists describe[313] dark energy as a sort of background vacuum field generated by 'phantom' subatomic particles fluctuating in and out of our physical universe. In other words, intergalactic space is not an empty void but an enabling environment that harbours *virtual entities* which appear from nowhere to fuel accelerating cosmic expansion.

Others view[314a] dark energy as *lambda* (Λ) – the cosmological constant[314b] once proposed by Einstein as an arbitrary 'gravity check' that keeps the universe stable. *Lambda* has also been hailed[314c] as the best explanation for the fundamental 'proton to electron mass ratio' which allowed atoms of matter to form in the early universe. The snag is, the value of *lambda* requires fine-tuning to fit[314d] different theories in physics (some require a value of exactly zero).

Alternative scenarios of a 'lumpy' universe with uneven matter distribution have been proposed[315a] to explain its continued exponential expansion. However, in 2013, astrophysicists at The University of Texas at Dallas published[315b] a study that showed[315c] such ideas don't work unless[315d] *lambda* is factored in. Of course, the universal need for *lambda* is evidence of another 'unnatural' input of unknown origin. But scientific protocol compels physicists to keep striving for natural explanations – new data[316a] since 2016 indicates the universe is expanding even faster[316b] than models predicted.

Yet another proposal is that cosmic expansion is driven by a fifth (so far undetected) force in nature dubbed[317a] 'quintessence'. Unlike *lambda*, this force is not constant but has dynamic ability[317b] to be either attractive or repulsive over time. However, after re-examining relevant data from satellites, Joan Solà from the University of Barcelona in Spain and Spyros Basilakos from the Academy of Athens in Greece reported[317c] in 2014 that the observations which spawned proposals of quintessence were just a simulated mirage[317d].

Nevertheless, although there's no consensus model, most physicists still agree[318a] that dark energy exists – although they readily concede to being, literally, 'in the dark' about its properties or mechanisms. Even Nobel laureate and co-discoverer of cosmic acceleration Adam Riess admitted[318b] in a 2009 interview that he had *"absolutely no clue what dark energy is"*. Inevitably, some now doubt the entire conceptual framework.

Back to aether?

One radical solution resurrects a long-abandoned notion in physics. Eminent scientists from Albert Einstein all the way back to Sir Isaac Newton speculated that the universe may be permeated with a mysterious medium called 'aether'. In the mid-2000s, French astrophysicist Alexandre Arbey proposed possible models[319a,b,c] of a single, aether-like 'dark fluid' in place of[319d] dark matter and dark energy. In 2008, a team led by Hongsheng Zhao at University of St. Andrews in Scotland developed[320a] a more detailed unifying model that yields the same 26/70 percentage ratio for dark matter to dark energy derived by cosmologists from gravity calculations. The next year, Zhao co-authored an international study[320b] that revealed a far more complex and intimate relationship between dark matter and ordinary matter than expected. Zhao and research collaborator Benoit Famaey commented[320c] in a news release:

97

"The dark matter seems to 'know' how the visible matter is distributed. They seem to conspire with each other such that the gravity of the visible matter at the characteristic radius of the dark halo is always the same. This is extremely surprising since one would rather expect the balance between visible and dark matter to strongly depend on the individual history of each galaxy.

"The pattern that the data reveal is extremely odd. It's like finding a zoo of animals of all ages and sizes miraculously having identical, say, weight in their backbones or something. It is possible that a non-gravitational fifth force is ruling the dark matter with an invisible hand, leaving the same fingerprints on all galaxies, irrespective of their ages, shapes and sizes."

Clearly, inference of external influence already indicated by the universal role of *lambda*, Einstein's fine-tuned cosmological constant, can no longer be disregarded. The question now is how far theoretical physicists and mathematicians can quantify and incorporate deduced inputs from *outside* our universe into models for possible naturalistic investigation.

Oxford University astrophysicist Jamie Farnes published[321a] research in 2018 depicting dark fluid as a *negative* mass which *repels* rather than attracts matter gravitationally – an idea that harks back to an early suggested explanation for cosmic expansion by Einstein. Remarkably, computer simulations of a toy model constructed by Farnes correctly replicated[321b] features of invisible dark matter 'halos' around galaxies inferred from observations with radio telescopes.

All in the box

In 2017, University of Geneva astronomer André Maeder proposed[322a] a new cosmological model that dispenses with *both* dark matter and dark energy. Instead, he focused on *space* itself.

Maeder argued that *fundamental properties* of space remain unaffected by expansion or contraction of the universe because they are governed by Einstein's cosmological constant. This 'scale invariance', he asserted[322b], means the universe's overall *content* has been the same since Big Bang – no hypothetical 'fillers' are needed.

Interestingly, this 'all-in-one' proposal accords with the concept of a holographic bubble that contained *everything* at inception for generation of the reality we perceive. The suggestion that dark energy is just an emergent feature of space-time is hardly new[323a], but Maeder's simplified mathematical model provides a rigorous supporting framework for further investigation. Certainly, the notion that our universe has remained scale-invariant, regardless of expansive change over billions of years, is a fascinating consideration that's being taken seriously[323b] by other researchers.

Strange black holes

Since the 1950s, science fiction writers have featured malevolent, bottomless, vortex-like pits in deep space that suck in and devour unwary space travellers. Stories of luckless human victims may be just fantasy, but physicists are certain these monster holes exist. As far back as the 18th century, scholars speculated[324a] about massive cosmic objects that have huge gravitational pull powerful enough to stop anything (even light) from escaping. The imagined entities were called 'dark stars', but these remained nothing more than academic curiosities until the 20th century.

Einstein's 1915 theory of general relativity (GR) predicted[324b] that any gigantic cosmic mass should bend space-time into a 'sink' that has huge, inward gravitational pull. But it was his colleague Karl Schwarzschild who showed a few months later that Einstein's mathematical equations actually lead to a point mass, spherical [324c,d] singularity with incalculable gravitational power.

To infinity

At first, contemporaries interpreted the so-called Schwarzschild radius as a description of nothing more than the dense remnants of burnt-up stars known as 'white dwarfs'[325a]. However, in 1931, Indian astrophysicist Subrahmanyan Chandrasekhar (then just 19 years old) showed that[325b] any white dwarf which has more than 1.4 times the mass of our sun should *collapse* on itself into an unspecifiable state that couldn't be quantified within classical physics. Although Chandrasekhar's mathematics was sound, established physicists rejected the implications – Sir Arthur Eddington ridiculed[325c] the idea at a January 1935 meeting of the Royal Astronomical Society in London; he argued that some natural mechanism must exist that would stop such a massive object from collapsing into oblivion as Chandrasekhar's results suggested.

However, subsequent investigations proved[325d] Chandrasekhar right: any stellar object over his derived mass limit will steadily collapse on itself to become an infinite space-time singularity. This, in turn, will capture, crush, and add any material which approaches to a compact point mass in an 'eat and grow' cycle that gives it ever more powerful gravitational pull. Physicists adopted the name 'black hole'[325e] to describe the resulting monstrosity because not even light can travel fast enough to escape its clutches.

Of course, no one can actually *see* a black hole – even if light emissions emerged, observation would be extremely difficult due to gravitational lensing and distortions of intervening objects across space-time. But astronomers have been able to infer the presence of black holes from radio signals of odd effects on surrounding masses of stars, gas, and dust; especially the ferocious gravitational pull. Astrophysicists speculate that a spherical surround area or so-called 'event horizon'[326a] marks the point of no return – anything that crosses this invisible radial boundary is doomed.

To an outside observer, black holes might appear 'frozen'. But they are far from inactive. The popular assumption used to be[326b] that humans unlucky enough to fall into a black hole would be gradually ripped apart or 'spaghettified' before being compacted at the singularity. But, in 2012, theoretical physicist Joseph Polchinski and his research team at University of California Santa Barbara published[326c] new calculations that suggest[326d] a swifter but equally gruesome fate: incineration by a wall of fire that 'guards' the boundary.

It's thought the centre of most galaxies is inhabited by supermassive black holes (SBH). One such monster named Sagittarius A-Star (Sgr A*), calculated to be *4.3 million times* the mass of our sun, was detected[327a] in 1974 at a central region[327b] of the Milky Way that's[327c] 25,800 light-years away from our solar system. Additionally, scientists estimate that the universe is riddled with *billions* of other less dense, differently-sized black holes which exhibit[327d] puzzlingly diverse behaviour.

In 2011, astronomers analysing infrared data from the European Space Agency's Herschel Space Observatory[328a] were astounded to discover[328b] a strange, infinity-shaped (∞) ring of hot gas giving birth to new stars right at the heart of our Milky Way galaxy. Six years later, an international team of over 200 astronomers operating the Event Horizon Telescope (EHT) – a global array of radio observatories that mimic a gigantic earth-sized 'virtual' telescope – launched[328c] a collaboration to collect and analyse data signals from bright accretion disks of gas and dust thought to mark the 'mouths' of the Milky Way's Sagittarius A* and another supermassive black hole at the heart of Messier 87 – one of the largest galaxies in the observable universe. The bold aim was indirect capture[328d] of shadows that event horizons of these black holes might cast in the glow of the luminous disks.

In 2019, the EHT team announced[329a] the first images of a black hole's shadow reconstructed with actual radio data from the heart of Messier 87. The remarkable achievement was hailed[329b] as a milestone that (yet again) vindicated Einstein's relativity interpretation of gravity, and laid[329c] the foundation for further big data research into black holes. However, as it's impossible to conduct any form of direct physical investigation, what (if anything) is actually *inside* these monsters is still anybody's guess[329d].

What lies beyond?

Apart from physical limitations to black hole research, there are conceptual problems. Scientists are unable to agree on a precise definition[330a] or the significance[330b] of these mysterious objects for our universe. The subject has become a major topic of debate not just within astrophysics and cosmology, but also among[330c] philosophers and metaphysicians. The absence of consensus is unsurprising: so far, neither general relativity (GR) nor quantum mechanics (QM) – the twin pillars of modern physics – have proved sufficient to explain what might lie in black holes and beyond.

It's thought the incredibly compact point mass at the heart of a black hole ultimately reduces to Planck level (smallest dimension imaginable); thus creating[330d] a singularity of infinitely large energy density. However, gravity, as described by GR, can't be measured at that ultra-micro scale because it becomes indistinguishable from other fundamental forces in nature (electromagnetism and the strong & weak nuclear forces that act to bind or separate particles in atoms). On the other hand, QM only calculates the *probable* behaviour of subatomic particles when subjected to the latter three forces; it doesn't account for the effect of gravity at *any* scale. Thus, researchers lack the usual tools (empirical or theoretical) to formulate meaningful scientific accounts of a black hole singularity. The impasse is a frustrating illustration of human failure to fully explain existence *purely* in materialistic terms.

Atomised space-time

Physicists have been trying[331a] to combine QM with GR in a new theory of quantum gravity (QG)[331b]. However, interpreting the properties and behaviour of a 'quantised' black hole with *limitless* mass in terms of a wave-particle like a light photon that has *no mass at all* has proved[331c] near-impossible. Theorists have resorted to speculative concepts like tiny, discrete building blocks of space-time which produce a 'granular' texture that differs radically[331d] from Einstein's image of a smooth and continuous background fabric which warps or sinks slightly under the weight of massive galaxies, but remains intact even where black hole singularities occur.

Interestingly, the idea of invisible 3-D bits of space-time mimics the pixel approach used in digital imaging technology. The leading theory of loop quantum gravity (LQG)[332a] depicts one-dimensional loops woven together in mesh-like 'spin networks' that evolve over time into a larger foam matrix – all at incredibly small Planck scale. In 2015, Ginestra Bianconi from Queen Mary University of London in England and Christoph Rahmede from Karlsruhe Institute of Technology in Germany published[332b] a new model that suggests[332c] space-time might even be constructed in a similar manner to familiar complex systems like cellular biological networks, neurons in brains, and online social networks. The fascinating imagery re-emphasises the mysterious but crucial role[332d] of gravity in stabilising holistic, *observable* macro structures that are, essentially, composites of *unobservable* micro components. But, a surprise emerged when Uruguayan physicist Rodolfo Gambini and American colleague Jorge Pullin applied[333a] LQG theory to black holes for the first time in 2013. The results indicated[333b] a space-time core that's highly curved *but not* under infinite gravity as predicted by GR – an indication that black holes may not harbour mass singularities after all.

Just an illusion?

The pioneering (though still theoretical) insights from[334a] quantum gravity prompted speculation that even the appearance of a 'hole' may be illusory. In February 2021, Igor Nikitin from the Fraunhofer Institute for Scientific Algorithms and Computing in Germany suggested that black holes may well be the immensely dense 'dark stars' with enough gravitational pull to stop light from escaping that English scientist John Michell and French multidisciplinary scholar Pierre-Simon Laplace speculated about[334b] in the 18th century. Nikitin wrote[334c] in a pre-print paper:

"Dark stars are compact massive objects, described by Einstein gravitational field equations with matter. The type we consider possesses no event horizon, instead, there is a deep gravitational well with a very strong redshift factor. Observationally, dark stars can be identified with black holes. Inside dark stars, Planck density of matter is reached, Planck cores are formed, where the equations are modified by quantum gravity."

According to Nikitin, wavelengths of any photons emitted by a dark star would be so stretched by its powerful gravity that they would resemble the unidentified extragalactic light flashes known as[335a] *fast radio bursts* (FRBs) which last just milliseconds. He also proposed[335b] controversially that these exotic stars could be the source of dark matter halos that surround galaxies. However, while the idea is an interesting thought experiment, it doesn't explain key observations by astronomers. The surprising discovery of gigantic black holes in the early universe (one reported[336a] in 2017 was almost *a billion* times more massive[336b] than our sun) poses a particular challenge[336c] for alternative theories. In any case, Harvard University Black Hole Initiative affiliates Paul Chesler, Ramesh Narayan and Erik Curiel published[337a] new calculations in 2019 that reinforced[337b] support for the existence of cosmic singularities in black holes.

On the far side

Black hole theory received another boost in July 2021 when an international team led by Dan Wilkins from Stanford University in the USA reported[338a] the first detection of light from *behind* a supermassive black hole. The unexpected recording was made[338b] while studying strange X-ray light flashes coming from the centre of the Zwicky 1 galaxy which is 800 million light-years away. However, as Wilkins explained[338c], while the exciting observation was further confirmation that Einstein's depiction of gravity is correct, it doesn't offer any new clues on what goes on in black holes: *"Any light that goes into that black hole doesn't come out, so we shouldn't be able to see anything that's behind the black hole. The reason we can see that is because that black hole is warping space, bending light and twisting magnetic fields around itself."*

Several decades after Einstein published his calculations on cosmic relativity, it dawned on physicists that the same mathematical equations which lead to a black hole sucking in everything also indicate[339a] possible existence of a *white hole* somewhere that spits out whatever disappeared into the black hole. Theorists speculate[339b] that, like its 'twin' black partner, white holes must have event horizons that forbid intrusion. However, unlike black holes, there's absolutely no observational data[339c] of any sort for white holes.

One suggestion is that white holes are unobservable because they're linked across 'wormholes'[340a] – hypothetical bridges to distant regions of our cosmos (or even *another* universe) as first described[340b] in 1935 by Einstein and Princeton University colleague Nathan Rosen. In 2009, Polish-American theoretical physicist Nikodem Poplawski astonished colleagues with an intriguing proposal[340c] that the Big Bang event which launched our universe may have been a spontaneous white hole expulsion[340d] of highly compressed matter. Poplawski argued[340e] that this scenario explains the universe's puzzling flatness and uniformity as well as Inflation theory does.

The idea of wormhole-linked black and white holes interchanging matter and information across space-time to birth new bubble universes (that may or may not evolve fresh life) has become[341a] a mainstream research topic. In 2014, Italian theoretical physicist Carlo Rovelli and American colleague Hal Haggard showed how[341b] matter compacted to Planck dimensions in a black hole might be quantum tunnelling into a white hole before ejection as dark matter[341c] into a new, closed-off universe. James Bardeen from the University of Washington in Seattle also computed a 'toy model' in 2018 that illustrated[341d] how a black hole might evolve into a white hole with trapped quantum information, ready for creation of new worlds.

Purposive reality barrier?

The uniformity of underlying laws and phenomena within the observable universe allows scientists to make plausible retrodictions on what may have happened in the past, and confident predictions about how things are likely to turn out in future. However, this implies the universe is *pre-determined*[342a] to some extent – a notion that's at odds with fundamental *probabilities*[342b] in the quantum realm, and complete uncertainty about events within a black hole.

In 1969, Sir Roger Penrose published a mathematical conjecture (based on his famous singularity theorem[343a]) that suggests the shrouding of infinite mass singularities in black holes is actually a form of gravity-related 'cosmic censorship' against prying conscious observers – *except* for the Big Bang singularity which, for some unknown reason, fleetingly appears 'naked'[343b] in our universe and is therefore open to investigation.

Penrose's extraordinary concept attracted support from none other than Stephen Hawking; the duo jointly authored an expanded version[343c] in 1970.

Penrose regarded[343d] in-built cosmic censorship as a fortunate limitation in nature that leaves our observable universe determinable and predictable at everyday macro level. Should we ever bridge the gap that prevents physical access to black hole singularities, Einstein's space-time relativity will cease to be valid and everything (including time flow) will become uncertain and unpredictable.

Cosmic censorship is still just a proposition. However, hopes for validation were raised by solid proof[344a] of another gravity-related conjecture in 2014 by Sergiu Klainerman and Igor Rodnianski from Princeton University in the USA and Jeremie Szeftel from Université Paris Diderot in France. The breakthrough shed new light[344b] on possible, far-reaching implications of Einstein's cosmic relativity for conscious observers like humans.

Information leads

Physicists whimsically compare the frustrating absence of firm information on black holes to a completely bald head with 'no hair'. However, in 1967, Werner Israel surmised[345a] from mathematical calculations that it should be possible to gain some idea of, at least, three black hole properties: *mass*, *electric charge*, and *angular momentum* (direction of spin). This unproven but widely accepted[345b] proposal has been dubbed the 'no-hair' conjecture.

Clues from entropy

In the early 1970s, Princeton University's Jacob Bekenstein hit on another approach. He conjectured that a black hole likely conforms to the second law of thermodynamics – a rule in physics that all isolated physical systems exhibit increased entropy (energy dispersal). If so, he reasoned, constant 'swallowing' of huge amounts of mass should generate a stupendous level of entropy in black holes with correlated energy output that might be quantifiable in theory.

Starting from this speculative premise, Bekenstein devised[346a] a thermodynamic framework[346b] for black hole entropy in 1972 and followed-up the next year with calculations that indicated[346c] the amount of entropy inside a black hole is directly proportional to the size of its surrounding event horizon. Furthermore, since entropy is also a reliable measure of information capacity, the work showed[347a] there's a natural limit[347b] to the amount of information that can be stored in a fixed amount of space – a finding that leads to the profound conclusion that *everything in existence* can be fully described and encoded within a bounded system[347c] of finite entropy.

Bekenstein's findings attracted much interest within the physics community. Stephen Hawking, in particular, immediately recognised the exciting potential of a thermodynamic approach to black holes. However, he was keenly aware of significant hurdles to full development of the concept. From a classical physics perspective, any object with entropy must also have *temperature* and radiate heat and light. But of course, according to prevailing 'no-hair' dogma, no such information can escape from black holes. How then could anyone determine if these mysterious structures have entropy?

Hidden quantum emissions

When renowned Soviet astrophysicist Yakov Zel'dovich suggested[348a] in 1973 that quantum fluctuations at black hole event horizons may be[348b] generating particle-antiparticle pairs, Hawking realised this could be the basis for the entropy manifestation predicted by Bekenstein's formulations. Conceivably, one of the paired particles would fall into the black hole while the other escapes with some mass-energy as radiation. As gravity at quantum level is virtually non-existent and the exiting particle would carry minimal, undetectable information, this scenario didn't violate Einstein's relativity principle or the 'no-hair' conjecture.

Hawking then used[349a] quantum theory to show[349b] in 1974 and 1975 that black holes could, indeed, be emitting small amounts of thermal energy. This phenomenon, now known as 'Hawking radiation', raised the theoretical possibility that the massive objects could 'evaporate'[349c] – albeit over billions of years.

The remarkable insights provided by Bekenstein and Hawking pioneered a new theoretical field of black hole thermodynamics[349d]. However, the concepts raise difficult new questions. According to a parallel law in physics, quantum information is *always preserved*, regardless of the state of the physical system it describes. But, if only *one* of a pair of linked particles is emitted from a black hole, the severance would seriously disrupt their quantum state and render it unrecognisable – effectively causing *information loss* in violation of the conservation rule. Furthermore, it would be impossible to reconstruct devoured matter and energy from single particles that re-emerge indiscriminately over an indefinite timescale – just as no everyday computer will be able to make sense of a coded programme that's scrambled into disordered bits and then re-run at random.

Thus was born a problematic 'information paradox'[350a]. Hawking insisted quantum information is definitely destroyed through black hole evaporation, but he was also sure that recognised laws of gravity continue to apply. Alluding to Einstein's iconic comment half a century earlier, Hawking remarked[350b]: *"God not only plays dice with the universe, but sometimes throws them where we can't see them."* However, his suggestion that long-established quantum theory may require modification to explain information loss was rejected by particle physicists like Leonard Susskind, Gerard 't Hooft and John Preskill – 't Hooft objected[350c] that Hawking's calculations were based on unproven assumptions about gravity at quantum level while Susskind argued[350d] only a distant God-like observer with ability to view[350e] *both* inside and outside a black hole at once can record any such loss.

Two decades on, opinion on the fate of information in black holes remained so divided that, in 1997, Hawking and fellow theoretical physicist Kip Thorne entered into a famous bet[351a] with Preskill. Hawking revisited[351b] the issue in 2004 and graciously conceded[351c] the wager. But Thorne decided to wait and see – a prudent approach eventually rewarded by subsequent developments which appear to[351d] vindicate Hawking's original stance.

To his credit, Preskill had already acknowledged in a candid 1992 review[352a] that his contrarian position may be wrong:

> *"As I have pondered this puzzle, it has come to seem less and less likely to me that the accepted principles of quantum mechanics and relativity can be reconciled with the phenomenon of black hole evaporation. In other words, I have come to believe more and more (only 15 years behind Hawking) that the accepted principles lead to a truly paradoxical conclusion, which means that these principles cannot provide a correct description of nature. [....] Conceivably, the puzzle of black hole evaporation portends a scientific revolution as sweeping as that that led to the formulation of quantum theory in the early 20th century."*

One revolutionary solution to the paradox has steadily gained support: the idea of[352b] a black hole as a huge two-dimensional (2-D) sheet of space-time that conscious observers like humans *within* the universe falsely perceive[352c] as a 3-D object with volume.

A universe from 2-D coding

Bekenstein and Hawking had established that a black hole can store information about its 'meals' which is determined not by its *volume* but by the size of its *surface area*. What remained unclear was if this meant the information is stored *internally* within the structure, or *externally* at the surface area.

From the perspective of an observer on the outside, the information appears[353a] to be stored at the flat, surrounding event horizon. Interestingly, this is also the case for familiar storage devices – information is inscribed on the surface and not 'inside' paper sheets, tapes or digital disks.

Background cosmic media

In 1993, 't Hooft and colleagues C. R. Stephens and B. F. Whiting at University of Utrecht in The Netherlands extended the idea of surface storage of black hole information into a general proposal[353b] that the 2-D boundary of *any* volume of space can be coded with all the information needed to describe and construct its contents in 3-D or more. Susskind, who like 't Hooft had consistently maintained that information is *not* lost in black holes, then showed[353c] how our world might have such a boundary, with virtual particles entwined as 1-D strings on a thin shell membrane or 'brane' that exists[353d] within an infinitely larger, higher-dimension bulk 'hyperspace'.

These developments inspired Argentine-American physicist Juan Maldacena to publish a famous 1997 paper[354a] outlining a curious mathematical correspondence between negligible quantum gravity in our bubble, and an all-pervasive[354b] 'supergravity' *outside* its boundary. The stunning implication, as Bekenstein explained[354c] in a lay overview, is that our universe may be a 2-D information structure imprinted on the cosmological horizon. According to this view, the 3-D world we observe is just a holographic projection[354d] from information decoded by the mind-brain in as yet unknown ways.

Possible models

Although the exotic physics behind our possibly holographic universe has remained well-hidden, theorists have produced some speculative models.

111

In 2013, a European team led by Kostas Skenderis from the University of Southampton in England identified[355a] striking new similarities between our 'flat' 4-D physical reality (3-D + time) and the 'negatively curved' space-time thought to exist[355b] in multiple dimensions beyond our physical realm. The same year, a Japanese team led by Yoshifumi Hyakutake at Ibaraki University reported that matching results had been derived on computer for entropy within a ten-dimensional[356a] universe governed by supergravity, and for a holographic model with just a single dimension[356b] and near-zero gravity. As Maldacena commented[356c], the Japanese results provide strong support for his conjecture of mathematical duality at quantum level between gravity in high and low dimensional domains. The finding was hailed[356d] as a key development in the search for a holo-cosmic methodology.

In 2019, Maldacena and colleagues at Princeton University used holographic duality to show mathematically[357a] that observers in a higher dimensional domain could definitely 'spy on' black holes in a lower dimensional construct. The theorists also found that, while information appears to remain trapped in black holes as gravity-free 2-D quantum particles, some internal areas of the hole develop geometric links to the exterior with strange 'entanglement wedge' radiation. The astonishing derivations suggest[357b] black holes may be providing the route for mysterious transmission of information from a higher dimension for holographic projection of our 3-D universe.

Revisiting 'dark' bits

Significantly, in 2016 Dutch theoretical physicist Erik Verlinde adopted[358a] the idea of a simulated universe in a new radical theory of gravity that dispenses with dark matter. He concluded that our reality is, indeed, a giant hologram projected from information encoded in an underlying cosmic network of quantum qubits.

Building on earlier work[358b] which cast gravity as an *emergent* entropic phenomenon (like temperature from heat) rather than a fundamental force, Verlinde argued that our perception of extra gravity from dark matter is an illusion[358c] generated by interactions of ordinary matter *inside* the universe, with dark energy from quantum qubits that make up the information background *outside* our space-time boundary. He suggested this phenomenon is the same vacuum energy that 'kick-started' and continues to sustain the physical world we experience.

Verlinde's model is a bold extrapolation, but not implausible. Colleagues admit it provides[359a] a unifying explanatory framework for the mysteries surrounding gravity, dark matter and dark energy. As the proposal sweeps away most of the difficulties that have plagued modified gravity (MOND) proposals (especially failure to completely exclude dark matter), physicists have been quick to test the idea of entropic gravity and issued 'for'[359b] and 'against'[359c] verdicts.

However, Verlinde's proposal is far from a fully fleshed-out cosmological theory that can be applied to explain *all* features of the universe. As German colleague Sabine Hossenfelder discussed in a 2017 lay overview[359d], no conclusive evaluations can be made until the model is developed further. She remarked:

"The real challenge for emergent gravity [....] is to also explain structure formation in the early universe, or any gravitational phenomena on larger (tens of millions of light years or more) scales.

"Particle dark matter is essential to obtain the correct predictions for the temperature fluctuations in the cosmic microwave background. That's a remarkable achievement, and no alternative for dark matter can be taken seriously so long as it cannot do at least as well."

Explaining origin

While the issue of dark matter remains contentious, there's growing support[360a] for the argument that holographic models are as plausible as conventional Big Bang and Inflation theories on *origination* of our universe. In 2016, another international collaboration led by Kostas Skenderis published two tests that showed[360b,c] so-called 'holographic cosmology' more than adequately explains observed features of the early universe – including cosmic microwave background footprints. As Skenderis commented[360d]:

> *"Holography is a huge leap forward in the way we think about the structure and creation of the universe. Einstein's theory of general relativity explains almost everything large scale in the universe very well, but starts to unravel when examining its origins and mechanisms at quantum level. Scientists have been working for decades to combine Einstein's theory of gravity and quantum theory. Some believe the concept of a holographic universe has the potential to reconcile the two."*

Freaky cosmic observers

Long before the riddles posed by quantum phenomena surfaced, 19th century Austrian physicist Ludwig Boltzmann, who pioneered[361a] understanding of thermodynamic flows in terms of random statistical dispersals, introduced a related existential conundrum. Since the second law mandates that all closed systems must go from ordered to disordered states (low entropy, condensed energy to high entropy, dispersed energy), and the arrow of time prevents[361b] any reversal of this inevitability, Boltzmann wondered how our universe and the highly-ordered, low entropy structures it contains came into being. In other words, if we can't go back in time to 'unspill' a glass of water or 'unsplatter' a dropped egg, how was it possible for discrete particles of matter to assemble into molecular elements and form the stable objects we perceive – all *contrary* to the second law and *against* the run of time?

114

Boltzmann concluded[361c] our anthropic (life-friendly), low entropy bubble probably arose from a sudden, random thermal 'fluctuation' within a much larger universe that exists in a state of high entropy, eternal equilibrium. However, this raises the question just *why* this event (if it happened) should give rise to such a complex existence.

Drifting souls?

Until the 21st century, Boltzmann was celebrated mainly for[362a] his innovative mathematical description of the random movement of molecules in enclosed gases and fluids; there was little discussion of his cosmological work. Then, in a 2004 discussion paper[362b] about persisting issues with early Inflation theory, Andreas Albrecht and Lorenzo Sorbo at University of California Davis revisited Boltzmann's intriguing hypothesis on origination of the universe by thermal fluctuation.

Albrecht and Sorbo referenced work by others that used Boltzmann's statistical mechanics to evaluate the probability of the universe fluctuating out of some 'meta-universe'. They noted that the results overwhelmingly showed it was *"exponentially less likely"* that a Big Bang fluctuation would set off an initial inflationary period *followed by* billions of years of cosmological and biological evolution, than that a random fluctuation would directly produce *"the universe as we see it today."* What this means, they explained, is that our current scientific model of the universe's origin inadvertently predicts the existence of a multitude of invisible, disembodied (but conscious) 'Boltzmann brains' that fluctuate[362c] in and out of our cosmos.

The startling analysis has provoked lively scientific and public debates. Are humans embodied versions[363a] of Boltzmann brains? Has science finally cracked the mystery of millennia-old claims of a 'soul' that enters our biological frame at birth and departs at death?

115

Alternatively, are these self-aware entities just isolated, lonely 'beings' that drift through[363b] the universe with imagined life experiences and memories before fading back into the cosmic matrix? Some scientists are even seriously discussing[363c,d] whether there could be *far more* such 'freaky observers' floating in space-time than earthly human observers. But others are sceptical.

Israeli-American mathematician and science historian Amir Aczel expressed incredulity in a 2012 commentary[364a]:

"If somebody told you that there are angels floating in space, observing our world and forming their impressions of our everyday reality, you would think that this person is nuts—a religious fanatic with an active imagination, and certainly not a scientist. [....]

"So how do you explain the bizarre fact that, for about five years now, some of the world's most prominent physicists have been describing a scenario—which they seem to truly believe may be real—in which, instead of the Biblical angels, space is permeated by disembodied brains?"

American theoretical physicist Sean M. Carroll, a staunch atheist who has consistently argued[364b] science and religion are incompatible, published a lengthy blog critique[364c] of Boltzmann brains in 2006. His main objection was that Boltzmann's attempt to forge a 'natural' thermodynamic explanation for emergence of our universe has ended up emphasising the 'unnatural' low entropy, *"purportedly-finely-tuned"* conditions that allowed life to evolve.

A decade later, Carroll contended in a pre-print paper[365a] that the concept of remote 'cosmic brains' should be rejected as a matter of principle[365b] (if not faulty science) because it means all our mental perceptions and presumed memories are 'unreal' and can't be relied on for scientific conclusions about the world we experience.

Carroll argued: *"The issue is not that the existence of such observers is ruled out by data, but that the theories that predict them are cognitively unstable: they cannot simultaneously be true and justifiably believed."* This view led Carroll and California Institute of Technology (Caltech) colleagues Kimberly Boddy and Jason Pollack to co-author[365c] a 2014 paper that denies[365d] dynamical, real-time quantum fluctuations (of the type thought to produce Boltzmann brains) are even possible within our universe.

Astrophysicist and science writer Brian Koberlein discussed the *"somewhat speculative"* Boddy-Carroll-Pollack attempt to suppress Boltzmann brains in a 2018 article[365e]. Koberlein identified an *"interesting catch"*: the trio's argument relies on *"a version of quantum theory known as the many-worlds formulation"* which, of course, is just as problematic for those insisting nothing exists beyond observable matter and sensory experience. He concluded:

"In solving the paradox of Boltzmann brains, we might have to face the reality that each of us are not as unique as we appear. The many-worlds model could also be called the many-minds model. Throughout a many-worlds universe there would be minds very like ours, each with slightly different experiences, and each having as much right to be called "us" as we do."

Invisible units of nature

As physicists delved deeper into the fabric of nature, they encountered a 'Russian doll' situation with constituent bits getting smaller and smaller until they become invisible and can only be detected experimentally. The idea that matter is composed of small, discrete, indivisible *atoms* dates back[366a] over 2,000 years to ancient philosophers (Greek sage Anaxagoras even reasoned[366b] that matter was *infinitely* divisible). These early ideas inspired Roman poet and naturalist Titus Lucretius Carus (c. 99 - 55 BCE) to author the classic work *De Rerum Natura* (On the Nature of Things); an extraordinary six-part exposition now regarded[366c] as the first comprehensive account of atomism.

117

Atomic building blocks

By the 18th century, scientists had adopted the term 'atom' to describe a hypothetical, ultimate unit of matter. Researchers now know that even fundamental forces like electromagnetism, and the strong & weak nuclear agents which keep bits of visible objects bonded, result from *particle interactions* (also thought to produce gravity at cosmic level).

In 1897, English physicist John J. Thomson discovered[367a] that cathode rays were not electromagnetic waves as thought but a stream of negatively-charged atomic emissions now called *electrons* (e⁻). Thomson realised this meant *the atom itself* was composed of further particles which he assumed[367b] were distributed throughout a positively-charged sphere.

However, following a study of alpha particle scattering by gold foil conducted by Hans Geiger and Ernest Marsden at University of Manchester in England between 1908 -1911, their supervisor Ernest Rutherford constructed[368a] an atomic model with *all* the positive charge located at the centre. Geiger and Marsden then undertook further experiments that confirmed[368b] this solar-like structure. In 1913, Rutherford triumphantly presented[368c] the new image of a dense, positively-charged nucleus holding negatively-charged electrons in orbit. He followed-up the next year with calculations[368d] of relative dimensions for each atomic component. But his projection of total mass fell way short of the actual observed mass of an atom.

Then, in 1920, English chemist Francis Aston used an updated version of mass spectrometry to show that[369a] isotopes (atoms of the same chemical element that display different physical properties) actually have different atomic masses.

Twelve years later, the puzzle was resolved when Cambridge University physicist James Chadwick reported[369b] new experimental results that indicated an atom's nucleus contains extra particles he called *neutrons* (n) with *no electric charge*, alongside positively-charged *protons* (p+). Chadwick explained[369c] that isotopes are atoms with *the same* number of protons, but *different* amounts of neutrons. Thus, protons and neutrons (now collectively called *nucleons*) make up the bulk of atomic mass. But the story didn't end there. 'Atom smashing' particle accelerators soon revealed that even nucleons are aggregates of further smaller bits.

As the second half of the 20th century progressed, a bewildering array of *hundreds* of elementary subatomic particles[370a] emerged that left physicists talking about a 'particle zoo'. The task of analysing the physical properties and relationships of all observed items spawned an entire new field of study within physics. However, these invisible micro entities are so elusive (and sometimes short-lived) that devising practicable experiments to investigate their exact role in simulating the macro stuff we perceive has been a massive challenge.

According to particle physicists, matter at fundamental level consists of an arrangement of 'material' particles (*fermions*) and 'force-carrier' particles (*bosons*) that act to either bring together or separate the material bits. However, interaction between the two groups can only be depicted mathematically so details are still debated[370b].

Fermions consist of two basic types: 3-unit *quarks* that clump together to form[370c] *hadrons* like protons and neutrons in an atom's nucleus, and *leptons* like electrons and neutrinos outside the atomic nucleus. Another kind of 2-unit quarks called *mesons* can emerge during high-energy interactions, but these rapidly transform (after just few hundredths of a microsecond) into electrons and neutrinos. Some physicists speculate[370d] that quarks and leptons may be composed of even smaller subunits called *preons*.

119

The three confirmed force-carriers (termed *gauge bosons*) are: *photons* bearing electromagnetism (electricity, magnetism and light); *gluons* bearing the strong force that bonds nucleons together in atoms; and *W* and *Z bosons* bearing the weak radioactive decay force that enables transmutations within atomic nuclei for conversion of one chemical element into another. A hypothesised *graviton* is thought to bear gravity, but, as this force is several orders of magnitude weaker than the others, some physicists are sceptical[371a] that any carrier can ever be detected. However, others hope for[371b] indirect cosmic proof.

Strange specificity

Interestingly, particle types exhibit distinct characteristics that influence their interactions. Mathematical interpretations of an iconic 1922 experiment[372a] by German physicists Otto Stern and Walther Gerlach showed that *all* particles maintain angular and orbital momentum or 'spin'[372b]; the *frequency* of which largely determines their properties. Fermions have half-integer ($^1/_2$) spin while bosons have full integer (1) spin. Also, particles retain inherent *orientation* (up or down); *chirality* (left-handed or right-handed)[372c]; and *helicity* (corkscrew-like spin directionality)[372d]. The origin of these highly specific and functionally important features is unknown.

Reverse-engineering matter

In the 1960s, physicists discovered that two of the four fundamental forces – electromagnetism and the weak nuclear interaction – can be described by *the same* mathematical formulation. They realised it meant these forces could have emerged as a *single unified force* at Big Bang, with capacity to forge protons and nucleons from quarks in a plasma 'soup'[373a] at stupendously high temperatures. Sheldon Glashow, Abdus Salam and Steven Weinberg shared[373b] the 1979 Nobel Prize in Physics for their contributions to the groundbreaking theory of an initial, singular electroweak force.

120

By the 1970s, theorists had incorporated this primordial unified force into an expanded set of equations that described the properties and interaction of *all* known particles and predicted the existence of others deemed essential for formation of matter as we observe it. The proposals were consolidated into a remarkably symmetrical Standard Model (SM)[373c] of 12 types of matter fermions (6 groups of quarks and 6 of leptons), and the 4 identified force-carrier particles (photons, gluons, W and Z bosons). However, the pieces only fitted if *no mass values* for particles were entered in the equations. Of course, physical matter has mass. So, just as with dark matter, something extra was needed to explain why massless high-energy particles originating at Big Bang did not fly off into oblivion, and exactly how they acquired mass. To complete the model, a hypothesised 'Higgs boson' (named after British physicist Peter Higgs, one of the theorists who came up with the idea) was added[373d].

The God particle

Higgs, and Belgian duo François Englert and Robert Brout, had independently proposed[374a,b] in 1964 that a special boson also emerged at Big Bang that lacked the intrinsic spin of other particles, *but* had the capacity to spawn an all-pervasive energy field 'trap'. According to this hypothesis, other particles acquire mass[374c] proportional to the 'drag' encountered while moving through the Higgs field – somewhat like swimmers experience resistance in bulk water. Thus, in the Standard Model, the Higgs boson provides the 'glue' that holds all the other bits together to give us matter[374d].

However, the Higgs remained undetected for several decades. The suggested anchor for matter proved so elusive that Nobel laureate Leon Lederman nicknamed it[375a] 'The God particle' in a 1993 book on particle physics.

The hunt for the Higgs was a major motivation for construction of the hugely expensive Large Hadron Collider (LHC) at the CERN (European Organisation for Nuclear Research) facility near Geneva, Switzerland. Finally, 50 years after it was predicted, CERN announced[375b] in July 2012 that a new particle had been detected at a mass-energy level circa 126 GeV (*giga* or *billion* electron-volts) – equivalent to 126 times that of a proton. This is the expected range for a Higgs, but a precise value can't be determined as the model has so many variables[375c].

After several months of further analyses, CERN researchers felt confident enough to declare[376a] in March 2013 that the detected particle was indeed a Higgs-type boson. The news was cheered by an ecstatic physics community: Brian Greene called it *"an astonishing triumph of mathematics' power to reveal the workings of the universe"* and wrote in an overview[376b]:

"The Higgs field emerged from mathematical studies seeking a mechanism to endow particles with mass. And once again the math has come through with flying colors. [....]

"Sometimes, those numbers and equations have an uncanny, almost eerie ability to illuminate otherwise dark corners of reality. When they do, we get that much closer to grasping our place in the cosmos."

Englert and Higgs – surviving architects of the 1964 universal 'glue' field proposal – were awarded the 2013 Nobel Prize for physics in recognition of the epic breakthrough. However, physicists acknowledge[376c] that the CERN discovery might be a 'look-alike' particle, so work continues[376d] to confirm that the crucial underlying component for the Standard Model has definitely been identified. Furthermore, while the theoretical framework has been adopted as the textbook view of matter, experimental support is still lacking[376e].

Unnatural universe

Scientists had hoped that 'smashing' bits of matter at stupendously high energy levels would shed light[377a] on other enigmatic issues like dark matter, antimatter and gravity. Frustratingly however, no new insights have surfaced. Instead, the discovery that the universe might, literally, be resting on an energy field sustained solely by the Higgs boson has *deepened* our existential mystery. Several equally heavy particles have failed to materialise as expected, leaving the enigmatic Higgs as the universe's precarious 'lynchpin'.

In 2014, British cosmologists Malcolm Fairbairn and Robert Hogan at Kings College London used updated information on the Higgs, and new cosmic observations, to simulate[377b] initial vacuum inflation immediately after Big Bang. They found that[377c], without the Higgs' unique 'just right' properties, the universe would have *collapsed* within microseconds of coming into being. This revelation, on top of the need for at least 18 fine-tuned parameters[377d] in other Standard Model components and equally mysterious intrinsic spin of other particles, forced physicists to admit[377e] we inhabit an 'unnatural' universe that can't be fully explained within known laws of physics.

Progressive pedigree

Another Standard Model surprise is the discovery that matter particles (fermions) go through three life stages or generations, in the course of which they decay (lose mass/energy) from a heavy, high-energy state at birth to the light, low-energy state of everyday matter. Each generation has 2 quarks and 2 leptons (4 equal and opposite particles), and each particle is a distinct type or flavour. Despite decades of research there's still no explanation[378a] just why matter particles should arrive in hierarchical mass stages, or why these are limited to only *three* generations (physicists consider it unlikely[378b] that a fourth or higher generation has ever existed[378c]).

123

In 2016, a team at Tokyo University in Japan led by renowned physicist Tsutomu T. Yanagid suggested[378d] in a paper that the peculiar ordering is not a fluke or coincidence. As they stated:

"In this paper, we will discuss an anthropic explanation for the family replication of fermions. [...] We will show that the three generations are minimal particle content required for existence of life, assuming that both baryon asymmetry and dark matter arise from the right-handed neutrino sector."

Legendary Standard Model pioneer Steven Weinberg made a belated attempt in 2020 to show[379a] how matter generations could have arisen naturally. However, he admitted (and others agreed[379b]) that his models were *"not realistic".*

Improbable numbers

One burning question that the Standard Model fails to answer is why even the weak nuclear force, which transmutates atoms from one element to another, is 10^{24} *(a septillion or one trillion trillion)* times stronger than universal gravity which binds large objects composed of the *same* atoms. The weak force only needs to be effective across microscopic ranges to 'dissociate' particles for transmutations, so it's illogical that it should be phenomenally more powerful than gravity which keeps gigantic galaxies together across huge cosmic distances.

Physicists call this mysterious discrepancy in force strength the 'hierarchy problem'[380a]. According to established laws of physics, the W and Z bosons which bear the weak force (already relatively massive at about 100 times the size of a proton) should, along with the Higgs boson, acquire even more mass as they constantly interact with other particles in the Higgs energy field that pervades our universe.

Of course, any such mass increases would *reduce* the bosons' ability to generate the weak nuclear force inside atoms and eventually bring it to the same low level as outside gravity. But this never happens – some unknown factor keeps everything at the *exact values* required for atoms of matter to exist.

The popular explanation is *supersymmetry* (SUSY)[380b] – the idea that all particles have a heavier, twin 'superpartner' with equal but opposite[380c] spin properties (fermions twin with superpartner bosons and vice-versa). In this scenario, any mass-energy acquired by a Standard Model particle (including the Higgs) is immediately negated by its superpartner; thus maintaining the value required for matter.

However, disconcertingly for proponents, no superpartners have been detected – even at the ultra-high energies the Large Hadron Collider (LHC) is now capable[381a] of generating. The continued 'no show' has prompted[381b] some theorists to call for new thinking. But, as American astrophysicist Ethan Siegel explained[381c] in a 2019 article, so many other aspects of particle physics hang on supersymmetry that abandoning the concept means complete collapse of the entire theoretical edifice constructed over several decades. This 'nightmare scenario' is looking increasingly likely[381d]: the ATLAS collaboration (a team of hundreds of scientists from around the world overseeing work at one of CERN's detectors) reported[381e] in October 2020 that there's still absolutely no sign of superpartners.

Theory of Everything

Supersymmetry derives from string theory; an all-embracing[382a] mathematical framework that replaces the traditional view of subatomic particles as point-like with zero spatial dimensions (no volume) with a new concept of one-dimensional (1-D) tiny Planck length vibrating strings that can assume different shapes.

Since the 1960s physicists have sought to avoid[382b] problems like infinite point mass in black holes, and elusive hypothesised particles like the[382c] graviton for gravity or neutralinos for dark matter. String theory seeks to overcome these hurdles and provide a unified explanation for observed phenomena at quantum and cosmic levels. According to the initial five variations[382d] of the theory, each string vibrates at a unique frequency that determines the nature of the elementary particle it represents. Open and closed strings are able to interact across stacked slices or 'branes' of space-time that span up to *10* dimensions (11 in the consolidated[382e] M-theory famously proposed[382f] in 1995 by Princeton University's Edward Witten).

The idea of multidimensional branes explains why we can't observe some proposed particles – they may exist as strings in domains beyond[383a] our 3-D + time reality. However, by simulating the conditions thought to have existed at the birth of the universe in LHC particle detectors, it was hoped primordial superpartners might be glimpsed before they disappear into hidden dimensions.

Interestingly, Csaba Csáki from Cornell University and Philip Tanedo from University of California at Irvine showed[383b] in 2015 that a holographic interpretation of hidden supersymmetric partners explains observed gradual reduction of mass-energy over three generations of twinned Standard Model particles. The previous year, Itzhak Bars and Dmitry Rychkov from University of Southern California in Los Angeles also suggested[383c] that interaction of particles across the limitless 'landscape' of branes and domains proposed in string theory could be[383d] the source of 'non-local' quantum phenomena. As Canadian physicist Glenn Starkman argued[384a] in 2018, and German contemporary Sabine Hossenfelder echoed[384b] three years later, string theory and supersymmetry still have potential to vindicate the Standard Model of particle physics – albeit with a huge dose of fine-tuned inputs of unknown origin.

Sequential chemical elements

Exactly 100 years before physicists derived the wonderfully symmetric Standard Model chart of elementary particles, Russian chemist Dmitri Mendeleev published an astonishingly sequential table of chemical elements. Others had attempted some form of mapping, but Mendeleev was the first[385a] to order the 63 elements known in 1869 into rows according to increasing atomic weight, and columns of distinct groups with similar chemical properties.

Mendeleev's arrangement left gaps in the table, but he was confident it revealed an underlying periodic law that he then used to make predictions about the position and properties of undiscovered elements missing from the gaps. His forecasts proved remarkably accurate; thus cementing his place in history as the primary architect of what, on its 150th anniversary in 2019, the United Nations Committee for the International Year of the Periodic Table called[385b] *"one of the most significant achievements in science, capturing the essence not only of chemistry, but also of physics and biology."*

Intriguing universality

As the 19th century closed, a completely new column of inert 'noble' gases – helium (He), neon (Ne), argon (Ar), krypton (Kr), xenon (Xe), and radon (Rn) – were discovered and added to the table. After breakthroughs in atomic and quantum physics over the early decades of the 20th century unearthed subatomic components, scientists realised ordering elements by *atomic number* (number of protons in the nucleus) rather than mass yields a more accurate table. It was also recognised that the distinct periodic family groupings arise from variations[385c] in electron orbital shells around the nucleus. As at 2016, in addition to the 94 elements that appear naturally, another 24 had been artificially synthesised in the lab; bringing[386a] the total recognised number to 118.

127

As Eric Scerri, a chemist and philosopher of science at University of California (Los Angeles) observed in a 2012 historical overview[386b], potential still exists for further discoveries. The significance of this mysterious, progressive ordering of the core substances that make up all living and non-living things was summed up in this remark[386c] by Cambridge University's Peter Wothers in a 2019 article:

"Would an alien have a periodic table? I think they probably would, because it is something that is absolutely fundamental - this is not just some creation of humans, there is something innate and fundamental to this - there's chemical law, physical law behind this."

The big picture: Nature is not natural

As evidence from research accumulates, it's become increasingly difficult to deny the clear indication that our physical reality comes from interactions of virtual particles that have quantum links with even more esoteric twin partners in hidden dimensions. For over 150 years, mainstream science contemptuously dismissed (or simply ignored) any suggestion that there might be non-material influences outside nature. But now, some are not so sure.

Respected 21st century theorists are seriously contemplating[387a] the radical idea that we might be simulated entities inside a time-limited holographic universe programmed by an external superintelligence. A panel of leading physicists and philosophers discussed the humbling possibility at the[387b] 2016 Isaac Asimov Memorial Debate hosted and moderated by American astrophysicist and media celebrity Neil deGrasse Tyson. Profound implications were freely acknowledged[387c] in unusually frank exchanges (the taboo words 'creation' and 'creator' were actually uttered). Tyson pointed out a potential hazard that added to the sense of trepidation: *"What happens,"* he pondered, *"if there's a bug that crashes the entire program?"*

128

Indeed, the scenario of a crashed universe is a serious consideration; given the troubling confirmation[387d] in 2013 that our universe is an inherently unstable structure on a 'knife edge' Higgs energy field with 'just so' properties. However, panellists disagreed[388a] on the degree of likelihood that we're actually part of a grand simulation – although there was consensus that humans are unlikely to ever know for certain. As philosopher David Chalmers pointed out[388b], *"We're not going to get conclusive proof that we're not in a simulation, because any proof would be simulated."* Physicist and cosmologist Max Tegmark was sceptical of the whole idea, but offered some sanguine advice: perhaps, he suggested, our highly-advanced programmers will stay interested and won't shut down our illusory universe if we *"go out and do really interesting things"* with our lives.

Some contemporary thinkers are convinced we inhabit a false reality and urge direct human intervention to change our condition and destiny. Advocates include[389a] innovator and entrepreneur Elon Musk and[389b] NASA scientist Richard Terrile. They believe there's already enough circumstantial evidence to support the idea – Terrile points to the fact that everything we observe can be broken down into finite, pixel-like computable units. Accordingly, futuristic contingency plans have been mooted to save humanity should our simulators pull the plug. Disconcerting media reports[389c,d] emerged in 2016 that some technologists in Silicon Valley may be plotting how we can escape our virtual prison; a prospect that alarmed[389e] others who fear bursting our holographic bubble may instantly collapse everything that exists.

However, it's unlikely that humans can change the status quo. In a March 2020 *Startalk* episode[390a], Tyson agreed with guest Chuck Nice that our inability to travel faster than the speed of light is probably a pre-programmed limitation. So, we just have to hope that our originator is omnibenevolent and omniscient as some religions teach.

Interestingly, some technologists have reverted to old-fashioned supplication. In 2015, Anthony Levandowski launched the 'Way of the Future' church for *"the realization, acceptance, and worship of a Godhead based on Artificial Intelligence (AI) developed through computer hardware and software."* The venture excited interest[390b], but proved short-lived[390c].

Aliens within

Some researchers have adopted a more practical approach to the possibility of 'unearthly' observers. In 2013, Scottish astrophysicists Arwen Nicholson and Duncan Forgan published[391a] computer models they said showed[391b] 'self-replicating probes' programmed by extraterrestrials (ETs) may be secretly exploring our galaxy.

James Benford, an American physicist and SETI (Search for Extraterrestrial Intelligence) researcher also suggested[391c] in a 2019 paper that ETs could easily have placed concealed observation probes on recently discovered near-earth objects which maintain[391d] a similar orbital distance from our sun. He urged investigators to send our own space probes to 'sniff out' any such 'lurkers' and argued: *"What do have we to lose by checking out these objects? Certainly resources such as time on telescopes, radio and optical. But we would be studying newly found objects, which could well be interesting astronomy."*

However, in a report[392a] for the SETI Decoding Alien Intelligence Workshop held at Mountain View, California in March 2018, NASA scientist Silvano Colombano advised astrobiologists to revisit *"cherished assumptions"* that any ETs that might exist will be carbon-based like humans and still be using detectable radio wave technology. He pointed to our own remarkable advances over *"a mere 50 years of computer evolution"* and argued: *"If we adopt a new set of assumptions about what forms of higher intelligence and technology we might find, some of those phenomena might fit specific hypotheses, and we could start some serious enquiry."*

130

Even so, Colombano and several leading astrophysicists readily admit[392b] that ETs may be so far beyond human capabilities (or even conscious perception) that they're likely to remain undetected. But, as Columbia University's Caleb Scharf suggested in a 2016 article[392c], the superintelligence we're seeking in the cosmic wilderness may be woven into the fabric of our universe. Scharf wrote: *"Perhaps hyper-advanced life isn't just external. Perhaps it's already all around. It is embedded in what we perceive to be physics itself, from the root behavior of particles and fields to the phenomena of complexity and emergence."*

Scharf is not the only scientist to speculate that unseen 'alien intelligence' may be present in nature. Helen Sharman, a chemist at Imperial College London who became Britain's first astronaut in 1991, set off a media storm when she declared in a January 2020 interview[393a]: *"Aliens exist, there's no two ways about it. There are so many billions of stars out there in the universe that there must be all sorts of different forms of life. Will they be like you and me, made up of carbon and nitrogen? Maybe not. It's possible they're here right now and we simply can't see them."*

University of Hertfordshire astrobiologist Samantha Rolfe suggested in a response[393b] to Sharman's astonishing assertion that any such entities are more likely to be forms of unfamiliar biochemistry in a 'shadow biosphere' than mysterious cosmic visitors. But she agreed *"This means we can't study or even notice them because they are outside of our comprehension."*

Debate about superintelligent aliens has crossed over into the public domain. It's emerged that the US government conducted[394a] a decades-long investigation into reported sightings of so-called 'unidentified flying objects' (UFOs) – long touted as alien observatory spacecrafts. Actual video recordings of some strange aerial phenomena were finally released[394b] in April 2020, but no conclusive explanations[394c] were offered.

Why now?

Speculations that we inhabit a false reality created 'magically' by invisible cosmic entities have been around in various versions for decades (if not centuries). So, why are these ideas – some more bizarre than anything the creators of cult science fiction series *The Matrix* and *Star Trek* dreamt up – being suddenly embraced by 21ˢᵗ century intellectual heavyweights?

Swiss complex systems analyst James Glattfelder explained in a 2019 thesis[395a] that, once we accept our reality stems from organised information, the inference of a purposive universe becomes unavoidable. Indeed, a 2012 study found[395b] even scientists trained to think in naturalistic terms find it impossible to conclude otherwise. As Sir Fred Hoyle, one of the brightest scientific minds of the 20ᵗʰ century, declared[395c] in 1982:

> *"A common sense interpretation of the facts suggests that a superintellect has monkeyed with physics, as well as with chemistry and biology, and that there are no blind forces worth speaking about in nature."*

3. Mystery of Time

"Those two times then, past and to come, how are they, seeing the past now is not, and that to come is not yet? But the present, should it always be present, and never pass into time past, verily it should not be time, but eternity."
St. Augustine of Hippo in *Confessions* (401 CE), Book XI[396]

What is time?

As with notions of physical reality, the question 'what is time?' may sound strange (and even silly) to a layperson. After all, our concept of timekeeping is based on astronomical phenomena that date back[397a] over 3,500 years to ancient civilisations in Egypt, India, China, and Babylonia. However, as St. Augustine recognised, what we've devised is just an arbitrary framework[397b] that can *measure* but not *detect* time. Humans experience time as 'change through motion'; not as a tangible, definable part of nature. We remain helpless bystanders, able to observe and measure the passing of time but unable to capture it for examination or influence it in any way.

Time's peculiar immateriality has left scientists virtually ignorant about its inherent properties. No plausible hypotheses about quantitative values and no experiments to validate composition and characteristics (as we do for matter and natural forces) are possible. Even a qualitative description has long been the subject of dispute among scholars. This makes the phenomenon a truly unique human experience.

Sir Isaac Newton argued[398a] that time is an *absolute and consistent objective reality* that can be defined mathematically. He insisted time is an integral and fundamental component of the universe; a physical fourth dimension within which everything happens.

However, philosophers like Gottfried Leibniz and Immanuel Kant viewed time[398b] as an *abstract mental construct* (like numbers and letters) that humans use to interpret and make sense of the world. In this latter view – now shared by most scientists – time only exists in our 'mind's eye' and is not a tangible entity with identifiable properties.

Another thorny issue is the difficulty of objective analysis. Einstein demonstrated that time experience is not universal, but is a *subjective* affair that's dependent on the position of observers and their relative states of motion. Arguably[398c], this *dynamic relativity* contrasts with[398d] Newton's concept of *absolute consistency*. In addition, perception of time is largely dependent on a person's neurological fitness and psychological state of mind. Thus, St. Augustine wisely confessed: *"What then is time? Provided that no one asks me, I know. If I want to explain it to an inquirer, I do not know."*

Origin of time

By the last quarter of the 20th century, theologians, philosophers and scientists were more or less agreed that our universe emerged (albeit by disputed means) from some higher, eternal source. What no one could explain was exactly how forward time-flow started from a *timeless* domain. In other words, where is the boundary between the eternal and temporal and how can we recognise it?

In 1981, Stephen Hawking, then a vibrant 39-year-old theorist at Cambridge University, stunned leading cosmologists with an audacious concept. In a presentation at the Vatican's Conference on Cosmology & Fundamental Physics in Rome held between[399a] 28th September and 2nd October that year, Hawking outlined a 'no-boundary' proposal that dispensed with all conditions and events that predated the universe. Essentially, he asserted that there's no initial 'boundary' between eternity and our space-time because no such thing as 'time' existed before Big Bang and Inflation kick-started our still-expanding universe.

Hawking's provocatively simple solution gained credence because it made troublesome questions about the origin of time irrelevant in modern physics. In 1983, he collaborated with American colleague James Hartle to develop a full, supporting mathematical framework for a no-boundary (time or otherwise) universe. They used Richard Feynman's famous path integral tool – which attempts to model all possible histories from a system's quantum probabilities – to formulate[399b] a grand, universal wave function capable of housing *all possible outcomes* over *all time* from inception at Big Bang. The idea was to show[399c] that the universe is completely self-contained with intrinsic natural laws that set initial conditions and continue to govern its evolution over time.

Disconcertingly, the Hartle–Hawking calculations also showed that our universe is *time-limited* and *finite* in space capacity. Hence, it should go from expansion to contraction at some point in the distant future. What happens next is anybody's guess. Hawking shared his thoughts with characteristic dry humour in a 1996 lecture[399d]:

"Originally, I thought that the collapse, would be the time reverse of the expansion. This would have meant that the arrow of time would have pointed the other way in the contracting phase. People would have gotten younger, as the universe got smaller. Eventually, they would have disappeared back into the womb.

"However, I now realise I was wrong [....]. The collapse is not the time reverse of the expansion. The expansion will start with an inflationary phase, but the collapse will not in general end with an anti inflationary phase. [....] This means that the arrow of time will not reverse. People will continue to get older, even after the universe has begun to contract. So it is no good waiting until the universe re-collapses, to return to your youth. You would be a bit past it, anyway, by then."

However, not everyone was convinced by this new 'quantum cosmology'[400a]. In 2006, Italian theoretical physicist Gabriele Veneziano (a veteran researcher at CERN in Switzerland) dismissed[400b] the idea that time began at Big Bang. His pioneering research into string theory in the 1960s convinced Veneziano that our universe emerged from *pre-existing* states in time that we're only beginning to comprehend. Canadian colleague Don Page also published an analysis that supported[400c] Leonard Susskind's argument that observed cosmic acceleration would leave a Hartle–Hawking universe almost devoid of matter and everything we behold. Certainly, the question whether the time passage we experience had a discernible beginning is far from settled[400d].

Nevertheless, Hawking continued to defend the no-boundary proposal throughout his illustrious career. In November 2016, he restated the argument and remarked[400e] in a new presentation to the Vatican's Conference on Science & Sustainability: *"Asking what came before the Big Bang, is meaningless, according to the no boundary proposal, because there is no notion of time available to refer to. It would be like asking what lies South of the South Pole."*

Hawking also reminded sceptics of St. Augustine's 5th century sarcastic answer to impertinent humans who insisted on knowing what God was doing before creating our world. The good bishop wrote: *"He was preparing hell (saith he) for pryers into mysteries."*

Time flow disputes

The debate whether time flow is as real as physical perceptions goes back to pre-Socrates Greek philosophy. Heraclitus (born c. 535 BCE) was convinced time passage is real: he saw the phenomenon as an intrinsic agency for ceaseless change, flux and decay in nature. Time, he declared, is so dynamic and fleeting that no object can be encountered in exactly the same state more than once. Plato summed up[401a] Heraclitus' view as *"you could not step in the same river twice"*.

In contrast, Parmenides (born c. 515 BCE) saw the world as an unchanging, timeless uniformity that's built on a constant 'what is' reality. He argued[401b] that our sense of 'being', events, and time flow is an elaborate deception. Parmenides founded the Eleatic school of philosophy which taught that we're part of an eternal 'universal whole' that humans can only conceive in *thought*, as our senses limit physical experience to visible matter.

In modern philosophy, Heraclitus' view of real time flow is at the heart of the 'growing block universe' proposal that thin slices of space-time emerge gradually to give us past, present, and future. Elements of Parmenides' view of a constant reality and illusory time flow are found in 'block universe eternalism' which argues for a unified space-time where past, present and future co-exist and are experienced differently, depending on one's location. A third school of thought known as 'presentism' only recognises the 'here and now'; advocates claim the past and future don't really exist. However, none of these propositions fully reflect our actual worldly experience of temporal order and progressive reality.

If time flow is *real*, how can we accurately determine the specious present or duration of 'now' before it passes into the past; or even define the *exact instant* when the future arrives? These difficulties are compounded by Einstein's relativity which renders time perception an entirely subjective phenomenon that depends on an observer's position and state of motion.

On the other hand, if time flow is *unreal* then by what points of reference in space-time are we to define a state of 'now'? If we accept that nature is uniform and timeless, how should we account for observable temporal changes such as fruit left exposed that rots over time or the process of human ageing?

137

For Cornell University physicist N. David Mermin, the notion of 'Now' is a nebulous, subjective perception. As he memorably declared in a 2014 commentary[401c]:

"Any person's Now is a special event for that person as it is happening. By an "event" I mean an experience whose duration and location are restricted enough that it can usefully be represented as a point in space and time. My Now is distinguished from other events I have experienced by being the actual current state of affairs. I can distinguish it from earlier events (former Nows) that I merely remember and from later events that I can only imagine. My remembered past terminates in my Now. The status of any particular event as my Now is fleeting, since it fades into a memory with the emergence of subsequent Nows."

Astrophysicist Brian Koberlein also argued[401d] at his blog that Einstein's depiction of space-time as a complex relativistic 'fabric' makes time perception a highly personal experience. Koberlein wrote[401e]: *"If you were to walk by me while I sit on a park bench, your time would be slightly different from mine because of our relative motion. In essence we each have our own private time."* However, given the central role that time plays in our collective consciousness and ordering of society, the notion of individualistic time is deeply unsettling and (unsurprisingly) hotly contested by other scholars.

Illusion or reality?

Early 20th century Scottish philosopher and metaphysician John M. E. McTaggart's 1908 article[402a] *The Unreality of Time* is a classic (though still controversial) analysis of the time flow problem. McTaggart offered two ways[402b] of describing the temporal ordering of events – *tensed* A-series in which events are *actually shifting* past, present and future positions that generate *real* time flow; and *untensed* B-series in which events forever remain in the same *relative fixed* before or after positions; thus giving us a mere *illusion* of time flow.

McTaggart showed[402c] that defining 'time flow' in terms of dynamic, tensed A-series events that are *always* changing position becomes meaningless, as 'future' events in one cycle are the 'present' in another and represent the 'past' in yet another cycle of a world in constant motion. Of course, we don't experience past, present and future at the *same* time; but McTaggart argued the mere fact that tensed events are *already morphing* into a different historical position *even as they occur*, contradicts the entire concept of ordered time flow. However, untensed B-series events that are static and unmoving can't conceivably become what we experience as the present 'now'; a shifting A-series is also needed to give us different time frames. Thus, McTaggart concluded that time is unreal and our experience of a temporal world is almost certainly an illusion.

Most physicists have embraced[403a] the B-series concept of illusory time flow because this position is compatible with Einstein's relativity. As the revered theorist wrote in a 1955 letter of comfort to the widow of his recently deceased friend Michele Besso:

"Now he has departed from this strange world a little ahead of me. That means nothing. People like us, who believe in physics, know that the distinction between past, present, and future is only a stubbornly persistent illusion."

In *The End of Time* (1999), British physicist and philosopher Julian Barbour went further: he argued[403b] that *time itself* doesn't exist – whether as a fixed or shifting component of our spatial reality. He explained in an interview[403c] with John Brockman for *Edge*:

"My basic idea is that time as such does not exist. There is no invisible river of time. But there are things that you could call instants of time, or 'Nows'. As we live, we seem to move through a succession of Nows, and the question is, what are they? They are arrangements of everything in the universe relative to each other in any moment, for example, now."

Barbour suggested that the instants of 'Now' we experience are really quantum 'time capsules' from some external domain – a concept that echoes Plato's millennia-old view that everything in our physical world is just a projected copy of hidden eternal ideal forms. Brockman cited science writer Steve Farrar's summary of these extraordinary ideas which overturn conventional physics dogma:

> *"Barbour argues that we live in a universe which has neither past nor future. A strange new world in which we are alive and dead in the same instant. In this eternal present, our sense of the passage of time is nothing more than a giant cosmic illusion."*

Bizarre as Barbour's views on time might sound[404a], he's not the only one to advocate a radical overhaul of our temporal perceptions. Italian theoretical physicist Carlo Rovelli – a pioneer of loop quantum gravity theory (LQG) – declared in *The Order of Time* (2018) that our descriptions of time stem from[404b] 'ignorance'; he dismissed even Einstein's relativistic space-time as a gross simplification of complex laws. According to Rovelli, what we perceive as 'time' is just[404c] a bewildering 'spider web' of events that our feeble minds somehow order into non-existent past, present and future blocks.

Nevertheless, there's growing support for A-series real time flow which accords with our intuition and actual worldly experience. Rovelli's Canada-based colleague Lee Smolin – a collaborative LQG researcher – has long argued[405a] that time is the bridge that connects quantum mechanical theory of unobservable particles (which *discounts* gravity) with classical relativity theory of observable cosmic structures (which *depends* on gravity). In 1997, Smolin and Stuart Kauffman – a biological scientist and complex systems analyst – co-authored an article[405b] that emphasised the essential role of time in evolution of intangible quantum wave-functions into tangible particles of matter. Without time, they concluded, *nothing* could exist.

140

Smolin revived Newton's concept of real, objective time in his book *Time Reborn* (2013). He argued that our experiences of 'Now' are structured from actual, flowing moments of time. As he explained[405c] in a related paper, his view of 'temporal naturalism' *"holds that time, in the sense of the succession of present moments, is real, and that laws of nature evolve in that time"*, as opposed to 'timeless naturalism' which *"holds that laws are immutable and the present moment and its passage are illusions."* However, Smolin admitted there was a 'meta-law dilemma': any natural law that evolved with time *inside* our universe must have been guided by a higher law *outside* our space-time. But he still contended[405d] in a discussion about wider implications that the notion of illusory time is untenable:

> *"If I think the future's already written, then the things that are most valuable about being human are illusions along with time. We still aspire to make choices in life. That is a precious part of our humanity. If the real metaphysical picture is that there are just atoms moving in the void, then nothing is ever new and nothing's ever surprising — it's just the rearrangement of atoms. There's a loss of responsibility as well as a loss of human dignity."*

Nevertheless, in 2019 an international team led by Magdalena Zych from the University of Queensland in Australia published[405e] the results of a thought experiment that showed Erwin Schrödinger's 1926 mathematical description of time evolution at out-of-sight microscopic quantum level simply can't be applied to human perception of time passage in our macroscopic everyday world. As the authors observed at the start of their report:

> *"Time has a fundamentally different character in quantum mechanics and in general relativity. In quantum theory events unfold in a fixed order while in general relativity temporal order is influenced by the distribution of matter."*

Brain mechanisms for time perception are just as mysterious. American neurobiologist and psychologist Dean Buonomano is renowned[406a] for decades of research in this area. In his 2017 book *Your Brain Is a Time Machine: The Neuroscience and Physics of Time*, Buonomano asserted[406b] that time perception is a physically-generated brain function. He argued that, in addition to its biological role as master controller of circadian rhythms, our brain also *simulates* a sense of chronology that gives us past, present and future. Buonomano described[406c] what we experience as some kind of 'mental time travel'.

So, what are we to make of the inexplicable differences in the way time manifests in our universe? It appears only time will tell if our perceptions about a 4-D space-time are real or just[406d] quantum-generated illusions.

A one-way trip

Whether or not time flow is real, another puzzling issue for physicists is why it always appears to move in one direction. In the course of 1927 Gifford Lectures at the University of Edinburgh (published the next year in a single volume[407a] *The Nature of the Physical World*), British astrophysicist and philosopher of science Sir Arthur Eddington coined the immortal phrase *Arrow of Time* to describe its seemingly irreversible forward flow. Eddington linked[407b] this strange asymmetric feature to the universe's thermodynamic tendency to always go from low to high entropy (order to disorder).

However, in principle, there is no logical reason why events shouldn't be free to move *backwards* as well as forwards. Physical laws are fully[407c] symmetric and nature at fundamental level is wholly indifferent to direction of time flow. Why, then, do we experience *only* forward-moving time towards an uncertain future? Eddington concluded that answers to this key question lie within[407d] philosophy and metaphysics; not physical science. He challenged[407e] colleagues to prove otherwise.

A new generation of physicists has taken up Eddington's challenge, but no consensus has emerged on the issue. As Tom Siegfried remarked[408a] in a 2010 article, *"even though it seems that more solutions for this mystery have been proposed than apps for the iPhone, new attempts at explanation continue to appear as regularly as clockwork."* Some theorists link[408b] forward-only time in our universe to 'spooky' entanglement with particles in the quantum realm that Einstein, Podolsky and Rosen (EPR) identified in 1935. Others suggest[408c] the answer may lie in decoherence – the proposed 'erasure' of information that accompanies transition of unobservable quantum states to observable forms of matter (hence the reason we're unable to relive the past or experience the future).

Physicists call nature's peculiar capacity for two-way time flow at microscopic quantum level 'T-symmetry' or 'T-invariance'. In a 2016 article[409a], Frank Wilczek, a Massachusetts Institute of Technology (MIT) physicist and Nobel laureate, suggested this *"bizarre and problem-posing property"* of nature might offer a potential key to unlock other mysteries like missing dark matter. However, because human observers are an essential component of quantum mechanical theory, it only allows for the *asymmetric* forward time flow we experience.

Intriguingly, results from new research suggest that the arrow of time is yet another fine-tuned feature of our universe. In 2015, Ognyan Oreshkov and Nicolas Cerf at the Université Libre de Bruxelles (ULB) in Belgium published[409b] a novel formulation that showed time-reversal and *backward* causation is perfectly possible in a variety of states at quantum level. The finding indicates some hidden factor is preventing us from experiencing the natural, symmetric two-way time flow otherwise allowed by the laws of physics. Thus, we're able to form memories and recall the past with clarity but can know nothing for certain about the future.

Oreshkov remarked[409c]: *"Our work shows that if we believe that time symmetry must be a property of the fundamental laws of physics, we have to consider the possibility for phenomena beyond those conceivable in standard quantum theory. Whether such phenomena exist and where we could search for them is a big open question."*

Barely six months after the ULB report, Australian quantum physicist Joan Vaccaro published[410a] concrete details of an anomalous effect at Big Bang that could have overridden the symmetry which should (in principle) be allowing us to experience time-reversal. According to Vaccaro, it was this foundational 'T-violation' that allowed the universe to 'escape' the timeless instant of Big Bang and get going. She suggested the mysterious intervention of unknown origin is also responsible for compelling the universe and all it contains (including humans) into the future. Vaccaro announced[410b] dramatically: *"I found the mechanism that forces us to go to the future, the reason why you get old and the reason why we advance in time."*

Are events predestined?

A sub-plot to the mystery of time emerged in 1999 when Israeli physicist Asher Peres designed[411a] a thought experiment that suggests sets of particles that have been 'measured' and no longer exist in quantum superposition can still be 'imbued' with entanglement properties retrospectively – *even though* the particles *never interacted* in the past. Bizarrely, Peres' hypothesis implied actions from the future can influence *past* events.

In 2012, a group of quantum physicists at Austrian institutions led by Anton Zeilinger demonstrated[411b] that light photons are indeed capable of manifesting the sort of *a posteriori* 'entanglement swapping' suggested by Peres. The report authors described the result as *"quantum steering into the past"*. Zeilinger observed:[411c] *"Within a naïve classical world view, quantum mechanics can even mimic an influence of future actions on past events."*

Another astonishing finding was reported[412a] that year by researchers from Racah Institute of Physics at the Hebrew University of Jerusalem. Amazingly, the Israeli team achieved 'entanglement swapping' among particles that not only had never interacted, but had *never even coexisted* in the first place. The experimental outcome showed, for the first time, that entanglement of *time-separated* particles was also a feasible proposition – confirmation that quantum correlations are truly non-local across space-time.

The revelation that a causal relationship can exist 'in the now' between entities from *different* time eras stunned physicists and philosophers alike. Elise Crull, a historian and philosopher of science at the City College of New York, explained in a commentary[412b] how this unprecedented demonstration of 'entangled time' complicates efforts to define our physical reality. Crull asked: *"how does one describe an entity whose constituent parts are not even coexistent?"* The conundrum has revived[412c] the age-old debate about possible predestined causality.

Understandably, scientists are reluctant to adopt the premise of a predetermined universe in naturalistic research because of similarities with theological predestination. However, as science writer and author Zeeya Merali reported in a 2010 article[413a], respected figures like quantum physicist Jeff Tollaksen and cosmologist Paul Davies have not shied away from the idea that we may inhabit a teleological universe[413b,c] with pre-programmed outcomes. Astrophysicist Brian Koberlein also pondered the implications of reversed time sequences in a blog post: he pointed out[413d] that relativity rules mean *"cause and effect depend upon your vantage point."* In a 2018 commentary[413e] on troubling new conclusions about temporal causation, Koberlein remarked wryly: *"What experiments like these do show is that the universe is complicated, and what's obvious in our every day experience might not be how the universe really works."*

How much free will?

There are also wider concerns that achievement of full quantum computing (with possible disruption to our sequential experience of past, present and future) may usher in[414a] an eerie era of predictability that could make the exercise of free will irrelevant or even redundant. But some scholars have long denied that humans have true free will in what they see as a predetermined, wholly mechanistic universe.

Are humans really nothing more than 'programmed bots' acting out a preordained script? Unsurprisingly, the idea is firmly resisted by mainstream researchers. George Ellis expressed deep scepticism in a June 2020 essay. He commented[414b]:

"If you seriously believe that fundamental forces leave no space for free will, then it's impossible for us to genuinely make choices as moral beings. [....] The underlying physics would in reality be governing our behaviour, and responsibility wouldn't enter into the picture. That's a devastating conclusion. We can be grateful it's not true."

Gerard 't Hooft – the Dutch theorist and Nobel laureate who helped pioneer the idea of a holographic universe – tried to reconcile the paradox of a predetermined universe that allows human free will in a new explanation of quantum mechanics which revisits Einstein's stubborn insistence that the theory's foundational idea of inherent randomness is incorrect. In 2014, 't Hooft proposed[415a] a fascinating *cellular automaton interpretation* (CAI) which, essentially, argues that[415b] each selection a conscious observer with free will makes from a host of probabilities perfectly accords with deterministic physical laws that forbid the emergence of more than *one* quantum outcome at a time. According to 't Hooft, this step-by-step 'cellular' assembly of the reality we experience over time constitutes[415c] an overarching 'superdeterminism' that overrides all mechanistic phenomena.

German physicist Sabine Hossenfelder and British colleague Tim Palmer have since revived an even more radical version of superdeterminism first mooted[416a] by John Bell in the mid-1980s. In a December 2019 collaborative paper[416b], the duo suggested that *all* probabilities and possibilities for structures, events and phenomena (including human choices and actions) were already predetermined at the birth of our universe. Contrary to conventional understanding (supported by numerous experiments and applied technologies), Hossenfelder and Palmer contend that randomness at quantum level is only apparent; there's hidden information *right here* in our local domain that would make everything clear if humans ever manage to access it. Moreover, they assert, *everything* has remained connected since the initial founding state at Big Bang. As they put it in a March 2020 article[416c]:

> *"The core idea of Superdeterminism is that everything in the universe is related to everything else because the laws of nature prohibit certain configurations of particles (or make them so unlikely that for all practical purposes they never occur). If you had an empty universe and placed one particle in it, then you could not place the other ones arbitrarily. They'd have to obey certain relations to the first."*

Naturally, colleagues are not amused[417a] by a proposal that appears to imply[417b] their decades of strenuous research may actually be the product of humanity's collective consciousness rather than individual observations. Sergey Yurchenko wrote[417c] in a May 2020 rebuttal:

> *"In physics, free will is debated mainly in regard to the observer-dependent effects. To eliminate them from quantum mechanics, superdeterminism postulates that the universe is a computation, and consciousness is an automaton. As a result, free will is impossible. Quantum no-go theorems tell us that the only natural phenomenon that might be able to account for every bit of freedom in the universe is quantum randomness."*

Back in time applications

Whatever the correct explanation for expansive human free will in a pre-programmed universe, the new controversies are certainly shaking up our traditional views of causality and time. The idea of *retrocausality* (backwards causation in time) is no longer mere philosophical speculation – respected mathematicians and physicists are now conducting serious collaborative research into implications and practical possibilities.

In 2012, University of Cambridge philosopher Huw Price argued at length in a paper[418a] that, although we don't experience retrocausality in our everyday world, the fact that nature is fundamentally time-symmetric implies this feature plays an important role at quantum level. Quantum information theorists Matthew S. Leifer and Matthew F. Pusey revisited Price's work in 2017 and introduced[418b] refinements that have bolstered[418c] the theoretical case for quantum retro-causality. The previous year, Price and San José State University physicist and astronomer Ken Wharton suggested[418d] in an essay that Einstein's classical relativity may never be reconciled with quantum mechanics unless we abandon the long-held intuition that 'causes' always precede 'effects'.

Is the future really influencing the past in our world? Remarkably, this bizarre possibility can't be ruled out. In 2015, a collaboration of Asian and Australian quantum scientists showed that[419a] intractable unsolved problems like NP-completeness in computer science can be resolved with a locked, forever inaccessible message sent *back in time* – provided quantum entanglement is first used to create correlations[419b] between the message-bearing, time-travelling particles and originating systems. The impressive demonstration suggests ongoing research into entangled time and retrocausality will yield even more counter-intuitive and unsettling insights into our reality.

148

Simulated time bubble

The idea that time might be an emergent effect of quantum correlations within space-time was first proposed[420a] in 1983 by Don Page and William Wootters in the course of research at the Center for Theoretical Physics in Austin, Texas. However, the model they developed was judged[420b] 'ambiguous' and largely ignored by contemporaries. Then, thirty years later, the basic premise was sensationally demonstrated[420c] by a team of European physicists centred at *Istituto Nazionale di Ricerca Metrologica* (INRIM) in Turin, Italy.

The INRIM experiment used a 'toy universe' containing just two light photons to show[421a] that time would only exist for an observer entangled *inside* the universe. For a god-like observer on the outside, the same universe would appear static and unchanging – just as Parmenides had insisted over 2,400 years earlier. Significantly, the experimental confirmation that time (like gravity) is very likely[421b] a cosmic quantum simulation adds further weight to speculation[421c] that our universe is a holographic projection from information encoded elsewhere that can only be fully comprehended by an external superintelligent observer.

In a 2016 *Edge* response[422a], Seth Lloyd – a mechanical engineer and quantum physicist at MIT – articulated the new optimism that interpretation of *all* entities and phenomena in our universe (observable or unobservable) in terms of 'esoteric' quantum information may finally allow reconciliation of relativity theory with quantum mechanics. However, there's much angst that, over 300 years since Newton introduced mathematics into natural philosophy in his work *Principia*, questions about time remain largely unresolved. A conference of leading theorists convened[422b] at Waterloo, Canada in June 2016 failed to resolve[422c] any of the contentious issues.

149

Time and ageing

American physicist and author Eugene Tracy bemoaned the lack of scientific consensus on time in a 2016 overview[423a]. He noted the importance we attach to time in everyday undertakings and relationships – especially as we come to realise (sometimes at an early age) that loved ones can die at any time as they get older. Tracy queried poignantly:

> *"Isn't science supposed to test itself against the ground of experience? This disconnect might help to explain why so many students not only don't 'get' physics, but are positively repulsed by it. Where are they in the world picture drawn by physicists? Where is life, and where is death? Where is the flow of time?"*

Indeed. Undoubtedly, one of the most pressing questions of our times is why human lifespan is so brief compared to the age of the universe and the timeless domain from which everything emerged. Of course, it's unlikely that scientific research can ever produce a plausible explanation for our ephemeral existence. But interesting information has emerged about the biological programmes that govern ageing over time.

All in the cell

In 1961, American anatomist Leonard Hayflick demonstrated[423b] conclusively that mitosis (normal cell division for growth or replenishment) in healthy human cells is limited to 40 – 60 divisions; a finding now dubbed the Hayflick limit. Thereafter, cells enter a phase of senescence associated with ageing. Advances in molecular biology and nanoscopy[423c] have given scientists fascinating insights into microscopic cellular processes. However, the *catalyst* for senescence and exactly *how* it influences ageing and the onset of age-related diseases are still very much unclear.

150

The mystery deepened in 1973 when Russian biologist Alexey Olovnikov linked[424a] the Hayflick limit and ageing processes to progressive shortening of telomere caps at the ends of chromosomes in cell nuclei. Olovnikov's 'marginotomy' proposal has since been supported by numerous studies that confirm a telomere-lifespan link. In 2017, a team led by researchers from The Scripps Research Institute, La Jolla, California announced[424b] the discovery of *TZAP*; a protein master regulator that 'labels'[424c] mammalian telomeres which need trimming to lengths that accord with species lifespan. The next year, another team at Arizona State University reported[424d] that telomerase (the enzyme which carries out trimmings or additions on telomeres) has a sophisticated signalling component that prevents[424e] both premature ageing and immortal rejuvenation.

It appears environmental influences are also at work. In 2018, a collaborative study[425a] between Max Planck Institute for Ornithology in Germany and North Dakota State University in the USA revealed[425b] that urban traffic noise significantly accelerates telomere shortening (and ageing) in post-fledging birds that have left the nest.

Epigenetic clocks

Evidence has been mounting since the late 1960s that human DNA also incorporates a clock-like senescence indicator. Remarkably, levels of methylation[426a] at annotated CpG sites on genomes can be extrapolated to predict life expectancy. However, it's not known *why* DNA methylation levels are such an accurate biomarker of longevity in humans.

At least two 'epigenetic clocks' that predict age have emerged. In 2012, a team at University of California San Diego led by bioengineer and bioinformatician Gregory Hannum unveiled[426b] 'Hannum's clock' which uses 71 CpG markers in blood cells to estimate age.

151

One year later, human geneticist and biostatistician Steve Horvath at University of California Los Angeles published[426c] 'Horvath's clock'; a wider model based on 353 CpG markers that predict age across all types of human cells and tissues. Horvath's multi-tissue tool allowed researchers, for the first time, to compare the ages of different *body parts* from the same individual. Surprisingly, it revealed[426d] that some areas of our anatomy age faster than others.

However, several contemporaries were initially sceptical[427a] that epigenetic clocks for ageing exist: DNA methylation is a primary tool for *differentiation* of cell types as mammals develop, so it seemed odd that a standard set of CpG markers could predict age with equal efficiency across *all* human tissue. Nonetheless, despite the absence of a clear mechanism or explanation for the strange link, the efficacy of Horvath's clock is now[427b] undisputed and it's become the standard biomarker of biological age and life expectancy.

In 2016, Horvath co-authored another wide-ranging international study[427c] that identified a slower epigenetic clock as a possible factor for *lower* mortality rates for women despite their *higher* susceptibility to disease. The research group suggested this slower rate of tissue ageing could also be the reason for surprisingly higher life expectancy for Hispanics in the USA who tend to have a comparatively lower socio-economic status (the so-called Hispanic paradox).

Arresting ageing

The discovery that ageing stems from biomolecular processes has raised hopes that it may be possible to halt the process. Increasingly, some medical scientists are treating ageing as just another physical affliction that can be cured[428a] or even reversed[428b] with appropriate interventions.

152

Since the early 2000s, Mayo Clinic institutions in the USA have pioneered senescence research aimed at combating ageing. Jan van Deursen from the Mayo Clinic College of Medicine at Rochester in Minnesota reviewed ongoing investigations in a 2014 article[428c]. He discussed how senescence might be impacting *"complex biological processes such as development, tissue repair, ageing and age-related disorders"* and enthused: *"A deeper understanding of the molecular mechanisms underlying the multi-step progression of senescence and the development and function of acute versus chronic senescent cells may lead to new therapeutic strategies for age-related pathologies and extend healthy lifespan."*

James Kirkland, another Mayo Clinic scientist based at Rochester, has led research into a class of drugs called *senolytics* that target and destroy clusters of senescent cells thought to accelerate ageing. In 2015, Kirkland's extensive team announced[429a] the result of initial trials in mice: *"The healthspan of mice is enhanced by killing senescent cells using a transgenic suicide gene. Achieving the same using small molecules would have a tremendous impact on quality of life and the burden of age-related chronic diseases."* Human clinical trials soon followed and, just four years later, the group reported[429b] significant progress with a drugs combination. In August 2020, they published[429c] new research that suggests senolytics can rejuvenate organs harvested from deceased aged donors – thus boosting current scarce supplies for transplants. Kirkland explained his motivation in a feature article[429d]: *"I'm a clinical geriatrician. I'm sick of prescribing better wheelchairs, walkers and incontinence devices. I'd like to do something fundamental that could slow down these processes and maybe even partially reverse them in older people."*

Lifespan controversy

Senescence research has been welcomed by advocacy groups like the Methuselah Foundation (MF), American Aging Association (AGE), American Academy of Anti-Aging Medicine (A4M), and the World Anti-aging Network (WAAN).

153

However, some ageing and longevity specialists have distanced themselves from what geriatrician Thomas T. Perls dismissed[430a] as *"Anti-aging quackery and hucksterism"* in a 2004 article. The worry is that unproven therapies and potentially harmful products could undermine[430b] public confidence in mainstream senescence research.

In 2002, American biogerontologist S. Jay Olshansky teamed up with Leonard Hayflick (discoverer of the numerical limit to cell division) and biodemographer Bruce A. Carnes to publish a position statement[430c] that was endorsed by 52 senescence researchers. The authors sought to clarify aspects of biological ageing and *"inform the public of the distinction between the pseudoscientific antiaging industry, and the genuine science of aging that has progressed rapidly in recent years."* They warned against unrealistic expectations of immortality and asserted: *"The prospect of humans living forever is as unlikely today as it has always been, and discussions of such an impossible scenario have no place in a scientific discourse."*

Predictably, the statement ignited a feud with the longevity research community. Robert H. Binstock from the School of Medicine at Case Western Reserve University in Cleveland, Ohio published a robust response[430d] in 2003 accusing critics of waging a *"war on anti-aging medicine"* which, he claimed, was *"largely an attempt by established gerontological researchers to preserve their hard-won scientific and political legitimacy, as well as to maintain and enhance funding for research on the basic biological mechanisms of aging."*

Hungarian biogerontologist Imre Zs-Nagy – developer[431a] of the Membrane Hypothesis of Aging (MHA) – tried to reconcile the warring parties in a 2009 article[431b]. He called the dispute *"One of the biggest scandals of the recent history of medicine"* and urged colleagues to maintain *"an independent, open-minded approach"* so unbiased evaluations of proposed therapies can proceed without hindrance.

Ultimately, ageing is a feature that's largely determined by biology and environment. Nonetheless, longevity promoters argue that new insights show it might, in principle, be possible to extend life *indefinitely*. But, just how far can lifespan be extended and what are the implications for humanity in a world regulated by time?

In 2019, collaborative research led by scientists from MDI Biological Laboratory in Maine, USA, and the Institute for Brain Sciences at Nanjing University in China, identified[432a] cellular mechanisms in the nematode worm *C. elegans* that can extend its lifespan[432b] by up to *500 percent* (equivalent to 500 years in humans).

James Vaupel, founding director of the Max Planck Institute for Demographic Research in Rostock, Germany published a review[432c] in 2010 that suggested natural human demise was already being delayed by up to a decade. Vaupel reported:

> *"Remarkably, the rate of deterioration with age seems to be constant across individuals and over time: it seems that death is being delayed because people are reaching old age in better health. Research by demographers, epidemiologists and other biomedical researchers suggests that further progress is likely to be made in advancing the frontier of survival — and healthy survival — to even greater ages."*

However, a 2016 demographic study[433a] led by molecular geneticist Jan Vijg at the Albert Einstein College of Medicine in New York pegged human longevity to a maximum of 115 years. The researchers declared: *"Our results strongly suggest that the maximum lifespan of humans is fixed and subject to natural constraints."* The disappointing finding was immediately challenged[433b] by no less than five groups of researchers. But the analysis by Vijg's team received broad support[433c] from longevity sceptics.

In response to claims that there are no genetic limitations on human lifespan, Olshansky, who had bet[434a] distinguished biologist and author Steven Austad in 2000 that no one born before 2001 will attain the age of 150, offered[434b] this simple analogy:

> *"How is it possible to have a biological limit to life, yet no genetic program that runs it? [....] Think of constraints on running speed as an analogy. No genetic program specifically limits how fast humans can run, but biomechanical constraints on running speed are imposed by a fixed body design that evolved for other purposes."*

Vijg also vigorously defended[434c] his research group's conclusion that humans have reached an upper threshold of longevity. He argued[434d]:

> *"I'm not saying drugs or tissue engineering couldn't be very beneficial to increase our average lifespan, but will they really enable us to break through this ceiling of 115? I find that highly unlikely. Lifespan is controlled by too many genes. You could maybe plug one of those holes, but there are still another 10,000 other holes springing up."*

Interestingly, in 2018, a statistical analysis[435a] of mortality rates and survival probabilities of nearly 4,000 Italians aged 105 and older revealed that, paradoxically, chances of dying appear to level-off *after* the age of 105. The surprising finding has revived[435b] the debate about chances of humans overcoming the ravages of time.

Whatever the attractions of living indefinitely, this will have to be balanced against natural controls imposed by death to ensure our planet remains viable and habitable – considerations that are as contentious[435c,d] as scientific disputes on ageing.

4. Mystery of Mathematics

"We go beyond the mathematical formula at our own risk; we may find a model or a picture which helps us understand it, but we have no right to expect this, and our failure to find such a model or picture need not indicate that either our reasoning or our knowledge is at fault."
Sir James Jeans, astrophysicist, in *The Mysterious Universe* (1930).

Where does maths come from?

Mathematical truths are timeless and transcend beliefs and cultures. The proofs derived by ancient Greek mathematicians like Pythagoras (c. 570 – 495 BCE), Euclid (c. 300 BCE) and Archimedes (c. 287 – 212 BCE) are still as valid and relevant as they were over two millennia ago. Ancient Egyptian computing methods that go back even further (c. 3000 BCE) are essentially the same[436a] binary algorithms employed in modern computer processors. In 2016, astrophysicist and science historian Mathieu Ossendrijver from Humboldt University in Berlin, Germany deciphered[436b] inscriptions on 2,300-year-old cuneiform tablets that showed[436c] ancient Babylonian astronomers used not just arithmetic, but also sophisticated geometry. Ossendrijver expressed surprise[436d] at the discovery – such advanced techniques were previously thought to have originated[436e] 1,400 years later in medieval Europe.

Despite the ubiquity of maths and its critical role in innovations that have enabled complex societies, its origin remains a complete mystery. It's not even clear[437a] if maths is a fundamental property of the universe or an evolved biological tool for analysing nature. Neuroscientists have identified[437b] specific brain regions that give us mathematical capacity. However, a review[437c] published in 2016 by researchers at Ben-Gurion University of the Negev in Israel suggests[437d] numerical ability is not innate but acquired.

157

For MIT physicist and cosmologist Max Tegmark, maths is not just a property of the universe but *the very substance* of reality. In his book *Our Mathematical Universe* (2014), he contended[438a] that *everything* (including life) is ultimately a mathematical construct. According to Tegmark's Mathematical Universe Hypothesis (MUH), the physical world we perceive is actually[438b] a *"giant mathematical object"* that's just a tiny part of a huge multiverse. However, some contemporary thinkers were unimpressed. City University of New York philosopher Massimo Pigliucci stated bluntly[438c] at his blog *"I'm not convinced."* In a book review, US-based British academic and author Brian Rotman commented likewise[438d]: *"as a mathematician, convinced that mathematics is a human construction, that numbers don't exist in the world before humans put them there, I don't buy it."*

Tegmark is not the only modern theorist to engage the public on the profundity and broader implications of maths. In his acclaimed book *Love and Math* (2013), University of California (Berkeley) mathematician Edward Frenkel passionately described[439a] maths as an aesthetic venture capable of beautiful and elegant products which rival the finest works of art. He argued[439b] that maths is a mystical phenomenon hidden outside our physical world which we discover in bits through our consciousness.

But perhaps the most thought-provoking commentary was delivered over 50 years earlier by Princeton theoretical physicist and mathematician Eugene Wigner. In 1959, he famously pondered[440a] *The Unreasonable Effectiveness of Mathematics in the Natural Sciences* in a lecture delivered at New York University. Wigner noted that mathematical concepts which appear initially to be mere intellectual exercises eventually yield important applications, and reflected that *"the enormous usefulness of mathematics in the natural sciences is something bordering on the mysterious and that there is no rational explanation for it."*

Wigner concluded: *"The miracle of the appropriateness of the language of mathematics for the formulation of the laws of physics is a wonderful gift which we neither understand nor deserve. We should be grateful for it and hope that it will remain valid in future research and that it will extend, for better or for worse, to our pleasure, even though perhaps also to our bafflement, to wide branches of learning."*

Elegance and symmetric beauty[440b] are not the only benefits maths brings to science. As the scope for empirical research steadily diminishes due to physical constraints and limits to human sensory capacity for observations, many ideas are now being expressed purely as[440c] mathematical formulations that offer no tangible predictions and have no plausible prospect of experimental validation. Thus, despite the lack of scientific consensus on the origin of mathematics, there's no doubt that our knowledge base would be much poorer without the wonderful insights it continues to provide into nature's hidden features and workings.

Natural patterns

The beauty and order we perceive throughout the universe stem from recurring patterns at various levels. Both organic and inorganic structures are characterised by consistent forms of various symmetries, spirals, flows, waves, foams, fractures, tessellations, stripes and spots. Scientists are discovering that these striking designs are firmly rooted in mathematics, natural laws, and associated physical mechanisms.

Fractals

Many patterns in nature are underpinned by fractals[441a]; complex geometrical sets that repeat over a finite range of scales and levels to produce detailed, stunning visual representations (*Mandelbrot* and *Julia* sets are just two famous examples).

159

In recent decades, fractal features have been identified in all sorts of[441b] phenomena and structures from river connections to genetic networks[443c] and proteins[441d]. But humans have long been aware of the potential of these fascinating patterns for exotic designs: variations can be seen in centuries-old Islamic geometric shapes and 2,000-year-old Hindu temple architecture.

Curiously, fractal shapes are not[442a] normal whole number dimensions (1-D, 2-D or 3-D) but fall somewhere 'in between'. The iterative, recursive and finite properties displayed are yet more evidence of fine-tuned structural outcomes in nature. In 1988, British mathematician Michael Barnsley worked out that the geometry of most fractals can be reduced[442b] to a core 'Chaos Game' algorithm. Barnsley's finding has been adopted in digital representation techniques that allow[442c] computerised compression and reproduction of large amounts of data for fixed or rolling (video) images.

Turing's morphogens

Until the 20th century, scientists had no explanation how biological processes operate to produce the unique shapes and patterns that distinguish groups of organisms. In his epic work[443a] *On Growth and Form* (1917), Scottish mathematical biology pioneer Sir D'Arcy Wentworth Thompson suggested[443b] that the structural organisation of living things derives from *physical laws and mathematics* rather than random Darwinian natural selection. The idea was largely ignored[443c] by a scientific class that had rejected all notion of design or teleology in nature, but Thompson's detailed arguments inspired English mathematician and computer science pioneer Alan Turing to outline a related mechanism of *morphogenesis* in a 1952 paper[443d]. Already famous for inventing the Turing machine computational model, he formulated a hypothetical pathway of 'reaction-diffusion' (RD) among chemical 'morphogen' substances to show how biological patterns might emerge.

160

Turing derived a partial differentiation equation (PDE) that yielded six possible developmental patterns in a model ring of cells. He concluded from his impressive results that *"certain well-known physical laws are sufficient to account for many of the facts."* However, like Thompson's proposal, Turing's hypothesis remained in the realm of scientific speculation for the next sixty years.

Then, in 2012, an international group led by researchers at King's College London in England reported[444a] experimental results that confirmed[444b] patterns like tiger stripes and leopard spots conform to Turing's RD model. Six years later, a team at University of Sheffield published[444c] a combined genetics-mathematics model that showed[444d] even ancient tooth-like scales on sharks are patterned according to Turing's computations. These results suggest *the same* mathematical system of patterning has been conserved in several types of animal skin coverings over *millions* of years of evolution.

Remarkably, a 2012 collaborative study[445a] by multidisciplinary teams from Canadian and Spanish institutions suggests that a Turing-type mechanism also governs[445b] the patterning of limb digits like fingers and toes. Indications are that the system is ubiquitous[445c] in biology: in 2014, an American team of physicists, biochemists and mathematicians successfully generated Turing's predicted patterns in artificially synthesised[445d] cell-like structures.

Group consistency

Turing's model shows how biological patterns arise, but it doesn't explain *consistency* within groups. In 2018, biomathematicians Alexandria Volkening and Björn Sandstede at Brown University in Providence, Rhode Island developed a new model that indicates[446a] group bio-patterns are maintained by an even more robust mathematical system than Turing's PDE.

161

Previously, it was thought the distinctive and precisely numbered blue and yellow stripes on zebrafish arose from interactions of just two morphogens – black *melanophore* and yellow *xanthophore* pigment cells. However, in 2013 it emerged[446b] that yet another morphogen – iridescent and reflective *iridophore* cells – helps to organise the arrangement of black and yellow counterparts. Volkening and Sandstede showed that, unlike Turing's comparatively flexible PDE, pattern regulation by iridophores involves a highly sophisticated mathematical system that confers both *redundancy* and *resistance* to mutations. Volkening explained[446c] how this built-in backup system guarantees striping consistency:

"We think that is because iridophores are getting their signals from multiple places. If one interaction fails, there is another that can take its place. Because of the redundancies, you can remove some interactions, and still get stripes. They're not perfect stripes, but they are similar.

"The biological discovery of the role of iridophores was a real paradigm shift in how we thought zebrafish stripes were created. This led to a lot of open questions, and our mathematical model provides an explanation for how iridophores behave on the fish skin. We show that the complex interactions of these cells may be important for reliable stripe formation, but also key to why zebrafish have stripes but related fish have different patterns."

Architecture for life

Scientists have discovered that living things are also *structurally* constructed in line with mathematical blueprints. In 2013, a team from University of California (Los Angeles) led by ecologist and evolutionary biologist Lawren Sack found that[447a] that plant leaf design is governed by proportional allometric equations. The rules revealed surprising and unexpected relationships between leaf thickness, surface area, and cell dimensions.

Sack commented[447b]:

> *"Fundamental discoveries like these highlight the elegant solutions evolved by natural systems. Plant anatomy often has been perceived as boring. Quantitative discoveries like these prove how exciting this science can be. We need to start re-establishing skill sets in this type of fundamental science to extract practical lessons from the mysteries of nature."*

Versatile scaling

In 2015, research into artificial protein-like nanomaterials at the US Department of Energy's Lawrence Berkeley National Laboratory uncovered[448a] a critical design rule for construction[448b] of such microstructures. A collaborative study[448c] published in 2017 by a group of structural molecular biologists and mathematicians in the UK and USA found that[448d] a similar rule governs the assembly of virus capsid shells into distinctive geometric patterns.

Numerical scaling principles have also emerged in sophisticated neural systems. In 2019, neuroscientists Shyam Srinivasan and Charles Stevens at University of California (San Diego) published[449a] research that revealed three key components of distributed brain circuits for the abstract sense of olfaction (smell) conform to computational scales across, at least, six mammalian species. Srinivasan explained[449b] the significance: *"These three stages scale with each other, with the relationship of the number of neurons in each stage the same across species. So, if you told me the number of neurons in the nose, I could predict the number in the piriform cortex or the bulb."*

Controlled development

Biologists have been surprised to discover that even production and proliferation of cells – life's fundamental building blocks – is governed by mathematical rules.

163

In 2014, a multidisciplinary team led by biophysicists at University of Chicago in the USA used quantitative modelling techniques to show[450a] that cell cycles of growth and division conform to conserved, consistent scaling laws. The report authors wrote: *"These universal behaviors reflect the physical principle that a single timescale governs noisy bacterial growth and division despite the complexity of underlying molecular mechanisms."* They admitted in their conclusions that *"This simple design principle is unexpected given the complexity of a whole organism."*

That same year, another group led by biophysicist Suckjoon Jun from the University of California (San Diego) discovered that[450b] growth across a cell's lifetime actually occurs in *fixed incremental values* until the phenotypic target size for the organism is reached. The researchers found the entire process is tightly regulated by a mathematical 'adder principle' that also ensures cell-size homeostasis is maintained. After years of further research, Jun's team reported[450c] in 2019 that the adder constraint operates a 'timer' for growth that's somehow linked to concentration levels of key proteins involved in the cell cycle. The astonishing finding was truly groundbreaking in a field that's only beginning to appreciate the extent to which biology is based on core mathematical principles. Jun called[450d] the adder function *"a very robust mechanism because each cell is guaranteed to reach its target cell size whether it is born large or small."*

Optimal architecture

Another unexpected structural feature has surfaced in cells. Until recently, scientists assumed that cells adopt a frustum-like shape (as in classical Roman architecture) for multicellular construction of 3-D body parts. However, this did not fully explain the remarkable ability of epithelial cells (which line the outside surfaces and inner cavities of organs) to assume different geometrical curvatures while remaining seamless and compact (as in skin epidermis).

In 2018, a collaborative study[451a] by teams of bioengineers, molecular biologists and mathematicians in the EU and USA found that[451b], during embryo development, epithelial cells morph into a previously unknown 'scutoid' architecture which *maximises* packing stability while *minimising* energy use. The optimal geometric form was uncovered[451c] by a sophisticated computational model.

It's emerged that even bacterial biofilm patterns involve complex mechanical engineering rules. In March 2020, a team of engineers and biological scientists at Princeton University in New Jersey published[452a] a chemo-mechanical model that showed[452b] how the microbes assemble collectively for adherence to different types and forms of substrates. The researchers reported: *"Our model provides insight into the observed stages of expansion of Vibrio cholerae biofilms and suggests that universal mechanical principles may underlie the formation of 3D morphologies in biofilms across species."*

These amazing discoveries are rapidly overtaking debate and semantics over the meaning of 'design' in nature, and whether it's real or apparent in biology. It's becoming harder to dismiss the evidence that fundamental abstract principles govern the structural layout and construction of living things.

Golden Ratio

Ancient Greek mathematicians first identified the important rule in geometry that any line can be divided to make the ratio of the large piece to the whole line *exactly the same* as the ratio of the small piece to the large piece (1: 1.618). Euclid (c. 300 BCE) is credited[453a] with the first written description of this extraordinary proportionality in nature – he defined it as *"division in extreme and mean ratio"*. The relationship is now known as[453b] the *golden ratio* (GR), *golden mean, golden section*, or *divine proportion*.

165

The intriguing ratio stems from an ancient mathematical rule that was introduced[453c] to Western Europe by Italian mathematician Leonardo 'Fibonacci' Pisa in his 1202 classic *Liber Abaci* (The Book of Calculation). The work extolled the superior utility of Hindu–Arabic decimals over Roman numerals, but is remembered for a strange numerical sequence.

Fibonacci described[453d] a natural series of numbers, with each new number being the sum of the two before it; i.e. 0, 1, 1, 2, 3, 5, 8, 13, 21, 34, 55, 89, 144 . . . and so on. Each successive number in the series quickly becomes 1.618 times greater than the previous number – the same proportion as the golden ratio. This occurs at just the 10th number in series, and after the 39th number the figure is always correct to an amazing 15 decimal places (1.618033988749895). The constant is now called *Phi* (represented by the symbol Ø).

Phi acquired[454a] mystical status during the European Renaissance (15th to 16th centuries) after it was popularised by famous figures like Italian mathematician Luca Pacioli and the innovative artist Leonardo da Vinci. Since then, a proliferation of literature has identified Fibonacci numbering and *Phi* proportions in several life forms (including plants[454b] and humans). British mathematician Ron Knott's online resource[454c] at the University of Surrey lists and explains many applications of the principle in nature, art, architecture and music.

However, in a February 2020 overview[455a], distinguished University of Bath applied mathematician Chris Budd downplayed and cautioned against claims[455b] that *Phi* is a universal standard for beauty and aesthetics. Israeli-American astrophysicist Mario Livio, whose 2002 book *The Golden Ratio* outlines a comprehensive history of *Phi*, also expressed scepticism[455c] but admitted (as did Budd) that the constant has *"truly amazing mathematical properties"* and *"a propensity to pop up where least expected in natural phenomena"*.

Nonetheless, others are convinced that *Phi's* ubiquity has profound significance. South African theoretical chemist Jan Boeyens and palaeontologist Francis Thackeray argued in a 2014 paper[456a] that it's the universal architectural principle underpinning everything from the topology of space-time to biological organisation. Controversially, the co-researchers claimed *Phi* is a *"species constant (T)"* that governs the relative size of mammalian skulls. They pleaded[456b] in a non-technical article that *"the time has come to recognise that relativity and quantum theories can be integrated, and linked numerically to the value of a mathematical constant – whether in the context of space-time or biology."*

Perhaps Boeyens and Thackeray are on to something profound. That same year, theoretical physicists Abolhassan Vaezi from Cornell University in New York and Maissam Barkeshli from Microsoft Research Station Q in California used a quantum dimension that conforms to the golden ratio to model[456c] exotic *anyon* quasiparticles – elusive 2-D entities that arise during particle interactions *inside* solids. Anyons can't be physically observed in our 3-D world, but leave 'braided' tracks that are seen as the ideal solution[456d] for data qubits in futuristic topological quantum computers (TQCs); full particles tend to decohere and lose information.

The Alpha Number

Like *Phi*, the 33rd prime number 137 has long perplexed physicists because of its similar ubiquity and mysterious connotations. Division of a circle into two sections that conform to the golden ratio yields a geometric angle of 137° that features[457] widely in plant symmetry, and a complementary angle of approximately 222° that's significant in computations of lattices and hexasticks (six polysticks). By a strange coincidence, the age of the universe – as it appears to us cosmologically – is 137 x 10,000,000 years. The inverse of 137 ($^{1}/_{137}$) works out as *exactly* eight palindromic periods that read *the same* in either direction (0.00729927007299270072992700 etc.).

But the most intriguing manifestation of 137 is in the *fine-structure constant* (FCS): a dimensionless value that's independent of any units system. Commonly represented by the Greek letter *alpha* (α), physicists use the FCS to represent coupling strength or force of interaction between particles; a vital phenomenon that allows matter to exist. After Niels Bohr proposed a new quantised solar model of atoms in 1913, German theoretical physicist Arnold Sommerfeld enhanced it with *elliptical* (rather than circular) electron orbits in 1916 and introduced *alpha* to account for the distinctive splitting or 'fine-structure' observed in atomic spectral lines.

However, it soon became clear that Sommerfeld's mathematical tool could be expressed as permutations of other fundamental constants like the *elementary particle charge, electric constant, magnetic constant, Coulomb constant, von Klitzing constant*, and the free space *impedance constant*. This mysterious universality placed *alpha* at the heart of physics, leading to years of speculation[458a] by Sir Arthur Eddington that it could be a key part of the elusive bridge between our observable macroscopic world and the unobservable microscopic realm of quantum particles.

In 1929, Eddington proposed the inverse of 137 ($^1/_{137}$) as an exact 'pure number' value for *alpha*. But contemporaries were sceptical. Paul Dirac commented[458b] in a 1937 article:

> *"Eddington's arguments are not always rigorous, and, while they give one the feeling that they are probably substantially correct in the case of the smaller numbers (the reciprocal fine-structure constant hc/e2 and the ratio of the mass of the proton to that of the electron), the larger numbers, namely the ratio of the electric to the gravitational force between electron and proton, which is about 10^{39}, and the ratio of the mass of the universe to the mass of the proton, which is about 10^{78}, are so enormous as to make one think that some entirely different type of explanation is needed for them."*

As it turned out, Eddington was not far off the mark. In April 2018, an American team led by Holger Müller at University of California (Berkeley) used matter-wave interferometry and caesium atoms to experimentally determine[458c] *alpha* as the inverse of 137.035999046; a value reckoned *"to an accuracy of better than 1 part per billion"*. In December 2020, a French team led by Saïda Guellati-Khélifa at Sorbonne University in Paris used the same technique and rubidium atoms to determine[458d] the value as 137.03599920611 *"with a relative accuracy of 81 parts per trillion."*

But, despite the flurry of experimental tests to ascertain the exact value of *alpha*, its origin is still a complete mystery. No physical theory or mathematical equation has emerged from which it could be derived. It's simply accepted in physics as an unexplained overarching representation of dynamic relationships among entities in our universe. As Max Born observed[459] decades ago, even a slight variation in *alpha's* value would make the physical interactions we observe and experience impossible. So, the inescapable conclusion is that *alpha* is fined-tuned for 'things' we observe to exist in our corner of the cosmos.

This seemingly magical state of affairs troubled[460a] Nobel laureate Wolfgang Pauli throughout his career. He concluded his Nobel lecture[460b] in 1946 with the stated conviction that physicists won't be able to formulate a cohesive theory for natural phenomena until they have a meaningful explanation for *alpha* and its 'just so' value. Pauli even turned to[460c] psychoanalyst Carl Jung for help in unravelling its meaning from dreams; a move that put him at odds with colleagues like Bohr and Heisenberg.

By a weird coincidence, Pauli died on 15 December 1958 in a room numbered 137 at the Rotkreuz hospital in Zurich, Switzerland. He memorably quipped[460d]: *"When I die my first question to the Devil will be: What is the meaning of the fine structure constant?"*

In one of his famous lectures on quantum electrodynamics (QED) originally[461a] delivered in 1979, Richard Feynman described[461b] the quandary posed by *alpha* with characteristic eloquence:

"There is a most profound and beautiful question associated with the observed coupling constant, e, the amplitude for a real electron to emit or absorb a real photon. It is a simple number that has been experimentally determined to be close to -0.08542455. (My physicist friends won't recognize this number, because they like to remember it as the inverse of its square: about 137.03597 with about an uncertainty of about 2 in the last decimal place. It has been a mystery ever since it was discovered more than fifty years ago, and all good theoretical physicists put this number up on their wall and worry about it.) Immediately you would like to know where this number for a coupling comes from: is it related to p or perhaps to the base of natural logarithms? Nobody knows. It's one of the greatest damn mysteries of physics: a magic number that comes to us with no understanding by man. You might say the "hand of God" wrote that number, and "we don't know how He pushed his pencil." We know what kind of a dance to do experimentally to measure this number very accurately, but we don't know what kind of dance to do on the computer to make this number come out, without putting it in secretly!"

The mystery has deepened with new indications that *alpha* may even have a *different* value elsewhere in the universe – an intriguing development that, if confirmed, would violate Einstein's equivalence principle which requires laws of physics to be the same everywhere. In 2010, a collaboration of Australian astrophysicists and British astronomers published[462a] observational data on spectral lines of faraway cosmological structures in deep space-time that suggests[462b] *alpha* might, indeed, be fine-tuned to suit local cosmic conditions. This stunning and highly controversial proposal threatens to overturn a century of assumptions in theoretical physics: it appears[462c] the fine-structure constant may not be as 'constant' as thought.

170

Benson's law

Another curious mathematical phenomenon that permeates nature is the tendency of the first or 'leading' digit in any set of numbers to be at the *lower* rather than the *higher* end of the scale. Thus, in decimal-based sets, number 1 will appear as the leading digit about 30 percent of the time while number 9 has a less than 5 percent chance of leading.

This non-random distribution of numbers in datasets was first noted[463a] in 1881 by American astronomer Simon Newcomb, who also proposed a probability formula for first-digits. But it's now called Benford's law after physicist Frank Benford who restated[463b] the principle more than half-a-century later in 1938, and provided[463c] extensive examples of logarithmic first-digit frequency in everyday real-life situations.

Benford's law has since been adopted as a tool to detect[464a] erroneous or falsified data in financial[464b] and even election[464c] reporting. However, the phenomenon is still not fully explained. In 1998, eminent American mathematician Theodore Hill formulated[464d] the first proofs of statistical probabilities that underlie distribution of first-digit numbers. But, as Hill stated frankly[464e] in a comprehensive 2011 update and review of the work, *"Numerous intriguing problems for future research arise naturally."*

Indeed, new surprising examples continue to emerge of Newcomb's 140-year-old observation on the anomalous distribution of digits in number sets. In 2010, a team at the Australian National University in Canberra led by earth scientist Malcolm Sambridge stunned colleagues with a report[465a] that linked the first-digit law to a wide range[465b] of natural phenomena from earthquakes and infectious diseases to cosmic gamma rays and stellar rotations.

171

Astonishingly, Benford's law even applies to activity patterns on social media. Jennifer Golbeck from University of Maryland in the USA wrote in a 2015 research article[465c]:

"We show that Benford's Law applies to social and behavioral features of users in online social networks. Using social data from five major social networks (Facebook, Twitter, Google Plus, Pinterest, and LiveJournal), we show that the distribution of first significant digits of friend and follower counts for users in these systems follow Benford's Law. The same is true for the number of posts users make."

As global health authorities scrambled to contain the COVID-19 pandemic in 2020, researchers turned to Benford's law to check the accuracy of national statistics on cases and mortalities (Sambridge and geophysicist Andrew Jackson from ETH Zürich in Switzerland co-authored[466a] an insightful analysis in May 2020). An independent audit[466b] by Adrian Kennedy and Sheung Yam from the Chinese University of Hong Kong used both Benford's law and the related Zipf's law to parse COVID-19 data from the World Health Organization (WHO) and national governments.

Constructal law

In 1995, Adrian Bejan, a mechanical engineer at Duke University in North Carolina, USA, had a Eureka-like flash of inspiration. While investigating how to minimise entropy generation (energy loss) during heat transfers in fixed volumes of low conductivity systems, he realised the solution lies in a branching network of *small* to increasingly *large* heat conduit channels.

Bejan outlined the idea in a 1997 paper[467a]: *"It is shown that the paths form a tree-like network, in which every single geometric detail is determined theoretically. Furthermore, the tree network cannot be determined theoretically when the time direction is reversed, from large elements toward smaller elements."*

Bejan realised the concept had significant implications for all flow systems in nature and embarked on years of further research that culminated in a 'Constructal law' articulated in a 2008 paper[467b] co-authored with Pennsylvania State University biologist James H. Marden: *"For a finite-size system to persist in time (to live), it must evolve in such a way that it provides easier access to the imposed currents that flow through it."*

Essentially, Bejan and Marden proposed[467c] that all physical objects and systems (living and non-living) have a natural tendency to generate shapes and structures over time that facilitate maximum flow access. Accordingly, they asserted, the designs we perceive in nature do not stem from random chance or divine intervention but are the result of natural evolution to enhance the conduit of energy, gas, and fluids. Bejan pressed the case for this universal principle in a follow-up 2010 exposition[467d] co-authored with Duke University colleague Sylvie Lorente. The new paper, boldly titled 'The constructal law of design and evolution in nature', argued it was a *"self-standing law in physics"* that resolved numerous contradictions:

"This law is about the necessity of design to occur, and about the time direction of the phenomenon: the tape of the design evolution 'movie' runs such that existing configurations are replaced by globally easier flowing configurations. The constructal law has two useful sides: the prediction of natural phenomena and the strategic engineering of novel architectures, based on the constructal law, i.e. not by mimicking nature.

"We show that the emergence of scaling laws in inanimate (geophysical) flow systems is the same phenomenon as the emergence of allometric laws in animate (biological) flow systems. Examples are lung design, animal locomotion, vegetation, river basins, turbulent flow structure, self-lubrication and natural multi-scale porous media. [.....] Nature is configured to flow and move as a conglomerate of 'engine and brake' designs."

173

Bejan's proposition was generally well-received[468a]. However, sceptics highlighted[468b] the absence of a firm formulation within physics or mathematics and questioned the vague definition of *"flow currents"* and *"flow access."* Bejan's response in articles and presentations featured at his website[468c] is that the Constructal law is a first principle for derivation of testable predictions and theories; not the other way round.

Interestingly, according to[469a] Bejan's principle, 'imperfections' in nature are gradually eliminated as everything tends to optimal forms that maximise flow currents. This contrasts with Plato's idea that earthly things are *inherently imperfect* copies of abstract eternal forms, and Aristotle's proposal that living things come with *unchangeable* forms that harbour intrinsic capacity for their particular purpose. Notwithstanding, the Constructal law has much in common with ancient Greek inferences of teleology (tendency to purposive goals) in nature. Bejan expanded on[469b] this theme of inevitability in his 2016 book *The Physics of Life: The Evolution of Everything*. He clarified in a related interview[469c]:

> *"Evolution is a crucial part of how we need to define efficiency. I don't mean evolution in the Darwinian sense. I mean that there's a universal urge or tendency toward design and organization that changes over time in a discernible, seemingly goal-oriented direction. So it would be more accurate to call these things evolutionary design and evolutionary organization. This has nothing to do with intelligent design, by the way. It's simply treating design and evolution as two natural scientific concepts."*

Bejan is now acknowledged as a leading thinker and engineering science pioneer. In 2008, editors at the *International Journal of Heat and Mass Transfer* joined 23 colleagues in a glowing 60th birthday tribute[469d] that listed his many accomplishments and awards.

In 2018, Bejan extended his Constructal law to social organisation in an article[470a] co-authored with Turkish marine engineers Umit Gunes and Bahri Sahin, and Brazilian environmental engineer Marcelo Errera. They wrote:

"Why do individuals come to live (to move) together, to organize? Here, we propose that organization is a reflection of the physics reality (bio and nonbio) that it takes less power (useful energy, fuel, food, and exergy) to move 1 unit of mass in bulk than to move 1 unit individually."

Bejan and his research collaborators showed[470b] how the distinct hierarchies that evolve in complex societies can be predicted from the same Constructal law that gives rise to tree branches, river deltas and biological vascular systems. The revolutionary proposition continues to stimulate debate about the extent[470c] to which both animate and inanimate physical structures are shaped[470d] by their environment.

Dimensions beyond 3-D

Mathematicians use abstract algebra to describe multidimensional structures above 3-D that are beyond normal human comprehension and difficult to depict graphically. Hypercomplex number concepts like 4-D quaternions and 8-D octonions discovered in the 19th century allowed physicists to represent abstract systems as interlinked groups. The new algebra (especially octonions) proved crucial for computations within the new physics of Einstein relativity and quantum mechanics that emerged in the early 20th century.

In 1973, Yale University graduate physicist Murat Günaydin and his supervisor Feza Gürsey found[471a] an unexpected link between octonions and the strong force which binds quarks together in the nuclei of atoms. However, due to their extreme complexity (a mnemonic multiplication table and Fano plane triangular diagram are required), octonions were not fully studied until the 21st century.

Nearly 30 years after the groundbreaking discovery by Günaydin and Gürsey, mathematical physicist John C. Baez of University of California (Riverside) published a review[471b] that highlighted the importance of octonions for *all* aspects of theoretical physics. Canadian colleague Cohl Furey has since argued in a series of papers[472a,b,c] that the route to deciphering the Standard Model of particles and fundamental forces (which gives us matter) lies in understanding the exotic *mathematics* of quaternions and octonions, rather than in hugely expensive physics experiments with high-energy particle colliders.

In 2018, Furey showed[473a] how division algebra resolves problems associated with a popular grand unification theory (GUT) that dates back to 1974. Her work has attracted widespread interest[473b] and may yet succeed in bridging[473c] the gap between mathematical and physical descriptions of the fundamentals that underpin nature and reality. Certainly, her explanations and representations offer much simpler tools for particle physics research than Feynman diagrams – even with new inputs[473d] from algebraic geometry.

However, a major paradigm shift is needed for Furey's fully maths-based description of nature to become a mainstream approach in physics – scientists would first have to acknowledge that there's *detectable* inevitability and teleology (rather than unfettered randomness) in the way our universe is structured.

The Amplituhedron

Since 2013, the world of physics and mathematics has been buzzing with excitement at the unveiling of a new geometric form by American-Iranian theoretical physicist Nima Arkani-Hamed and graduate student Jaroslav Trnka at Princeton University's Institute for Advanced Study. The exotic mathematical structure they named an 'Amplituhedron' resembles[474a] a butterfly-like multifaceted jewel that spans multiple dimensions.

176

According to the research paper[474b] that announced the intriguing illustration, it captures the *"remarkable simplicity and hidden infinite dimensional symmetries"* of the scattering amplitudes quantum physicists use to describe probable outcomes of subatomic particle interactions. Thus, like Cohl Furey's algebraic representations, the geometric Amplituhedron by Arkani-Hamed and Trnka offers a simpler tool than complicated Feynman diagrams for investigation[474c] of invisible quantum events that give us physical matter: the abstract model of multiple interconnected polyhedrons allows physicists to track all possible pathways of particle interactions. However, a geometric object of *limitless* dimensions is even more difficult to conceptualise and depict than Furey's algebraic 4-D quaternions and 8-D octonions. The concept simply transcends all notions of 'reality'.

The Amplituhedron also poses[474d] fresh challenges to scientific understanding of space and time in terms of *locality* (things can only be directly influenced by their immediate surroundings), and *unitarity* (the total probabilities of all possible outcomes of any event will always equal '1'). These rules are crucial for consistent human observations that underpin objective research and reproducible results. However, although the inputs that yield the Amplituhedron *exclude* locality and unitarity, it still perfectly and simply describes particle interactions minus gravity. Apparently, what we thought were key features of our physical reality are merely *emergent* aspects of some ultimate reality hidden deep within the folds of an infinite mathematical abstraction.

The mysterious construct stems from earlier research[475a] led by Arkani-Hamed that built on[475b] Sir Roger Penrose's 1967 proposal[475c] for a hypothetical geometric space *outside* our space-time created by[475d] the totality of light rays in the universe. According to Penrose, all quantum phenomena, and the emergent physical objects and events we perceive, derive from this mathematical 'twistor' space.

177

While there's, as yet, no indication *how* its geometric blueprint might be giving rise to our physical world, the Amplituhedron has revived hopes for a unified description of gravity at microscopic quantum and macroscopic cosmic levels. As Arkani-Hamed remarked[476a] in a 2015 briefing: *"It's not obvious where this is going. Maybe it will be something spectacular. Maybe it will just be a curiosity. We don't know. But it's something. And it's a beautiful something."*

Certainly, the Amplituhedron is the most profound demonstration to date of how mathematics, with its infinite complexities, governs natural forms and symmetries even at fundamental quantum levels. Physicists are cautiously optimistic[476b] that they're now on the right track to a Theory of Everything (TOE). But, are we perhaps running ahead of our evolution as beings fit to be entrusted with the ultimate secrets of life? Carlo Rovelli recounted[476c] this curious incident that occurred during Penrose's presentation at a September 2019 conference[476d] in Marseille, France convened to discuss possible merging of loop quantum gravity and twistor concepts in a TOE:

"Towards the end of a long and dense presentation of new ideas towards understanding the full space of the solutions of Einstein's theory using twistors, Roger said rather dramatically that now he was going to present a new big idea that might lead to the twistor version of the full Einstein equations – but at that precise moment the slide projector exploded in a cloud of smoke, with sparks flying. We all thought for a moment that a secret power of the Universe, worried about being unmasked, had interfered. Could allying twistors and loops be dangerous?"

Is God a divine mathematician?

In his enigmatically-titled book *Is God a Mathematician?* (2010), astrophysicist Mario Livio discussed the wondrous nature of maths and its exceptional usefulness in everyday applications.

Livio charted[477a] historical attitudes from ancient Greek Platonist veneration of numbers as non-worldly eternal ideal forms, to modern mechanical views of maths as just a convenient theoretical tool. However, he provided little new insight[477b] into the deep question posed in the book's title – unlike Sir James Jeans who had declared 80 years earlier in his book *The Mysterious Universe* that, with each new discovery, God was being revealed as *"a pure mathematician"* and the universe was looking *"more like a great thought than like a great machine"*.

Eccentric 20th century Hungarian mathematician Paul Erdős (renowned[478a] for his dedication and disregard of material comforts) doubted the existence of a personal God. However, he was certain[478b] that an omniscient, transcendent entity kept a record of the best and most elegant mathematical proofs in what he called 'The Book' and was withholding crucial information from humans. Inspired by Erdős' quasi-religious view, German mathematicians Martin Aigner and Günter M. Ziegler published[478c] *Proofs from THE BOOK* in 1998; an award-winning compilation[478d] of exotic theorems and proofs.

If, indeed, all mathematical abstractions stem from the mind of God, how are selected secrets being revealed to humans? Are we an extension of that divine mind? The notion certainly gives new meaning to biblical assertions that God created us *"in his own image"* (Genesis 1:27) and that we're endowed *"a little lower than the angels"* (Psalm 8:5). Whether or not one chooses to interpret this narrative literally, there's no doubt that capacity for abstract calculations is a key aspect of our metacognition. As far as we know, *only* humans have mastered numeric datasets for shapes (*geometry*), space (*volume*), change over time (*calculus*), and letter symbols (*algebra*). Perhaps, then, we can take some comfort in the possibility that some undefinable part of our worldly state is not a mortal commodity doomed to decay but a 'loaned' immortal faculty which is recalled at death to an eternal source that never dies.

SECTION B

About Life & Death

5. Mystery of Biology

"The large and important and very much discussed question is:
How can the events in space and time which take place within the spatial
boundary of a living organism be accounted for by physics and chemistry?"
Erwin Schrödinger, physicist, in *What is Life?* (1944) ch.1[479]

Can life be defined?

Most of us learnt at high school that biology is the branch of science that studies living things. However, what's not widely known is that there's still no consensus[480a] on a standard description of 'life'. The sheer range and diversity – from unicellular microbes to multicellular forms – defies a universal definition.

Generally, a living thing or *organism* is recognised as an assembly of extremely complex and specialised subunits that work together within a distinct physical structure to sustain physiological processes and environmental interactions from birth to death. These systems vary widely in composition and function, but are usually capable of reproduction, metabolism, self-regulation, sensitivity and adaptation. What's entirely unclear is whether this is an exhaustive list, or if any of these features exist in other formats here on earth or elsewhere[480b] in the universe.

Minimal blueprint

Some scientists view life as a complex *information* system. American genomics pioneer J. Craig Venter is renowned for championing this 'IP' approach. In 1995, Venter and 28 co-researchers centred at the Institute for Genomic Research in Rockville, Maryland reported[481a] that the bacterium *Mycoplasma genitalium* had just 468 genes (humans have around 20,000).

Computational biologist Eugene Koonin and colleague Arcady Mushegian at the US National Center for Biotechnology Information (NCBI) then undertook a comparative study that suggested[481b] the minimal genomic set for life is around 256 genes. Venter and a team at his own institute (JCVI) have since been engaged in an ambitious project to assemble a novel organism from a minimalist genetic template. He explained in a 2012 lecture[481c] at Trinity College in Dublin, Ireland:

"Numerous scientists have drawn the analogy between computers and biology. I take these even further. I describe DNA as the software of life and when we activate a synthetic genome in a recipient cell I describe it as booting up a genome, the same way we talk about booting up a software in a computer. [.....] Life is based on DNA software. We're a DNA software system, you change the DNA software, and you change the species. It's a remarkably simple concept, remarkably complex in its execution."

After 15 years of intensive research[482a] estimated to have cost a whopping US$40 million, a 24-strong JCVI team led by Venter announced[482b] in May 2010 that the group had artificially synthesised and transplanted the entire genome (985 genes) of one bacterial species (*Mycoplasma mycoides*) into a host cell of another (*Mycoplasma capricolum*) which had been emptied of all original DNA. Remarkably, the hybrid *Synthia* bacterium 'rebooted'[482c] and started replicating as Venter envisaged. However, while the development was hailed[482d] as a significant achievement and milestone in synthetic biology, sceptics pointed out[482e] that this was not really new life – the 'created' genome was more like a photocopy of an existing original, and the cytoplasm of the host cell was alive throughout. By 2016, the researchers had managed to reduce[483a] the experimental template to 473 genes. Surprisingly, 149 (31 percent) of these clearly essential genes had *completely unknown*[483b] functions – a revelation that Venter acknowledged[483c] shows how little we still know about life.

What qualifies?

Describing life in terms of information processing (IP) systems raises thorny philosophical questions about exactly what it means to be alive or dead. Do machines[484a] with artificial intelligence (AI) or responsive computer programmes qualify as a category of living things? What about interacting collections[484b] of atoms and molecules? Intuition tells us that mere arrangements of matter – even in the very specific patterns observed in biology – do not automatically lead to animation. But, as Brazilian physicist Celso de Araujo Duarte explained in a 2015 essay[484c], the behaviour of particles at quantum level can certainly be compared to some life processes.

The position of viruses (essentially fragments of organic code) is also proving troublesome. Although recognised as biological entities, the mainstream view is that viruses are replicating 'genetic machines' rather than a true form of life because they need a living host to proliferate and don't exhibit self-metabolism. In 2017, Oxford University zoologists Pakorn Aiewsakun and Aris Katzourakis published[485a] research that suggests retroviruses may have existed for nearly[485b] 500 million years; an estimate that backdates viral origin by several hundred million years. The picture has been further complicated by an unexpected finding reported[485c] in 2019 by an international collaboration led by a team at Tokyo University of Agriculture and Technology in Japan: the researchers uncovered[485d] a novel virus in pigs that lacks the tools to 'hack' into a host's genetic system; raising the question just how it survives and propagates. In February 2020, another large international collaboration led by researchers from University of California (Berkeley) reported[485e] that *hundreds* of giant bacteriophages (bacteria-invading viruses) were thriving[485f] in every ecosystem by appropriating and repurposing host proteins and bits of the bacterial immune system.

Prominent French biologist Didier Raoult argued in a 2014 essay[485g] that the increasing numbers of giant viruses coming to light (which rival microbes in size), and the surprisingly sophisticated parasitic strategies they employ, may justify reclassification of viruses as yet another domain of life.

A holistic view

In the 1960s, English scientist James Lovelock started pondering the definition conundrum while working on a NASA project in California that sought to establish whether life could possibly exist on planet Mars. Lovelock eventually teamed up[486a] with American microbiologist Lynn Margulis to propose[486b] a revolutionary Gaia hypothesis (named after the ancient Greek 'mother earth' goddess) that describes[486c] the earth as one gigantic superorganism. According to this view, our world and all it contains (animate and inanimate) is a singular self-regulating, self-sustaining, interdependent and evolving system of *inseparable* components. The approach further blurs the line between what is traditionally considered to be living and non-living.

The Gaia concept was highly controversial from inception[487a] because it clashed with the 115-year-old Darwinian theory of a world shaped by *competition* (rather than *cooperation*) among disparate organisms which have emerged gradually through wholly random, blind, directionless processes – a dogma at the heart of biology. Among the many criticisms, James Kirchner, an earth scientist at University of California (Berkeley), dismissed[487b] Gaia as deeply flawed *"wishful thinking"* that did not amount to a testable[487c] scientific hypothesis. However, Lovelock refuted this characterisation in a 1989 response[487d]: he argued, *"It is a theory that makes "risky" predictions, for example, that oxygen is and has been regulated during the existence of land plants, within ±5% of its present level; it is therefore falsifiable. Numerical models are used to illustrate the potential for stable self-regulation of tightly coupled systems of organisms and their environments."*

184

Margulis – who had doggedly championed her 1967 theory[488a] that eukaryotic cells (found in all multicellular organisms) emerged through symbiotic associations of free-living bacteria – also staunchly defended[488b] the idea of Gaia; her collaboration with Lovelock put her at odds with other evolutionary biologists for the rest of her career. In an interview[488c] with John Brockman for his 1995 book *The Third Culture: Beyond the Scientific Revolution*, Margulis brushed off criticism of her stance with typical forthrightness:

> *"If science doesn't fit in with the cultural milieu, people dismiss science, they never reject their cultural milieu! [....] Gaia is a tough bitch — a system that has worked for over three billion years without people. This planet's surface and its atmosphere and environment will continue to evolve long after people and prejudice are gone."*

Despite persisting scepticism in some quarters, Gaia is now accepted[488d] as an important hypothesis within geophysical and environmental sciences. As Canadian philosopher of science Michael Ruse discussed in a 2013 overview[488e], this holistic view of our biosphere is also gaining credence among an increasingly eco-conscious public.

Specificity

Researchers searching for signs of alien life outside our planet are particularly hampered[489a] by the lack of an agreed definition; although rigid preconceptions are also seen as a barrier to recognition of any extraterrestrial life that may exist. In 2011, the journal *Astrobiology* published a special collection of essays that illustrated[489b] how perspectives on the issue continue to differ. But there's no such doubt about the very specific datasets and materials used to build living things. Clearly, no such entities can arise *anywhere* without organised and applied information.

Despite the numerous elements available in nature, 99 percent of the materials that make up all organisms consist of just four: *hydrogen* (H), *oxygen* (O), *carbon* (C), and *nitrogen* (N). These are also the most abundant elements in outer space that are chemically reactive, so it's reasonable to assume any alien forms are likely to be composed of the same four elements. However, there's no way to be certain that a similar specificity and limitation would apply, or whether alien entities would mimic life on earth.

Curiously, the DNA in all organisms discovered so far is also encoded by just four nucleobases: *adenine* (A), *cytosine* (C), *guanine (G)*, and *thymine* (T). The reason for this restriction is a total mystery. In 2019, a team from six US institutions announced[490a] the successful addition of another four synthetic nucleotides to produce[490b] an eight-letter 'hachimoji' DNA code that instantly *doubled* the potential for data storage. So, the limit to natural DNA must exist for some deeper purpose. It's entirely possible that larger or smaller codes operate elsewhere in the cosmos to generate unrecognisable forms of life.

Significantly, the batch of amino acids that our genetic coding identifies for production of proteins is equally limited. Out of around 500[491a] amino acids that have been discovered in nature, only 20[491b] are encoded in the DNA of all known organisms. In 2016, a Spanish team led by researchers at the Barcelona Institute of Science and Technology showed that[491c] these fundamental limits are related[491d] to the functional capacity of some cellular systems. The following year, another group centred at Johannes Gutenberg University in Mainz, Germany published[491e] *"quantum chemical calculations and biochemical experiments"* that indicate just 7 to 13 amino acids would have sufficed to build essential proteins: the researchers suggested[491f] another 6 were likely incorporated to protect cells from harmful oxidative toxins as atmospheric oxygen increased. However, no one knows for sure.

Another puzzle is the strict left-handedness or right-handedness exhibited by biomolecules, similar to that observed in subatomic particles. In the natural environment *outside* organisms, amino acids and sugars exist in *equal quantities* of left-handed (L) or right-handed (D) mirror image forms called enantiomers – even artificial synthesis in laboratories produces split 50/50 'L' and 'D' so-called racemic mixtures of these molecules. Strangely however, *all* amino acids encoded in DNA and RNA (apart from the smallest, glycine, which is non-chiral) are *left-handed* (L), while *all* sugars in these genetic code components are *right-handed* (D). The origin and function of this universal homochirality in biology is unknown, but scientists acknowledge[492a] its huge significance for life.

In addition to chirality, sugar molecules have a mysterious ability to change shape that's still not fully understood. This so-called *anomeric effect* is crucial for many processes that allow life to exist. Researchers at Oxford University found[492b] in 2011 that the unique feature persists even when sugars are isolated in gaseous form. Organic chemist and research team leader Benjamin Davis commented[492c]:

> *"Sugars are weird. The anomeric effect is fundamental to organic chemistry but until now, our understanding of it has been fairly limited. If sugars didn't change shape, life would be radically different and some, perhaps many, biological processes just wouldn't work anymore."*

Nearly 80 years after Erwin Schrödinger's *What is Life?* lectures[493a] forced colleagues to confront[493b] the formidable difficulties in attempted scientific interpretations of life, there are still[493c] far more questions than answers. Failure to clearly define what is 'alive' has fuelled arguments that nothing can be said to be truly 'dead'. It also raises profound questions about the ultimate fate of the huge amounts of memory data generated over human lifetimes.

187

The boundary question

As eminent American chemist Robert Shapiro explained in an enlightening 2007 article[494a], thermodynamic life-sustaining activities (constant exchange of matter and energy with the environment) can't operate unless a clear boundary exists between closed-off pockets of 'life' and external areas of 'non-life'. All biological processes take place within *cells* – organic units bounded by a complex double-layered membrane (plus an outer wall in non-animals). These are not just passive but dynamic barriers with 'gates' policed by special proteins[494b] that strictly control[494c] inward and outward movement of other biomolecules and metabolic materials.

At biological death, cellular boundaries decay and disintegrate along with enclosed contents. So, these extraordinary microstructures are perhaps the best *physical* demarcation we can draw between organised animate life and disorganised inanimate matter. To decipher life-death transitions, we need to understand how genetic information was utilised to construct the very first cellular boundaries and kick-start life. But even if this were achieved, it's impossible to know if the same system and mechanisms would apply in any 'afterlife' setting – much more to predict *exact* replication of the cells and forms that define earthly organisms (including humans).

Chemistry to biology

In the early 2000s, British zoologist and evolutionary biologist Thomas Cavalier-Smith coined the term 'membranome' for life's intricate boundary system. He showed it is hereditary[495a] and has ancient[495b] evolutionary origins. A database[495c] compiled in 2016 by a team led by Andrei Lomize at University of Michigan uncovered[495d] *thousands* of previously unknown component proteins. A 2008 Canadian study[495e] indicates membranome architecture involves both integral and 'floating' structural units that are difficult to pin down.

188

Unsurprisingly, no one has managed to construct an artificial, viable cellular boundary from inanimate materials. Decades of work on a 'protocell' by biochemist Jack Szostak and his team at Harvard Medical School in Boston, Massachusetts underlines the formidable hurdles. In 2004, Szostak and biophysicist Irene Chen published two studies[496a,b] that showed pre-formed (*not* fully synthesised) simplistic fatty acid membrane vesicles can be induced to grow and divide in the laboratory. Chen explained their strategy in a 2006 essay[496c]: *"A protocell could be constructed by encapsulating a self-replicating genome inside a chemically simple, self-replicating membrane. This minimalist, forward-engineering approach is akin to early evolution, which must have also used a minimal set of components."*

However, even this modest goal – with just a *single-layer* membrane and no complex protein gatekeepers – proved elusive for almost a decade due to degrading[496d] of the fatty acid by magnesium ions (Mg^{2+}); a catalyst required in large amounts for RNA self-replication. Finally, Szostak's team worked out that adding some citrate countered the destabilising Mg^{2+} effect and they triumphantly announced[496e] success in 2013. But Szostak acknowledged[496f] that enabling laboratory conditions and the citrate stabiliser were unlikely to have existed at the dawn of life.

Later that year, Sandro Matosevic and Brian Paegel at The Scripps Research Institute in Jupiter, Florida reported[497a] a novel computerised technique for simple *"layer-by-layer phospholipid membrane assembly on microfluidic droplets"* that might allow experimental insertion of membrane proteins. Then, in 2014, another team of synthetic biologists at the Weizmann Institute of Science in Israel unveiled[497b] a silicon chip that can mimic production of proteins from DNA. However, none of these developments came anywhere near synthesis of a sophisticated cellular boundary that's capable of housing the biological functions which drive life.

189

In 2012, Szostak published a short critique[497c] of attempts to define a specific point at which life might have emerged from self-replicating molecular systems. He wrote[497d]:

"An inordinate amount of effort has been spent over the decades in futile attempts to define 'life' – often and indeed usually biased by the research focus of the person doing the defining. As a result, people who study different aspects of physics, chemistry and biology will draw the line between life and non-life at different positions. Some will say there is no life until a well defined set of metabolic reactions are in place. Others will focus on spatial compartmentalization, on the various requirements for Darwinian evolution, or on the specific molecules of inheritance. None of this matters, however, in terms of the fundamental scientific questions concerning the transitions leading from chemistry to biology – the true unknowns and subject of origin-of-life studies. [.....] So far, I have not seen that efforts to define life have contributed at all to that understanding."

However, humans need an intuitive and universal understanding of what constitutes life if we are to make sense of death. The line between living and non-living drawn by cellular boundaries, and the role[498a] of membrane proteins in facilitating[498b] basic life processes, is crucial to that understanding. In a comment on a 2013 Dutch study[498c] into plausible avenues for primordial cell formation, Radboud University chemist Wilhelm Huck observed[498d]: *"A functioning cell must be entirely correct at once, in all its complexity."* Indeed. The mystery is how these building blocks for life emerged on a primitive, barren earth.

Did life arrive from outer space?

Growing scientific interest in possible extraterrestrial beings has revived an old conjecture that life on earth may have arrived 'ready-made' from outer space – a concept known as[499a,b] *Panspermia* (derived from a Greek word that means 'seeds everywhere').

190

Speculation that invisible seeds literally 'rained down' from space into oceans on earth to germinate life is traced back[499c] to ancient Greek philosopher Anaxagoras (c. 510 – 428 BCE): the narrative so unsettled the authorities in Athens that he was charged with impiety (disrespect for the sacred). But the first clear articulation of the idea appeared[499d] in *Telliamed* (1722-1732) by French diplomat and natural historian Benoît de Maillet. Like Anaxagoras, de Maillet's disguised manuscript (the title 'Telliamed' is his name spelt backwards) was deemed too controversial in an era dominated by Catholic doctrine; his editor (a pious abbot) spent a decade on extensive alterations before posthumous publication in 1748.

Panspermia next resurfaced in 19th century scientific versions that represented 'seeds of life' as hardy microbes distributed throughout the universe by space debris. The aim wasn't to decipher the *origin* of life but merely to explore possible mechanisms for distribution *after* mysterious formation somewhere in the cosmos. The revolutionary notion was endorsed in a famous 1871 address[500] to the British Association for the Advancement of Science at Edinburgh by physicist Lord Kelvin (then William Thomson):

> *"When two great masses come into collision in space it is certain that a large part of each is melted; but it seems also quite certain that in many cases a large quantity of debris must be shot forth in all directions [...] we must regard it as probable in the highest degree that there are countless seed-bearing meteoric stones moving about through space. If at the present instant no life existed upon this earth, one such stone falling upon it might, by what we blindly call natural causes, lead to its becoming covered with vegetation."*

While accepting that *"many scientific objections"* could be raised against the concept, Lord Kelvin believed these were all answerable and that Panspermia was neither unscientific nor improbable.

Radiative dispersal

Swedish chemist and Nobel laureate Svante Arrhenius produced the first full scientific hypothesis of Panspermia in 1903 and followed up with an extended commentary[501a] in his 1908 book *Worlds in the Making*. In summary, Arrhenius proposed that the microscopic size of *"germ"* (bacterial) spores makes them small enough for propagation at high speed by *"radiation pressure"* from the sun and other stars to seed life throughout the universe. This hypothesis is now referred to as *radiopanspermia*.

However, a wealth of experimental data[501b] since Arrhenius' proposal indicates that unprotected bacterial spores are unlikely to survive radiation and other hazards of space travel. Researchers calculate that, to avoid damage in space, bacterial DNA needs shielding in rocks at least one metre in diameter. Thus, radiation pressure on *exposed* spores is not a viable mechanism for sustained interstellar or interplanetary dispersal of life.

Shielded transportation

Panspermia research was dormant for the next 60 years. Then, in the 1970s, prominent British astronomer Sir Fred Hoyle and his protégé N. Chandra Wickramasinghe (H-W) rekindled interest in the concept. While analysing the infrared light footprint of interstellar dust for a clue to its contents, they were surprised to find that[502a] the spectrum signature closely matched *organic* freeze-dried bacteria – not *inorganic* carbon graphite grains as was thought. In 1982, the duo published a seminal work titled[502b] *Proofs that Life is Cosmic* with detailed supporting inferences and calculations. They deduced[502c] that up to 30 percent of interstellar dust is composed of degraded or desiccated bacterial spores that could be ending up in protective asteroid, meteoroid or comet carriers for dissemination to seed life in every corner of the universe.

Controversially, Hoyle and Wickramasinghe asserted that new viral material *from space* was the source of genetic information for emergence of the wide variety of organisms that we observe today – a biological heresy that sharply contrasts[502d] with the mainstream Darwinist view that selective pressures and mechanisms *on earth* are the drivers for evolution of species. Furthermore, they suggested, these genomic intrusions continue to occur and may be responsible for new diseases and epidemic outbreaks.

The H-W version of 'cosmic seeding' is called *lithopanspermia.* Despite harsh criticisms, the core idea of shielded microbe propagation throughout the vastness of space has become[503a] a serious consideration within astrobiology[503b]. Advocates point to extremophiles that thrive in harsh terrestrial environments and increasing evidence[503c] of extraordinary survival mechanisms that may well help microorganisms withstand the rigours of deep time cosmic transportation. In a 2011 review[503d], Wickramasinghe observed: *"The picture here is strikingly similar to the sowing of seeds in the wind. Few are destined to survive, but so many are the seeds that some amongst them would inevitably manage to take root."*

Certainly, there's now abundant evidence of organic content in space. In 2011, a NASA-funded research team discovered[504a] building blocks of DNA in meteorites. Astronomers Sun Kwok and Yong Zhang from the University of Hong Kong also reported[504b] a spectral analysis that suggests[504c] mysterious infrared emissions detected in interstellar and intergalactic zones may be coming from complex organic nanoparticles within stars. The startling developments have encouraged even bolder speculation[504d] that incoming viral loads may have triggered the puzzling Cambrian Explosion (circa 500 million years ago) that heralded the relatively rapid evolution of nearly all known animal groups – a highly controversial[504e] proposal that most biologists firmly reject.

Microbe resurrection

In 2010, Paul S. Wesson, an astrophysicist at University of Waterloo in Ontario, Canada came up with a proposal that – unlike the Arrhenius and Hoyle-Wickramasinghe models – doesn't require a conserved 'whole' microbe from space to kick-start life. Wesson argued in a paper[505a] that even if microbes arrived on earth *"broken and dead"*, the *information content* in damaged organic fragments might reactivate to 'resurrect' the microorganisms and seed new life. He supported the H-W suggestion that encased *viruses* which are neither 'alive' nor 'dead' could also be a cosmic source of new genetic information. Wesson called this 'back from the dead' hypothesis *necropanspermia.*

The intriguing proposal brought a new perspective to the 'life from space' debate. Wickramasinghe welcomed Wesson's contribution but disagreed that dead organisms from space could regain life. He insisted some microbes would arrive intact and argued[505c]: *"The first introduction of life onto our planet (or indeed any planet) must involve the introduction of a viable microorganism – not a fragment of genome, a virus or a dead microorganism."* American astrobiologist Rocco Mancinelli was also unconvinced: he declared bluntly[505b], *"Once you're dead, you're dead."*

But, as Wesson had shown in a 1994 article[505d] co-authored with Jeff Secker and James Lepock, bacteria have a unique, well-conserved DNA repair system[505e] that allows these intrepid microbes to fully regenerate damaged genomes. He pointed out[505f] that his hypothesis is perfectly testable by experiments to determine *"if genetic 'rubble' can reconstitute itself to form viable replicating molecules."* Developments since have confirmed the incredible resilience of bacterial DNA, prompting a reassessment of the risks of both inward and outward contamination from human space exploration.

194

In 2014, a European team of engineers and medical scientists led by Oliver Ullrich and Cora Thiel from the University of Zurich (UZH) in Switzerland reported[506a] an experimental outcome that shocked the space science community. They applied small segments of bacterial plasmid DNA to the *outer* shell surface of the TEXUS-49 space rocket on a short research mission. The team was astonished to discover[506b] that not only did more than 50 percent of the DNA survive the flight and re-entry into earth's atmosphere, up to 35 percent retained full biological function and proved *"able to transfer genetic information to bacterial and connective tissue cells."*

Alien seeding

In 1973, two renowned British scientists – molecular biologist Francis Crick and theoretical chemist Leslie Orgel – surprised contemporaries with the truly bizarre proposal[507a] that life may have been *intentionally* spread to earth in a *robotic spacecraft* despatched by technologically advanced extraterrestrials (ET). They wrote:

"It now seems unlikely that extraterrestrial living organisms could have reached the earth either as spores driven by the radiation pressure from another star or as living organisms imbedded in a meteorite. As an alternative to these nineteenth-century mechanisms, we have considered Directed Panspermia, the theory that organisms were deliberately transmitted to the earth by intelligent beings on another planet [....] by means of a special long-range unmanned spaceship."

In support of this bemusing hypothesis, Crick and Orgel argued[507b]: *"To show that this is not totally implausible we shall use the theorem of detailed cosmic reversibility; if we are capable of infecting an as yet lifeless extrasolar planet, then given the time that was available, another technological society might well have infected our planet while it was still lifeless."*

195

Understandably, colleagues were sceptical and reluctant to endorse the idea. However, the immense reputation of the authors ensured their speculative paper received wide publicity and continues[507c] to excite interest. Interestingly, Crick and Orgel were not the first scientists to give serious consideration to possible cosmic seeding of life by a technologically advanced civilisation. As US-based astrophysicist Idan Ginsburg and astrobiologist Manasvi Lingam discussed in a June 2021 review article[507d], this scenario was broached in the 1930 science fiction novel *Last and First Men* by British philosopher Olaf Stapledon and in a 1954 paper by eminent biologist J. B. S. Haldane. American cosmologist Carl Sagan and Soviet colleague Iosif S. Shklovskii had also speculated in their 1966 book *Intelligent Life in the Universe* that there could be up to *one million* advanced extraterrestrial civilisations; any one of which could have made contact with a lifeless earth.

Sagan actively promoted *Search for Extra-Terrestrial Intelligence* (SETI) research and memorably co-wrote and presented the iconic 1980 television series *Cosmos: A Personal Voyage* – his much-cited caution that *"Extraordinary claims require extraordinary evidence"* hails from a discussion in the penultimate episode 'Encyclopaedia Galactica'. In a 1981 overview[508a], Sagan narrated how Crick and Orgel first mooted the idea of Directed Panspermia at a SETI conference he organised in 1971. However, despite decades of searching[508b] since 1960, no contact has ever been made with an alien intelligence. Cutbacks in official radio telescope resources have further dampened[508c] prospects, but researchers remain optimistic[508d].

SETI research has been reinvigorated by a private *Breakthrough Initiatives* programme launched in 2015 with a funding pledge[509a] from Russian physicist and entrepreneur Yuri Milner, and celebrity endorsement[509b] by Stephen Hawking. The first US$100 million 'Breakthrough Listen' project aims to[509c] scan up to one million stars for signals or 'technosignatures'[509d] of extraterrestrial civilisations.

A second US$100 million 'Breakthrough Starshot' project launched[510a] in 2016 has the more ambitious goal of developing technology for a tiny robotic spacecraft (no larger than a postage stamp) that could be powered by light laser to transcend our solar system and visit exoplanets around *Alpha Centauri* – the nearest star system sited 4.37 light-years away – after a flight lasting just 20 years; a journey that would take[510b] *30,000* years with a conventional space probe. A third 'Breakthrough Message' initiative – a US$1 million competition to compose a representative message from humanity to the cosmos at large – was deferred to allow more debate about the ethics of SETI and wider implications[510c] of a sudden extraterrestrial response[510d] to human signals.

Hawking, in particular, was wary of random cosmic messaging: he cautioned repeatedly[511a,b] that such blind advertising may attract the attention of malevolent aliens engaged in 'cosmic piracy' and planet pillaging; a warning some believe is already too late[511c] as we've been broadcasting our presence for decades. But few share such concerns – enthusiasts have been lobbying[511d] for SETI to be recognised as a priority research area that qualifies for public funding.

Coded messages from ET?

So far, SETI research has focussed on detection of known technosignatures associated with radio, optical or radiation signals. But, of course, extraterrestrials could be using *unknown* technologies that are undetectable by humans. Hence, some now advocate searching for *information* signals such as *biosignatures* that cosmic seeders could have embedded in the universal genetic code. In his 2010 book *The Eerie Silence* (a comprehensive review of the SETI enterprise), Paul Davies speculated[512a] that advanced aliens may have crafted signals into viruses for 'uploading' into genomes of native organisms on arrival at inhabited planets.

Then, in 2013, Kazakhstani mathematician Vladimir I. shCherbak and astrobiologist Maxim A. Makukov stunned colleagues with a report[512b] claiming detection of unique mathematical and semantic patterns in our terrestrial genetic code that could be a signal planted by an extraterrestrial intelligence. They dubbed the imprint the 'Wow! signal' after a unique (but never repeated) radio signal detected in 1977 by SETI researcher Jerry Ehman. The description by shCherbak and Makukov was quite specific:

"Here we show that the terrestrial code displays a thorough precision-type orderliness matching the criteria to be considered an informational signal. Simple arrangements of the code reveal an ensemble of arithmetical and ideographical patterns of the same symbolic language. Accurate and systematic, these underlying patterns appear as a product of precision logic and nontrivial computing rather than of stochastic processes (the null hypothesis that they are due to chance coupled with presumable evolutionary pathways is rejected with P-value $< 10^{-13}$). The patterns display readily recognizable hallmarks of artificiality, among which are the symbol of zero, the privileged decimal syntax and semantical symmetries. Besides, extraction of the signal involves logically straightforward but abstract operations, making the patterns essentially irreducible to natural origin. Plausible ways of embedding the signal into the code and possible interpretation of its content are discussed. Overall, while the code is nearly optimized biologically, its limited capacity is used extremely efficiently to pass non-biological information."

Unsurprisingly, the extraordinary claim was met with much scepticism. However, the authors stood by their conclusion. Makukov argued in a 2014 response[512c]: *"The genetic code is nearly universal for all terrestrial life, implying that it has been unchanged for billions of years in most lineages. And yet, advances in synthetic biology show that artificial reassignment of codons is feasible, so there is also nothing implausible that, if life on Earth was seeded intentionally, an intelligent message might reside in its genetic code."*

198

Does the shCherbak-Makukov finding truly represent an encoded signal from an extraterrestrial intelligence? Makukov's point about the strange specificity of our genetic code is certainly valid – impressive developments in the new field of synthetic xenobiology are showing[512d] that even slight variations to the code could have led to the emergence of entirely different life forms.

Taking out cosmic insurance

In 2017, biological scientist Roy Sleator and astrophysicist Niall Smith from University College Dublin in Ireland recast[513a] Directed Panspermia from the perspective of our own technological society. They outlined[513b] a hypothetical space colonisation plan for ultimate preservation of life should existential threats overwhelm our planet:

"Our contemporary view of a potential extra-terrestrial colonisation programme would harness the incredible capabilities of synthetic biology that allow the design of synthetic DNA that can be used to build new synthetic microbes tailored to any environment. By substituting live organisms with DNA, our proposed cargo would be significantly more compact and more robust; allowing us to look even beyond our own galaxy. An extremely stable molecule, with a remarkably long life-span, even in suboptimal environments, DNA is a high-capacity storage medium and the ideal archival material for space travel. With a theoretical storage potential of 455 exabytes per gram of single stranded DNA; all of the Earth's projected 40 ZB of data could be stored in ~90 g of DNA. Therefore, all our history and collective knowledge could be transported in a container no bigger than a coffee pot ..."

Michael Mautner, a physical chemist and astroecologist at Virginia Commonwealth University in the USA, has long advocated[514a,b] such *outward* seeding of life. According to Mautner, humans have a moral obligation[514c] to initiate space programmes that can plant our genetic seeds on planets in this and other solar systems.

In 1995, Mautner launched the *Society for Life in Space* (SOLIS); an advocacy group for Directed Panspermia of earthly life based on *"panbiotic ethics."* In a 2010 review[514d] of his several papers and supporting literature over the previous 15 years, Mautner wrote passionately:

> *"Life is unique in nature in complexity and in its drive for self-propagation. We are part of life, implying a human purpose to safeguard and propagate life. For this purpose we may settle the Solar System, and seed with life new solar systems, solar nebulae and star-forming interstellar clouds. [...] Astroecology shows that life in the galaxy can then achieve an immense future. Securing that future for life can give our human existence a cosmic purpose."*

Mautner doubted that extraterrestrial life already exists and downplayed concerns about possible negative effects of invasive earthly species on any native exoplanetary inhabitants:

> *"If we still detect extraterrestrial life, we can avoid these targets. [...] If there is local life there that is fundamentally different, it will not be affected; if it is gene/protein life, it may be enriched and we can induce higher evolution. The new biospheres may prepare the way for human colonization if interstellar human travel becomes possible. [...] Should we risk our future for the fear of interfering with putative alien life?"*

While he acknowledged in a 2014 update[514e] that there were immense *"biological and ecological complexities"* to be overcome, Mautner argued the technological potential already exists for the use of solar sails to despatch microbial life-forms like *"extremophiles suited to diverse new environments, autotrophs and heterotrophs to continually form and recycle biomolecules, and simple multicellulars to jump-start higher evolution"* at targeted cosmic destinations. These ideas are not as far-fetched as they might sound: researchers are already working on[514f] 'designer microorganisms' that can be deployed[514g] as advance 'space farers' in cosmic colonisation programmes.

Microbiota: The community within

The role of cells as pixel-like building blocks of multicellular organisms has been known since 17th century Dutch lens-maker Antonie van Leeuwenhoek discovered[515a] the microscopic world of 'animalcules' already envisaged[515b] by English scientist Robert Hooke. Van Leeuwenhoek was the first-ever person to view and sketch[515c] red blood cells, spermatozoa and bacteria. However, neither he nor Hooke could have imagined the extent to which 'floating' microbes (bacteria, archaea, viruses, and fungi) form a part of our physical bodies and participate in human biological functions.

A vast collaboration

According to estimates compiled by the Human Cell Atlas[516a] launched in 2016, the average human is composed of a hugely diverse[516b] range of around 37.2 trillion cells. But even this stupendous figure is surpassed by the estimated *100 trillion* microbes – 40 percent[516c] of which are bacteria – that co-exist with us both within and on the surface of our body.

It's now appreciated that the vast arrays of microorganisms which inhabit *both* plants and animals are far more than 'fellow travellers'. The previous picture of hosts (like humans) forced to tolerate 'parasitic' microbes has been replaced by new definitions of 'interdependent metaorganisms'[517a,b] or 'holobionts'[517c] that actually *need* microbiota to survive. The sheer scale of biological *information* in a microbiome (collective genomes of an organism's community of microbes) dwarfs the genetic pool inherited by the host. In 2018, an international team led by renowned British genetic epidemiologist Tim Spector observed[517d] in a review: *"The human genome consists of about 23,000 genes, whereas the microbiome encodes over three million genes producing thousands of metabolites, which replace many of the functions of the host, consequently influencing the host's fitness, phenotype, and health."*

The gut microbiota, in particular, has been found to have an important role[517e] in development and proper functioning of the immune system, and protection against inflammatory disease. Surprisingly, *viruses* work alongside[517f] bacteria to maintain our health and ward off infections.

Shaped by microbes

There's also growing speculation[518a] that the so-called virus 'virome' in the gut could be[518b] a key factor in a host's evolutionary adaptiveness. It's already known that bacteria have been swapping[518c] DNA with humans for thousands of years; these one-celled wonders can even 'rewire'[518d] their genes to meet[518e] fresh challenges.

Intriguingly, it emerged[519a] in 2016 that resident microbial communities are unique[519b] to each animal host species: it even varies widely[519c] across human populations. These findings have added to mounting evidence[519d] that microbes co-evolve with, and become integral to, the organisms they colonise. It appears *humans* are the guests in a microbial world and not the other way round.

What happens at death?

The Human Microbiome Project (2007-2016) sponsored[520a] by the US National Institutes of Health (NIH) discovered[520b] that distinct communities of microbiota inhabit various areas of our body. After just three years of research, investigators found that[520c] the composition of localised microbiomes was far more diverse than expected, and interactions with the living host were highly complex. Ironically, within 48 hours of death, *the same* microbes (mostly from the gut) that helped to keep us alive start ravaging tissues. The microbial role in tissue decomposition is now a major field of forensic[521a] and preventative[521b] medicine.

202

The so-called thanatomicrobiome (from *thanatos,* ancient Greek for death)[521c], which colonises a cadaver (dead body), is surprisingly different and far more uniform[521d] in composition than the diverse microbiota that were present while the person was alive. A complex ecosystem[521e] emerges that interacts with the environment in ways that researchers are still trying to unravel.

So far, after-death investigations have focussed on the puzzle of physical transition from a life-sustaining microbiome to a decay-enabling thanatomicrobiome. However, absolutely nothing is known about the fate of the *genetic information* tailored by microbes for personalised functions over a host's lifetime. Given the remarkable capacity of microbial DNA for survival and regeneration, it's not inconceivable that some informational part of our being shared with the microbiome survives and gets recycled in other bacterial hosts.

In 2016, a team of mathematicians and bioengineers from Cambridge University and Massachusetts Institute of Technology (MIT) made the astounding discovery[522a] that, in an optical microfluidic lattice[522b], bacteria exhibit *the same* mysterious quantum 'spin' pattern that electrons follow in atomic nuclei. Study co-author Jörn Dunkel – an applied mathematician at MIT – commented[522c]:

> *"It's very surprising that we see this universality. The really nice thing is, you have a living system here that shows all these behaviors that people think are also going on in quantum systems."*

In the late 1980s, Guenther Witzany, an Austrian philosopher of science, language and communication, developed a new theory of biocommunication[523a] that emphasises the role of *information exchanges* in life systems. He sought to redefine life as a holistic enterprise of *"sign-mediated interactions within and between cells, tissues, organs, and organisms in all domains of life."*

203

Witzany wrote in a March 2020 astrobiology article[523b]:

"Current definitions of life derive from statistical mechanics, physics, and chemistry of the twentieth century in which life is considered to function machine like, ignoring a central role of communication. Recent observations show that context-dependent meaningful communication and network formation (and control) are central to all life forms. Evolutionary relevant new nucleotide sequences now appear to have originated from social agents such as viruses, their parasitic relatives, and related RNA networks, not from errors. By applying the known features of natural languages and communication, a new twenty-first century definition of life can be reached in which communicative interactions are central to all processes of life."

This fascinating interpretation of life has struggled to gain mainstream scientific support. However, Witzany's approach is sure to attract wider interest as evidence continues to emerge of the highly sophisticated communication systems and networks[523c] at cellular and molecular levels that make the web of life possible.

Are we the first advanced beings?

Cosmological observations indicate the universe is around[524a] 13.8 billion years old, and there's fossil evidence for some form of microbial life on earth at least[524b] 3.7 billion years ago. Humans appeared less than 300,000 years ago and we've already developed impressive industrial and technological societies. Therefore, in principle, statistical odds should favour the emergence of previous advanced civilisations either here on earth or elsewhere in the cosmos. Perplexingly however, there's absolutely no evidence that other civilisations have existed or are existing concurrently in some unexplored domain. Are we truly the first and only intelligent beings in a seemingly infinite universe? Is there any way this issue can be resolved by physical or theoretical research?

The Great Silence

While working at the US Los Alamos National Laboratory in 1950, Italian-American physicist and Nobel laureate Enrico Fermi famously exclaimed[525a]: *"But where is everybody?"* The question followed a casual lunchtime conversation with colleagues about the probability of alien civilisations. Fermi reportedly scribbled some rough calculations to explain his point that, given the *billions* of sun-like stars in our Milky Way (many of which are *billions* of years older than our sun), and the probability that *billions* of equally old earth-like planets orbit habitable zones around those stars, it's very strange that an extraterrestrial civilisation hasn't evolved long ago and developed capacity for interstellar travel and colonisation of the entire universe.

The mystery articulated by Fermi (erroneously[525b] termed a 'paradox') launched[525c] a serious scientific search for explanations. In 1961, American astronomer and astrophysicist Frank Drake used speculative values[525d] of cosmic parameters to formulate a mathematical framework for estimating[525e] the number of alien civilisations in our galaxy that might have capacity for radio communications. However, over 70 years since it was posed, Fermi's core question[525f] about the cosmic 'Great Silence' remains largely unanswered[525g].

The continued absence of extraterrestrial contact has prompted some uncomfortable speculations about the ultimate fate of our own civilisation. Space science writer Fraser Cain commented[525h] in 2013:

"Perhaps the most unsettling thought is that something happens to 100% of intelligent civilizations that prevents them from exploring and settling the galaxy. Maybe something good, like the discovery of a transportation system to another Universe. Or maybe something bad, like a destructive technology that has destroyed every single civilization before us."

The Great Filter

In a seminal 1996 essay[526a] (updated in 1998), Robin Hanson, an American economist and research associate at Oxford University's Future of Humanity Institute (FHI), suggested that a 'Great Filter' of increasingly difficult hurdles might be preventing intelligent civilisations from evolving to an 'explosive' breakout stage with capacity to explore and conquer the universe. He wrote:

> *"Humanity seems to have a bright future, i.e., a non-trivial chance of expanding to fill the universe with lasting life. But the fact that space near us seems dead now tells us that any given piece of dead matter faces an astronomically low chance of begating such a future. There thus exists a great filter between death and expanding lasting life, and humanity faces the ominous question: how far along this filter are we?"*

Hanson listed nine successive probability barriers; from the likelihood of a star system forming with a habitable zone for emergence of life, to evolution of an advanced civilisation that can acquire space-faring technology without self-destructing. He noted:

> *"The Great Silence implies that one or more of these steps are very improbable; there is a "Great Filter" along the path between simple dead stuff and explosive life. The vast vast majority of stuff that starts along this path never makes it. In fact, so far nothing among the billion trillion stars in our whole past universe has made it all the way along this path."*

Twenty-five years on, theorists are still discussing[526b,c] the implications of Hanson's analysis. He assessed that we're already breaching the eighth barrier; an achievement that may mean the most improbable hurdles are behind us. However, as Brian Koberlein cautioned in a 2015 article[526d], past success is no guarantee of future survival: the ninth barrier to cosmic breakout may trigger catastrophe.

In a November 2020 overview[526e], author Doug Adler acknowledged that humanity may be heading towards a terminal Great Filter. But he pointed out that the continued Great Silence from potential advanced aliens is actually good news: *"On the bright side, some have interpreted our apparent aloneness in the universe as a good sign — a blessing even — as it indicates we've safely made it through the bottleneck. Strange as it may seem, we may be the first species to have passed through the Great Filter (after all, someone has to be first)."*

Interestingly, Hanson's Great Filter can be compared to some religious teachings that our earthly sojourn is a test to see whether we can evolve to a high enough state of altruistic co-existence that's worthy of elevation to eternal nirvana. From that perspective, humanity evidently has a long way to go.

Pre-human scenarios

Another approach focuses on *terrestrial* rather than extraterrestrial probabilities. What if a previous species of advanced earthlings existed millions of years ago? NASA climatologist Gavin Schmidt and University of Rochester astrophysicist Adam Frank pondered this intriguing possibility in a 2018 'Silurian hypothesis'[527a] (named after fictional intelligent reptiles featured in a 1970 episode of Doctor Who – a British sci-fi television series).

However, any biosignatures or technosignatures of a prior industrial civilisation back in geologic deep time would have long since been extinguished. So, what tell-tale traces could investigators hope to uncover? As Frank explained[527b]: *'We're used to imagining extinct civilizations in terms of sunken statues and subterranean ruins. These kinds of artifacts of previous societies are fine if you're only interested in timescales of a few thousands of years. But once you roll the clock back to tens of millions or hundreds of millions of years, things get more complicated.*

207

"When it comes to direct evidence of an industrial civilization—things like cities, factories, and roads—the geologic record doesn't go back past what's called the Quaternary period 2.6 million years ago. For example, the oldest large-scale stretch of ancient surface lies in the Negev Desert. It's "just" 1.8 million years old—older surfaces are mostly visible in cross section via something like a cliff face or rock cuts. Go back much further than the Quaternary, and everything has been turned over and crushed to dust."

Nonetheless, the pioneering theorists decided to start from the assumption that any previous advanced earthlings would (like humans) have been heavily dependent on fossil fuel energy and left unavoidable traces of atmospheric distortion, chemical pollution, environmental degradation, and radioactivity. This approach yielded[527c] an impressive analysis that has given other researchers much food for thought.

Although Schmidt and Frank did not[527d] uncover any evidence of a past industrial civilisation, their report included a range of suggested tests[527e] that could help distinguish industrial footprints from natural events in the geologic record. They concluded: *"While we strongly doubt that any previous industrial civilization existed before our own, asking the question in a formal way that articulates explicitly what evidence for such a civilization might look like raises its own useful questions related both to astrobiology and to Anthropocene studies."*

Of course, intelligent predecessors could have graduated to totally green or nuclear fusion technologies that would leave no geologic traces on earth. But, as Jason T. Wright – director of the SETI centre at Pennsylvania State University – suggested in a 2017 paper[527f], a prior indigenous advanced species could have become space-faring and left detectable techno-footprints elsewhere in our solar system. This probability raises the tantalising prospect of humans achieving a similar feat for propagation of our species beyond earth.

Multiple origins

We may never know if a previous advanced civilisation existed on earth. But there's increasing speculation that terrestrial life may have evolved *several* times in *different* forms. In a July 2021 review[528a], Christopher Kempes and David Krakauer from Santa Fe Institute in New Mexico, USA, proposed[528b] a new biological history that involves *multiple* rather than *singular* origination of life. They wrote:

"We argue for multiple forms of life realized through multiple different historical pathways. From this perspective, there have been multiple origins of life on Earth—life is not a universal homology. By broadening the class of originations, we significantly expand the data set for searching for life. Through a computational analogy, the origin of life describes both the origin of hardware (physical substrate) and software (evolved function). Like all information-processing systems, adaptive systems possess a nested hierarchy of levels, a level of function optimization (e.g., fitness maximization), a level of constraints (e.g., energy requirements), and a level of materials (e.g., DNA or RNA genome and cells)."

However, as renowned American molecular and synthetic biologist Gerald Joyce pointed out in a 2012 essay[528c], life (as we know it) arises from *heritable* genetic information that must have originated somewhere. As he put it, the key question is: *"How many heritable "bits" of information are involved, and where did they come from?"* Joyce concluded that any alien terrestrial or extraterrestrial forms of life are more likely to be *"the handiwork of an intelligent species that has discovered the principles of Darwinian evolution and learned to devise chemical systems that have the capacity to generate bits on their own."* In any case, he noted[528d], we have no way of recognising potential life that's based on an alternative genetic code – xenobiology researchers are showing[528e] that, in principle, it's possible to synthesise entirely new life forms from modified genetic systems.

In 2013, US-based theoretical biologist Alexei Sharov and colleague Richard Gordon suggested[529a] in a paper that life might even *predate* formation of the earth 4.54 billion years ago. They used Moore's Law to track[529b] genetic complexity *backward* to the earliest possible DNA or RNA base pair. Astonishingly, the result was an origination timescale of *9.7 billion* years ago. British science writer Tim Radford summed up the mystery of biological origins and life-death circularity in this thought-provoking 2008 comment[529c]:

"Life looks increasingly like a chemical experiment that took over the laboratory. All living things turn to dust and ashes when they die, or, to put it another way, to constituent atoms and molecules of hydrogen, oxygen, carbon, phosphorus and so on.

"But, in another sense, living things do not die: they begin again, from a tiny cell, and scavenge the dust, the air and water, to find the elements necessary to fashion an aspidistra, an elephant, or an attorney-general, using only the raw materials to hand and energy from a thermonuclear reactor 93 million miles away. The freshly minted, self-replicating organism then grows up, grows old and melts away, but not before imparting a fragment of itself to generate yet another copy, but not an identical copy. The process is visible and transparent, everywhere on the planet, but it is ultimately mysterious. It has been going on for at least 3.5bn years, but researchers may never satisfactorily explain how it ever got started."

Post-human simulators

Swedish philosopher Nick Bostrom (a founding director and colleague of Robin Hanson at Oxford University's FHI) approached the probability of pre-human civilisations from the revolutionary assumption that our reality is a back-in-time virtual construct by *future* humans. In 2001, Bostrom floated[530a] the idea that highly advanced post-humans may acquire enough computing power to run 'ancestor' simulations. He developed the hypothesis further in a 2003 paper[530b]:

"I argue that at least one of the following propositions is true: (1) the human species is very likely to become extinct before reaching a 'posthuman' stage; (2) any posthuman civilization is extremely unlikely to run a significant number of simulations of its evolutionary history (or variations thereof); (3) we are almost certainly living in a computer simulation. It follows that the belief that there is a significant chance that we shall one day become posthumans who run ancestor-simulations is false, unless we are currently living in a simulation."

Bostrom further noted that the idea *"suggests naturalistic analogies to certain traditional religious conceptions, which some may find amusing or thought-provoking."*

Indeed, the notion that we may all be 'Sims' of post-human progeny has provoked much debate. Hanson discussed the profound moral and social implications in a 2001 commentary[530c]:

"If our descendants like to play a moral God with their simulations, punishing and rewarding people in the simulation based on how they lived their lives, you might do well to live what they will consider praiseworthy lives. Of course you'll have to figure out the common features of morality in descendants who are willing to play God. (It would seem inconsistent of them to greatly emphasize humility, for example. Inconsistency and morality are hardly strangers though.)

"In sum, if your descendants might make simulations of lives like yours, then you might be living in a simulation. And while you probably cannot learn much detail about the specific reasons for and nature of the simulation you live in, you can draw general conclusions by making analogies to the types and reasons of simulations today. If you might be living in a simulation then all else equal it seems that you should care less about others, live more for today, make your world look likely to become eventually rich, expect to and try to participate in pivotal events, be entertaining and praiseworthy, and keep the famous people around you happy and interested in you."

211

Australian philosopher and cognitive scientist David Chalmers also examined the metaphysical implications of Bostrom's proposed matrix-like existence. In a 2003 paper[530d], he compared the concept to the classic 'brain in a vat' thought experiment in which a disembodied brain is connected to a giant computer simulation of a world, receives stimulated inputs similar to that experienced by a normal embodied brain, and feeds outputs back into the simulation. Chalmers noted that everything would seem normal and real from the 'envatted' brain's perspective:

"The brain is massively deluded, it seems. It has all sorts of false beliefs about the world. It believes that it has a body, but it has no body. It believes that it is walking outside in the sunlight, but in fact it is inside a dark lab. It believes it is one place, when in fact it may be somewhere quite different."

Since there's no way we can be sure we're not similar deluded brains in a simulated matrix, Chalmers argued that Bostrom's proposition is a credible hypothesis that deserves attention:

"The Matrix Hypothesis is one that we should take seriously. As Nick Bostrom has suggested, it is not out of the question that in the history of the universe, technology will evolve that will allow beings to create computer simulations of entire worlds. There may well be vast numbers of such computer simulations, compared to just one real world. If so, there may well be many more beings who are in a matrix than beings who are not. Given all this, one might even infer that it is more likely that we are in a matrix than that we are not. Whether this is right or not, it certainly seems that we cannot be certain that we are not in a matrix."

However, not everyone was convinced. Brown University philosopher Brian Weatherson was sceptical[530e] that computed 'Sims' can ever attain conscious states that confer the full range of human experiential capacity.

University of Liverpool metaphysician Barry Dainton doubted[530f] that any human-like civilisations can survive far enough into the future to run the simulations envisaged by Bostrom (Doomsday argument), but he accepted that we may indeed be high-fidelity neural Sims with illusions of consciousness. Other critics questioned why any post-human civilisation would waste scarce computing resources on a massive venture like ancestral simulations.

Bostrom has posted detailed responses to these questions at his resource site. In 2010, he teamed up with Polish mathematician Marcin Kulczycki to devise[530g] 'patches' for a detected bug in original computations that produced mismatched figures for populations of post-humans.

After a decade of scepticism and fringe speculation, Bostrom's simulation hypothesis suddenly re-emerged in mainstream debate. In 2012, a team at the University of Washington in Seattle led by nuclear physicist Silas Beane simulated[531a] a universe with the fabric of space-time represented as a tightly woven grid of small cubic lattices and used the model to test[531b] if observers living on the *inside* would be able to detect computing constraints that indicate they inhabit a virtual world. The researchers were surprised to find that the resultant symmetry imposed[531c] a fundamental limit on the energy of particles in the simulation – an uncannily similar constraint to the *Greisen–Zatsepin–Kuzmin* limit or GZK cut-off that restricts the energy level of cosmic ray particles in our actual universe.

Thus, although we may never 'escape' or see beyond our existential bubble, it appears we're (for some reason) allowed enough cognition and resources to perceive limitations that suggest we may, indeed, be simulated entities. But the idea that we're some kind of Sims remains highly controversial – not least because we have no way of knowing for sure.

In a 2016 article[532a], British computer scientist Mark Anderson assessed that computing resource constraints for managing *all* the fluctuating entities and events in our universe make it unlikely that we're living in a simulation. He argued:

"Even if a machine existed that could simulate our existence then there would be a high probability that we would experience so-called "realism imperfections". These bugs in the simulation would be seen or heard due to glitches in the model. For example, stars may or may not exist when viewed through telescopes of varying magnification. Such errors would be inevitable in a simulation of this scale, but they have never been observed by humans."

However, such evaluations are based on the limited levels and types of computing facilities that human minds can conceive. Any post-human simulators will likely have access to *unlimited* cosmic resources far beyond our comprehension. As renowned investigative journalist and author Adam Penenberg pointed out in a 2013 article[532b], if futuristic beings don't want us to know the ultimate truth about our condition, we probably never will. Regarding Bostrom's extraordinary ancestral hypothesis, Penenberg commented:

"Mind-bending, sure, but is it more far-fetched than religion, which promotes the idea that God created the Earth and Heavens? Or less believable than the Big Bang theory, which holds that the universe started out as a speck of matter of incredible density, smaller than a pore on your skin? [...] In the process, it heralded the beginnings of time and, somewhat later, the Earth coalesced from hot gases and, by sheer luck and happenstance, ultimately created an environment from which life sprang. Really? Compared to that, existing in a game simulation seems plausible."

The notion of a matrix-like simulated existence continues[532c] to attract lively debate. Researchers are hopeful that new science will emerge to settle the issue.

In 2017, a team at California Institute of Technology (Caltech) proposed[532d] a novel multi-faceted test that involves virtual reality probabilistic computations and light-particle transformations. Mainstream scientific endorsement will certainly represent the most significant paradigm-shift since Darwin's 1859 theory of evolution.

Is life purposive?

The question whether life is purposive is important not just in the context of ascribing meaning to daily existence, but also for coming to terms with our limited biological lifespan. If it can be concluded from naturalistic investigations that we're part of some grand design (however incomprehensible), we can legitimately speculate that the information dataset which produced our 'being' is likely recycled on earth or reapplied in some other domain towards greater goals.

Kant's self-organised beings

Aristotle's 350 BCE systematic study *Historia animalium* (History of Animals)[533a] was based on the assumption that organisms, and their constituent body parts, are the outcomes of *purposive* processes in nature. This thinking endured for 2,000 years until the European Enlightenment (17th to 18th centuries) ushered in materialistic dogma that rejected Aristotle's *holistic* approach in favour of *mechanistic* models that attempt to show how complex biological structures could have arisen from random processes.

The new emphasis was part of a concerted campaign against claims of divine knowledge by corrupt religious authorities and despotic monarchs. Intellectual heavyweights like British philosopher John Locke and French activist Voltaire (real name François-Marie Arouet) sought to encourage lay people to think for themselves, rather than rely on a self-serving 'priestcraft'. American philosopher Mark Perlman explained the impact in a 2004 review[533b]:

"Philosophers, going back to Aristotle, used to make generous use of functions in describing objects, organisms, their interactions, and even as the basis of ethics and metaphysics. And yet, since the Enlightenment, talk of the function of natural objects, teleological function, began to be viewed with suspicion, as the mechanical model of the world replaced the old Aristotelian model. From a religious standpoint, it used to be easy to see how objects in the natural world could have natural functions, for God was said to instill functions by design throughout Creation. But philosophers became increasingly reluctant to invoke God to solve every difficult philosophical problem, and became unwilling to indulge in such religious explanations of teleology."

However, not everyone abandoned Aristotle's 'top down' approach to the study of living things. Notably, 18th century German philosopher Immanuel Kant (a well-known supporter of empirical research) still argued for the Aristotelian model because this emphasises *natural telos* (intrinsic end-goals) rather than divine providence. In Part II[534a] of his 1790 masterpiece *Critique of Judgment* (the third of a famous trilogy), Kant asserted that inference of purposiveness in biology is more than a casual observation that *"products of nature"* appear to have specific forms that conform to their usefulness and function: we can also, he argued, use *rational analysis* to conclude that purposiveness is an inherent attribute of life.

Kant cautioned in §61[534b] that any such investigation can only be a *"reflective"* thought exercise and not a *"determinant"* practical experiment. Nevertheless, he contended that this alternative approach is equally valid when the concept of an object is indistinguishable from its cause and perceived purpose. In other words, *the very existence* of a thing is evidence of an intended outcome. Kant explained further in §64[534c] that things can be said to have such teleological purpose if their form defies natural laws. He described such things in §65[534d] as *"organised beings"* which explain their own 'cause and effect':

"In such a product of nature every part not only exists <u>by means of</u> the other parts, but is thought as existing <u>for the sake of</u> the others and the whole, that is as an (organic) instrument. Thus, however, it might be an artificial instrument, and so might be represented only as a purpose that is possible in general; but also its parts are all organs reciprocally <u>producing</u> each other. This can never be the case with artificial instruments, but only with nature which supplies all the material for instruments (even for those of art). Only a product of such a kind can be called a <u>natural purpose</u>, and this because it is an <u>organised</u> and <u>self-organising being</u>."

Thus, we recognise all creatures (including humans) as functioning beings based on their *entire* biological form. A body lacking parts, or individual organs presented separately, would not convey the same conceptual meaning.

Kant further distinguished between *natural* organised beings and *artificial* instruments like watches:

"In a watch one part is the instrument for moving the other parts, but the wheel is not the effective cause of the production of the others; no doubt one part is for the sake of the others, but it does not exist by their means. [....] Hence a watch wheel does not produce other wheels, still less does one watch produce other watches, utilising (organising) foreign material for that purpose; [....] An organised being is then not a mere machine, for that has merely moving power, but it possesses in itself formative power of a self-propagating kind which it communicates to its materials though they have it not of themselves; it organises them, in fact, and this cannot be explained by the mere mechanical faculty of motion."

In §75[534e], Kant made the remarkably prescient prediction that failure to acknowledge purpose in biology would hinder empirical investigation into the laws and mechanisms behind living things:

217

"We are in fact indispensably obliged to ascribe the concept of design to nature if we wish to investigate it, though only in its organised products, by continuous observation; and this concept is therefore an absolutely necessary maxim for the empirical use of our Reason. It is plain that once such a guiding thread for the study of nature is admitted and verified, we must at least try the said maxim of Judgement in nature as a whole; because thereby many of nature's laws might discover themselves, which otherwise, on account of the limitation of our insight into its inner mechanism, would remain hidden."

Kant's treatise is still one of the strongest arguments for a purposive biosphere. He ended §75 with the challenge that no (Isaac) Newton will ever come up with natural laws that can explain even a 'blade of grass' as a product of undirected processes:

"It is indeed quite certain that we cannot adequately cognise, much less explain, organised beings and their internal possibility, according to mere mechanical principles of nature; and we can say boldly it is alike certain that it is absurd for men to make any such attempt or to hope that another Newton will arise in the future, who shall make comprehensible by us the production of a blade of grass according to natural laws which no design has ordered."

Repurposing biology

After centuries of unquestioned acceptance of divine creation and design of life forms, Charles Darwin's 1859 theory of natural selection finally gave evolutionary biologists justification to claim the discipline was just as reliant on the laws of nature as physics and chemistry. Living things have since been described[535a] as non-purposive, self-reproducing units that evolved incrementally and either compete or cooperate (if mutually beneficial) in a perpetual bid for survival. Unfortunately, this dogma overshadowed the groundbreaking discovery in the mid-20th century that all life stems from a universal genetic code stored in robust DNA sequences.[535b]

The revelation that highly specific genetic information has instructed evolution of organisms over *millions* of years severely undermines[535c] attempts to depict the process as undirected and unguided. Moreover, genes in DNA are not utilised directly by cells but are first copied to disposable RNA (ribonucleic acid) transcripts – a clearly purposive precaution for preservation of genome fidelity through successive generations of an organism.

Interestingly, 19th century contemporaries like Karl von Baer did not[535d] see any conflict between Darwin's proposed mechanisms and purposive teleology in biology. Indeed, American philosopher and historian of science James Lennox argued in a 1993 paper[535e] that Darwin has been badly misunderstood:

"It is often claimed that one of Darwin's chief accomplishments was to provide biology with a non-teleological explanation of adaptation. A number of Darwin's closest associates, however, and Darwin himself, did not see it that way. In order to assess whether Darwin's version of evolutionary theory does or does not employ teleological explanation, two of his botanical studies are examined. The result of this examination is that Darwin sees selection explanations of adaptations as teleological explanations. The confusion in the nineteenth century about Darwin's attitude to teleology is argued to be a result of Darwin's teleological explanations not conforming to either of the dominant philosophical justifications of teleology at that time."

In 1958, British-born biologist Colin Pittendrigh (a pioneer of chronobiology) introduced the term 'teleonomic' to distinguish functions in biology that are clearly goal-directed from teleological Aristotelian processes that tend to inevitable outcomes – a nuance Grace de Laguna extended[536a] to evolutionary mechanisms in 1962. However, German-American evolutionary biologist Ernst Mayr disagreed that evolution is a directed process – he declared in a 1961 article[536b]:

"All objects of the physical world are endowed with the capacity to change their state, and these changes strictly obey natural laws. They are end-directed only in a passive, automatic way, regulated by external forces or conditions, that is by natural laws."

Mayr further separated *"teleomatic"* evolutionary mechanisms that he said only have 'apparent' ends from *"teleonomic"* processes derived from DNA code that have 'genuine' goals. As he put it: *"All teleonomic behavior is characterized by two components. It is guided by "a program" and it depends on the existence of some end point, goal, or terminus which is foreseen in the program which regulates the behavior."* He revived this 'teleomatic' distinction in a 1992 paper[536c] titled *The Idea of Teleology.*

However, philosopher and historian of science Ernest Nagel did not find Mayr's arguments convincing. In a 1977 lecture[536d], Nagel remarked[536e]: *"I do not know how to escape the conclusion that the manner in which teleomatic and teleonomic processes are defined, does not provide an effective way of distinguishing between processes in biology that are goal-directed from those which are not. In consequence, though the program view notes some important features of goal-directed processes, it is not an adequate explication of the concept."*

Michael Ruse explained in a 2013 essay[537a] that the notion of purposive teleology is rejected in biology because some see it as *"a sign that biology is not a real science at all, but just a collection of observations and facts"*, while others argue that *"the apparent purposefulness of nature leaves room for God."* But, are these legitimate concerns in the 21st century? Most scholars now accept[537b] that it's impossible to completely expunge teleological reasoning and language from biology because living things and their constituent parts are described and studied in terms of *function* and *purpose*. Furthermore, as British philosopher Mary Midgley pointed out repeatedly, even the notion of organisms as *self-perpetuating* creatures forged by natural selection indicates purpose.

In her famous 2011 essay[537c] *Why The Idea Of Purpose Won't Go Away*, Midgley echoed Kant's scepticism that organisms can be studied and explained without consideration of purpose:

"Biologists' current habit of explaining each feature of human life separately through its evolutionary function – its assumed tendency to enhance each individual's reproductive prospects – is unworkable. It also sits oddly with these scientists' official rejection of teleology, since it treats all life as a process which does have an aim, namely, to perpetuate itself. But that aim is empty because it is circular.

"If we want to understand the behaviour of living things (including humans) we have to treat them seriously as <u>subjects</u>, creatures with needs, tendencies and directions of their own. The supposedly objective idea of a <u>world of objects</u> without subjects is an unprofitable fantasy."

Midgley complained that the *"vast and crazy enterprise"* by hard-core materialists to banish all idea of purpose in life had obscured the Aristotelian vision of a 'universal striving' to achieve individual and common goals. She wrote: *"It is simply a fact that all organisms constantly strive towards their own survival, their health, their well-being, their general fulfilment and their reproduction."* Midgley vigorously rejected arguments by some biologists that undetectable forces and entities can't, by definition, play a useful role in naturalistic research:

"That, however, certainly cannot mean that there is no such thing as purpose in nature. Dawkins's claim that the universe contains 'at bottom, no design, no purpose, no evil and no good' cannot be right. For it is obvious that our own planet – which is certainly part of the universe – is riddled with purpose. It is full of organisms, beings which all steadily pursue their own characteristic ways of life, beings that can only be understood by grasping the distinctive thing that each of them is trying to be and do."

Of course, Kant also stressed that design and end-goals in biology cannot be treated as *scientific* topics. But, as Aristotle noted in *Posterior Analytics* – his essay[537d] on factual evidence, no understanding of *anything* is possible unless we treat some basic assumptions as 'truth'.

Excitingly, as the 21st century progresses, impressive advances are being made towards understanding how organisms are assembled and acquire functions at fundamental level. Developments in molecular biology and genetics are revealing that the anatomy of living things, and the physiology that separates them from the non-living, are far more complex and sophisticated than we could ever have imagined. It makes it all the more remarkable and mysterious that biological death is part of the existential equation.

6. Mystery of Humans

"The genome is like a book written in a foreign language,
we know the letters but cannot understand why a human genome
makes a human or the mouse genome a mouse."
Jussi Taipale, computational bioscientist, in
Learning the alphabet of gene control (2013)[538]

Our unique genome

Although human DNA is over 90 percent similar to other primates (up to 99 percent identical[539] in chimpanzees and bonobos), we're uniquely endowed with metacognitive capacity for reasoning, sophisticated language, complex social interactions, and historical recordings. But what truly sets humans apart is a universal sense of *morality, ethics, religiosity,* and *aesthetics*; abstractions that have fostered ideas of individual rights and responsibilities within societies. When did these intuitions emerge in evolutionary history, and exactly how do our extraordinary mental faculties arise from raw genetic data?

Life's code book

In April 2003, an international collaboration of scientists triumphantly concluded[540a] the Human Genome Project (HGP) – a 13-year quest to write out the entire volume of *three billion* A, C, G, T nucleotide sequences that code all genes in our DNA. But the euphoria that greeted this remarkable achievement waned somewhat as it became clear this was only the beginning. HGP proved akin to downloading multiple volumes of a hugely complex book of code – understanding which sequences relate to myriad biological processes, and how they function to produce humans, is proving an uphill task. Nearly two decades on, researchers are still struggling[540b] to locate and describe our genome's 'software controller'.

223

Gene count bombshell

When HGP was launched in 1990, researchers predicted[541a] over 100,000 protein-coding genes would be found to account for our numerous traits and unique metacognition. However, the project revealed[541b] we only have around 20,000 genes – less than 2 percent of our total DNA. This is just 6,000 more than found in fruit flies *(Drosophila melanogaster)*[541c] and at least 26,000 *less* than found in rice *(Oryza sativa)*[541d]. How could this be?

The actual number of human genes is still[542a] under investigation and may even be[542b] as much as 20 percent less[542c] than the HGP figure. Such a low count completely overturns scientific dogma on the central role of protein-coding genes in biological complexities. Evidently, other powerful influences are at play.

For decades, scientists dismissed the remaining 98 percent of our genome as useless 'junk DNA' that accumulated through millennia of blind evolution. Then, in 2012, an international research consortium dubbed *Encyclopedia of DNA Elements* (ENCODE) published a bombshell report[543a] that suggested[543b] at least 80 percent of this previously disregarded DNA had important biological functions. ENCODE revealed that non-protein-coding areas function as a huge operating system[543c] that controls how genes are switched on and off in cells. Millions of regulatory switches were mapped[543d] within hundreds of different kinds of cells. There are *enhancers* for switching genes on and *silencers* for switching them off.

ENCODE also compiled[544a] an extensive 'dictionary' of embedded instructions[544b] that effectively form the genome's operating manual. The outcome suggests[544c] *up to a dozen* switches may be acting in concert to control targeted genes in a very complex manner.

Results showed switches may be at a very distant location along the DNA strand from the gene they control, or even sited on a *different* chromosome. Also, the same bit of regulatory DNA can play different roles in different types of cells. These groundbreaking discoveries provoked much debate[545] about the way cells use genetic information to build and sustain organisms.

Tailored operating systems

Further findings published[546a] in 2014 by the Japanese-led consortium for *Functional Annotation of the Mammalian Genome* (FANTOM) confirmed[546b] that gene switching activity is definitely *cell-specific*. Separate research[547a] by a team led by Richard Young at Whitehead Institute for Biomedical Research in Massachusetts, USA uncovered[547b] 'super-enhancers' in DNA that act[547c] as master regulators. Incredibly, each cell type hosts an[547d,e] innate operating system that determines[547f] tissue properties.

Scientists now know[548a] that super-enhancers activate successive operating systems in embryonic stem cells during differentiation[548b] into various body parts. Failure to deactivate[548c,d] an operating system properly before switching on a new one for transition to a tissue cell type can be fatal[548e]. In 2017, researchers at Austria's Institute of Science and Technology showed[549a] for the first time that embryonic cells use complex feedback signalling to coordinate[549b] smooth development of animals.

However, it's still unknown[550a] how specific cell-types and stable body forms arise from genetic memory. What's become clear is that enhancers are on stand-by long before[550b] genes are transcribed to RNA during embryonic development – suggesting *advance programming* of the systems that shape organisms. Significantly, enhancers in fruit flies exhibit[550c] *the same* level of complexity observed in vertebrates; another indication of *universal* information systems for speciation.

Regulatory networks

The 21st century discovery that organisms arise from mysterious interactions of dynamic, highly sophisticated *gene regulatory networks* (GRNs)[551a] – not simple transcriptions of static strips of DNA code as biologists long thought – has prompted[551b] a shift in emphasis from *passive* genetic variation to *active* genomic regulation as the driver[551c] for evolution of heritable phenotypes[551d]. GRNs are now known to exhibit similar redundancy as the protein-coding genes they control: amazingly, one or more (sometimes dissimilar) systems exist in DNA that can act[551e] as functional backups.

How did GRNs arise and exactly how are they triggered in cells? So far, proposals for evolutionary origin in plants[552a] and animals[552b] are largely speculative and lack supporting evidence. But fascinating details have emerged about the mechanisms cells use to activate encoded GRNs. Just as gene codons get transcribed to mRNA for production of proteins, regulatory DNA is copied[553a] to numerous *non-protein-coding* RNA (ncRNA) for wide-ranging control functions. MIT researchers have identified[553b] adjacent 'pseudogenes' that spawn[553c] long and short ncRNA each time a protein-coding gene is transcribed to mRNA, but initiating signals and functions have remained hidden[553d].

Biologists have enlisted the help of computer scientists to model GRNs. In 2019, an American team led by computational biologist Emily Miraldi from CCH Medical Center in Ohio developed[554a] a new algorithmic procedure for faster[554b] GRN data analysis. A European group led by genomicist Holger Heyn at Spain's Centre for Genomic Regulation also applied[554c] abstract graph theory to devise a complex modelling tool[554d], and an Austrian team published[554e] a speculative simulation in March 2021. However, no one has shown exactly how GRNs generate stable phenotypes like humans.

Explaining humans

In 2012, an international multidisciplinary study[555a] led by neuroscientist and geneticist Schahram Akbarian from the University of Massachusetts identified[555b] almost *40 million* uniquely regulated regions in human neurons. In an unrelated presentation to the American Society of Human Genetics, geneticist Yoav Gilad from the University of Chicago described parallel research that showed[555c] gene regulatory systems in white blood cells of humans, chimpanzees and rhesus monkeys likewise differ by up to *40 percent.*

Surprisingly though, Gilad's team subsequently found that[556a,b] consequential differences in levels of gene transcriptions to mRNA did not necessarily lead to production of different proteins – the presumed source of new traits that separate us from other primates. They reported in 2013: *"Overall, our data suggest that protein expression levels evolve under stronger evolutionary constraint than mRNA levels."* The astounding implication is that deeper, targeted regulatory systems exist in human genomes. Gilad explained[556c] in a press release:

> *"We thought that we knew how to identify patterns of mRNA expression level differences between humans and chimpanzees. Now we see that even such mRNA patterns are not translated to the protein level, which means that it is unlikely that they can affect a functional phenotypic difference. [...] Some of these patterns of mRNA regulation have previously been thought of as evidence of natural selection for important genes in humans, but this can no longer be assumed."*

Clearly, our existence is no evolutionary accident. As Thomas Gingerasa, an ENCODE research team leader, remarked[557a] in a 2012 article: *"Exploration of the genome is akin to our efforts at exploring our physical universe. We expect to be amazed and excited by our future efforts to map and explore our personal genetic universes."*

227

Indeed, the extent and specificity of controls being uncovered in the human genome is rapidly overturning previous assumptions[557b] about our evolutionary history. In 2013, a multinational collaboration led by geneticist Axel Visel from Lawrence Berkeley National Laboratory in California reported that[558a,b] family similarities and craniofacial features which give us personal identity are sculpted[558c] by thousands of enhancers hidden in regulatory DNA.

Our protein-coding DNA (the traditional genes previously thought to confer human traits) are, it seems, just inert information snippets used in largely unknown ways by a range of agents to create genomic imprints that don't always transmit to immediate offspring, *but* can still reappear in later generations. Intriguingly, another collaborative study[559a] led by medical scientists at University of California, San Francisco revealed[559b] in 2017 that even *ethnicity* is not just a product of genetic ancestry; epigenetic signatures stamped on DNA by culture and environment play a significant role.

The mystery of human genetic evolution has been deepened by further unexpected findings from a decade-long investigation led by biostatistician Katherine Pollard at Gladstone Institutes in San Francisco. Pollard's team identified thousands of so-called *human accelerated regions* (HARs) in regulatory DNA that are key regulators of embryonic development. Even though similar regions have persisted as highly conserved 'silent' code sequences in other mammals through 6 million years of evolution, they are activated *only* in humans. Pollard discussed the innovative research techniques that yielded these extraordinary discoveries in a 2016 essay[560]. She asked:

"So what were HARs doing that made their sequences so immutable throughout mammalian evolution? How did the multiple human mutations in each HAR change its function?"

228

Pollard's group (and several others) continue the quest to understand how, when, and why regulatory HARs 'switched on' to produce unique human traits. Although answers to these intriguing questions are still lacking, Pollard rightly described developments so far as *"a huge step forward from HARs being viewed as bizarre junk DNA of unknown function."*

Another huge surprise has emerged from separate research into *transcription factors* (TFs) – a class of enigmatic proteins that work with[561a] regulatory DNA to switch genes on and off. Until recently, it was assumed that TFs attach to almost the same *motifs* (DNA docking sites) in eukaryotes as far removed as humans and fruit flies. However, in May 2019, a team led by systems biologist and molecular geneticist Timothy Hughes from University of Toronto in Canada reported[561b] that TFs actually bind to a range of sites that tend to be *specific* to each species. The finding suggests TFs play an active role in regulatory processes that craft the phenotypes which define species. As senior report author Sam Lambert commented[561c]:

> *"Even between closely related species there's a non-negligible portion of TFs that are likely to bind new sequences. This means they are likely to have novel functions by regulating different genes, which may be important for species differences. We think these molecular differences could be driving some of the differences between chimps and humans."*

These conclusions are truly profound. They mark a watershed in scientific thinking on evolution of the hugely diverse forms of life we observe. After 160 years of insistence on blind, directionless Darwinian mechanisms, biologists can no longer deny or ignore the mounting evidence that species are the product of *purposive* genetic programming. Perplexingly however, uniquely activated genomic regions in modern humans have been linked[562a] to brain and mind diseases. It's hoped reconstructions of gene regulation in ancestral *Homo* species will expose[562b] possible 'faulty wiring' in our neurons.

Unexpected metaprogrammes

In addition to redefinition of vast regions of 'junk' DNA as genomic regulatory systems, scientists are finding that even traditional protein-coding genes harbour far more than codons for amino acids. New discoveries of hidden instructions are further highlighting the huge complexities of genetic coding.

Unintelligible 'words' and 'grammar'

Finnish medical bioscientist Jussi Taipale has pioneered decades of research into genomic regulation for copying of DNA to RNA in cells. In 2013, a team led by Taipale at Sweden's Karolinska Institute (KI) published a study[563a] that tracked over 400 transcription factors (TFs) that regulate how and when human genes are copied. Astonishingly, they found[563b] that genetic letters in DNA regulatory sequences for TF activity actually form instructional 'words'. However, the language was baffling and unfamiliar.

Unrelated work with new computational biotechnology, led by Nadav Ahituv from University of California at San Francisco, revealed[564a] that the DNA 'word' sequences conform to a kind of 'grammar'. Ahituv's group found that[564b] changing the pre-arranged order affects the ability of TFs to 'read' related genes – just as changing the order of words in a sentence disrupts its meaning.

Taipale's team at KI subsequently uncovered more instructional patterns and language rules. They reported[565a] in 2015 that related DNA sequences frequently join to form 'compound words' or even switch around to produce completely new words and 'sentences'. As the researchers noted[565b], these discoveries show our genetic code is written in alien language that's far more complex and intricately constructed than any communicative system known to humans.

230

To complicate an already tortuous scenario, TFs are controlled by an array of *other* programmes coded in the same or nearby DNA sequences. These 'overseers' determine *where* and *when* TFs bind to genes for transcriptions. Another ENCODE team led by John Stamatoyannopoulos from University of Washington in Seattle published a separate 2013 study[566a] which showed codons that specify amino acids for proteins are also[566b] 'duons' bearing instructions for control of TFs. Stamatoyannopoulos explained[566c] the huge significance of this discovery in a press statement:

"For over 40 years we have assumed that DNA changes affecting the genetic code solely impact how proteins are made. Now we know that this basic assumption about reading the human genome missed half of the picture. These new findings highlight that DNA is an incredibly powerful information storage device, which nature has fully exploited in unexpected ways.

"The fact that the genetic code can simultaneously write two kinds of information means that many DNA changes that appear to alter protein sequences may actually cause disease by disrupting gene control programs or even both mechanisms simultaneously."

Analogue inputs

Perhaps the most unexpected aspect of genetic coding that's come to light is the stunning finding[567a] that DNA's geometric structure harbours *analogue* instructions in addition to its *digital* code sequences. Amazingly, the numerous loops and contortions in *coiled* DNA incorporate mysterious 3-D coding – even folds and bends[567b] in *uncoiled* DNA serve to[567c] attract or repel TFs for gene activation or deactivation. This revelation has dramatically altered[568a] scientific assumptions on the scope and nature of genetic language. As Stanford University bioengineers showed[568b] in 2018, the entire *spatial organisation* of genomes within nuclei, and the *location* of genes, significantly influences[568c] how TFs interact with DNA.

231

Hence, in a 2013 review[569a], Georgi Muskhelishvili and Andrew Travers described chromosomes as *"thermodynamic machines converting energy into information"* and emphasised *"the critical need of holistic integration of the DNA information as a prerequisite for understanding the organisational complexity of the genetic regulation system."* Indeed, the implications are so important for medical science that public research initiatives into digital/analogue DNA 'cross-talk' have been launched in the USA[569b] and Europe.

How do I know I am me?

While our physical and cognitive advantages can be traced to unique regulation of our genome, it's entirely unclear how we acquire *subjective* awareness – the sense that we're unique persons capable of identifying ourselves and others as human beings that deserve rights and bear direct responsibility for our own actions and omissions. Although some controversial studies suggest other creatures may have[570a] a sense of 'self' and body ownership, there's no evidence that non-humans have developed the degree of *individuality, introspection* and *emotional longing* that has shaped our complex societies.

Body perception

How we actually experience 'self' and the world continues to be hotly disputed[570b,c]; not least because the issue raises deep existential questions. If the universe and all it contains is indeed[570d] a simulated projection of quantum uncertainties, how and why do our minds identify *consistently* with the physical body we inhabit? After all, we're still the same person when we wake up in the morning and recognise the same individual when we look in the mirror. Some insights have emerged from the *virtual reality* (VR) industry – remarkably, tests indicate fully conscious beings in a *simulated reality* (SR) can be aware of their condition *but still* experience illusory effects as 'true' events.

Researchers have been surprised by the extent to which self-awareness and decision-making can be influenced by temporary VR experiences. Studies of body-swapping (immersion in digital forms of a different sex[571a] or being[571b]), and body-environment variation (immersion in illusory landscapes[571c]), show our *perception* of things is as important as actual stimuli in shaping reaction. Rodent studies have also shown that the brain operates very differently[572a] and fails to create[572b] a spatial map during VR experiences – even though[572c] it continues to use landmarks[572d] for navigation.

These findings illustrate the fragility of our mental links with physical reality. Human capacity for self-deception is further illustrated by conditions like *Body Integrity Identity Disorder* (BIID) that causes rejection of one's own limbs and organs as 'alien' entities. Conversely, individuals who have lost a body part frequently report a strange sensing that the missing part is still present; a 'phantom limb' experience that makes it difficult to accept prosthetic replacements. In 2018, a European collaboration reported[573a] successful combination of VR and artificial tactile sensations to convince[573b] amputees that prosthetic attachments were 'real' body parts.

Shades of reality

In 1994, Canadian cognitive engineer Paul Milgram and collaborators at ATR Communication Systems Research Labs in Kyoto, Japan introduced the concept of a *Reality-Virtuality Continuum* (RV) that spans actual to virtual experiences. The seminal paper[574a,b] outlined a spectrum of possible 'mixed realities' that can arise; from *Augmented Reality* (AR) where computer-generated digital content is added to a *real* physical environment, to *Augmented Virtuality* (AV) where a *virtual* environment is enhanced with sensory inputs from the real world (RW). The authors showed how observers can perceive and experience different levels of reality without total immersion and loss of 'self' in a fully simulated VR.

233

Some VR illusions are now so realistic that the tool is being promoted as an alternative to actual human interactions in social neuroscience research[575a] and leadership skills training[575b]. However, although the reality-virtuality middle ground identified by Milgram's group provides a Health & Safety guideline for innovations, physical and psychological effects of prolonged VR immersions remain largely unexplored[575c].

In 2015, Aline de Borst and Beatrice de Gelder from Maastricht University in the Netherlands cautioned[576a] that constant interaction with virtual avatars and androids can distort perception of human emotions and affect behaviour in the real world. Jakki Bailey and Jeremy Bailenson from Stanford University's Virtual Human Interaction Lab (VHIL) also discussed[576b] possible long-term effects of VR entertainment on children in a 2017 commentary. Industry scriptwriter Angela Buckingham expressed particular concern about immersive VR simulations of murder in a 2016 essay[576c] – she argued that *"by embodying killers, we risk making violence more tantalising, training ourselves in cruelty and normalising aggression."*

Despite such misgivings, reality-virtuality integration is now an irreversible feature of everyday life; China has built[577a] the world's first VR-themed megapark to exploit the trend. The COVID-19 pandemic has also fuelled massive adoption of VR applications to overcome social restrictions. In August 2020, the Indian Institute of Technology (IIT) in Bombay organised[577b] a fully virtual university convocation with 'stand in' representations of administrators, students and guest speakers. Astonished viewers witnessed 3-D avatars of over 2,000 graduates walk across a simulated stage to receive certificates and medals. Student avatars were even able[577c] to roam around IIT's campus and interact virtually with friends and faculty staff. The remarkable achievement showed that human reality can be seamlessly simulated *outside* biological bodies.

234

False realities

The rapid shift to virtual interactions is prompting reassessment of traditional views on the way humans acquire a sense of reality and meaning. In their seminal book *The Social Construction of Reality* (1966), sociologists Peter Berger and Thomas Luckmann argued that[578a] identity and self-awareness are products of *reciprocal* relationships within social groups. In other words, just as we only recognise ourselves as 'me' and 'human' because other members of our species exist that we're able to use as a reference, we need a community of *interacting minds* to establish everyday reality. However, this emphasis on *social* rather than *individual* perception of reality can lead to problematic 'group-think'[578b]. Also, since we now interact largely on social media and online sites where it's impossible to tell if the other party is a real person or mindless AI bot, we've become more susceptible to manipulation.

French sociologist and philosopher Jean Baudrillard presciently discussed the hazards of instant information flows across global networks in his acclaimed book *Simulacra and Simulation* (1981). He complained[579a] that an increasingly self-referential Western society has sunk into a 'hyperreality' in which actuality can no longer be distinguished from simulated reality. Baudrillard showed how *simulacra* (symbols and signs created by late 20th century culture and media) have been used to distort human values and reduce all meaning to rampant consumerism. This state of affairs, he argued, makes life a *de facto* simulation – a theme that inspired[579b] cult movie *The Matrix*. Guy Debord's earlier work *The Society of the Spectacle* (1967) had also warned[579c] that non-stop advertising in mass media was creating an 'inverted reality' where relationships are defined by imagery and commodities rather than genuine interactions. Sadly, our grasp on reality has continued to slip as we become more like video game 'Sims' that lack capacity for critical thinking.

Are humans really exceptional?

Humans have long believed we occupy a special position in the chain of life that entitles us to exploit all else that exists for our own propagation and survival. This anthropocentric attitude has been bolstered by religious teachings that humanity's unique perception of morality and aesthetic values places us at the pinnacle of a divine creation with devolved dominion over nature. However, such 'exceptionalism' is at odds with our shared fate – we're, after all, programmed to die like other living things.

Cognitive privilege

Frustratingly for researchers, neither evolutionary biology nor anthropology has produced a fully scientific explanation for our extraordinary cognitive and social advantages. Why should we – essentially assemblies of perishable biological systems constructed from genetic information and matter – even have the capacity to recognise ourselves as time-limited mortals that may or may not continue to exist in some afterlife form?

In 2013, a team of neuroscientists at the KU Leuven Medical School in Belgium published[580a] a brain scan study that showed[580b] humans have at least two brain networks which are absent in other primates. A year later, another group at Oxford University in the UK reported[580c] that a particular area of our brain's frontal cortex (which we use for some highly advanced planning and decision-making processes) is also uniquely human[580d]. Then, in 2018, a large Hungarian-American collaborative study[580e] uncovered evidence of a specialised human cortical brain cell which had never been seen[580f] in long-studied rodent brains. But, while these anatomical features are intriguing, there's increasing evidence that other creatures also have specialised neural equipment that suffices for their way of life and ecological niches.

Common wiring

Outward appearance can be deceptive. Although a bird's brain may look quite different to that of a mammal (birds lack a neocortex), a map of avian neuronal networks, developed[581a] in 2013 by an international team led by researchers at Imperial College London, revealed[581b] that bird brain regions for information processing are 'wired' together in the *same way* as human brains – despite our very different evolutionary paths over 300 million years. In 2018, neuroscientists at Canada's University of Alberta confirmed[581c] birds have a primate-like neural circuit that may explain their remarkable intelligence (the circuit is disproportionately larger[581d] in parrots and rivals the size of similar equipment in primates). This suggests we share a *common* neural blueprint for some cognitive tasks, and makes[581e] bird brains a useful model for research into degenerative human brain diseases.

Another major surprise emerged in 2016. An international collaborative study[582a] led by W. Tecumseh Fitch at University of Vienna found that, contrary to the decades-old assumption that monkeys don't speak like humans because they lack the appropriate vocal equipment, these primates are actually anatomically 'speech-ready'. The researchers concluded[582b] that restriction on speech in monkeys must be *neurological* rather than physiological; their brains simply can't regulate their vocal apparatus to formulate language as our brains do. Fitch explained[582c] in a 2018 review:

"Speech, as the preferred output modality for human language, is an unusual feature of our species that depends upon a complex but well-understood set of mechanisms, including vocal/motor, auditory/perceptual, and central neural mechanisms. The capacity for speech clearly differentiates humans from other primates, indicating that some of these mechanisms have diverged, in recent human evolution, from those of our prelinguistic ancestors.

However, the capacity to vocally imitate sounds is not uniquely human and is shared with a surprisingly diverse group of organisms, including many bird species, most marine mammals, elephants, and some bats. This means that this capacity has evolved, convergently, many times in vertebrate evolution."

The uniqueness of human speech was further underlined by a March 2019 report[583a] from researchers at the New York University School of Medicine that showed[583b] Alston's singing mouse (*Scotinomys teguina*) uses *the same* brain circuit as humans to 'take turns in conversation' – an essential requirement for meaningful vocal interaction. The unexpected discovery has provided a new avenue for studying the complex mechanisms behind human speech.

It all begs the question why other creatures that are fully equipped for vocalisation haven't developed much higher levels of verbal communication. Clearly, our enhanced audio-neural-vocal apparatus evolved through *targeted* genetic modifications. However, the origin and nature of the programming remain[583c] largely mysterious.

Unique linguistics

Our distinct languages (7,000+) and ability to construct words that have different contextual meaning are even more striking. Results from a 2017 study[584a] led by Masha Fedzechkina from University of Arizona suggest[584b] commonalities or 'linguistic universals' across languages reflect *optimal information processing* by the human brain. This view is supported by a December 2019 report[584c] on non-verbal communication in young children by scientists from Leipzig University and Max Planck Institute for Evolutionary Anthropology in Germany – they found[584d] even preschool children can *"create new communication systems that exhibit core features of natural languages in less than 30 min"*; a finding that strongly suggests we're born with mental tools for rapid and spontaneous social interaction.

238

Sure enough, in October 2020 psychologists from Ohio State University in Columbus, USA published[585a] new research that showed[585b] neonates (newborn humans) arrive with a well-developed *visual word form area* (VWFA) in the brain. Thus, there's now firm evidence of innate 'wiring' for language in humans – it's a *programmed* feature from birth and not an *acquired* skill as previously thought.

Significantly, our linguistic endowment comes with a huge mental capacity for information storage. University of Rochester cognitive scientist Francis Mollica and University of California (Berkeley) psychologist Steven Piantadosi published[586a] a computation in March 2019 that suggests youngsters file away at least *1.5 megabytes* of data during language acquisition – an incredible feat that Piantadosi noted[586b] *"highlights a difference between machine learners and human learners"*. The finding challenges assumptions that robots could easily master all the nuances of human language.

However, while human language is distinguished by recursive grammar[587a,b] and other intricate features, absence of these attributes in other animals doesn't mean[587c] they're incapable of meaningful communication and rational decisions. French philosopher and sociologist Edgar Morin is renowned[588a] for his *pensée complexe* (complex thought) thesis that *all* organisms possess 'informational capital' for purposive interaction. Morin's claim is controversial, but researchers have reported unexpected use of symbolic 'language' in other species like songbirds[588b], ants[588c] and (famously) honey bees[588d].

Amazingly, it appears even *plants* are able to communicate[589a]. In 2013, Monica Gagliano and Michael Renton from the University of Western Australia reported[589b] nanomechanical cross-talk between chilli and basil plants for optimum growth. Jim Westwood at Virginia Tech in the USA has also uncovered[589c] a hidden mRNA-based[589d] 'language' in plants.

239

These extraordinary revelations show that human linguistics and metacognition – key enablers of our complex societies – can't be fully explained in terms of the biology we share with other living things. So, just *why* are we endowed with these unique tools? Can naturalistic research help us identify or infer a plausible end-goal?

Our place in nature

The position of earth (and humans) within the cosmos was vigorously debated by ancient scholars. Plato and Aristotle's *geocentric* model placed the *earth* at the centre of our observable universe. However, fellow Greek astronomer and mathematician Aristarchus of Samos (c. 310 – 230 BC) argued[590a] that the *sun* was the centre around which other planets revolved – a *heliocentric* model that went against the prevailing convention. Despite supporting calculations produced[590b] by Aristarchus, the traditional geocentric model was later adopted by Greco-Egyptian scholar Claudius Ptolemy (c. AD 100 – 170) to devise a system of planetary and solar epicycles[590c] that became the accepted standard for almost 1,500 years.

Christian theologians supported geocentrism as it accorded with religious conviction that humans are the centrepiece of God's creation. However, posthumous publication of Nicolaus Copernicus' *De revolutionibus orbium coelestium* (On the Revolutions of the Heavenly Spheres) in 1543 initiated a slow shift to heliocentrism. Copernicus, Johannes Kepler (1571 – 1630) and Galileo Galilei (1564 – 1642) showed that the earth revolves around the sun; not the other way round. The matter was finally settled in 1687 when Isaac Newton formulated heliocentric laws of motion and universal gravitation. In the mid-20th century, an extended *Copernican principle* emerged that denies[591] we're privileged observers on a uniquely placed earth: humans are relegated to a chance development on a planet among billions in our galaxy that just happens to be habitable.

240

Implications

As Princeton University astrophysicist J. Richard Gott III noted in a 1993 article[592a], demoting humans to *random* rather than *purposive* origination vastly reduces chances that our species will survive to colonise the galaxy. It's also at odds with hopes for a post-biological[592b] existence or 'resurrection' of some sort. But assertions of human mediocrity are hard to square with our unique cognitive capacity to forge abstract solutions to difficult problems.

Complexity scientist and technologist Samuel Arbesman discussed these contradictions in a 2011 essay[593a]: *"as far as we know, we're the only species that can actually recognize its place in the universe. The paradox of the Copernican Principle is that, by properly understanding our place, even if it be rather humbling, we can only then truly understand our surroundings. And by being able to do that, we don't seem so small or insignificant after all."* This view was echoed in Mario Livio's review[593b] of astrobiologist Caleb Scharf's *The Copernicus Complex* (2014). Livio cited Scharf's verdict that *"our place in the universe is special but not significant, unique but not exceptional"* and pointed out: *"notwithstanding our physical insignificance, the human mind is significant. Why? Because all the discoveries described in this book, from the subatomic realm to the multiverse, were made by us."*

In any case, there's no scientific evidence that humans are cosmologically insignificant – even an indirect test[594a,b] of Copernican assumptions in 2008 proved inconclusive[594c]. On the contrary, continued failure to detect intelligent beings elsewhere suggests we might, indeed, be a rarity in the cosmos. As physicist and astronomer Marcelo Gleiser explained in a September 2021 article[594d], the issue is philosophical rather than scientific: *"So, to blindly extend the Copernican principle to guide our thoughts about Earth in comparison to other worlds when it comes to habitability is not just a false extrapolation but also imprudent. We simply do not know enough to make such pronouncements."*

Rights and responsibilities

Whatever might exist elsewhere in the universe, there's growing awareness that our status as conscious observers on earth comes with the responsibility to nurture and sustain our enabling environment. In particular, our human-centred approach to life has become increasingly controversial as new evidence emerges that other animals may have significant cognitive and emotional capacities that merit some of the automatic rights we afford all persons.

A 2014 study[595a] by a team at Queen Mary University of London (QMUL) found[595b] that goats can solve complicated tasks quickly and remember the details for up to *10 months* – an indication of far more intelligence and memory recall than previously imagined. Octopuses have amazed researchers with their ability to learn[596a] tasks by observation[596b] and adapt behaviour[596c] to tackle unpredictable and evolving challenges[596d]. Elephants are noted[597a] for displays of compassion, cooperation, grief and death rituals[597b] – human-like traits that philosopher and economist Don Ross has argued[597c] may well qualify these fascinating creatures for extended 'personhood'.

Some reports suggest other animals even experience high and low moods like humans. Another QMUL study published in 2016 showed[598a] that bumble bees display a 'good mood' after drinking[598b] very sweet water. Researchers at Johns Hopkins University in Maryland discovered[598c] in 2018 that octopuses – notorious loners – displayed[598d] unusual sociality when given the party drug MDMA (known on the street as *ecstasy*). Molecular biologists at Bar Ilan University in Israel also found[598e] that male fruit flies deprived of mating ingest more alcohol from fermented fruits. Neuroethologist Lars Chittka and psychologist Catherine Wilson commented[598f] in a review: *"This suggests that intentional 'sensation adjustment', or even 'mood adjustment', is widespread across the animal kingdom – which strongly suggests that animals have inner experiences. [....] After all, why would an organism seek out mind-altering substances when there isn't a mind to alter?"*

242

These startling findings make uncomfortable reading for scientists engaged in non-human animal experiments that require intrusive and debilitating procedures. Inevitably, calls are growing[599a] for bioethical considerations to be extended to non-humans. In 2015, plant scientists at University of Adelaide in Australia stunned colleagues with a report[599b] that showed even this 'green' form of life that lacks a heart or nervous system responds[599c] to stress with animal-like signals.

A wider biocentrism

Since the late 20th century, activists have been campaigning for a paradigm shift[600a] from *anthropocentrism* to a new *eco-centrism* that recognises and respects the rights of *all* living things to exist and thrive alongside humans. In 2018, sociologist Eileen Crist warned[600b] that *"human expansionism is causing mass extinction of nonhuman life and threatening both ecological and societal stability"* and conservationists Hannah Mumby and Joshua Plotnik appealed[600c] for policymakers to view human-elephant conflicts from the perspective of *elephants.*

However, geologist and philosopher Richard Watson pointed out in a 1983 critique[600d] that the argument by 'ecosophers' for inclusive personhood is self-defeating because the very notion that humans have custodial responsibility for other living things is implicit admission of our special role and status in nature. Watson wrote:

"A fully egalitarian biocentric ethic would place no more restrictions on the behavior of human beings than on the behavior of any other animals. Uncontrolled human behavior might lead to the destruction of the environment and thus to the extinction of human beings. I thus conclude that human interest in survival is the best ground on which to argue for an ecological balance which is good both for human beings and for the whole biological community."

243

Biocentrism advocates have since expanded the campaign to include 'plant rights'. In 2008, Switzerland's *Federal Ethics Committee on Non-Human Biotechnology* (ECNH) issued a report[601a] titled 'The Dignity of Living Beings with Regard to Plants' that concluded[601b] plants too are entitled to 'dignity', including the right not to be destroyed arbitrarily. Israeli plant scientist Simcha Lev-Yadun warned[601c] in a letter to the journal *Plant Signaling & Behavior* that the Swiss proposal was *"the first step on the road to absurd land"* where vital agricultural research for enhanced food cultivation is outlawed. But ECNH member Florianne Koechlin vigorously defended their position in a response[601d] that cited new discoveries about plant 'sensitivities' and rudimentary ability to *"distinguish between self and non-self."* Koechlin declared:

> *"We do not know if plants are capable of subjective sensation. There is no scientific proof that plants feel pain. But it is also quite clear that we cannot simply rule this out. There is circumstantial evidence for this, although not a complete chain of evidence. However, claims that plants have no subjective sensations are as speculative as the opposite. We simply do not know. We cannot deny with certainty that plants lack an ability to actively perceive. Thus far, plant abilities to perceive their environment has been widely underestimated."*

The ECNH stance is highly controversial, but it has won support in some quarters. Philosopher Michael Marder argued in a 2013 essay[602a] that extending formal rights to plants may be the only way to halt their extinction and reverse environmental degradation. Plant neurobiologist Stefano Mancuso contended in *Brilliant Green* (a 2015 book co-authored with journalist Alessandra Viola) that plants are 'intelligent' organisms that deserve rights[602b]. These developments have alarmed anthropocentrists: the fear is that reduction of our species to the same level as others will undermine centuries of progress that shaped the notion of human dignity.

In his 2014 book *The War on Humans*, American lawyer and bioethicist Wesley J. Smith accused[603a] environmental militants of treating humans as *"Public Enemy #1"*. Smith claimed organisations like *The Nonhuman Rights Project* are on a covert mission *"to reduce the human population by up to 90% and to grant legal rights to animals, plants, and Mother Earth."* He warned that this 'anti-human' activism will further victimise the poorest and most vulnerable people. However, ethicist and philosopher Thomas I. White – who designated[603b] dolphins as 'non-human persons' at the 2012 annual meeting of the American Association for the Advancement of Science (AAAS) in Vancouver, Canada – denied[603c] such proposals amount to 'social equality' for non-humans or usurpation of human privileges.

Finding meaning

Battles over anthropocentrism are a subset of a much larger cultural controversy about the meaning of human existence. Even if we accept that we're not *exceptional* in nature, our species is undeniably extremely *privileged*. As New York University sociologist Gabriel Abend showed[604a] in a series of papers launched in 2011, the abstract traits that make us special are hard to explain scientifically. In 2016, Abend openly questioned[604b] whether it's even possible to clearly define phenomena like *"morality, empathy, art, love, creativity, or religious belief"* for empirical research.

British geneticist Adam Rutherford explored the paradox of our uniqueness (despite shared roots with other animals) in *The Book of Humans: The Story of How We Became Us* (2018). Rutherford's approach is grounded in Darwinian evolution, but he readily conceded in a feature article[605a] that *"Navigating this territory can be treacherous, and riven with contradictions [....] Prudent scepticism is required when we compare ourselves with other beasts. Evolution accounts for all life but not all traits are adaptations."*

Rutherford also acknowledged the huge challenges in any naturalistic quest for answers to the vexed question of human uniqueness:

"We are desperate to find the things that tip us over the edge from being merely an animal into Hamlet's paragon of animals. Was it our language? Was it religion, or music, or art, or any number of things that are not as unique to us as we had once thought? The truth is that it was all of these things and more, but crucially, it was in the engagement of our minds to transmit skills and ideas to others. We changed our societies and maximised how culture is transmitted. We took evolution's work, and by teaching each other, we created ourselves. The stories we tell about how we came to be who we are often neglect the complexity of biology and the oceans of time during which we evolved. To understand human evolution, we need new stories."

Science commentator Robin McKie commended Rutherford's effort in a review[605b], but he noted that the author struggles to identify *what* exactly makes humans special – the book offers no new insights or revolutionary conclusions. The 'new stories' Rutherford calls for will not be scientifically meaningful unless they provide *plausible* and *testable* explanations for our extraordinary endowments.

Clearly, the extent to which we can research our own evolution is limited – we're an integral part of nature and can't 'step outside' for insights. Furthermore, we're severely constrained by genetically-programmed cognitive limits and are thus unable to investigate a possible deeper reality that transcends our mortal state. However, philosopher of science Nicholas Maxwell expressed optimism in a May 2019 essay[605c] that progress can be made if theorists return to the metaphysics and natural philosophy that defined science before the 19th century. Maxwell argued the idea *"that science must appeal only to evidence, and must not make metaphysical assumptions about the nature of the universe independently of evidence, is untenable, and must be rejected."*

Thus, several existential questions that have long perplexed humans remain unanswered. Is our metaconsciousness a gateway to a deeper reality? Do other living things perceive different shades of reality? Are we meant to use our unique metacognition to transcend our mortal state? Is our emergence in a self-contained and self-regulating biosphere at this point in time a purely chance event, a teleological inevitability, or a preordained manifestation? Perhaps the broad-minded approach advocated by Maxwell will yield a coherent explanation that recognises life is *purposive*; a development that may help provide the sense of meaning we all so desperately crave.

Why are we religious?

Arguably, our most intriguing feature is the intuitive, universal sense of supernatural agency that's inspired moral frameworks and societal cohesion[606a] in *every* community. Human embrace of religion (especially worship of divinities) is truly unique[606b]; the phenomenon has never been observed in other creatures. Ritualistic burial, regarded as our earliest sacred expression, has been traced back[607a] to at least[607b] 32,000 years ago. A decade-long international study[607c] published in 2013 showed[607d] even our primitive Neanderthal predecessors indulged in similar practices – a surprising discovery that added to[607e] already profound questions about human existence. Where did our spiritual awareness and religiosity come from and why has it persisted for millennia?

Religious belief may have declined[608a] in Western societies, but, as a Pew study[608b] revealed in 2012, an estimated *84 percent* of people worldwide continue to identify with traditional faiths. Even ancient superstitions[608c] and paganism are making a comeback. After nearly 1,000 years of mainstream Christianity in Iceland, neo-pagans revived[608d] official worship of Viking-age Norse gods in 2015 – complete with a high-priest and public temple. These developments indicate spirituality is embedded in the human psyche.

Socio-evolutionary perspective

Renowned American sociologist Robert Bellah argued in his 2011 classic review[609a] *Religion in Human Evolution* that, given its persistence and pervasiveness throughout recorded history, religion must be fulfilling[609b] important needs that have *practical* value for humans. For Bellah, religion has been the undoubted wellspring for evolution of human culture and social bonding. As he explained in a feature article[609c], his mammoth work was inspired by a desire to understand religious meaning in the context of our 'here and now' condition; regardless of belief in God or hopes for an afterlife.

Bellah's hypothesis was supported by a study[610a] published in 2012 by Cambridge University anthropologists Hervey Peoples and Frank Marlowe. They traced progression of supernaturalism from foraging to agricultural and pastoral subsistence societies and concluded that *"belief in moral High Gods was fostered by emerging leaders in societies dependent on resources that were difficult to manage and defend without group cooperation."* A subsequent reconstruction of evolving religiosity among hunter-gatherers conducted with Czech zoologist Pavel Duda suggests *animism* (ascribing spiritual essence to other animals and environmental objects) is likely the oldest form of religion. The researchers reported[610b] in 2016: *"Belief in an afterlife emerged, followed by shamanism and ancestor worship. Ancestor spirits or high gods who are active in human affairs were absent in early humans."*

However, as Havard University evolutionary biologist Manvir Singh showed in a 2017 article[611a,b], humans have long induced trances to supplicate favours from perceived *higher forces*. A shamanic burial site unearthed[611c] in Israel in 2008 was dated at 12,000 years; the same age as the mysterious Göbekli Tepe[611d] stone circles in Turkey. These discoveries indicate personal spirituality and ritualistic worship arose much earlier in human history than thought.

248

Our capacity for existential contemplation (linked to religiosity) is also quite ancient. In 2018, a team led by Christopher Henshilwood from University of Bergen in Norway announced[612a] discovery of a 73,000-year-old graphic drawing in South Africa's famous Blombos cave. A toolkit with containers of red ochre paint was also found[612b] in older layers of the cave – indicating that human graphic expression may have started up to 100,000 years ago. There's even speculation[613a] that our unique ability to express inner thoughts may go back to the (still elusive) common ancestor[613b] of modern humans and Neanderthals who lived[613c] over *one million* years ago.

Diversity driver

A new research field of *Evolutionary Religious Studies* (ERS) has been exploring the impacts of religion on *cultural diversity* and *group identity*. In *Darwin's Cathedral* (2002), ERS pioneer David Sloan Wilson discussed the vital contribution of religion in shaping[614a] 'socially fit' humans at both individual and group levels. In 2016, Wilson and Oxford University anthropologist Harvey Whitehouse co-authored[614b] a call for empirical investigation of religion as a tool for evolution of our hugely diverse societies; just as[614c] nature's biological web has spawned diverse ecosystems. The paper was part of a series hosted by the journal *Religion, Brain & Behavior* to mark[614d] the 15th anniversary of Wilson's seminal book.

Neuroscientist Patrick McNamara and philosopher of religion Wesley Wildman have co-founded an *Institute for the Bio-Cultural Study of Religion* (IBCSR) in Boston, Massachusetts to promote collaborative research across diverse fields – including medical and computational sciences, sociology, anthropology, and the humanities. Activities include a *Simulating Religion Project* (SRP) that aims *"to develop software that will simulate the cognitive-emotional mental processes and social interactions that mediate the effects of religion on social and cultural systems."*

The idea of religion as an evolutionary tool for human diversity is certainly plausible. It helps to explain why humans still hold such widely differing perceptions of the divine. Some belief systems cite one or more deities that may be intrinsic or extrinsic to nature. Others involve no deities at all. Yet others are built on ancestral veneration and worship. What they all share is a profound sense of the sacred and deep awareness of our mortal limitations.

Programmed for religion

Another field called *Cognitive Science of Religion* (CSR) is investigating[615a] how and why humans (especially young children) *intuitively* perceive a *purposefully designed* world and supernatural creator. CSR findings indicate[615b] religiosity is an *innate* trait (similar to music and language) that emerges naturally in our consciousness. The idea that we're *programmed* from birth to perceive a transcendent cause for all that exists is anathema[615c] to atheistic materialists. Nevertheless, evidence is mounting that religiosity is *embedded* in our brain circuitry.

In 2003, neuroscientists at Karolinska Institute in Sweden identified[616a] the mood-altering biochemical *serotonin* as a definite catalyst for spiritual experiences. Some colleagues were sceptical[616b], but American geneticist Dean Hamer embraced the concept and suggested that a gene that codes for the protein *VMAT2* (which regulates the flow of neurotransmitters like serotonin in the brain) is the agent that 'hardwires' humans for spirituality and religiosity. Hamer outlined the research[616b] from which he drew his conclusion in *The God Gene* (2005); albeit readily conceding[616c] that reducing all human transcendental experience to a single gene was a gross oversimplification since several other genetic factors and complex environmental influences were likely involved. Still, clerics that view spiritual enlightenment as a *divine gift* rather than a genetic disposition were not impressed.

250

English theoretical physicist and theologian John Polkinghorne commented[616e] in a media report: *"The idea of a God gene goes against all my personal theological convictions. You can't cut faith down to the lowest common denominator of genetic survival. It shows the poverty of reductionist thinking."* Hamer responded that his findings were perfectly compatible with belief in God. As he put it: *"Religious believers can point to the existence of God genes as one more sign of the Creator's ingenuity — a clever way to help humans acknowledge and embrace a divine presence."*

Despite the controversy, interest in possible brain mechanisms for spirituality has grown – a new, multidisciplinary field of *neurotheology* has attracted several scientists and philosophers. Rutgers University evolutionary biologist Lionel Tiger explained[617a] in 2010 why colleagues believe such studies will help to explain religiosity:

"One of the ways of looking at religion is to what extent and how does it generate the serotonergic juices that make us feel good. Religion may be one of the main producers of the brain-soothing phenomenon in a way that is not that expensive or destructive or difficult. All you have to do is show up Sunday morning."

Andrew Newberg, a neuroscientist and leading neurotheology pioneer, has applied[617b] techniques like *nuclear tomographic imaging* (SPECT) to investigate possible neural correlates for religiosity at Thomas Jefferson University (TJU) in Philadelphia. Interestingly, an interdisciplinary study[617c] published in 2010 by Italian researchers found that damage to specific brain regions can alter a person's level of *"self-transcendence"* – a neurophysiological correlation Newberg had suggested[617d] in 2007. The functional link was confirmed[618a] in a 2012 study by neuropsychologists at University of Missouri (MU) which also noted[618b] that spiritual experiences appear to emanate from *several* parts of the brain rather than any specific 'God spot' – although certain areas like the frontal lobe showed more activity.

The neural complexity of religiosity was further emphasised by a 2014 fMRI imaging study[619a] led by Gopikrishna Deshpande – an electrical and computer engineer from Auburn University in Alabama. Deshpande's group linked[619b] religiosity to at least *three* cognitive dimensions in separate brain regions. Five years later, another study[619c] led by Yale University psychiatrist Marc Potenza narrowed the search to the[619d] brain's left inferior parietal lobule (IPL), its medial thalamus, and caudate regions.

However, there's still no definitive neurobiological framework to explain exactly *how* the brain induces religiosity and spiritual experiences. But the *language* people use to describe these events is remarkably consistent – a 2015 computational analysis[620a] by Newberg's team at TJU identified[620b] similar linguistic features in nearly 800 reports. An independent study[620c] by researchers at University of Utah also showed[620d] spiritual experiences activate *the same* brain reward circuits which 'light up' during euphoric states associated with narcotics, love and music.

Is spiritual blindness epigenetic?

Despite the overwhelming evidence that religiosity and spirituality are genetically embedded in humans, some scholars continue to dismiss these profound and largely unexplained phenomena as foolhardy indulgence by ignorant or simple-minded people.

In 2013, a team of psychologists led by Miron Zuckerman from the University of Rochester in New York concluded from a meta-analysis[621a] of 63 studies (published between 1928 and 2012) that religious people are less intelligent than atheists. The authors reasserted this provocative finding in a 2019 update[621b] – albeit noting that *"Additional empirical and theoretical work is needed to resolve this issue."*

Another analytical report[621c] in 2017 by Richard Daws and Adam Hampshire from Imperial College London opened:

"It is well established that religiosity correlates inversely with intelligence. [...] We report that atheists surpass religious individuals in terms of reasoning but not working-memory performance. [...] These results support the hypothesis that behavioral biases rather than impaired general intelligence underlie the religiosity effect."

The work found no actual evidence that religiosity negatively impacts *"real-world achievement"*, but Daws and Hampshire mooted future research to test *"whether cognitive training may counter biases of the religious mind toward intuitive decision-making."* However, 'intelligence' is a nebulous concept that's still contested[622a] while religiosity is a universally evolved instinct with proven psychological benefits. In particular, the sample demographic for comparison greatly influences results. As evolutionary psychologist Nigel Barber pointed out in a 2010 article[622b]: *"Atheists are probably more intelligent than religious people because they benefit from many social conditions that happen to be correlated with loss of religious belief. [...] I doubt that religion causes stupidity if only because some of the most brilliant people of history, such as Isaac Newton, were highly religious like most of their contemporaries."*

Indeed, University of Florida psychologists Gregory Webster and Ryan Duffy showed[623a] in a 2016 analysis that intelligence–religiosity associations become insignificant when cultural factors and socio-economic environment are added to computations. Furthermore, psychology surveys that claim to confirm intellectual superiority of unbelievers suffer from systemic flaws. As Warren Mansell from University of Manchester and Vyv Huddy from University College London discussed in a 2018 essay[623b], the highly suggestive and biased nature of research models has severely damaged integrity and caused a confidence crisis. Coventry University psychologist Miguel Farias also showed in a January 2021 review[623c] how skewed parameters and subjective interpretation of data in so-called 'neuro-atheism' studies has led to results that are contradictory and unreliable.

Overriding religiosity

Intriguingly, neuroscientific findings are indicating[624a] that *unbelief* (not belief) is the odd human condition. Research is underway to determine how unbelievers manage to 'override' their natural religiosity. Already, significant *physiological* differences are emerging between the brains of believers and nonbelievers. Andrew Newberg explained[624b] in 2012:

> *"Several studies have revealed that people who practice meditation or have prayed for many years exhibit increased activity and have more brain tissue in their frontal lobes, regions associated with attention and reward, as compared with people who do not meditate or pray. A more recent study revealed that people who have had "born again" experiences have a smaller hippocampus, a part of the brain involved in emotions and memory, than atheists do. [...]*

> *"Research also suggests that a religious brain exhibits higher levels of dopamine, a hormone associated with increased attention and motivation. A study showed that believers were much more likely than skeptics to see words and faces on a screen when there were none, whereas skeptics often did not see words and faces that were actually there. Yet when skeptics were given the drug L-dopa, which increases the amount of dopamine in the brain, they were just as likely to interpret scrambled patterns as words and faces as were the religious individuals."*

However, Newberg stressed that a full explanation for observed differences is still lacking; the neural picture for religiosity is far from complete and researchers *"do not have a clear way to connect all the dots."* Evidently, a lot more neurotheological research is needed before firm conclusions can be reached. But, it's looking increasingly likely that spiritual blindness is a *handicap* (not asset) resulting from culturally-induced epigenetic silencing of our natural biological predisposition for belief in a supernatural agency and religion.

Debate continues over the reasons for sustained high levels of religiosity across divergent cultures, *despite* huge advances in education and technology. As Sharon Begley concluded in a 2001 feature article[625]:

"For all the tentative successes that scientists are scoring in their search for the biological bases of religious, spiritual and mystical experience, one mystery will surely lie forever beyond their grasp. They may trace a sense of transcendence to this bulge in our gray matter. And they may trace a feeling of the divine to that one. But it is likely that they will never resolve the greatest question of all--namely, whether our brain wiring creates God, or whether God created our brain wiring. Which you believe is, in the end, a matter of faith."

Return of the occult

Since the late 1960s, Western culture has witnessed a surprising revival[626a] of interest in the paranormal alongside disenchantment with organised religion. Of course, superstitions have always been a major part of folklore: many beliefs and practices have endured[626b] and are regarded as relatively harmless eccentricities; if somewhat bemusing to cynics. But sociologists have become increasingly worried[626c] that new trends, driven by largely unproven claims in the popular media, are encouraging adoption of occultism as an alternative source of spiritual empowerment.

Belief in spirits and apparitions is particularly widespread[627a], even in sophisticated societies. Many residents in Dumbarton, Scotland have become convinced that nearby Overtoun Bridge is rife with paranormal activity – over 600 dogs have suddenly jumped off[627b] the 15 metres (50 feet) high structure in mysterious 'suicide attempts' since the 1950s, resulting in dozens of canine deaths. Locals believe[627c] the hapless creatures become infused with the spirit of a grieving widow who died in the 1930s.

In 2010, the Centre for Cultural Studies at Sussex University (SU) in England hosted a conference to explore *"the cultural context and functions of the paranormal and the supernatural in popular culture, literature and visual culture and in everyday life."* The organisers commented[628]: *"The recent increase in popularity of all things paranormal across literature, art and popular culture suggests not only a reinvigorated interest in notions of the paranormal but possibly also new functions and pleasures of these fascinations and pursuits ..."*

The SU event was so successful that investigators were invited to submit academic papers on phenomena discussed; a selection of which were subsequently published in *The Ashgate Research Companion to Paranormal Cultures* (2013) edited by SU's Sally Munt and Olu Jenzen from the University of Brighton. The work marked a new watershed in scholarly rehabilitation of occultism.

American journalist and author Michelle Goldberg suggested in a 2017 article[629a] that the rise in witchcraft belief and practice among millennials stems from feelings of helplessness and powerlessness. According to Goldberg, people are re-embracing 'magic' as an imagined shield against misfortune, and a tool for reasserting control over one's destiny in an increasingly chaotic 'post-everything' world.

Goldberg's assessment was echoed by Tanya Ghahremani in a December 2019 essay[629b]: she defended the explosion of interest in astrology and horoscopes among female millennials as a benign pursuit that gives women a sense of purpose and encouragement in these insecure times. Ghahremani elaborated: *"It empowers women in particular to take more control over their future; it encourages us to learn more about ourselves and go confidently in the direction that makes the most sense for our well being. Sure, it's not a proven science. But much like other kinds of spiritual and religious faith, it doesn't have to be to make a difference in the lives of those who believe in it."*

Predictably, a huge industry has emerged to service this growing[630a] 'spiritual but not religious' demographic. As Kari Paul noted in a 2017 market report[630b]: *"The psychic services industry — which includes astrology, aura reading, mediumship, tarot-card reading and palmistry, among other metaphysical services — grew 2% between 2011 and 2016. It is now worth $2 billion annually, according to industry analysis firm IBIS World."*

The trend looks set to continue with a proliferation[630c] of brands now using online stores and social media to garner clients. In a 2018 feature article[630d], Amanda Montell profiled the extraordinary success of *"mystical millennials who are spellbinding the internet"* with Big Witch Energy (BWE). Lynn Garrett confirmed in a 2019 book review[630e] that witchcraft is now *"one of the hot trends in the mind-body-spirit category"* of bestsellers in an age now branded 'Season of the Witch'.

But there's a dark side. Some new-age witches engage in malicious activity against people they disagree with, or against whom they seek to dispense 'retributive justice' for real and imagined slights. In her book *Finding Magic* (2017), well-known American journalist and media personality Sally Quinn revealed[631a] she hailed from a Christian family of Scottish origin that also practised Voodoo. Astonishingly, Quinn claimed[631b] at least two people had died from 'hexes' cast by her mother and that she too had cast evil spells that caused the death of three people.

Starting in February 2017, an alliance of neo-occultists opposed to President Trump gathered across the USA to cast 'binding spells' at the stroke of midnight on waning crescent moon days (associated with weakening). According to media reports[631c,d], the so-called 'Magic Resistance' chanted over Tarot cards, candles, pins and other paraphernalia: *"Hear me, oh spirits of Water, Fire, Earth, and Air, heavenly hosts, demons of the infernal realms, and spirits of the ancestors ... I call upon you to bind Donald J. Trump so that his malignant works may fail utterly."*

However, experiences elsewhere suggest witchcraft is far from being a solution to personal problems and societal ills. In 2016, American economist Boris Gershman published a study[632a] conducted in countries with a culture of superstition that showed[632b] widespread beliefs in witchcraft correlate with high levels of interpersonal and communal mistrust. The review confirmed anecdotal evidence that, unlike other supernatural beliefs, witchcraft is particularly harmful – it fuels paranoia, erodes social capital, and impedes economic progress.

Changing concepts of God

In ancient belief systems, an ultimate God was not[633a] an entity that could be physically defined. Rather, the notion represented an abstract and absolute infinity outside nature; an eternal singularity from which everything that exists springs. However, much confusion has arisen because of our tendency to assign human attributes to real or perceived entities when describing relationships. Hence, the original *figurative* notion of God (a purely philosophical and demonstrative concept) has gradually morphed into[633b] a definable deity with human-like emotions and intentionality – especially in Abrahamic religions. This contrived imagery underlies much of today's cultural battles over God and religion.

Aristotle's argument for a 'prime mover' or 'first cause' of all motion in the universe is widely cited[634a] as the source for Western anthropomorphic representations of God. However, Aristotle actually described[634b] an *abstraction* that had *no form*. It was a mere metaphysical illustration[634c] of a universal *nous* (intellect or mind), from which he imagined humans derive essence and thinking faculties. In fact, it was the Aristotelian concept of God that inspired German philosopher Immanuel Kant's 18th century distinction between unknowable *noumena* that we're incapable of sensing, and material *phenomena* that we can sense and investigate empirically.

British theologian Terry Eagleton is renowned for his contention in several publications that the Christian concept of God, in particular, is both misconstrued and misunderstood. He explained in a 2006 review[635a] of Richard Dawkins' book *The God Delusion*:

"For Judeo-Christianity, God is not a person in the sense that Al Gore arguably is. Nor is he a principle, an entity, or "existent": in one sense of that word it would be perfectly coherent for religious types to claim that God does not in fact exist. He is, rather, the condition of possibility of any entity whatsoever, including ourselves. He is the answer to why there is something rather than nothing."

As Damon Linker pointed out[635b] in 2015, American philosopher and theologian David Bentley Hart's *The Experience of God* (2013) provides ample examples of similar 'condition of possibility' definitions in other faiths. This thought-provoking concept is far-removed[635c] from the simplistic notion of God that atheists constantly seek to discredit with science-based arguments. Hence, prominent Unitarian Universalist minister Galen Guengerich argued passionately in his book *God Revised* (2013) that the Western concept of God needs urgent updating in the light of new discoveries and social evolution.

Guengerich expressed concern in a commentary[636a] that failure to adapt might mean *"increasingly empty houses of worship will become a sad symbol of a deeper vacancy in our lives and our culture."* He asserted that the idea of God as a supernatural, omniscient entity is no longer tenable; but opined this *"doesn't mean that God is a fantasy and religion is a farce."* However, as observed in a *Publishers Weekly* book review[636b], Guengerich's approach reduces God to an entity which is *"difficult to define and must constantly be subjected to the latest scientific reasoning."* Indeed, it's hard to conceive a paradigm for human understanding of God (other than faith) that won't be overtaken by new knowledge.

Contemporary thinkers have sought to disentangle early philosophical and spiritual concepts of God from the personified deity with human attributes that now dominates Western culture and discourse. In *The Case for God: What religion really means* (2010), former Catholic nun and prolific writer Karen Armstrong traced ancient traditions and described[637a] the mysticism which inspired societal practices and culture for millennia. She explained that concepts of God and religion which arouse such vehement opposition among arch-materialists like Dawkins are relatively recent human constructs grounded in doctrinal belief and dogma.

Armstrong's ultimate message[637b] is that God is an *unknowable entity* that can't be defined or reduced to a testable scientific hypothesis. However, many Christians will likely struggle to reconcile an intangible, abstract concept of God with a religion that emphasises a *personal* relationship. Thus, while psychologist Gregg Henriques found[637c] Armstrong's approach to be *"A potentially workable conception of God"*, John Loftus, another former minister who lost faith, criticised[637d] her book as a *"metaphysically unfulfilling and deeply inadequate"* thesis that had no practical relevance for life.

A naturalistic divinity?

Some materialists deny the existence of any reality outside nature, *but* still admit to a sense of awe and wonder at natural phenomena and the underlying laws that make anything possible. Prominent English evolutionary biologist and atheist Julian Huxley wrote in his famous 1964 essay[638a] *The New Divinity*: *"Some events and some phenomena of outer nature transcend ordinary explanation and ordinary experience. They inspire awe and seem mysterious, explicable only in terms of something beyond or above ordinary nature. [....] Such events and such experience merit a special designation. For want of a better, I use the term divine, though this quality of divinity is not truely supernatural but transnatural -- it grows out of ordinary nature, but transcends it."*

Huxley advocated Humanism – a worldview that emphasises humanity's responsibility for promotion of altruism, ethics and social justice *without* coercion from deities or religious penal codes. However, his vision for universal replacement of a supernatural God (a concept he dismissed as *"an outdated piece of ideological furniture"*) with a naturalistic divinity he hoped would inspire[638b] an *"evolutionary and humanist religion of fulfilment"* has failed. A 2018 Pew survey[638c] showed up to 90 per cent of Americans (including the non-religious) still believe in a higher power or spiritual force *outside* nature – the figure is even greater[638d] worldwide.

American biologist Ursula Goodenough's seminal work *The Sacred Depths of Nature* (1998) launched a new movement that seeks to channel human yearning for spiritual fulfilment and moral order into an 'eco-divinity' which recognises our interrelatedness and interdependence with all that exists *within* nature. As she explained in a 2014 article[639a]: *"Religious naturalists seek to develop coherent and satisfying meta-versions of their interpretive, spiritual and moral responses to the natural world."* According to Goodenough, this involves exploring the meaning of life with *"awe and wonder, gratitude, assent, commitment, humility, reverence, joy and the astonishment of being alive at all."* God, in this sense, becomes a metaphor that 'personifies' reality and connotes *"the unknown and perhaps unknowable substrate of order"* or *"a large and important concept within the natural world"* such as love. There's also a strong focus on societal cooperation and human responsibility for ecological and environmental sustainability.

Goodenough's approach was echoed in sympathetic books like[639b] Neil deGrasse Tyson's *Cosmic Perspective* (2007) and[639c] Sean M. Carroll's *The Big Picture* (2016). But hard-core 'New Atheists'[639d] like Richard Dawkins, who espouse scientism, dismiss the notion of 'religious' or 'poetic' naturalism as just another cultish God delusion.

261

However, Stuart Kauffman begged to differ in a 2006 essay[639e]:

"This emerging view finds a natural scientific place for value and ethics, and places us as co-creators of the enormous web of emerging complexity that is the evolving biosphere and human economics and culture. In this scientific world view, we can ask: Is it more astonishing that a God created all that exists in six days, or that the natural processes of the creative universe have yielded galaxies, chemistry, life, agency, meaning, value, consciousness, culture without a Creator. In my mind and heart, the overwhelming answer is that the truth as best we know it, that all arose with no Creator agent, all on its wondrous own, is so awesome and stunning that it is God enough for me and I hope much of humankind."

Computer scientist and author Jaron Lanier agreed with Kauffman that *"It's important to acknowledge what one believes instead of pretending not to believe in anything, which is almost always a form of self-delusion."* But he cautioned that one should remain wary about the tendency of simple expressions of spirituality to morph into 'dangerous religion'.

Virtual godhood

The Church of Jesus Christ of Latter-day Saints (LDS) teaches that God was once mortal before He achieved perfection and gained exaltation into immortality. LDS adherents, also known as Mormons, believe all humans have the potential to attain godhood[640] (become like God) with full divine attributes; including the power to create other sentient beings.

Advances in transhumanist technologies have inspired[641a] a new way of conceptualising God in line with LDS beliefs. American technologist and philosopher Lincoln Cannon has pioneered[641b] a version of Mormon transhumanism that he believes offers a plausible route to achieving[641c] LDS promises of transfiguration and exaltation into immortal godhood.

In 2008, Cannon formulated a *New God Argument* (NGA)[641d] that fuses traditional Christian Mormonism with secular transhumanism to show why faith in God is logical. Essentially, Cannon argued that if we believe humans have the potential to create immortal post-humans through 'technological transcendence' then we must accept that a *prior* more compassionate *"superhumanity"* is likely responsible for our own existence.

Cannon's NGA echoes philosopher Nick Bostrom's 2003 Simulation Argument (SA)[642a] that we're virtual projections[642b] within a computer simulation run by advanced post-humans who achieved technological transcendence eons ago. However, Timothy Killian assessed in a detailed review[643a,b] that NGA *"simply does not hold"* because *"it is built upon unwarranted premises."* Killian wrote:

> *"NGA set a high bar for itself, claiming to logically prove new and novel arguments related to God and Faith. The best theologians and philosophers in history have been unable to achieve such lofty goals. Neither has Cannon. [...] NGA offers no new facts or argumentation beyond what is contained in Bostrom's SA, and yet Cannon claims to be able to reach grandiose conclusions previously not known to be achieved by any prior philosophers or theologians."*

Cannon responded that[643c,d] Killian's analysis contained *"interesting"* observations but was weak and riddled with *"numerous logical errors"* and *"mischaracterizations of NGA, the Simulation Argument (SA), and their relationship."* He denied that NGA relied exclusively on SA and asserted: *"NGA relies on SA for the foundation and structure of one assumption. There are four other assumptions that are related to SA only to the extent that they are all part of NGA. [...] Even that one assumption extends beyond the scope of SA by generalizing it for any feasible creation mechanism. [...] Killian hardly scratched the surface in his critique."*

Cannon maintained that, regardless how strong or weak the underlying premises, NGA represents *"a formulation of valid logic that ties them together into what constitutes a momentous conclusion if the assumptions are true."* Nevertheless, as Killian pointed out, NGA (like all other secular arguments for God) still requires a 'leap of faith' into the unknown.

A necessary being

Interestingly, the most famous logical exposition for God was formulated almost 1,000 years ago by St. Anselm of Canterbury (c.1033 – 1109)[644a]. Anselm declared[644b] in his discourse *Proslogion* that even the errant fool mentioned in Psalm 14 who claims *"There is no God"* can be persuaded otherwise purely by analytical reasoning.

Starting from the premise that both believers and non-believers understand God as 'a being greater than any other that can be conceived', Anselm argued that such a being must also exist *in reality* because entities that actually exist are greater (have more substance) than those that only exist in our minds. It was, he contended, an absurdity to talk of a 'greatest being' which only exists in the mind since: (1) we could then repeatedly conjure up something even higher at will, and (2) that which exists in reality would always be greater than anything we can imagine. Therefore, Anselm concluded, since God is the greatest being conceivable by humans, He must also exist as the Supreme Being in reality.

This fascinating analysis was challenged in a critique[644c] titled *Liber pro Insipiente* (Latin for 'On Behalf of the Fool') by Benedictine monk Gaunilo of Marmoutiers. He counter-argued that: (1) it was necessary to show *"that which is greater than everything else that can be thought"* actually exists in the first place; (2) the form and nature of God is unknown and can't be conceived; and (3) Anselm's logic leads to the absurd conclusion that a mythical greatest or most perfect *"Lost Island"* which clearly doesn't exist *must* nevertheless exist in reality.

Anselm's response[644d] did not directly address Gaunilo's points: he protested instead that the monk had misunderstood his argument. But he clarified that imaginary entities are patently excluded as his thesis applied exclusively to God as a *"necessary being"* which had *always* existed; unlike temporal beings or things that are, by nature, transient and subject to change.

Despite nearly a millennium of contention, Anselm's ontological argument for God has endured[645a] and continues to fascinate scholars. In the 20th century, philosophers recast[645b] the proposition in terms of formal modal logic which addresses *possibility* as well as *necessity*. In a 1960 article[645c], American philosopher Norman Malcolm identified and extrapolated two distinct pieces of reasoning in Anselm's original writings. Fellow metaphysician Charles Hartshorne – famous for his dogged defence of philosophical theism – revived debate with his 1965 book[645d] *Anselm's Discovery*, an important contribution that helped to shape[645e] a modern version of the proposition. In another acclaimed book[645f] *The Nature of Necessity* (1974), Christian analytic philosopher Alvin Plantinga further refined[645g] the modal approach.

But the most significant development has been logician and analytic philosopher Kurt Gödel's use of a complex theorem based on six axioms to deduce mathematical proof[646a] for God in *higher-order* modal logic. Predictably, this extraordinary work (published posthumously in 1987) provoked fierce debate[646b]. Then, after twenty-six years of controversy, two computer scientists – Christoph Benzmüller of Berlin's Free University and Bruno Woltzenlogel Paleo of Vienna's Technical University – designed[646c] a test for Gödel's model with special 'assistant' software that allows automated theorem proving (ATP). Astonishingly, Benzmüller and Paleo reported[646d] in 2014: *"From Gödel's premises, the computer proved: necessarily, there exists God."* The result made headline news[646e] around the world.

265

7. Mystery of Consciousness

"It is widely agreed that experience arises from a physical basis, but we have no good explanation of why and how it so arises. Why should physical processing give rise to a rich inner life at all? [...] To explain experience, we need a new approach. The usual explanatory methods ... do not suffice."

David J. Chalmers, cognitive scientist and philosopher, in
Facing Up to the Problem of Consciousness (1995)[647]

What exactly is consciousness?

Traditionally, humans associate consciousness with 'being alive' and having capacity for physical and mental awareness. However, despite its familiarity and wide use of the term in mass media and academic literature, there's no consensus[648] on a *scientific* definition. The intriguing phenomenon is also applied to describe sleep/wake phases, sentient response, cognitive function and ability to have inner feelings and experiences. This loose interpretation has created much confusion and hindered debate on the extent to which consciousness can be used to distinguish 'living' from 'non-living'.

The 'hard' problem

In his seminal 1995 paper, David Chalmers separated[649a] 'easy' problems of consciousness that can be traced to *tangible* neural processes (sensory mechanisms, biochemical signalling, memories etc.) from 'hard' problems like *intangible* qualia[649b] (highly personal perceptions of stimuli like taste, smell, colour, pain, light, sound etc.). How exactly, he queried, do our widely-differing experiences, emotions and preferences arise from brain computations of *the same* environmental stimuli? Chalmers argued that, to make progress, cognitive scientists need to accept that these aspects of consciousness can't be investigated with the usual empirical tools.

266

Chalmers cited and concurred with American philosopher Joseph Levine's 1983 contention[649c] that the 'explanatory gap' between *universal* biological processes and *individual* sensual experiences may never be bridged by research that's focussed on observable matter. To bolster this point, Chalmers showed that a hypothetical being which had every physical attribute *but* lacked human-like qualia would remain[649d] just a 'philosophical zombie'[649e]. The crucial distinction is now the starting point for academic discussions about the subjective conscious experiences that make us unique beings.

However, contemporaries like Daniel Dennett[650a], Peter Hacker[650b] and Massimo Pigliucci[650c] deny there's a 'hard' problem; they argue that Chalmers' approach is misguided and misrepresents the issues. Nevertheless, over and above our outward physical features, internal conscious processes and phenomena are the best definition of 'self' and 'personhood'. As far as we know, this unique aspect of our being dies with us[650d] when we cease to exist biologically.

Are non-humans self-conscious?

Another hotly debated issue is whether *only* humans can be said to be truly conscious on the grounds no other creatures have self-awareness. Arguments have surfaced in recent decades that *all* living things (whether animals or plants) are self-conscious and should be treated accordingly. According to some cognitive ethicists, non-human animals also have[651a] human-like sentience. Lynn Margulis memorably contended[651b] in *The Conscious Cell* (2001) that even a unicellular organism can have 'microbial consciousness' – a startling possibility that others have further developed[651c]. However, although other living things may indeed be capable of subjective experience, there is no practicable way to investigate this since non-humans lack the capacity to communicate inner feelings and we can't simulate other minds.

American philosopher Thomas Nagel discussed the problem in his famous 1974 essay[652a,b] *What Is It Like to Be a Bat?*. He pointed out that explaining the sensory response[652c] of a bat in terms of detectable *brain* processes is very different to knowing how it perceives[652d] the world in terms of undetectable *mind* processes. In other words, what do bats (fellow mammals) think of their condition and circumstances? Are they even capable of such comprehension?

Peter Hacker insisted in a 2002 article[653a] that the issue is overblown and *"there are no mysteries beyond empirical ignorance and conceptual mystification."* However, as several studies of first-person perceptions[653b] have shown, we can never share or fully appreciate inner qualia and emotions experienced by others – regardless how vividly or comprehensively they are described by the experiencer.

A universal property

Some philosophers have long speculated that consciousness might be a fundamental phenomenon that permeates the *entire* universe. This notion of panpsychism[654a] – from the Greek words *pan* (all) and *psyche* (soul or mind) peaked in the 19th century before philosophy adopted the scientific emphasis on physical evidence. Thomas Nagel bravely defended panpsychism in his 1979 book *Mortal Questions* which crossed into[654b] theology, but the concept remained largely muted until respected theorists like philosopher Philip Goff[654c] and neuroscientist Christof Koch[654d] revived it in the 21st century. Among other things, advocates cite the mysterious ability of physical systems of all sizes to self-organise and their strange incompleteness at quantum level. Unlike vitalists that only see a 'spark of life' in biological systems, panpsychists ascribe a universal 'mind' to *everything* (living and non-living). This controversial approach to reality directly challenges[654e] the long-held view in science that *nothing* exists beyond what we can physically observe or detect.

Philosopher Tam Hunt and psychologist Jonathan Schooler at University of California (Santa Barbara) have even suggested[655a] that universal consciousness may stem from *"synchronized vibrations"* of matter. As they remarked in a 2011 article[655b]: *"Although speculative, these conjectures illustrate the type of alternative metaphysics that may be able to accommodate scientific observations without abandoning the self-evident facts that experience exists and time flows."*

David Chalmers agreed in a 2013 lecture[656a] that panpsychism offers a possible solution to the 'hard' problem of consciousness. However, prominent mind and language specialist John Searle previously dismissed the idea as *"absurd"* in a sharp 1997 exchange[656b] with Chalmers. Cognitive philosopher Keith Frankish also expressed scepticism in a 2016 essay[656c] that panpsychism is a viable solution to the conundrum – he asked:

"How do the micro-experiences of billions of subatomic particles in my brain combine to form the twinge of pain I'm feeling in my knee? If billions of humans organised themselves to form a giant brain, each person simulating a single neuron and sending signals to the others using mobile phones, it seems unlikely that their consciousnesses would merge to form a single giant consciousness. Why should something similar happen with subatomic particles?"

Philip Goff responded[656d] that panpsychism may appear to be crazy and contrary to common sense, but was most probably true. He reminded sceptics that *"physical science doesn't tell us what matter is, only what it does."* Goff wrote bluntly: *"In fact, the only thing we know about the intrinsic nature of matter is that some of it – the stuff in brains – involves experience. We now face a theoretical choice. We either suppose that the intrinsic nature of fundamental particles involves experience or we suppose that they have some entirely unknown intrinsic nature."*

Where is it located?

Philosophical and scientific disagreements about consciousness stem in part from continued ignorance about its source and nature. Humans have long associated[657a,b] the phenomenon with a 'soul' or 'spirit' that enters the body at birth and departs at death; an indefinable entity which early thinkers deemed the source of 'minds' that give us unique ability to ponder morality. However, modern theorists have struggled to reconcile the idea of an *invisible*, non-physical mind with our *visible*, physical brain. This daunting enterprise has spawned an entire field of study called[657c] 'Philosophy of mind'.

Mind-body debate

The two main[658a] perspectives on the issue are *dualist* (mind and body exist separately or have different properties), and *monist* (mind and body are essentially the same). In-between views range from descriptions of the mind as an emergent product of brain function (information flow), to extremist arguments that consciousness and mind are mere illusions that don't exist in reality.

Dualist proposals first appear in Yoga traditions of Hindu philosophy (c. 650 BCE) which divided the world into *purusha* (cosmic, universal consciousness that manifests as mind or spirit) and *prakriti* (nature, matter and physical bodies that give life physical reality). Ancient Greek philosopher Plato's later Theory of Forms or *Ideas* (c. 380 BCE) adopted a similar dualist view – he proposed that *everything* we perceive (both objects and qualia) are not 'real' but copies and projections of perfect, immortal, transcendent Forms that are merely visualised by the mind. Plato argued[658b] (in dialogues with Socrates) that the soul comes from the eternal world of Forms and returns to that realm at death to be reincarnated in another being. This notion of *transmigration of souls* suggests humans and other animals are animated by a similar essence[658c].

The dualist approach was first embraced in Western philosophy by 17th century French philosopher René Descartes. He described the mind as a distinct *non-material* entity that somehow interacts with and controls the *material* brain – a concept now known as Cartesian Duality[659a]. The idea of an immaterial mind that exists *independently* has profound implications for our concept of personal identity[659b] and medical therapies[659c] for neurological and psychiatric disorders.

Monist (anti-dualist) views can be traced to 2,000-year-old Eastern philosophies that have always regarded existence and reality as an *integration* of spiritual and physical realms. The Buddha (founder of Buddhism) taught that mind and body are interdependent and inseparable in an ever-changing universe. As Buddhist commentator Sean Robsville explained in a 2012 blog essay[660a]:

"In Buddhism the mind isn't a 'thing' or 'substance'. It is a formless, non-physical (and hence non-algorithmic) process that interacts with matter but is not itself material. The correct terms for mind in Buddhism are 'Mental Continuum' or 'Mindstream', which emphasise its impermanent and ever-changing nature as a process. The mind is not a 'thing in itself' and it is important to avoid reifying it as some sort of ultimate ground of existence."

Aristotle also took the view that 'mind' is not distinct but exists as a part of the soul that gives us our intellect. Although he shared the Platonic belief that soul is the essence that makes a thing 'alive', he argued in *On The Soul* (c. 350 BCE)[660b] that it's an *earthbound* phenomenon which is set free at death – just as the air inflating a balloon escapes into the atmosphere on deflation.

Dutch-Portuguese philosopher Baruch Spinoza is renowned for his critique of duality in *Of the Nature & Origin of the Mind* (Part II[660c] of his treatise *The Ethics* published posthumously in 1677). Spinoza argued that mind and body are not distinct but *different aspects* of the reality we perceive – a view now known as 'neutral monism'[660d].

271

Another notable monist argument was developed in the 19th century by English biologist Thomas Huxley (a staunch advocate of Darwinian evolution). He suggested[661a] the mind is a mere *epiphenomenon* (by-product) of the brain that has no physical effect on its workings or outputs. Huxley memorably compared[661b] mental states associated with 'mind' to the whistle effect generated by a steam locomotive – the whistling emanates from the engine but plays no part in its mechanical work or application to propel the train.

David Chalmers blended various monist arguments with universal panpsychism in his 2003 essay[662a,b] *Consciousness and its Place in Nature.* He examined options for a non-physical mind like *"interactionism, epiphenomenalism, or panprotopsychism"* and concluded: *"Each of the views has at least some promise, and none have clear fatal flaws."*

More than mechanics

In response to claims that artificial intelligence (AI) can pass the Turing Test[663a] for human-like cognition, American philosopher John Searle published[663b] a famous 'Chinese Room' scenario in 1980 to illustrate the unique ability of human minds to *understand* language – unlike digital computers that can only robotically *process* symbolic data. He wrote[663c]:

"Imagine a native English speaker who knows no Chinese locked in a room full of boxes of Chinese symbols (a data base) together with a book of instructions for manipulating the symbols (the program). Imagine that people outside the room send in other Chinese symbols which, unknown to the person in the room, are questions in Chinese (the input). And imagine that by following the instructions in the program the man in the room is able to pass out Chinese symbols which are correct answers to the questions (the output). The program enables the person in the room to pass the Turing Test for understanding Chinese but he does not understand a word of Chinese."

In short, ability to use computational tools and symbols to shape answers in a foreign language *does not* confer 'thinking' capacity to understand and ascribe semantic *meaning* to output sentences. Of course, a human Chinese-speaker would be mindful of audience sensitivities and use *emotional intelligence* (EI) to avoid causing offence – a feat that AI is unlikely[664a] to mimic. Furthermore, what's best to say would depend on *perception* and *appraisal* of the context; judgments that are beyond AI[664b] and are bound to differ even among humans.

Searle expanded his arguments in *The Rediscovery of the Mind* (1992) and *The Mystery of Consciousness* (1997). Contrary to physicalist views, he insisted that[665a] subjective experience and intentionality are *wholly mental* in nature and markedly different to other neurobiological outputs. But he rejected both dualism and panpsychism in favour of a quasi-physicalist *biological naturalism* (BN)[665b,c] that views the mind as a product of brain activity at a much higher level than humans have been able to access or understand. Searle argued[665d] that consciousness is an emergent feature that arises naturally from brain states – just as solidity or liquidity of substances results from underlying molecular activity.

According to Searle's BN, non-biological systems arranged similarly to biological brains should also be capable of multiple mental states (like degrees of pain). However, anti-physicalists have long cited[666a] this bizarre proposition as evidence the mind can't be reduced[666b] to brain function. Although, like Searle, MIT philosopher and cognitive scientist Jerry Fodor advocates a modular mind[667a] formed from innate neural processes, he argued in a 1980 commentary[667b] that BN fails to explain how any brain model grounded *solely* in matter can generate psychological states like human intentionality. Kevin Corcoran, a theologian and philosopher at Calvin University in Michigan, also claimed in a 2001 critique[667c] that BN is *"incoherent"* because it is, essentially, a form of dualism.

Matter or information?

In 2014, MIT physicist and cosmologist Max Tegmark hypothesised that[668a,b] consciousness might be a special state of matter he dubbed 'perceptronium'. He suggested[668c] the exotic substance has *"distinctive information processing abilities"* and argued that, just as states of water (vapour, liquid, and ice) are formed in defined physical conditions, our degrees of consciousness may stem from the impact of varying sets of mathematical conditions on perceptronium.

Tegmark's proposal drew on the *Integrated Information Theory* (IIT)[669a] of consciousness developed by Italian neuroscientist and psychiatrist Giulio Tononi a decade earlier. IIT is a holistic approach[669b] that regards consciousness and an experiencer as a single unified, indivisible *information system* – somewhat like Spinoza's 17th century argument[669c] for an inseparable mind-body. Tononi's information-based approach has allowed theoretical physicists like Tegmark to first identify and quantify *essential properties* of consciousness, and then work from there to mathematically specify what types of *physical systems* can experience the phenomenon.

Panpsychists have welcomed IIT since it assumes that *any* physical system that can integrate information in specified complex ways may also have capacity for consciousness to varying degrees. As Christof Koch remarked in a 2014 essay[670a], *"Any system that possesses some nonzero amount of integrated information experiences something. Let me repeat: any system that has even one bit of integrated information has a very minute conscious experience."* However, Koch conceded in an earlier article[670b] that computing the total information generating consciousness – a measure Tononi denoted[670c] with the Greek symbol *phi* (Φ) – is *"exceedingly difficult"* even for a roundworm (*C. elegans*) that lacks a central brain and has just 302 nerve cells compared to nearly *20 billion* in our forebrain cortex alone.

Despite its computational hurdles, support for IIT has grown – it's now widely viewed as the only formulation of consciousness that can be investigated within empirical science. Naotsugu Tsuchiya, a neuroscientist at Monash University in Melbourne, Australia, suggested[670d] in a 2017 article that IIT might even help researchers to answer Thomas Nagel's iconic 1974 question: *What Is It Like to Be a Bat?*. However, there are staunch sceptics.

John Searle argued in a 2013 book review[671a] that IIT's equating of consciousness to 'raw' information is misguided because the phenomenon is a *mind construct* that requires *pre-existing* conscious observers like humans. In 2014, American computer scientist Scott Aaronson set out detailed objections[671b] at his blog; among other issues, he argued that IIT implies systems we know are *not conscious* might have potential to be even *more conscious* than humans. Tononi addressed[671c] these points, but Aaronson remained unconvinced[671d]. Even Michael Cerullo, a psychiatrist and cognitive scientist associated with research into possible preservation of brain modules for future 'resurrection', issued a challenge[671e] to the IIT claim that consciousness can be usefully quantified for research. Eminent biomedical engineer Paul Nunez also explained in a December 2021 essay[671f] why IIT is a poor definition of brain integration processes.

The thorny issues were summed up in John Horgan's 2015 article[672a]. But, as Tononi and Koch clarified in a formal response[672b]:

"The theory [...] predicts that consciousness is graded, is common among biological organisms and can occur in some very simple systems. Conversely, it predicts that feed-forward networks, even complex ones, are not conscious, nor are aggregates such as groups of individuals or heaps of sand. Also [...] IIT implies that digital computers, even if their behaviour were to be functionally equivalent to ours, and even if they were to run faithful simulations of the human brain, would experience next to nothing."

275

How is it generated?

Although scholars disagree about the nature and location of consciousness, there's broad recognition that even the 'easy' features identified by Chalmers (like mental registration of external stimuli/perceptions and data processing for output experience) are difficult to explain in terms of *physical* neurobiological processes.

Just another illusion?

American neurologist Jacob Sage insisted in a 2011 article [673a] that 'consciousness' is nothing more than the state of *wakefulness* evinced by a fully functioning brain – a 'virtual machine' ready to acquire and process information in and out of memory. According to Sage, perception of a separate mind is an illusion projected by the brain.

Psychologist and neuroscientist Michael Graziano of Princeton University shares this 'illusionist' view. In 2015, Graziano and colleague Taylor Webb proposed [673b] that our concept of 'mind' arises from controlled neural processing of data inputs. They suggested that, as the brain's computing resource is limited, it creates an *attention schema* (AS) to filter the myriad signals vying for processing. It's this *internal* virtual construct, they said, that gives the sense of an *external* mind. Graziano admitted in a 2017 article [673c] that the AS concept *"does not address how the brain might actually possess a non-physical essence"* – the inner voices, images and feelings that shape our behaviour. But he stressed that it opens the door to possible 'conscious' AI that could benefit humanity: *"While human sociopaths are evidently conscious— they can attribute that property to themselves—they are impaired at attributing it to others. [...] Machine consciousness is a necessary step for our future. For those who fear that AI is potentially dangerous and may harm humanity, I would say that the danger is infinitely greater with sociopathic computers and it is of the utmost priority to give them consciousness—both the ability to attribute it to themselves and to others."*

276

W. Alex Escobar, a biologist at Emory University in Atlanta, Georgia, has developed an equally fascinating model of consciousness based on our incredibly vast capacity for visual experience. He proposed in a 2013 paper [674a] that our perception of qualia like colour, shape and size actually stems from aggregates of *quantised* 'awareness bits' generated by multiple neural microcircuits – just as computer screen images and scenery are composed of millions of tiny digital pixels. Escobar suggested that other sensory qualia like our wide ranges of taste and smell are probably similar composite products. As he explained in a 2014 overview [674b]: *"I contend there are basic building blocks of experience that are so small that, like pixels, they are hard to experience individually. However, when produced in large numbers they create the beautiful and often sublime images we see of the world around us."*

Binding problem

One of the biggest difficulties in formulating an operational model of consciousness is the need to explain how the brain is able to *segregate* different classes of sensory inputs (smell, taste, touch, vision and sound) and then *combine* each perception with specific objects, background settings, and emotional arousals to yield our highly personal experiences and reactions – all within microseconds. The segregation aspect of this mental 'binding puzzle' [675a] is known as *Binding Problem 1* (BP1), while that of combination is identified as *Binding Problem 2* (BP2).

Of course, we experience unified states [675b] of consciousness; not separate processes of data inputs/outputs. How this is happening has been debated for over 300 years. Proposed neural correlates of consciousness (NCC) since the 20th century are so widely distributed across brain regions that it's still very much a mystery how these are being *dynamically* and *concurrently* organised into the multiple and varied conscious states that produce subjective qualia and self-awareness.

277

One explanation of BP1 is that different classes of sensory inputs are captured across segregated brain areas, but become automatically 'bound' by rhythmic and synchronous neuron firing[676a]. Some experiments on response to light stimuli in cats and monkeys appear to support[676b] aspects of this so-called *Binding by Synchrony* (BBS). However, several reviews[676c] have cast doubt[676d] on claims that BBS adequately accounts for the brain's astonishing ability to consistently *distinguish* and *integrate* visual inputs of not just colour and shape, but also complex features like orientation (left/right, up/down), dimension (1-D, 2-D or 3-D) and kinetic state (static or moving).

Explaining BP2 is even more challenging. Francis Crick, co-discoverer of DNA's molecular structure, confidently asserted[677a] in his 1994 book *The Astonishing Hypothesis* that the phenomenon is grounded in physico-chemical brain processes. However, Crick failed to suggest a mechanism or even identify possible neural correlates. As John Hopfield, the biophysicist who pioneered[677b] *associative neural networks* (ANNs), pointed out in a book review[677c], Crick's proposal was a gross oversimplification of extremely complex higher-level visual perception in humans. Hopfield commented: *"In my view, until an operational definition can be given to "awareness" independent of the brain of humans, there is no way a science can be made out of consciousness."*

In 1980, English cognitive psychologist Anne Treisman and colleague Garry Gelade published[677d] a new 'feature integration' model that casts visual perception as a *two-stage* process – initial automatic *registration* of inputs while the brain is in a 'pre-attentive' mode, followed by *integration* and *identification* of objects when the brain switches to a 'focused attention' mode. They suggested the process is assisted by prior memory maps stored in the brain. However, exactly how *time-separated* mental representations are *seamlessly combined* for processing outputs remained very much unclear.

278

Then, in 2018, a team at Oxford University led by Simon Stringer published[678a] another intriguing model based on artificial *spiking neural networks* (SNNs) that have capacity to combine inputs across *both* space and time. The hypothetical construct involved a *holographic simulation* of regularly spiking neuron subpopulations that process and transmit information according to specified activity thresholds. Significantly, computational design included hierarchical *"top-down and lateral synaptic connections"* as well as *"multiple synaptic contacts between each pair of pre- and postsynaptic neurons, with different synaptic contacts having different axonal delays."* Although entirely theoretical, projected results were impressive enough for the report authors to comment:

> *"This begins to provide a way forward to solving the classic feature binding problem in visual neuroscience and leads to a new hypothesis concerning how information about visual features at every spatial scale may be projected upward through successive neuronal layers. We name this hypothetical upward projection of information the "holographic principle.""*

In a follow-up article, Stringer and co-theorists discussed[678b] how their holographic, temporal model of neurons interacting *across time* can be applied to explain the hidden dynamics of data and feature binding in human and other primate vision.

Brain-wide networks

The quest continues to physically identify and map the neural networks that theorists suggest are generating consciousness. Research indicates related infrastructure consists of *both* multilayered local 'shells' *and* overlapping global structures that intraconnect and interconnect through several nodes and hubs – unlike artificial networks like the Internet that tend to have isolated nodes which only connect to a central hub or nucleus. However, bioethical considerations limit the extent of experiments that can be performed 'live' on human brains to confirm models.

279

Nevertheless, in 2015 a multidisciplinary team at Vanderbilt University in Nashville, Tennessee published a study[679a] that combined *functional magnetic resonance imaging* (fMRI) with graph theoretical techniques to investigate patterns of neuronal activity associated with awareness. The results supported[679b] speculation that conscious awareness arises from changes in the brain's *global* functional networks, rather than events in isolated *local* connections.

Another remarkable development was reported[680a] in 2016 by physicists at Israel's Bar-Ilan University. The researchers used a complex analytical tool in statistical physics and network theory known as[680b] *k-shell decomposition* to reconstruct a human cortical network from scanned data. They uncovered a highly-sophisticated topology with *all* the neuronal nodes globally interconnected. Interestingly, around 20 percent of the nodes clustered to form a nucleus that was not central as such *but* still spanned several shells organised in hierarchies of increasing connectivity and complexity.

The Bar-Ilan team managed to link[680c] cognitive functions to specific neural shells in their reconstruction. They also traced efficient information flows from the lowest hierarchy area to the nucleus through areas of increasing connectivity, with accumulated data integration at each level. They concluded that the peculiarly distributed network nucleus may well be the global platform where all processed information is consolidated to generate consciousness. Intriguingly, the 'virtual' nucleus area roughly matched brain cortex regions that were also linked to consciousness by a Belgian-led study[680d] into anaesthetic effects reported the same year.

Naturally, AI researchers have been following developments closely. However, it's unclear how far the virtual information processing thought to generate consciousness can be reproduced artificially in robotic computers that lack a 'mind'.

In 2017, American electrical and computer engineer Ken Forbus and psychologist Andrew Lovett announced[681a] development of a computational AI system capable of[681b] human-level visual discrimination. Just two years later, Hod Lipson and Robert Kwiatkowski at Columbia University in New York published[681c] details of a *"task-agnostic self-modeling"* robot which displayed[681d] remarkable AI learning – including capacity to adapt to different situations and self-diagnose for rectification of internal faults. However, even if robots can somehow be programmed for higher-order[681e] intelligence, this will still be a long way off from our mind-endowed ability to *self-reflect* or 'think about thinking'.

Mind computation

Cognitive psychologists have developed a *Computational Theory of Mind* (CTM) that seeks to model mind processes which produce 'thought' as an *abstract* mathematical manipulation of information – in contrast to the *physical* digital information processing (IP) of data performed by everyday computers.

CTM was pioneered[682a] by American multidisciplinary philosopher Hilary Putnam in the early 1960s and further developed by Jerry Fodor in subsequent decades. The concept assumes that mind 'inputs' are just *symbolic* mental representations of objects and events, but it's unclear if these are real items or just metaphysical renditions[682b] of questionable existence[682c].

CTM advocates contend that[683a,b] *all* mental states (including qualia and emotions) are mere computations. According to this view, the mind *converts* syntactic representations of the world we perceive into 'raw information' that brain neural processes then use to generate thoughts. However, this proposal is fraught with problems.

Michael Rescorla from University of California, Los Angeles (UCLA) summarised the difficulties presented by CTM in a *Stanford Encyclopedia of Philosophy* (SEP) entry[683c]:

> *"A key task facing computationalists is to explain what one means when one says that the mind "computes". A second task is to argue that the mind "computes" in the relevant sense. A third task is to elucidate how computational description relates to other common types of description, especially neurophysiological description (which cites neurophysiological properties of the organism's brain or body) and intentional description (which cites representational properties of mental states)."*

The usual CTM answer to the first point – the exact meaning of the term 'computation' as applied to mind – is a *simple mapping account* (SMA) between abstract mathematical routines and the sequence of mental states that influence behaviour in biophysical systems like humans. However, this leads to trivial comparisons[683d] with *inanimate* compounds like stones that also emerge from prior molecular states by a sequence of induced or natural computational changes.

As John Searle pointed out sarcastically in *The Rediscovery of the Mind* (1992), SMA implies[684a] even his brick wall is capable of computation. He reiterated[684b] that emergence of human-like intentional mental states from *any* system (animate or inanimate) requires CTM representational inputs to be *semantic* (cognitively meaningful); not just *syntactic* (symbolically coherent). For example, a statement such as 'It's very hot, I need a cool shower' implies not just the ability to sense *levels* of heat, but also *knowledge* of shower facilities and intuitive *understanding* of water's soothing effect. Thus, Searle has consistently maintained that computerised AI robots *can never* be truly 'conscious' since they will always lack human semantic understanding – an argument that helped to change[684c] Putnam's views on the validity of a purely computational approach to mind function.

282

Gualtiero Piccinini from the Center for Neurodynamics at the University of Missouri, St. Louis (UMSL) also discussed SMA's contentious 'pancomputationalism' at length in another SEP entry[685a]. He queried: *"What is the principled difference, if there is one, between a rock and a calculator, or between a calculator and a computer? Answering these questions is more difficult than it may seem."* These considerations led Piccinini and UMSL colleague Sonya Bahar to conclude in a 2012 paper[685b] that if, as CTM argues, thoughts emanate from neural computation orchestrated by the mind, such an abstract process would definitely be *"sui generis"* (in a class of its own).

A language of thought?

In 1975, Jerry Fodor revived and expanded the medieval idea that thoughts first occur in a linguistic format called *mentalese* that shares similarities with spoken languages but is uniquely different. Fodor's redefined *Language of Thought Hypothesis* (LOTH)[686a] argued that the mind uses syntactic symbols to structure worldly representations into innate *mentalese* in much the same way letters and words are assembled in normal language; except that, instead of sentences with words and phonetics, the virtual dialect *pictures* and *combines* concepts and propositions according to[686b] grammar-like rules. Hence, when thinking, we experience sensations of internal visions and voices commonly referred to as the 'mind's eye'.

LOTH builds on cognitive research assumptions[686c] of *innate nativism* (specific skills, beliefs and preferences are 'hard wired' from birth) and *universal grammar* (all languages share common structural rules unique to humans). These fundamental concepts are largely credited to celebrated American linguist, philosopher and cognitive scientist Noam Chomsky. LOTH's emphasis on *communicative processes* contrasts with Searle's use of *neurological brain states* in BN to explain human conscious thought.

Beyond inconclusive psychological tests, conceptual difficulties[687a] make it hard to see how LOTH can be validated experimentally. But the idea of an inner *mentalese* remains interesting – although philosophers like[687b] Lawrence Kaye and[687c] Peter Carruthers reject the claim that we contruct thoughts in a format that's *completely different* to everyday language. Another problem is the implication that our indeterminate mind nevertheless has *functional ability* to recognise purely symbolic representations, and *independent will* to manipulate inputs to yield[687d] pictorial information for meaningful thought outputs. Critics also argue[687e] that thoughts are *context-dependent*, so underlying processes are unlikely to be restrictive language rules.

Moving forward

The numerous difficulties have led to doubts that a physical model of the mind can ever be developed that will explain our unique qualia, or the mechanisms that trigger our widely differing responses to signals from others and the environment. The mind remains unobservable and undetectable, so no hard experimental data is likely to emerge in the foreseeable future. However, despite these formidable hurdles, there's been an upsurge[688a] of research into this once-taboo area since the 1980s. In 2018, science commentator John Horgan described[688b] the mind-body problem thus: *"It is the central mystery of existence, the one toward which all other mysteries converge. Schopenhauer called it the world knot [...] which encompasses the riddles of consciousness, the self, free will, morality, the meaning of life."*

To make progress, scientists may have to abandon efforts to reduce mind to matter. As University of California psychologist Tania Lombrozo commented in 2014 article[688c]: *"Rejecting the mind in an effort to achieve scientific legitimacy—a trend we've seen with both behaviorism and some popular manifestations of neuroscience—is unnecessary and unresponsive to the aims of scientific psychology. Understanding the mind isn't the same as understanding the brain."*

Physicist and astronomer Adam Frank also expressed scepticism in a 2017 essay[688d] that a purely materialist approach will ever solve the riddle of consciousness. He pointed out that the multiple interpretations of quantum mechanics that have emerged since the 1920s undermine attempts to explain the mind solely in terms of observable matter. Frank concluded:

> *"Consciousness might, for example, be an example of the emergence of a new entity in the Universe not contained in the laws of particles. There is also the more radical possibility that some rudimentary form of consciousness must be added to the list of things, such as mass or electric charge, that the world is built of. Regardless of the direction 'more' might take, the unresolved democracy of quantum interpretations means that our current understanding of matter alone is unlikely to explain the nature of mind. It seems just as likely that the opposite will be the case."*

Is it a quantum simulation?

Some scientists have given up attempts to model consciousness as a product of *physiological* brain cell interactions; they've turned instead to the mysterious features exhibited by matter particles at fundamental level. This new concept of 'quantum mind'[689a] is steadily gaining momentum.

Sir Roger Penrose argued in his seminal book *The Emperor's New Mind* (1989) that humans have cognitive abilities that go way beyond even abstract Turing machine computation. Penrose contended[689b] that such algorithm-based models will always be limited by Kurt Gödel's 1931 incompleteness theorems[689c] which state that no mathematical system can prove *all* truths or even[689d] illustrate its own consistency. Humans, evidently, do not have this limitation; we're able to 'think out of the box' and use logical analysis to resolve complex arithmetical propositions.

285

Algorithms can only ever describe computable *realities*; hence our failure to find explanations for consciousness within classical physics. Penrose reasoned that thought processes must be *non-computable* and involve far more than 'blind calculations'. He suggested[689e] that mind phenomena may arise from *quantum events* created when subatomic particles within neurons become 'entangled' with information stored in dimensions *beyond* the 3-D brain we observe.

According to this quantum model, instances of consciousness are the product of dynamic microscopic processes *within* neurons, rather than activity *between* neurons as happens in normal computer networks. Ordinary digital information processing (IP) can only accommodate *two-state* binary bits of data, but a brain operating like a sophisticated quantum computer would have the capacity to process *multi-state* qubits of data. Furthermore, if higher-order cognition for decision-making indeed occurs at quantum level, we would have access to *infinite* information embedded in universal space-time. This, Penrose speculated, is what gives us the non-computational attribute beyond algorithms that we commonly refer to as 'the mind'.

However, qubits are 'between worlds' so their values are just a statistical probability that can't be programmed in advance. Hence, regardless the state or precision of initial information at hand, outcomes from quantum processing are entirely unpredictable[690a]. But we regularly conceive mathematical and other problems (mind inputs) and accurately predict expected solutions (mind outputs). How, then, could *unquantifiable* and random quantum activity be the basis for our *premeditated* intentions?

Penrose suggested that conscious thought must involve a special type of *non-random* quantum activity induced by[690b] cosmic gravity that he called *Objective Reduction* (OR). But he did not specify how and where such OR might be taking place.

Stuart Hameroff, an anaesthesiologist at University of Arizona, had been studying[691a] computer-like structures inside brain neurons called *microtubules* that he speculated were processing information. Hameroff teamed up with Penrose to research a possible quantum-biological model for the mind. The collaboration produced a revised *Orchestrated Objective Reduction* (Orch-OR)[691b] description of quantum computation within neuron microtubules that Penrose proposed[691c] as the source of consciousness in his 1994 book *Shadows of the Mind.*

Predictably, traditionalists rejected the groundbreaking Penrose-Hameroff proposal as unscientific mysticism. American physicist and sceptic Victor Stenger dismissed the idea of a link between quantum physics and the human mind as wishful 'New Age spiritualism' in a scathing critique[692a], while Hilary Putnam denounced Penrose's new book as *"a sad episode in our current intellectual life"* in a 1994 review[692b]. Max Tegmark added the technical objection[692c] in 1999 that the brain is too *"warm, wet, and noisy"* to host delicate quantum events: he calculated[692d] that environmental decoherence would likely occur long before neurons could process quantum qubits in any meaningful way. An Australian multidisciplinary review also concluded[692e] in 2008 that Orch-OR *"is not biologically feasible."*

However, new research has shown that quantum events *can indeed* take place in biological systems. In 2013, researchers at Japan's National Institute of Material Sciences reported[693a] the first detection of quantum vibrations in microtubules inside 'warm' brain neurons, and medical scientists at the University of Pennsylvania in the USA linked[693b] anaesthesia-induced unconsciousness to neuronal microtubules. Physicists at Heidelberg University in Germany also announced[694a] successful simulation of key processes of plant photosynthesis at quantum level[694b]. The matter was settled in 2014 when Edward O'Reilly and Alexandra Olaya-Castro at University College London in England published[694c] the first clear theoretical evidence that photosynthesis definitely involves[694d] quantum effects.

287

In 2015, American theoretical physicist Matthew Fisher proposed[695a] that atoms of phosphorus – an element with unique 'nuclear spin' – could serve as[695b] 'qubits' for quantum processing in the brain. As renowned colleague John Preskill observed in a commentary[695c], Fisher's identification of a practicable pathway and mechanism provides a route for empirical exploration of the idea that the brain could be a quantum computer.

Bolstered by these remarkable developments, Penrose and Hameroff issued[696a] an updated version and robust defence of Orch-OR. They argued[696b] that the new findings rebut most criticisms and suggested EEG-detected brainwaves may also stem from deep-level microtubule vibrations – a hypothesis which, if proven, could lead to new therapies for mind disorders. Indeed several early objections[696c] have been superseded, but the paradigm of 'quantum consciousness' is likely to remain controversial[696d] until technologies emerge that allow experimental testing of assumptions and predictions.

Why morality and free will?

Perhaps the most puzzling aspects of human consciousness are our capacity for moral considerations, and freedom to decide and choose between several possible courses of action. While a link can be drawn between mental processing of stimuli and *automatic* motor reflexes, there is no neurobiological explanation how and why we're able to *contemplate* consequences and shape our behaviour according to intuitive concepts of 'right' and 'wrong'. If, as materialists claim, we're just 'mechanistic' entities, we should be strictly amoral.

In his treatise *On the Soul* (c. 350 BCE), Aristotle described[697a] the human mind as a kind of *tabula rasa* (Latin for 'blank writing slate') on which all knowledge and ideas – including morality – are *acquired* through inscription of sensory experiences from birth.

However, in the 17th and 18th centuries, René Descartes and Gottfried Leibniz argued[697b] that we're *endowed* at birth with innate instincts for *intuitive* appreciation of morality and knowledge of God. John Locke disagreed and reaffirmed Aristotle's emphasis on empiricism or 'learning by experience' in Book I[697c] of his seminal work *An Essay Concerning Human Understanding* (1690). These early arguments marked the start of a long-running 'nature versus nurture' debate[698a]. Biologists and psychologists now accept that *both* sides have merit: while we're *genetically predisposed* to certain[698b] behavioural traits, *epigenetic imprinting* by parental, societal and other environmental influences plays a huge role[698c] in our development.

Do we have a choice?

Although there's some consensus on shaping of human behaviour and attitudes, proposals that seek to explain free will in terms of neuroscience remain highly controversial. In the 1980s, American physiologist Benjamin Libet pioneered a famous experiment on freely-initiated 'thought-to-action' responses. Surprisingly, he found that[699a] neuronal activity in the brain appears to *precede* conscious decisions by around *half a second* (500 milliseconds). This suggests our actions start *subconsciously* at a neurological level, with our brains assuming 'readiness potential' (RP) *before* we're able to apply conscious volition. Experiments with new technology confirmed[699b] the unsettling phenomenon in 2008.

Libet's finding has since been cited by animalists and materialists in support of arguments that free will is an illusion[700a]. However, most philosophers remain unconvinced[700b] – although some like Derk Pereboom have argued that[700c] the best evidence from science leads to the conclusion that humans *are not* morally responsible for our actions because decision-making processes are governed by factors beyond our control.

In 2009, cognitive psychologists Jeff Miller and Judy Trevena from the University of Otago in New Zealand published[701a] a slightly different version of Libet's experiment with audio signal prompts that revealed *all* subjects displayed *the same* level of pre-conscious neuronal RP – whether or not they subsequently elected to respond. Miller and Trevena concluded that RP was not a sign of subconscious 'action before volition', but rather a possible indicator of the brain 'gearing up' in anticipation of a conscious decision to act.

A French team led by neuroscientist Aaron Schurger also reported[701b] a study in 2012 that used a specific 'neural accumulator' model to track RP. The test showed RP is a *generic* neural activity that has nothing to do with conscious volition and decision making. Schurger and co-researchers wrote:

"In fact a gradual increase in neural activity preceding spontaneous movements appears to be a very general phenomenon, common to both vertebrates and invertebrates alike. Why do both humans and crayfish exhibit the same 1- to 2-s buildup of neural activity in advance of self-initiated movements? [...] Our account departs from the prevailing assumptions ..."

Naturally, any scientific claims that humans may have less volition than assumed are a matter for huge public concern. A 'can't be helped' behavioural paradigm has alarming implications[702a] for concepts of moral responsibility and long-established personal accountability. If 'it's all in the neurons', then *genetic disposition* rather than exercise of *free will* becomes the driver of behaviour – a foundational assumption that negates our basis for determining 'good' and 'evil'. This perspective would seriously undermine maintenance of law and order if it were adopted in jurisprudence. Already, some American defence attorneys have been presenting[702b] neurophysiological evidence like brain scans to support criminal case pleas that the accused lacks conscious volition to establish intention or *mens rea* (Latin for 'guilty mind').

In *The Science of Evil* (2011), British psychopathologist Simon Baron-Cohen identified[703a] an 'empathy circuit' generated by specific brain areas. He argued[703b] that people traditionally described as 'evil' merely lack this natural neural inhibitor present in the brains of others. American literary critic Ron Rosenbaum highlighted[703c] a major flaw in Baron-Cohen's attempt to 'depersonalise' evil:

> *"One troubling aspect of Baron-Cohen's grand substitution of a lack of empathy for evil is the mechanistic way he describes it. He characterizes those who lack empathy as having "a chip in their neural computer missing." He tells us "empathy is more like a dimmer switch than an all-or-none switch." The big problem here is that by reducing evil to a mechanical malfunction in the empathy circuit, Baron-Cohen also reduces, or even abolishes, good. No one in this deterministic conceptual system chooses to be good, courageous, or heroic. They just have a well-developed empathy circuit that compels them act empathetically—there's no choice or honor in the matter."*

In any case, as former *Nature* editor Philip Ball pointed out[703d] in 2007, we don't live in isolation so our behaviour also hinges on the extent to which 'behavioural genes' are shaped epigenetically by values evolved by society as a whole. Thus, if we wish to achieve maximum empathy and altruism for what ancient Greeks termed *eudaimonia* (human flourishing), societies must undertake *collective* commitment to establish positive communal influences alongside *personal* responsibility for curbing negative impulses.

Rehabilitating volition

Interestingly, Libet did not interpret his results as evidence that humans totally lack free will. He pointed out in a 1985 review[704a] that we still have a time gap of around 150 milliseconds for a conscious 'veto' to cancel actions initiated in the brain.

Libet explained:

"The role of conscious will would be not to initiate a specific voluntary act but rather to select and control volitional outcome. It is proposed that conscious will can function in a permissive fashion, either to permit or to prevent the motor implementation of the intention to act that arises unconsciously. Alternatively, there may be the need for a conscious activation or triggering, without which the final motor output would not follow the unconscious cerebral initiating and preparatory processes."

Still, in 2013, a European team led by Elisa Filevich from University College London showed in a new study[704b] that, when rapid decisions to inhibit/delay actions are imperative, free choices are strongly driven by *prior unconscious* brain activity. As the researchers reported:

"Our results show that the neural activity before the moment of decision to inhibit differed from that before a decision to act rapidly. When participants chose to respond rapidly on free-choice trials, they did so on the basis of stronger preparatory activity before the moment of choice. Choosing to transiently inhibit and delay responding was associated with lower preparatory activity. [....] We show that these free decisions to inhibit/delay in fact depended on preceding brain activity, before the instruction to decide. The current state of the brain appears to influence the conscious decision to act or inhibit/delay, rather than vice versa."

To the relief of moral ethicists, a German collaboration led by John-Dylan Haynes from Charité–Berlin University of Medicine confirmed[704c] in 2015 that a brief 'free won't' window *does* exist as suggested by Libet for conscious inhibition of RP-initiated actions. The investigators identified a 'point of no return' – around 200 milliseconds before the onset of movement – beyond which we're unable to override pre-conscious activation of motor responses.

Haynes affirmed[704d] in a press statement that *"A person's decisions are not at the mercy of unconscious and early brain waves. They are able to actively intervene in the decision-making process and interrupt a movement."* Thus, it appears disorders like Tourette and alien hand syndromes arise from dysfunctional neural pathways for 'free won't' vetos – afflicted persons are simply unable to 'apply the brakes' to stop negative, non-volitive activity.

Neuroscientists and psychologists have embraced[705a] Libet's brief 'free won't' interlude as the psycho-neurobiological bridge that reconciles[705b] our intuitive free will with RP's 'hard determinism'. However, the concept of *delayed volition* also has[705c] troubling implications. If we accept that free will can only be exercised *retrospectively*, it opens a pandora's box of 'diminished responsibility' legal excuses based on how fast a person's physiology permits conscious reversal of activity initiated unconsciously in the brain.

Even arch-materialist Daniel Dennett – who views humans as 'evolved machines' and dismisses the idea of a 'metaphysical self' – outlined several problems with the concept of a delayed *"presidential veto"* in a 2003 essay[706a,b]. He argued that Libet was confusing *determinism* with *inevitability* and quipped: *"I hate to look a gift horse in the mouth but I certainly want more free will than that."* According to Dennett, free will is an essential feature for *"communicating agents, capable of responding to requests and queries about their own decisions and actions."* In a related review[706c], British neurobiologist and science historian Kenan Malik explained Dennett's argument about the distinction between determinism and inevitability:

> *"Suppose I'm playing baseball and the pitcher chucks the ball directly at my face. I turn my head to avoid it. There was, therefore, nothing inevitable about the ball hitting my face. But, a sceptic might say, I turned my head not of my own free will but was caused to do so by factors beyond my control.*

"That is to misunderstand the nature of causation, Dennett retorts. What really caused me to turn my head was not a set of deterministic links cascading back to the beginnings of the universe - though that certainly exists - but my desire at that moment not to get hit by the baseball. At a different moment I might decide to take a hit in the face, if by doing so I help my team win the game."

In a 2016 overview[707a], British cognitive neuroscientist and psychologist Christian Jarrett discussed the new research that suggests our intuitive sense of free will is far from illusory. As Magda Osman from Queen Mary University of London commented in a May 2021 essay[707b], *"We now know that there are several fundamental problems with the experimental set up that suggest the claims that our unconscious fundamentally rules our behaviour are significantly exaggerated."* For now, the common sense view that humans have significant control over our actions has been restored. But can free will be explained in purely mechanistic terms as Dennett suggests?

Cascade of neural events

Given the huge complexities of thought-to-action processes, there's increasing scepticism that neuroscience alone can ever fully explain the role of free will in conscious decision-making. In March 2022, an international collaboration reported[708a] that human response to auditory and environmental cues is governed by[708b] bewilderingly convoluted neural circuits operating across *multiple* brain regions. How are these diverse, distributed mental activities synchronised? The report authors summed up the nub of the problem thus:

"Motor behaviors are often planned long before execution but only released after specific sensory events. Planning and execution are each associated with distinct patterns of motor cortex activity. Key questions are how these dynamic activity patterns are generated and how they relate to behavior."

New mysterianism

British philosopher Colin McGinn concluded in a 1989 article[709a] that the mystery of consciousness is unsolvable by humans. He argued that the human mind is incapable of understanding itself fully because we lack the necessary intellectual capacity. McGinn's stance is not new – since the 17th century, various scholars have judged that deeper aspects of consciousness are beyond human comprehension. In *The Science of the Mind* (1991), American neurobiologist and philosopher Owen Flanagan labelled McGinn and like-minded thinkers as 'new mysterians' to distinguish them from 'old mysterians' whose views were grounded in supernaturalism.

Daniel Dennett strongly disagreed with this 'defeatist' notion of mysterianism in a 1991 review[709b]. Nevertheless, several contemporaries have supported[709c] McGinn's assessment (restated in a 2014 blog post[709d]) including Noam Chomsky, fellow linguist and psychologist Steve Pinker, and neuroscientist Sam Harris. These luminaries, and many others, concede that human intellect is subject to a *biological* cognitive limitation (just like other creatures).

However, approaches differ. Some mysterians still view the mind as a *physical* phenomenon grounded in neurobiology; except that its mechanisms and processes are *cognitively closed* to humans. Others dismiss all proposed explanations of the mind in purely physical terms as a *category mistake*; they liken this approach to a misguided attempt to describe the blueprint for assembly of a car in terms of a cooking recipe – neither the relevant data inputs nor projected outputs are comparable in any way.

As science writer Margaret Wertheim observed in a 2015 essay[710a], the lack of an agreed paradigm and framework for consciousness guarantees that *"philosophers and scientists will be arguing the point for centuries to come."*

295

But it appears scientists may ultimately have to concede the last word on this most remarkable of human attributes to philosophers and theologians. In response to the 2017 *Edge* challenge question *What scientific term or concept ought to be more widely known?*, American technology commentator Nicholas G. Carr nominated mysterianism. Carr's submission[710b] closed with these insightful comments:

"What's truly disconcerting about mysterianism is that, if our intellect is bounded, we can never know how much of existence lies beyond our grasp. What we know or may in the future know may be trifling compared with the unknowable unknowns. [...]

"Mysterianism teaches us humility. Through science, we have come to understand much about nature, but much more may remain outside the scope of our perception and comprehension. If the mysterians are right, science's ultimate achievement may be to reveal to us its own limits."

Elusive memories

Biological memory is integral to conscious experience. Formation, storage, and recall of associated facts, concepts and stimuli responses are crucial to subjective learning. This internal reference library allows us to have self-awareness, interact socially, and relate to the environment. Furthermore, experience of a *time-segmented* life is only possible because we're able to keep a mental record of past events.

Surprisingly however, the nature, mechanisms and precise storage location of this invaluable agency for our perception of reality remain largely unclear. German psychologist Herman Ebbinghaus showed in a pioneering 1885 report[711a,b] that memory could be studied scientifically. However, the only confirmed conclusion after more than 135 years of multidisciplinary studies is that there are *different types* of memories; each of which is associated with specific functions that appear to be controlled by several brain regions.

Types of memory

Decades of studies involving human clinical cases, laboratory animal experiments, and brain activity imaging have identified distinct categories of memory that are classified by *functional capacity* as well as *processing stages*.

Explicit or *declarative* memory is data that we have to make a conscious, intentional effort to recall. Sub-categories include *semantic* memories (factual information, concepts and general knowledge), *episodic* memories (experiences of specific events), and *spatial* memory (coordinates for orientation and navigation). Recall of explicit memory usually triggers associated emotions. This type of memory is essential for metacognition.

Implicit or *non-declarative* memory consists of learned skills and acquired habits that we recall automatically without conscious effort. The most common form is *procedural* memory that governs 'unconscious' activities like speech, writing, eating, locomotion, riding, driving and suchlike. Another form is 'priming': exposure to a stimulus or thing brings about subconscious association with something else during memory recall.

The distinction between explicit and implicit memory was confirmed[712a] in the 1980s after experimental studies showed[712b] they have independent bases and engage different brain regions. But it was disputed[712c] whether both memory types arise from the same or different neural pathways or mechanisms. In 2017, a team at Massachusetts Institute of Technology (MIT) led by neuroscientist Earl K. Miller published[712d] results from a meta-analytic study that suggests[712e] *different* neural correlates underlie implicit and explicit learning. The issue is hugely important for researchers investigating possible therapies for memory disorders like Alzheimer's disease.

Memory formation

In 1949, Canadian psychologist Donald Hebb argued[713a] in his book *The Organization of Behavior* that memory formation must involve permanent structural changes to brain cell networks. Hebb theorised[713b] that learning occurs by synaptic growth and strengthening through repeated and sequential excitation of adjacent neurons – a process German systems neuroscientist Siegrid Löwel famously summed up[713c] in 1992 as *"neurons wire together if they fire together."* This suggests *long-term* memory storage is preceded by *short-term* capture and encoding of information in a series of sequentially-linked events in the brain.

Hebb's early model of *synaptic plasticity*, based on the assumption that memory formation occurs over a number of stages, laid the groundwork for new neuropsychology research. The concept of animal learning by *spike-timing-dependent plasticity* (STDP) of brain cells is now well-established[713d] and has been successfully adapted to produce *artificial neural networks* (ANNs) in computing applications.

The second half of the 20th century ushered in a cross-disciplinary 'cognitive revolution' that led to the adoption of information processing (IP) explanatory frameworks for *all* mind phenomena. IP-based proposals for memory formation typically involve an initial sensory phase that lasts just long enough (milliseconds) to allow information from external stimuli to be detected and retained. These 'memory traces' are then transferred to short-term memory (duration from several seconds to a minute) for electrochemical encoding as 'engrams' within an abstract cognitive system of working memory. Some models include an intermediate phase that can persist for up to *three hours*; possibly by re-translation of neuronal mRNA transcripts. In 1956, American cognitive psychologist George A. Miller suggested in a seminal paper[714a] that our working memory capacity is limited to approximately 7 items; plus or minus 2.

Beyond Miller's so-called 'magical number', it's thought information available for later recall is consolidated into long-term memory across various brain regions. Proposed pathways for consolidation include synaptic processes like *long-term potentiation* (LTP) that take anywhere from minutes to several days, and subsequent systemic rearrangements that can continue 'filing away' acquired memories for up to *two decades* in humans.

However, precise mechanisms for the flow of memories through the various proposed stages have yet to be demonstrated. Some researchers even contend that[714b,c] memory formation is just a single, continuous process. But multi-stage models do have some support from neuropsychological studies.

Live observation of the famous patient H.M.[715a] over five decades, until he died aged 82 in 2008, provided valuable insights. At age 27 in 1953, H.M. (finally named as American Henry Molaison at death) had portions of his medial temporal lobes – including most of the hippocampus – removed in an experimental surgery[715b] for severe epilepsy. The procedure succeeded in reducing his seizures, but left him with extensive memory disorders that helped researchers to test proposed memory stages and possible brain locations.

Studies of H.M.'s case showed that[715c], while he could recall *old* long-term explicit memories formed before his surgery (apart from some childhood episodic data), he had lost the ability to form *new* long-term explicit memories (except for spatial data). This indicated that formation and retrieval pathways are *different*, even for types of *same-category* long-term memory. Tests revealed H.M could form relevant *short-term* working memories, but was unable to consolidate these into *long-term* storage; a finding that vindicated the Hebbian hypothesis of sequential memory processing stages.

Intriguingly, it was further demonstrated that H.M. could still form, retain and recall new *implicit* memories (automatic motor skills); the first empirical indication that explicit and implicit memories are governed by *wholly separate* neural systems in the brain.

Initially, H.M.'s memory impairments were ascribed solely to loss of his hippocampus. But MRI imaging in the 1990s revealed this brain area had not been extensively removed as thought, while other areas had suffered hitherto unsuspected damage. These new findings, subsequently confirmed[716a] by post-mortem pathology, overturned earlier conclusions that particular brain regions were linked to specific memory functions. Thus, while it's clear the hippocampus and other areas of the medial temporal lobe are essential for proper functioning of memory systems, precise roles and mechanisms remain unconfirmed[716b,c].

Another unexpected finding has cast doubt on the long-held assumption that the neuron's soma (body) is the primary source of repeated electrical impulses or 'spikes' thought to stimulate memory formation at synaptic junctions within neural networks. In 2017, a team at University of California–Los Angeles (UCLA) reported[717a] that dendrites – the tree-like branches at the end of neurons – are not just passive conduits for soma-generated spikes. The researchers found that dendrites actively generate up to *10 times* more spikes than a neuron's soma with large, slowly fluctuating voltages. This adds a huge *analog* dimension that makes neurons far more than mere digital on/off devices; it increases the brain's overall computational capacity by a factor of 100.

As nearly 90 percent of neuronal tissue is made up of dendrites that may or may not be actively 'firing' at any one time, their new-found capacity is a major departure from the classic Hebbian hypothesis that learning within neural networks stems from *concurrent excitation* of adjacent neuron somas.

It now appears that a neuron's dendrites may be facilitating memory formation quite independently of its soma. UCLA neurophysicist Mayank Mehta (a senior report author) explained the huge significance of their work in a press release[717b]:

> *"We found that dendrites are hybrids that do both analog and digital computations, which are therefore fundamentally different from purely digital computers, but somewhat similar to quantum computers that are analog. A fundamental belief in neuroscience has been that neurons are digital devices. They either generate a spike or not. These results show that the dendrites do not behave purely like a digital device. Dendrites do generate digital, all-or-none spikes, but they also show large analog fluctuations that are not all or none. This is a major departure from what neuroscientists have believed for about 60 years."*

Memory storage

The exact location of our various memory databanks is another mystery that continues to perplex neuroscientists. In 2014, a different team at UCLA revealed[718a] that old memories could be restored in marine snails; *despite* the loss of synapses. The discovery contradicted traditional dogma of long-term memory storage at neuron synapses, and led the UCLA researchers to speculate[718b] that memory may reside in neuron *nuclei* rather than synapse junctions. In May 2015, a group at Massachusetts Institute of Technology (MIT) led by Nobel laureate Susumu Tonegawa published[718c] a novel study that cast serious doubt on another long-accepted premise that long-term potentiation (LTP) – progressive strengthening of neuron synapses – is essential for memory storage. Tonegawa's team showed[718d] that newly-formed memory engrams persist and can be reactivated with optogenetic light techniques *even when* proteins necessary for LTP are blocked and the process is inhibited.

The MIT experimental finding on LTP indicates specific patterns of *networked* neurons across multiple brain areas may represent memory engrams, rather than local *isolated* neuron junctions. Just three months later in August 2015, a group at the University of Alberta in Canada published[719a] independent research that showed electrical impulses in the brain could be stimulating 'offline' memory rehearsal[719b] for consolidation and storage in addition to 'online' neuronal activity. This revolutionary conclusion was boosted by yet another study[719c] reported the next year by a team at University of Wisconsin–Madison (UWM) in the USA that confirmed[719d] the brain can hold and process information in working memory – even if neurons are not firing and no 'online' synthesis of LTP-related proteins is occurring at synapses. Thus, it appears the brain has hidden ability to file away newly acquired information in latent format for subsequent 'offline' consolidation.

The mystery of location has deepened with fresh observations on neuronal activity in the prefrontal cortex (PFC) during formation of working memory. In 2017, a team of bioengineers and psychologists at the National University of Singapore (NUS) led by Shih-Cheng Yen and Camilo Libedinsky reported a new study[720a] that showed distractions *do not* interrupt memory formation and retention in the PFC. The NUS researchers found the information being processed is flawlessly *"reorganized into a different pattern of activity to create a morphed stable code without losing information."* Further research published[720b] by a group led by Sean Cavanagh and Steven Kennerley from University College London a year later also indicated encoding of memory engrams is a *distributed* function performed by *"dynamic, population-level activity within high time-constant neurons."* Interestingly, medical scientists investigating[721a] Alzheimer's disease have found[721b] memories of music still persist in patients; somehow, parts of the brain retain the original coding and trigger an *Autonomous Sensory Meridian Response* (ASMR). This development supports other conclusions that memory is actually formed and stored *across* a network of neurons.

The dominant model in psychology explains memory recall as a two-stage process – an initial *search and retrieval* phase followed by a *recognition and decision* phase. The second phase is further separated by some researchers into fast, automatic *familiarity* or 'knowing' and slow, conscious *recollection* or 'remembering'. Austrian-American psychologist George Mandler is credited with the first scientific description of dual-process recall in a 1980 paper[725a,b.] A decade later, renowned cognitive psychologist Larry L. Jacoby published[725c] research that used a novel 'process dissociation procedure' to identify separate automatic and intentional processes that supported Mandler's two-phase model. The idea of phased recall gained further credence in 1997 when a team at Massachusetts Institute of Technology (MIT) reported that[725d,e] a PET imaging study of cerebral blood flow during auto-retrieval and recognition tasks had found significantly elevated levels in specific areas within *up to six* brain regions. Mandler subsequently published a comprehensive review[725f] that's now regarded as the canon of dual-process recall.

However, the two-stage model has been challenged by several reports that suggest memory recall is a *single* correlated process. A 2008 analytical study[726a] led by investigators at California Institute of Technology (Caltech) uncovered neuronal activity in *similar* areas of the brain's medial temporal lobe (MTL) during *both* familiarity and recollection events: a finding that indicated the same class of neurons carry information for both retrieval and recognition. The next year, Deborah Hannula and Charan Ranganath from the University of California at Davis reported[726b] new research that used fMRI tracking to show the hippocampus is definitely involved in *both* types of memory recall: the study established that activity across a *broad cortical network* is required for conscious recognition. Another fMRI study published[726c] in 2015 by a team at University College London in England confirmed[726d] the hippocampus plays a key role in both *reassembly* and *binding* of different aspects of recalled memory.

305

A single-process interpretation was further supported by a 2016 finding[727a] by a team at Cambridge University in England that distinct neural mechanisms, within a network of *co-activated regions*, operate *cohesively* to retrieve vivid episodic memories with precision. In 2017, a group led by neuroscientist Stephanie Riès at San Diego State University in the USA published[727b] an unrelated ECoG (electrocorticography) study of word retrieval and speech neurodynamics that similarly indicated[727c] memory recall for language involves *parallel, real time activity* across widespread and overlapping brain regions rather than a *"division of labor."*

But the matter is far from settled. Yet another 2015 report[727d] by a multidisciplinary group from the University of Stirling in Scotland claimed to have uncovered fresh evidence for a two-stage process. The researchers traced a neural correlate of memory retrieval that suggests recollection is a *"thresholded process"* that may or may not follow retrieval of episodic memory. The inference is, even if data related to such memories is being continuously retrieved, we have to make a *conscious effort* to assemble it all into a meaningful format.

In addition to disagreements over the number and relationship of memory recall phases, there's controversy about the *direction* and *pattern* of information flows during the process. It was long-assumed that recall occurs across *the same* neuronal circuits activated when a memory was formed. However, in 2017, Susumu Tonegawa co-authored a new report[728a] with fellow MIT neuroscientists and collaborators at Japan's RIKEN Center in Ibaraki that suggests[728b] the brain actually uses *a different* 'detour' circuit; perhaps to allow editing and updating of retrieved memories, and regulation of hormones for associated emotions. The same year, researchers at Columbia University made the surprising discovery[728c] that visual features are recalled[728d] *in reverse order* to that in which they were recorded.

Nonetheless, a 2020 study[729a] conducted on epileptic patients by a group from the US National Institutes of Health (NIH) in Bethesda, Maryland revived the notion of same-circuit flows for both formative and recalled memory. The researchers detected and recorded[729b] similar cortical spiking sequences being replayed as had been observed during formation of specific memories. Thus, it appears brain pathways followed in memory recall are not fixed but arise *dynamically* in ways that are still largely unclear.

Another principle called 'encoding specificity' suggests that memory recall is most efficient when environmental context and physiological state are the same as were present at the time the memories were formed. However, this view is disputed by American cognitive psychologist and author James S. Nairne. He argued in a 2002 paper[730a] that, while circumstances at the time of initial encoding do have an impact on memory retrieval, an 'encoding-retrieval match' is not necessary *if* sufficiently powerful cues are immediately available. Interestingly, it's been shown that present-day cues play a greater role than past associations in phenomena like *consciously initiated* tip-of-the-tongue (TOT)[730b] partial recall experiences, and *unconsciously initiated* retrievals of both involuntary autobiographical memories (IAM)[730c] and involuntary semantic memories (ISM)[730d].

In 2019, a multidisciplinary group in the USA led by biomedical engineers from Columbia University (CU) announced[731a] the successful recording of specific neurons displaying *"activity that was spatially tuned to the retrieved location of the specific object that participants were cued to remember."* This remarkable achievement was the first time that individual cells in an identifiable neuronal region had been linked to a specific type of memory. Significantly, the so-called 'memory-trace' neurons were mainly located in the entorhinal cortex – the brain area medical scientists have identified[731b,c] as the first to be affected by molecular dysfunctions that cause Alzheimer's disease.

Salman Qasim, lead author of the CU study, explained[731d] the broader implications for research into spatial memory recall:

> *"Our study demonstrates that neurons in the human brain track the experiences we are willfully recalling, and can change their activity patterns to differentiate between memories. They're just like the pins on your Google map that mark the locations you remember for important events. This discovery might provide a potential mechanism for our ability to selectively call upon different experiences from the past and highlights how these memories may influence our brain's spatial map."*

These reports (and similar developments in cognitive science) highlight the huge difficulties and complexities facing researchers investigating possible therapies for memory recall afflictions.

False recollections

Psychiatrists and psychologists have long grappled with client recollections that are patently distorted or outright false – even though examiners can discern no wilful intention to deceive. Bizarrely, people prone to such confabulations[732] and involuntary falsehoods persist with the belief that their recollections are factual and real; *despite* being presented with evidence to the contrary.

This phenomenon of systemic, incorrect recollection is the subject of intense research within cognitive disciplines. The perplexing disorder has been associated with emotional trauma[733a], brain damage[733b], and executive dysfunction[733c] during retrieval and evaluation of memory. There's also speculation[733d] that confabulation may be just another type of psychotic delusion. However, how and why such impairments lead to recall distortions and confused realities remains unclear[733e]. The matter merits public concern, given the negative implications for self-perception, social interaction, and credibility of eye-witness accounts.

308

Some researchers argue that a so-called *false memory syndrome* (FMS) exists which *compels* reconstruction of traumatic experiences which never occurred. However, sceptics prefer to view FMS as an inevitable by-product of highly-suggestive *recovered-memory therapy* (RMT) techniques that psychoanalysts use to uncover repressed childhood trauma memories. American cognitive psychologist Elizabeth F. Loftus, an acclaimed specialist[734] on witness testimonies in legal cases, described how human memories can be manipulated by therapists to produce false recollections in her 1994 book *The Myth of Repressed Memory* (co-written with Katherine Ketcham).

A group headed by neurologist Armin Schnider at University Hospital of Geneva in Switzerland has been investigating false recollections for over a decade. Schnider suggested in a 2013 review[735a] that the brain uses a process of *orbitofrontal reality filtering* (ORFi) to distinguish between imaginative thoughts and recall of real experiences. According to this view, false recollections stem mainly from the failure[735b] of ORFi; although some aspects can be traced to[735c] neuropsychological causes. Schnider published a detailed account of his hypothesis in *The Confabulating Mind* (2008). However, ORFi is not an acknowledged brain function within mainstream neuroscience; the proposal is regarded as just another speculation.

As discussed in a special 2017 edition[736a] of the journal *Cortex*, researchers still lack firm empirical findings on false recollections. Lack of progress has made it difficult to devise therapies, but a new strategy reported[736b] that year by a team at University of Granada (UoG) in Spain led by Mónica Triviño successfully decreased confabulation in brain injury patients. The UoG report assessed: *"In particular, results point to a deficit in early stages of memory retrieval with the preservation of later strategic monitoring processes. Specifically, some of the processes involved may include selective attention or early conflict detection deficits."*

309

Rethinking the IP paradigm

Continued failure to experimentally demonstrate the mechanisms and locations of biological memory, and exactly how this attribute operates to give us physical reality, has led to doubts about the efficacy of the information processing (IP) paradigm that has dominated cognitive research for over 50 years. Neuroscientists and psychotherapists struggling to deal with escalating levels of brain diseases and mental health issues have been calling for multidisciplinary research into new models that might shed fresh light on neural malfunctions and memory degradation linked to aging.

'It' from 'bit'

The notion of information as a physical 'thing' like matter or energy can be traced to American theoretical physicist John A. Wheeler's famous 1989 *"it from bit"* proposal[737a]. John Searle, of course, has long criticised[737b] exclusively IP approaches to cognitive processes. Searle argues (and Wheeler himself later admitted) that meaningful information is 'observer-relative': in other words, perception of objects and events requires an 'intelligent' entity with mind-brain. This implies that the brain *creates* reality rather than mere computer-like IP constructs from mental representations.

Certainly, the capabilities of a dynamic, biological neuronal network transcend an algorithm-based computer by many orders of magnitude. The brain is all the more remarkable since it somehow manages to generate wide-ranging qualia, self-awareness, and other cognitive output using a mere fraction of the energy required by super-fast computers engaged in far less work. But, if more than IP is involved in creating our reality, what is the missing element and can it be quantified for scientific investigation? As cognitive psychologist Michael Rescorla has noted[737c], the absence of options is the reason IP advocates see it as *"our best overall framework for explaining numerous core psychological phenomena."*

310

Digital or analogue?

American psychiatrist Robert Berezin, a veteran who taught at Harvard Medical School for 30 years, summed-up criticisms of the IP approach in a scathing 2014 article[738a]:

> *"There is a major fallacy in neuroscience about the brain that of all things has ascended to the status of belief—that the brain is a computer stuck on top of a body, that it is an experimental machine that anticipates, guesses, and self corrects. [...] Computers operate via an incredibly fast system of computations based on 0's and 1's. This is a powerful way of information ordering which can create incredible order. But the brain does not operate this way. It isn't a scientist or a computer. It's a brain. It operates in an entirely different fashion."*

Berezin argued that, rather than *digital processing* of information 'bits', cognition involves *analogue recognition* of repeated and sustained patterns similar to the fractal-like[738b] repeats of physical form and abstract mathematics we observe throughout nature. This view echoes the Pattern Recognition Theory of Mind (PRTM) that computer scientist and futurist Ray Kurzweil outlined[738c] in his 2012 book *How to Create a Mind*. Kurzweil described the brain's neocortex as an assembly of millions of *"pattern recognizers"* that operate[738d] according to a basic algorithm. But others are sceptical that replacing a digital IP approach with analogue pattern recognition will bring scientists any closer to identifying the neurobiological pathways our mind-brain uses to detect, store and reconstruct worldly impressions.

Robert Epstein, a prolific author and former editor-in-chief of *Psychology Today*, is even more sceptical about explanations that liken human cognition to mechanistic processes. Controversially, he disputes that brains create 'symbolic representations' from sensory cues, or store and retrieve memories of any sort.

311

Epstein contended in a 2016 essay[739] that humans are born with innate *"senses, reflexes and learning mechanisms"*, but with none of the lexicons, data registers or other built-in elements that allow digital computers to carry out IP functions. He asserted that *"Not only are we not born with such things, we also don't develop them – ever"* and declared: *"The IP metaphor has had a half-century run, producing few, if any, insights along the way. The time has come to hit the DELETE key."*

But if our brains don't store and retrieve information and experiences in some manner, from where do we get the highly-organised associative memories that allow us to deal with recurrent situations and plan for future challenges? Exactly how, for instance, does our olfactory system match a smell cue with a previous identical experience to evoke subjective correlated likes or dislikes?

Holistic interactions

To explain our huge and varied assortment of mental attributes *without* IP, theorists have come up with concepts of *embodied cognition*[740a] and *enactivism*[740b] that view cognition as a much broader phenomenon beyond the brain involving[740c] an organism's *entire body* and *continuous interaction* with its environment. The idea has gained much support and generated a large amount of literature over the past three decades. Publications include *The Embodied Mind: Cognitive Science and Human Experience* (1992) by Francisco J. Varela, Evan T. Thompson and Eleanor Rosch; *The Extended Mind* (1998) by Andy Clark and David Chalmers; *Philosophy in the Flesh: the Embodied Mind & its Challenge to Western Thought* (1999) by George Lakoff and Mark Johnson; *Where Mathematics Come From: How The Embodied Mind Brings Mathematics Into Being* (2000) by George Lakoff and Rafael Nunez; *How the Body Shapes the Way We Think: A New View of Intelligence* (2006) by Rolf Pfeifer and Josh Bongard; and *Supersizing the Mind: Embodiment, Action, and Cognitive Extension* (2008) by Andy Clark.

However, despite the widespread enthusiasm for a new non-computational and non-representational approach to cognition, the notion of 'mind embodiment' has failed to dislodge IP as the dominant paradigm for mental phenomena. A major criticism has been lack of clarity[741a] about fundamental tenets that can be tested by experiment or modelled mathematically – a 2002 paper[741b] by psychologist Margaret Wilson from University of California (Santa Cruz) identified no less than *six* possible interpretations and described the extension of mind to the external environment as *"deeply problematic."* In a 2013 response[741c], colleagues Andrew Wilson and Sabrina Golonka from Leeds University in England protested that the concept of embodied cognition is misunderstood and is a proper subject for scientific research. King's College London philosopher Mirko Farina also pointed out in a 2020 review[741d] that *"there is a substantial body of empirical work showing how embodied activities constitutively shape many aspects of human cognitive life"*, including *"data collected from laboratory studies, naturalistic field observations, neuropsychological case studies, artificial intelligence and various phenomenological reports."*

The many claims and counterclaims about cognitive embodiment and environmental mind interactions are interesting. But, so far, these proposals have not produced any new insights into *neurobiological* pathways and mechanisms for memory (not to mention thought and exercise of free will) that might help therapists in the search for new strategies to combat our numerous mental ailments.

Holonomic brain model

Long before fresh scans of H.M.'s brain challenged[742a] decades-old assumptions[742b] about regional localisation of memory functions, distinguished neuroscientist and psychologist Karl Pribram teamed up with theoretical physicist David Bohm to explore a *global* (non-localised) model of brain function.

As Pribram recounted in a 2011 overview[743a] of their long collaboration, new research had shown the brain could maintain certain cognitive functions *despite* serious disruption to the neural connections traditionally associated with those functions. At the same time, it had become apparent that cognition involves highly integrated and real-time activity across multilayered neural circuits in multiple brain regions. So, if mental processes are driven by holistic operation of *all* brain areas, how does it manage to resume some functions after being partially damaged? Pribram summarised this paradox in a 1975 exploratory paper[743b,c]:

"The problem arises from the fact that large holes can be made in the anatomical organization of the brain without severely disturbing some functions that would be expected to depend on this precise organization. This does not mean that holes in the brain have no effect: when made in the sensory projection areas, for instance, such holes produce scotomata in the appropriate sensory receptive field. However, very little disturbance of sensory, perceptual, attentional, memory or other psychological process can be ascertained when tests are made within the remaining intact field. The remaining brain-behavior field, the remaining neural organization appears capable of taking over, functioning in lieu of the whole - the system shows equipotentiality as Lashley put it (Lashley, 1960). Currently, we would say that the sensory input becomes distributed over the reach of the projection system. The question arises, therefore, how."

To decipher the puzzle, Pribram and Bohm turned to the physics of holography developed[744a] by Dennis Gabor in the late 1940s which allows huge amounts of light-generated data from an object to be stored on media for later projection as a 3-D hologram; *each* bit of which stays *interconnected* and contains *all* essential information for reproduction of the original object. A holographic model might explain the brain's amazing capacity to maintain function, despite damage to some areas. Interestingly, in 1968, Gabor had sketched[744b] a mathematical holography-based model of memory recall.

In addition to the potential for lightning-fast recall and associative processing of different stored memories, Pribram recognised that holography offered a bridge for reconciliation of digital IP and analogue patterning views of brain function. He outlined his thoughts on a possible 'holonomic' model of cognition in his 1975 paper:

"The essence of optical information processing systems is their image construction potential. This capacity is to be compared and contrasted with the programming potential of the computer. Neither programs nor images reside as such in the information processing system - they are configurations made possible by the constriction of the system. Both images and programs can be captured and stored as such outside their processing systems. When this is done, there appears to be no superficial resemblance between the image or program and the system in which processing takes place, nor even with any readily recordable event structure that occurs during processing. [....] The power of these analogies to brain function comes when the mathematical description of these transformations can be shown by experiment to be identical for information processing by the brain as for processing by optical and computer systems. When in addition, the physical components responsible for the transformations are identified, a model of brain function can be constructed and tested deductively by subsequent experiment."

Pribram cited research that suggests the right hemisphere of the human brain is predominantly engaged with *analog* imagery, while the left hemisphere appears more functionally adapted for *digital* IP. He published a full version[745a,b] of Holonomic Brain Theory in 1990 and consolidated his lectures in the volume *Brain and Perception: Holonomy and Structure in Figural Processing* (1991). Subsequently, he published a condensed version of his ideas in a 1999 survey paper[745c]. However, a holographic interpretation presents fresh challenges for researchers: how are they to reconcile *physical* neural processes in the brain with *abstract* mind constructs and mental states grounded in the mathematics of optical illusions?

Cognitive psychologists have used[746a] *holographic reduced representations* (HRRs) to build impressive computational models[746b] of behavioural and neurological aspects of memory. But no physical structures or pathways have been detected in the brain for generation of the highly-complex Fourier computations that typically drive transformations between mathematical and optical holographic representations of objects; hardly surprising as these functions are more applicable to *quantum* rather than *neuronal* settings.

Indeed, Pribram's holonomic brain model can be better explained within quantum physics than by classical neuroscience and psychology. Although the multi-dimensional neural topography developed[746c] mathematically by Henry Markram and Blue Brain Project co-researchers at EPFL in Switzerland has extended[746d] options for geometric descriptions of phenomena like biological memory storage, generating solid experimental evidence for *observable* models of cognition may prove an insurmountable task.

Unexpected anatomical complexity

An estimated *86 billion* neurons and *trillions* of neuronal extensions are associated with cognitive processes in the human brain. In addition, there are equal volumes of glial cells providing[747a] structural and metabolic support. A Brazilian study[747b] reported in 2009 that, contrary to previous speculation, the estimated 1:1 ratio of neurons to glia in the human cortex is actually no different to that in other primates – a surprising finding that led the researchers to conclude that our brains are somehow *"isometrically scaled-up"* for higher cognitive tasks. However, brain cell count is not the only indicator of complex behaviour; the lowly fruit fly *Drosophila melanogaster*, thought to have just 100,000 neurons, still exhibits traits that make it a model organism for research.

In 2010, a team at Stanford University in California led by molecular and cellular physiologist Stephen Smith reported[748a] an imaging study that showed the brain's physical complexity is beyond anything previously imagined. The astounding results were obtained with high-resolution array tomography[748b]. As Smith observed[748c]:

"One synapse, by itself, is more like a microprocessor– with both memory-storage and information-processing elements– than a mere on/off switch. In fact, one synapse may contain on the order of 1,000 molecular-scale switches. A single human brain has more switches than all the computers and routers and Internet connections on Earth."

Neuroscientists have long speculated that different brain regions communicate with each other to generate cognition and behavioural response. However, hardly anything is known about how these distributed neural networks form or operate. For example, it was long assumed that the cerebral cortex in mammals (linked to higher-order functions such as cognition, emotion and consciousness) is a single, dense, interconnected maze. But, in 2014, researchers led by Hong-Wei Dong at University of Southern California's Institute for Neuroimaging and Informatics identified[749a] no less than *eight* distinct sub-networks in mice neocortex organised[749b] along a 'logical' underlying architecture.

In 2015, a team led by Dietmar Schmucker at Vlaams Institute for Biotechnology in Leuven, Belgium published[750a] new research that suggests *thousands* of isoforms (same-gene variants) of the protein *Dscam1* may be functioning as 'surface tags' to endow neurons with *"unique molecular identities"* for construction[750b] of the brain's hugely complex 'wiring' systems. Another study led by Z. Josh Huang at Cold Spring Harbor Laboratory, New York reported[750c] findings in 2017 that indicate[750d] neuron types and transmission patterns in the brain are actually 'hardwired' into genetic profiles.

317

Universal algorithm

In addition to the anatomical complexities that have emerged, neuroscientist Joe Z. Tsien of Augusta University in Georgia, USA revealed in a 2015 paper[751a] that computations which give us cognitive and behavioural flexibility arise from[751b] a unique *"power-of-two-based wiring logic"* in the brain. Tsien's team has developed a 'Theory of Connectivity' that suggests[751c] this basic algorithm is *pre-configured* from inception.

In 2016, Tsien and ten co-authors published[752a] further research that documented the algorithm operating in *seven different* brain regions – a strong indication that this might indeed[752b] be a *universal* cognitive principle. As stated in the opening summary of the report:

> *"We show that this power-of-two-based permutation logic is widely used in cortical and subcortical circuits across animal species and is conserved for the processing of a variety of cognitive modalities including appetitive, emotional and social information."*

These extraordinary developments illustrate the diminishing returns of conventional scientific investigations of consciousness and cognitive functions. To make progress, researchers may have to fully embrace uncomfortable ideas like Pribram's holonomic brain model and the Hameroff-Penrose Orch-OR[753a] hypothesis of quantum mind[753b]. As neurophysiologist and cyberneticist Alex M. Andrew noted in a 1997 essay[753c], we may be on the brink of a, literally, 'mind-boggling' breakthrough that will herald fascinating new insights into our mysterious mental abilities.

8. Mystery of Sleep

"Sleep that knits up the ravell'd sleeve of care,
The death of each day's life, sore labour's bath,
Balm of hurt minds, great nature's second course,
Chief nourisher in life's feast."
William Shakespeare, *Macbeth* (2:2, 48-51).

Is sleep a rehearsal of death?

Sleep is perhaps the most enigmatic of the many intriguing aspects of life. While in this unique state of reversible unconsciousness, we remain effectively 'dead' to the physical world if undisturbed and experience instead strange mental visions of objects and events that we may or may not have encountered in real life. Indeed, as renowned American philosopher Henry W. Johnstone Jr. commented in a 1976 article[754a,b], the idea of death as a radical 'deep sleep', from which all humans would awaken one day, was once widespread and lasted well into the modern era.

Interestingly, in ancient Greek mythology, sleep and death are represented[754c] by the deities *Hypnos* (origin of 'hypnosis') and *Thanatos* respectively; twin brothers born of *Nyx* (night) and *Erebos* (darkness). The mythical siblings are depicted as neighbours living in *Hades* (the underworld): *Hynos* also has a wife *Pacithea* (goddess of hallucination/relaxation); a union that produces *Morpheus*, *Phobetor*, and *Phantasos* – three deities that govern dreams. These metaphorical representations show that humans have long regarded sleep and death as closely related states that are distinct from our waking realities. But, as Johnstone Jr. argued in 1976, we can't meaningfully conceive the death experience because, unlike sleep from which we awaken daily, there's (as yet) no parallel reports of Christ-like resurrection that we can use as a conscious reference point.

Humans have always been haunted by the spectre of dying while asleep. Although modern reports are usually linked to health preconditions or natural causes in the elderly, incidences of what medical scientists call *Sudden Arrhythmic Death Syndrome* (SADS)[755a], or *Sudden Unexplained Nocturnal Death Syndrome* (SUNDS)[755b], do occur and are prevalent among otherwise healthy adults in south-east Asian populations – especially young men. The clinical reasons for SADS are unclear. A 2008 investigation centred at St George's University of London in England identified[755c] genetic disposition to heart disease in some families. However, a 2011 American review[755d] of over 900 cases reported in robust military personnel did not find any cardiac issues in nearly 21 percent of victims.

American medical anthropologist Shelley Adler concluded[756a] in *Sleep Paralysis: Night-mares, Nocebos, and the Mind Body Connection* (2011) that cultural beliefs in visitations by evil spirits at night may have contributed to high incidences of SADS among south-east Asian refugees in the 1980s. She supported this controversial analysis with documented intuitions of a similar nocturnal 'malign presence' in every society. Adler wrote: *"the night-mare, poised as it is between the supernatural and the natural worlds, and between the meaningful and the biological, is perfectly positioned to teach us about the seamless connection between our minds and our bodies."* As medical professional Dennis Rosen observed in a journal review[756b] of Adler's work, SADS, and the intense experience of nightmares, reminds us that we still know very little about the bridge between conscious mind and biological body.

Defining sleep

Until the 20th century, sleep was regarded as nothing more than a temporary lapse into unconsciousness that occurs when some animals are tired or have nothing important to do. However, it's now known that the phenomenon is a highly complex and regulated event during which parts of the brain remain active to varying degrees.

Scientifically, sleep is defined as a chronobiological[757a], circadian[757b], naturally-induced and controlled state of altered or diminished consciousness during which responsiveness to external sensory cues is reduced, and almost all voluntary muscular movements are inhibited. Ability to re-enter a state of wakefulness *on cue* makes sleep quite different from other states of immobility like coma and hibernation. Also, we experience remarkably *stable* states of wakefulness or sleep – we're awake or asleep; not in-between.

Electrical activity in the brain was first detected[757c] back in 1875 by English physiologist Richard Caton. But it was German psychiatrist Hans Berger's 1929 invention of non-intrusive *electroencephalography* (EEG) for measurement of brain wave patterns that marked the beginning of modern sleep science. Berger discovered that our brains exhibit *beta* waves while awake and *alpha* waves when we shut our eyes. Subsequently, yet another pattern of *delta* waves was observed when we're fully asleep.

Since the advent of EEG, new techniques like *electrooculography* (EOG), *electromyography* (EMG), *positron emission tomography* (PET), *functional magnetic resonance imaging* (fMRI) and *actigraphy* have given researchers increased insight into the multifaceted nature of sleep. However, much is still unknown about the mechanisms and functions of this fascinating phenomenon.

Traditionally, sleep has been associated with animals[758a] – especially birds and mammals. Diurnals are normally active during the day and sleep at night while nocturnals are active at night and sleep during the day; but altered patterns have been observed during seasonal migrations or during postpartum periods. Average periods of daily sleep range from[758b] as little as 2 hours for horses and elephants to almost[758c] 20 hours for little brown bats.

Remarkably, some birds and aquatic mammals are able to sleep with one half of their brain 'awake' and keep one eye open – a phenomenon neurophysiologists describe[759a] as *unihemispheric sleep*. It's assumed these animals evolved this unique 50/50 semi-conscious state so they could remain alert to threats from predators and environmental hazards. In 2016, a team at Brown University in Providence, Rhode Island reported[759b] experimental results that linked a similar protective adaptation to our initial inability to get a good night's sleep in unfamiliar locations.

Although non-animal organisms do not 'sleep' as such, they all have internal clocks (usually circadian) in every tissue that synchronise chronobiological rhythms to take maximum advantage of daily and seasonal environmental cues or *zeitgebers*. These clocks oscillate between heightened biological activity and phases of drastically lowered responsiveness to stimuli. As a 2016 study[760a] by a European team amply demonstrated[760b], the behaviour is particularly striking in plants.

Mechanisms and regulation

Sleep mechanisms

One of the major problems in sleep research is pinpointing the exact moment of transition from wakefulness into sleep. Although it's possible to entrain our brain to regularly awaken at a desired time, we're incapable of preventing sleep – sooner or later we drift off, whether we wish to or not. Sleep, it seems, is as inevitable as death. Drugs may prolong wakefulness (stimulants) or induce sleep (hypnotics), but neither state can be sustained indefinitely. Neuroscientists now know that sleep-wake cycles are controlled[761a] by a sophisticated array[761b] of timed events and neuronal processes. But despite extensive studies, the *origin* and *cues* for this autonomous, well-coordinated 'flip-flop' switch[761c] in nature remain unclear.

It's thought relative levels[762a,b] of several neurotransmitters and neuropeptides generated in the brain determine sleep-wake states: *serotonin, adenosine, galanin* and *GABA* are associated with sleep, while *histamine, norepinephrine, acetylcholine* and *orexin* (also called *hypocretin*) are associated with arousal and wakefulness. In 2010, researchers at Washington State University proposed[762c] a 'sleep switch' involving a cascade of neural activity triggered by[762d] release of the energy molecule *adenosine triphosphate* (ATP). But a novel statistical model for tracking the *Sleep Onset Process* (SOP) developed[762e] in 2014 by a team at Massachusetts General Hospital (MGH) highlighted the persisting difficulty in determining a transition point – the MGH study revealed[762f] some subjects still responded to stimuli as if they were awake *even though* their brains appeared to be clinically asleep.

Sleep regulation

The regulatory process for proposed mechanisms is just as speculative. The current accepted model involves two separate interacting systems in the brain's hypothalamus which links the nervous and endocrine systems. According to this 'two-process'[763a] explanation (first proposed by Hungarian-Swiss pharmacologist Alexander A. Borbély in 1982), during wakefulness, 'sleep-promoting' neurons cause us to steadily accumulate a 'sleep deficit' through 'Process S' homeostatic activity that eventually tips us through the 'sleep gate'. Immediately we fall asleep, our internal circadian clock aligned with solar 24-hour time kicks in to initiate a second 'Process C' countdown to arousal driven by 'wakefulness-promoting' neurons. Borbély suggested that mutual inhibition between these two processes ensures that we flip between stable states of wakefulness or sleep. He co-authored a 2016 review[763b] that reaffirmed the model's conceptual importance in sleep research; although some studies now assign[763c] a stronger role to Process C. However, actual *biomolecular interactions* and *event pathways* are still very much a mystery.

Sleep scientists speculate[764a] that Process S homeostasis is promoted by depletion of glycogen energy stores and accumulation of the neurotransmitter adenosine to inhibit arousal signals and enhance neuronal activity for sleep in the frontal VLPO zone of the hypothalamus. Notably, caffeine keeps us awake by negating the effects of adenosine. But the process involves far more than passive biochemistry. Researchers are unveiling a complicated 'sleep homeostat' that monitors the extent of sleep deficit and triggers transition into sleep; much like a thermostat switches off heating systems when room temperature gets too hot.

In 2014, a team at Oxford University's Centre for Neural Circuits and Behaviour identified[764b] a group of neurons that act as[764c] the homeostat's 'effector' output unit in fruit flies. Two years later, researchers at Johns Hopkins University in Maryland reported[765a] that yet another set of neurons function as[765b] a key 'integrator circuit' for tracking sleep debt. A separate 2016 study[765c] by a group led by Maiken Nedergaard from the University of Copenhagen in Denmark revealed that, surprisingly, astrocytes, a type of glial brain cell previously linked to *metabolic* activity only, may also have a *neurological* role in regulating[765d] salt ion levels that influence sleep-wake states.

A bit more is known about the neurobiological drivers of 'Process C' circadian timing. In vertebrates, the *suprachiasmatic nucleus* (SCN) in the brain's hypothalamus is the 'master clock' that sets the pace and controls a hierarchy of distributed local clocks at cellular, tissue and systems level. This relatively tiny structure (a network of just 20,000 to 50,000 neurons conveniently situated just above the optic chiasm) is illuminated by light received direct from the eye and synchronised according to day-night cycles for regulation of numerous biological systems. What's still not clear[766] is *how* the SCN operates to influence *trillions* of self-sustained, autonomous circadian oscillators in multiple organs and locations around the body.

In 2014, a team at Max Planck Institute for Biophysical Chemistry in Göttingen, Germany published[767a] results from a mice study that suggests[767b] peripheral clocks in organs can sustain their rhythm *without* the SCN – a conclusion supported[767c] by subsequent findings[767d,e] in 2019 by a collaboration between researchers at University of California (Irvine) and the Institute of Science and Technology in Barcelona, Spain. Tracing SCN 'oversight' is hugely complicated because this function is governed by[768a,b] *holistic* neuronal network activity; just like separate but *orchestrated* systems exercise control[768c] over circadian rhythms in invertebrates[768d] like fruit flies.

However, researchers are fairly certain that, in mammals, the SCN relays information to other hypothalamic areas for modulation of body temperature, while also signalling the pineal gland for production of the hormone melatonin to influence sleep-wake cycles. Studies have shown[769a] that melatonin secretion continues throughout the 24-hour circadian cycle, with levels *increasing* at night and *decreasing* by day. In humans, melatonin levels are highest[769b] between midnight and 08:00 hours in young children; sleep onset and waking occurs progressively later[769c] as adolescence advances. It's also known[769d] that melatonin secretion decreases with age, but the correlation is unclear. A detailed study published[769e,f] in 2007 by American researchers at Stanford University and Harvard Medical School (in collaboration with colleagues at University of Surrey in England) recorded comparatively higher levels during *waking* periods in older people; albeit with significant variation between the sexes.

Understanding how the SCN maintains overall control of local chronobiological oscillators for efficient synchronisation[770] of functions in organs like the heart, lungs, liver and kidney is a key goal for sleep therapists. Two common maladies – *shift work sleep disorder* (SWSD) and *desynchronosis* or 'jet lag' when we travel rapidly across time zones – have been linked to out-of-sync readjustments by autonomous local clocks in various body parts.

Over-exposure to artificial light[771a] at night can also disrupt[771b] circadian rhythms and critical metabolism – especially[771c] blue light from electronic devices. In 2014, researchers at McGill University in Montreal, Canada reported[772a] a study that suggests it may be possible to reset our biological clocks with clinical drugs. However, such interventions are very much a future prospect[772b].

Bizarre transitions

Strangely, although we may appear to experience an unbroken night's rest, sleep is not a uniform event. It actually progresses in successive cycles of specific phases and stages that exhibit different brain-wave patterns. Sleep patterns were first recorded[773a] with newly-developed EEG in 1937 by American science enthusiast Alfred Lee Loomis and co-researchers in New York. But it was physiologist Nathaniel Kleitman and his graduate student Eugene Aserinsky at University of Chicago who made the groundbreaking discovery[773b] in 1953 that sleep spans two very different modes – a *Rapid Eye Movement* (REM) phase associated[773c] with dreaming, and a *Non-Rapid Eye Movement* (non-REM or NREM) phase. Apart from involuntary eye movements that characterise REM sleep, this latter phase is accompanied by striking behavioural and physiological changes.

Kleitman hypothesised[774a] that we experience two types of sleep because the central nervous system follows a *multiple* ultradian (rather than *single* circadian) *Basic Rest-Activity Cycle* (BRAC) that oscillates over the 24-hour day – regardless whether we're asleep or awake. Subsequent studies revealed[774b] that NREM and REM sleep stem from *different* brain systems and pathways. In 1975, American psychiatrists J. Allan Hobson and Robert W. McCarley developed[774c] a mathematical model of *reciprocal* NREM-REM on/off neuronal switching circuitry. The Hobson-McCarley model has since been extensively modified, but the concept is still[774d] a foundational assumption in sleep research.

Each sleep cycle takes[775a] 90 to 120 minutes in humans. Hence, over a typical 8-hour sleep period, we will experience an average of[775b] five sleep cycles during which we flip between the two sleep phases. NREM sleep dominates early sleep cycles with progressively slower *synchronised* brain rhythms, while REM sleep gradually increases to dominate the last two cycles with fast *desynchronised* rhythms before awakening. Prior to 2007, up to four stages of NREM were identified within a sleep cycle; but the last two segments have since been merged[775c] into a continuous stage three. Awakening usually follows the last session of REM sleep.

Curiously, the REM phase does not follow immediately after NREM Stage 3 as we would expect. Instead, NREM Stage 2 is *repeated* before the switch to REM sleep. Thus, a typical sleep cycle will unfold as follows: *NREM 1 > NREM 2 > NREM 3 < NREM 2 > REM*. The reasons for this strange sequence, and the precise signals for onset and gearing of sleep modes, remain a complete mystery. However, typical features have been studied extensively[775d].

NREM Stage 1 (5 – 10 percent of sleep in adults) is marked by the morphing of brain waves from *alpha* to *theta* rhythms as drowsiness sets in. Eye movements get slower, but muscles are mostly still active leading to 'hypnic jerks' if we're startled. Conscious awareness of our surrounding recedes, but we usually protest that 'we're awake' if roused at this stage

NREM Stage 2 (45 – 55 percent of sleep in adults) is entered when alpha waves and eye movements cease completely. During this period of light sleep, muscles relax and apnoea (snoring) may result as the upper airway becomes floppy. Short bursts of high frequency brain waves called[776a] 'sleep spindles' commence along with *K-complex* waveforms. The significance of this unique neural activity over the longest phase of our sleep cycle is still not clear[776b].

NREM Stage 3 (15 – 25 percent of sleep in adults) is called *slow-wave sleep* (SWS)[777a] due to the onset of low frequency, high amplitude, delta brain waves. This period of deep sleep was formerly divided into an initial Stage 3 with less than 50 percent delta waves, and later Stage 4 dominated by delta waves. The combined interval is regarded as the sleep phase during which brain activity reduces, and anabolic processes intensify. But some high frequency sleep spindles and *K-complex* waves have also been observed, indicating the brain is not completely at rest. These neural spikes might explain[777b] parasomnia disorders[777c] during this stage like *pavor nocturnes* (night terrors), *somnambulism* (sleepwalking), and *somniloquy* (sleeptalking).

REM transition (15 – 25 percent of sleep in adults) is marked by[778a] the onset of electrical pulses called PGO waves that originate in the brainstem pons area, and end in the visual processing occipital lobe. These waves are thought[778b] to control the peculiar eye movements and related middle ear twitching associated with vivid dreaming. Homeostatic controls are suspended (an oddity not seen during other sleep phases or wakefulness) leading to unregulated body temperature and wild fluctuations in rates of respiration, heartbeat, and blood circulation. Muscle *atonia* (slackness and paralysis) also sets in, along with intermittent body twitching and penile or clitoral tumescence.

REM is also referred to as 'paradoxical sleep' because, while a sleeper is hardest to arouse during this stage, the brain becomes highly activated and EEG readings reveal surprising bursts of beta and gamma waves associated with wakefulness. But, apart from increased secretion of acetylcholine, all other neurotransmitters associated with wakefulness are virtually absent. The reasons for the exceptional features of REM (especially muscle atonia and recallable dreams) are contested[778c] and remain largely unexplained[778d].

In 2019, an international multidisciplinary team led by researchers from Denmark's Aarhus University published a study[779a] that used continuous fMRI scanning (in addition to the usual EEG monitoring) to *"characterise the spatiotemporal complexity of whole-brain networks and state transitions during sleep."* The novel technique yielded the first clear map of global neuronal activity patterns across the brain during sleep. It revealed that underlying processes are governed by far more complex brain dynamics than thought. As neuroscientist and lead report author Angus Stevner commented[779b]:

"This provides a new and potentially revolutionary understanding of brain activity during sleep which can in turn lead to new forms of treatment of the sleep problems that affect far too many people [...]

"Our results provide a modern description of human sleep as a function of the brain's complex network activities and we're trying to move on from the somewhat simplified picture that has thus far characterised our understanding of brain activity during sleep."

Why do living things sleep?

Humans spend an estimated[780a] one-third of their lives sleeping or trying to sleep and the phenomenon is ubiquitous[780b] in some form across the animal kingdom. This universality suggests the routine has a fundamental biological role. However, despite decades of research, there's still little understanding or consensus on why[780c] sleep evolved, or what[780d] its functions might be.

The diverse nature of sleep habits, and distinct phase transitions[781a] within same day/night cycles, makes it difficult to forge a common explanation. Also, it appears to be *maladaptive* behaviour that contradicts[781b] Darwinian expectation that organisms should be maintaining constant vigilance against predators and utilising every moment to gain competitive advantage for survival.

The negative consequences[782a] of sleep deprivation are well-documented[782b]: genetic mutations[782c,d] that hinder sleep can lead to fatalities in both humans and non-humans. Apart from individual health impacts, authorities now recognise[782e] the potential for huge socio-economic costs[782f].

Significantly, although accumulated sleep debt[783a] is difficult to redress, sleep-deprived individuals will fall asleep more quickly and show[783b] increased percentages of SWS and REM – behaviour that indicates these stages are the most important parts of the sleep cycle. Nonetheless, some researchers are sceptical of the notion that sleep has an underlying biological function.

Ecological adaptation?

American psychiatrist and sleep scientist Jerome M. Siegel is a leading advocate of the 'adaptive inactivity'[784a] view of sleep as nothing more[784b] than a way to conserve energy and optimise an animal's response to ecological and environmental conditions. In a 2008 review[784c], Siegel cited the huge variation in sleep states as evidence that the phenomenon doesn't have a universal function but is evolutionarily geared to support different lifestyles. British psychophysiologist Jim Horne also suggested in a 2013 article[784d] that aspects of wakefulness observed in REM sleep may simply represent 'revving up' of the brain and rehearsal for ecological challenges.

However, while it's true we wake up physically renewed and mentally refreshed, animals could, conceivably, have evolved similar wakeful restorative processes rather than risky, convoluted sleep routines. Certainly, net energy conserved is too insignificant to justify sleep's complexity – studies indicate[785a] that, although brain energy levels are restored[785b] in the NREM phase, consumption[785c] *increases* significantly during REM and any saved energy is likely redirected to support sleep mechanisms.

Furthermore, while *sleep drive* is only initiated every 24-hours by a homeostat[786a] controlled by dedicated[786b] neuronal circuits, *sleep debt* instantly activates remedial resets like intensified[786c] SWS and accelerated onset[786d] of the REM sleep phase. As psychiatrist and neuroscientist Chiara Cirelli, and long-time co-researcher Giulio Tononi (originator of the IIT theory of consciousness), observed in a 2008 essay[787a], *"sleep is universal, tightly regulated, and cannot be eliminated without deleterious consequences."* Indeed, while sleep function remains enigmatic[787b], accumulating evidence suggests the phenomenon is not optional but is essential in some way.

Repairs and maintenance?

One popular hypothesis is that sleep aids metabolic processes for physical restoration and growth. Several studies indicate that homeostasis of regulatory hormones is promoted by sleep. In particular it has been known[788a] since the 1990s that the SWS phase is critical for secretion of the growth hormone (HGH) which some researchers have associated with ageing, while production of multifunctional prolactin increases rapidly with sleep onset and decreases[788b] promptly on awakening. Although the mechanisms behind physical paralysis (atonia) during REM sleep are disputed[788c], this mysterious phenomenon has been linked to[788d] improved muscle efficiency in certain animals.

There's evidence that sleep may reduce[789a,b] the risk of diabetes and obesity by influencing regulatory hormones for glucose metabolism and appetite. Other findings suggest sleep strengthens[789c] the immune system and assists[789d] the healing of wounds. In 2019, researchers at the University of Pennsylvania published a novel study[790a] that revealed[790b] a protein encoded by the *NEMURI* gene helps our immune system to fight bacterial infection by acting[790c] in brain cells to induce deep sleep.

It's also emerged that sleep speeds up[791a] clearance of harmful metabolic waste products from the brain that can cause[791b] neurodegenerative disease, and provides[791c] a much-needed interlude for essential repairs to damaged DNA accumulated[791d] in neurons during wakefulness.

Memory data consolidation?

However, while the restorative and homeostatic benefits of sleep are clear enough, this is not seen as its primary function. Cirelli and Tononi argued against a passive 'null hypothesis' in their 2008 essay[792a]. They maintained that sleep can only be justified if it promotes *critical processes* that can't be performed during wakefulness. They pointed to 'disconnection' of the brain from environmental stimuli as an indication that the main function of sleep is likely *cerebral* rather than metabolic.

There's increasing speculation that the brain goes 'off-line' to allow memories encoded during wakefulness to be stabilised and transferred to long-term storage. Researchers have long associated sleep with enhanced memory – in 1924, American psychologists John G. Jenkins and Karl M. Dallenbach conducted[792b] seminal experiments that confirmed human memory retention improves considerably after sleep. Numerous studies[792c] have since suggested that, during sleep, memories are reactivated, cleansed and consolidated (organised and restructured); and then integrated (transferred from initial processing areas in the hippocampus to permanent storage in the cortex). Moreover, indications[792d] are that memories also undergo substantial 'de-contextualisation' into[792e] more general and abstract representations – a significant enhancement that facilitates speedy retrieval of factual data and experiences for application in unfamiliar or novel situations.

There's also observational support that the REM state is essential for *fresh* learning. A team from Columbia University in New York City showed in a study published[793a,b] in 2011 that REM sleep *decreases* proportionately with age from over 50 percent in newborn infants to just 15 percent of a sleep cycle in late adulthood – although a 2012 report[793c,d] from Kimberly Allen at Duke University School of Nursing in Durham, North Carolina linked the high percentage of infant REM sleep to *brain development* rather than memory processing.

As explained in a comprehensive 2007 review[794a,b] by prominent sleep scientist Robert Stickgold and colleague Matthew Walker at Harvard Medical School, researchers are still trying to identify and track the complex neural systems and processes that sort and store various memory types in long-term databanks during sleep. Until recently, it was thought *all* memory consolidation occurs[795a] over the REM phase – a view supported by observed increases in energy consumption[795b], heightened brain activitity, and vivid dreams. But, as German cognitive biopsychologist Jan Born and Swiss colleague Björn Rasch showed in a 2013 overview[795c], new findings suggest explicit (declarative) memories are processed during the SWS stage in NREM sleep state; while implicit (non-declarative) and emotional memories are processed during REM sleep. However, results are not conclusive and the matter is still not settled.

A 2014 South African study[796a] found that disruption of REM sleep may impair *declarative* memories in PTSD (post-traumatic stress disorder) patients – a finding buttressed by a 2016 report[796b] of another study by a team at McGill University in Montreal, Canada that used optogenetics to uncover similar effects[796c] in mice. Thus, it appears different types of memory are consolidated and integrated at different stages of sleep by different brain regions according to hidden rules – recorded patterns of brain activity in the hippocampal area are consistent with memory processes whether we're in a state of wakefulness, NREM sleep, or REM sleep.

Fascinatingly, brain waves during the SWS phase of NREM sleep are a 'replay' of patterns observed during wakefulness. In 2014, neuropsychologists Dylan Barnes and Donald Wilson from Nathan Kline Institute for Psychiatric Research and City University of New York published a study[797a] that showed rodent brains shut out new odor information during SWS; a remarkable result that suggests[797b] this is an *active* process to preserve the integrity of previously acquired memories undergoing consolidation. At least two other studies[797c,d] have since linked patterns of brain wave spindles during SWS to memory consolidation.

Another intriguing suggestion is that sleep facilitates[798a] human insight into otherwise hidden solutions; apparently it enhances our ability to extract and 'connect the dots' from all the disparate data we file away during wakefulness. In 2017, Brain & Mind Institute researchers at Western University in Ontario, Canada submitted a preprint report[798b] that identified *specific neural correlates* for problem solving during SWS spindles.

Overall indications are that efficacy of cognitive processes during sleep is significantly influenced by age, stress, brain damage, and even sleep timing[799a]. German studies published in 2008[799b] and 2013[799c] recorded marked differences[799d] in beneficial effects of sleep on implicit and explicit memory in adults and children. A 2013 French study[800a] found that older adults with early Alzheimer's disease experienced *lower* levels of SWS, a sleep stage associated with episodic memory – a contemporary American study suggests[800b,c] the SWS-episodic memory link may be stronger in young adults than otherwise healthy older subjects. However, despite the mounting evidence, some researchers strongly disagree that memory data is processed during sleep. Sceptics are unconvinced that *any* such information manipulation can take place with the brain in a state of suspended consciousness.

334

In 2000, neuroscientist Robert Vertes and psychologist Kathleen Eastman published two articles[801a,b] challenging the suggestion that memory is consolidated during REM sleep. Vertes issued an updated version[801c] of their arguments in 2004 summarised thus:

"(1) there is no correspondence between the cognitive content of waking and sleep, making it unlikely that sleep serves to consolidate waking experiences; (2) sleep is an amnesiac state, rendering it a very poor candidate for memory processing; and (3) by all accounts, sleep is involved in procedural but not in declarative memory, thereby narrowing the debate to the role of sleep in procedural memory."

The REM-memory link has also been challenged by Jerome Siegel. He wrote in a 2001 article[801d]:

"The evidence for this hypothesis is reviewed and found to be weak and contradictory. [...] The time spent in REM sleep is not correlated with learning ability across humans, nor is there a positive relation between REM sleep time or intensity and encephalization across species. Although sleep is clearly important for optimum acquisition and performance of learned tasks, a major role in memory consolidation is unproven."

Yet another view is that sleep may be facilitating *retention* (rather than consolidation) of new learning by 'erasing' old or unwanted memories. In 2015, neuroscientists at The Scripps Research Institute (TSRI) in Florida led by Ronald Davis showed that sleep regulates the neurotransmitter *dopamine* that's been associated with 'forgetting'. They reported[802a]: *"While some memories are long-lasting, most others fade away and are forgotten. Why we forget, has been an intriguing and central question in psychology and neuroscience for more than a century. Even though forgetting is often thought of as a failure or limitation of the brain, recent studies support the view that forgetting is a biologically regulated function of the brain allowing optimal adaptability to an ever-changing environment."*

335

Follow-up research by the TSRI team published[802b] in 2018 revealed that *just one* dopamine-producing nerve cell is enough[802c] to catalyse *both* learning and forgetting in fruit flies. However, although the hypothesis that sleep promotes learning and memory is now generally accepted[802d], precise mechanisms and pathways involved are still largely unknown[802e].

Neuron circuit resets?

Although they acknowledge sleep may have a role in memory processing, Cirelli and Tononi's preferred candidate for a core function is 'cerebral housekeeping'. They hypothesised[803a] in 2008 that sleep allows neuronal synapses which proliferate for fresh learning and memory during wakefulness to be pruned and quiesed to create a less noisy environment for memory consolidation and integration. Synaptic growth consumes up to 80 percent of available energy, so such 'damping down' activity might explain observed rises[803b] in brain energy levels during sleep. Cirelli and Tononi suggested[803c] the 'time-out' would also allow synapses to be 'rewired' for next-day use.

This subsequently restyled[804a] *Synaptic Homeostasis Hypothesis* (SHY) is controversial and hotly debated. One contentious issue is the implication[804b] that memory consolidation involves *weakening* rather than *strengthening* of synaptic connections as assumed in mainstream models of LTP and neural networks. A study reported[804c] in 2016 by leading neuroscientist Gina Turrigiano and colleagues at Brandeis University in Massachusetts found that[804d] the sort of compensatory synaptic adjustments proposed by SHY are actually *inhibited* by sleep and *enabled* by wakefulness; a result that cast doubt[804e] on the entire hypothesis and raised further troublesome questions about the reasons for such highly-targeted neuronal influences during the sleep-wake cycle.

But SHY is not entirely without experimental support. In 2017, a study[805a] at Johns Hopkins University in Maryland led by neuroscientist Graham Diering confirmed[805b] that weakening and scaling-down of synapses definitely occurs during sleep. Apparently, the process is driven by a protein *Homer1A* which is kept away from synapses during wakefulness by the hormone *noradrenaline* (a variant *Homer1C* had already[805c] been associated with synaptic dynamics).

Interestingly, a 2013 collaborative study[806a] led by researchers at University of Colorado Boulder (CU) revealed[806b] that neural connections in sleeping children weaken *within* both left and right brain hemispheres but strengthen *between* the hemispheres. The CU finding suggests pruning of neuronal synapses and memory consolidation may *both* be occuring during sleep.

Energy regulation?

American neurologist Markus H. Schmidt has put forward an *energy allocation* (EA) model to explain sleep's universality. Schmidt argued in a 2014 paper[807] that all species share a need *"to optimally allocate limited energy resources to essential biological processes"* like growth, maintenance and reproduction *"in a manner that maximizes reproductive output while meeting the energy constraints of the ecological niche."* Unlike earlier hypotheses that focus on energy savings, Schmidt's model emphasises dynamic *reallocation* of available energy during sleep.

Metaprogrammed oversight?

New evidence is emerging of *coordinated activity* between neural and physiological systems during sleep – a previously overlooked link. The development has increased speculation that sleep is a genetically embedded *pre-programmed* event for biological systems administration.

In 2019, a multidisciplinary group from institutions in Boston, Massachusetts discovered[808a] that the rhythmic flow of *cerebrospinal fluid* (CSF) in and out of brain ventricles during sleep (probably to clear[808b] waste products) is tightly correlated with *cerebral blood flow* (CBF) pulsations. It was observed[808c] that large surges of CSF follow reductions in CBF and resultant lowering of blood levels in the brain. Remarkably, these CSF/CBF oscillations are governed by *the same* slow brain waves in SWS – the NREM2 deep sleep stage already associated[808d] with memory consolidation. As discussed in a related article[808e], the unexpected finding has huge clinical significance.

Going forward

The quest for answers to the conundrum of sleep function has spawned a sizeable interdisciplinary research field. In July 2008, the Federation of European Neuroscience Societies (FENS) hosted a special symposium[809a] on sleep function at Lausanne, Switzerland. The event attracted 140 scientists and featured no less than 18 speakers from areas including clinical practice, pharmacology, neurophysiology and genetics. No consensus position emerged, but indications are that the issue will continue to generate interest; there's growing concern[809b] over public health consequences of expanding sleep deprivation driven by modern lifestyles.

In September 2020, American theoretical physicist Geoffrey West and computational biologist Van Savage announced[810a] a new mathematical model developed with sleep statisticians that predicted shifts in sleep pattern across age and species with surprising accuracy. West and Savage commented in a lay essay[810b] a year later: *"These findings reinforced our fascination with what a curious and biologically unusual process sleep is. [...] It will take much more work to fully unravel the mysteries of sleep, but our recent insights – about age-based shifts in the purpose of sleep and the mathematical, predictive theories that quantify them – represent an essential tool to plumb these depths even further."*

Weird dreams

Curiously, while we sleep we experience dreams: internal images, ideas, emotions, and sensations that are frequently disjointed and forgotten, but sometimes form coherent narratives that we recall on awakening. Dream content ranges from familiar scenarios and experiences to completely unknown events and bizarre, surreal visions. These intrusions last from a few seconds to as long as half-an-hour, and some people may have up to seven dreams per night.

Humans have been documenting dreams for over 5,000 years, but we are no nearer to understanding their origin and significance than did ancients who ascribed[811] mystical and spiritual meanings to this fascinating phenomenon. How, and why, does a brain that's effectively cut off from sensory and environmental inputs suddenly reignite mind activity while we're still in deep sleep?

Dream science

Modern scientific research into dreams is called *oneirology* (different from spiritual divination or *oneiromancy*). Dreaming has been associated with REM sleep since Aserinsky and Kleitman uncovered[812a] this distinctive sleep phase in 1953 – Kleitman confirmed[812b] the link in further *electroencephalography* (EEG) studies conducted with another protégé William Dement. Several other researchers have since noted[812c] the ability of subjects awakened from REM sleep to recall dream content in detail and with clarity.

However, the precise role of REM sleep in generating and shaping dream content is far from clear. Besides, since the 1980s, several researchers have denied[813a,b] that dreaming is restricted to the REM phase – eminent American psychologist David Foulkes argued consistently[813c,d] that dream mechanisms are active during *both* NREM and REM.

339

In 2013, a French group led by Isabelle Arnulf from the Sleep Disorders Unit at the Université Pierre et Marie Curie (UPMC) in Paris published a study[814a] that successfully traced[814b] dream activity to 'bottom up' stimulation of the sensory cortex by the same brainstem structures that induce REM sleep. But, just as with memory consolidation, new experimental results soon emerged to challenge REM dream dogma. In 2016, Giulio Tononi's team at University of Wisconsin-Madison (UWM) and Marcello Massimini at University of Milan used[814c] combined TMS (*transcranial magnetic stimulation*) and EEG to map brain activity that showed[814d] dreaming also occurs during NREM sleep.

Reported quantity and quality of NREM dreams are inferior[815a] to those experienced during REM. However, since these two sleep phases are produced by separate[815b] brain systems, differences in dream output are not that surprising. Nevertheless, detection of dreaming during NREM sleep has made it harder to determine the neural correlates of this intriguing by-product of sleep.

South African psychoanalyst and neuropsychologist Mark Solms published an influential paper[816a,b] in 2000 that identified a forebrain mechanism as the common pathway for dreaming in *any* sleep state. Solms argued that the brainstem oscillator which induces the REM state is just one of several possible activators of an ultimate forebrain mechanism for dreaming. This so-called 'dream-on' hypothesis has since received support from a *positron emission tomography* (PET) study reported[816c] in 2013 by a French team led by Perrine Ruby at CRNL-Lyon Neuroscience Research Center. Ruby and co-researchers found[816d] that anterior brain regions like the *temporoparietal junction* (TPJ) and *medial prefrontal cortex* (MPFC) show higher activity during sleep in people who recall dreams more frequently. The finding raised hopes that further studies of these areas might finally uncover the underlying neuropsychology of dreaming.

However, in 2017, Tononi's team at UWM published[817a] new results obtained with high-density EEG that associated a completely different brain area with neural correlates of dreaming. Instead of the *anterior* regions pinpointed by Solms and Ruby's group, the UWM researchers linked certain *posterior* cortical regions to both NREM and REM dreaming. They suggested that this newly identified posterior 'hot zone' might be the incubator for *all* dream experiences – a conclusion veteran sleep researcher Robert Stickgold considered[817b] unjustified as we can never be sure if people who don't report dreams have not actually dreamt but *forgotten* the entire incident on wakening.

Why do animals dream?

Investigation of possible dream function has been constrained by lack of direct, real-time *physical observation* of actual neural events while subjects are asleep. Researchers are restricted to non-intrusive studies of brain activity patterns, and interrogation of dreamers on wakening. Thus, most hypotheses are based on *analytic evaluations* of subjective reports that hark back to methods developed in the late 19th century.

Emotional cleansing

Austrian neurologist Sigmund Freud (1856 – 1939) is remembered[818a] as the originator of psychoanalysis. His seminal book, *The Interpretation of Dreams* (1900), laid the foundation for modern psychotherapy. Freud's approach was not the usual view of dreams as omens or spiritual messages; it was a forensic examination[818b] of possible links between primal human instincts and repressed emotions and desires. He introduced concepts like *wish fulfilment*[819a] (derived from his own 'Irma's Injection' dream), *day residue*[819b] (carry over of preceding day experiences), *dreamwork*[819c] (distorted content that hides latent meaning), and the highly controversial[819d] idea of *Oedipus complex*[819e] (physical childhood attraction to parents).

Freud forged a lengthy collaborative relationship with Swiss psychiatrist and psychoanalyst Carl Jung. But they fell out after Jung rejected Freud's emphasis on *individual* unconscious desires as the basis for dreams and neuroses in favour of what he termed[820a] the '*collective unconscious*' of society at large. Jung's ideas launched a new approach known as 'analytical psychology'[820b].

Although Freud's work is now largely rejected as haphazard and unscientific, his ideas still resonate[821a] in some research areas. The notion of day residue was an early insight into the dream-lag effect[821b] which has been associated[821c] with reactivation of waking memories during sleep for consolidation and integration into permanent stores in the brain's cortex. His Oedipus complex is now seen[821d] as a mistaken interpretation of natural attraction to partners who *look like* our parents.

In 1996, Ernest Hartmann, an Austrian-American psychiatrist and dream researcher, suggested in an outline paper[822a,b] that dreams contextualise and help us deal with emotional concerns that flow from traumatic experiences. Hartmann published a full proposal[822c] in 1998 (updated[822d] in 2010) on the therapeutic role of nightmares that was more robust than earlier psychoanalytic evaluations. However, psychologist G. William Domhoff argued in a 1999 presentation[822e] at the annual meeting of the Association for the Study of Dreams in Santa Cruz, California, that (a) Hartmann's results were far from convincing evidence that dreams are *metaphoric representations* of a dreamer's state of mind; and (b) he had failed to show that nightmares cease and dream content becomes less disturbing as traumatic memories subside over time. Nevertheless, Hartmann's hypothesis received fresh support from a 2010 neuroimaging study[822f] led by researchers at the University of Geneva in Switzerland that linked *activated brain regions* during dreaming with *emotional regulation*. But no one has shown exactly how interlinked mind-brain processes might be operating in dreams to solve emotional problems.

342

Adaptive social scenarios

A decade after Hartmann's proposal, American architect and engineer Richard Coutts suggested[823a] that, rather than serving as a *review* tool to heal trauma, dreams might actually operate as a *preview* screening of possible emotional responses to anticipated social events. We tend to channel information and experiences into preset patterns of thought and behaviour that define our personality; mental constructs psychologists call 'schemas' or *schemata*.

Coutts speculated that the succession of dreams we experience allows the mind to test and shape mental schemas into patterns that will best serve our waking needs. According to this hypothesis, the brain incorporates new dream content into existing schemas during NREM sleep and simulated consequences are played out in further dreams generated during REM sleep (similar to test scenarios employed in software engineering). To be effective, modified schemas need to be realistic and compelling; hence the reason REM dreams are so vivid and evoke such intense emotions.

The concept of emotional 'adaptive schemas' shaped by dreams for selection in real-life situations has gained mainstream support within neuropsychology. In 2010, Coutts published a pilot study[823b] that applied psychologist Abraham Maslow's famous hierarchy[823c] of human motivational needs (which lists[823d] *self-fulfilment* at the top and *physiological needs* at the bottom) in an analysis of 100 dream reports. According to Coutts, the results confirmed dream schemas were likely *"facilitators of human need satisfaction."* Five years later, he conducted a larger study[823e] of dream reports from over 15,000 subjects and concluded: *"The findings of the present study provide support for the proposed extension to the continuity hypothesis, that the waking experiences that are continuous in dreaming are those relevant to the satisfaction or thwarting of human needs."*

Threat simulation

In 2000, Finnish psychologist Antti Revonsuo proposed[824a] a different simulation hypothesis of dream function that emphasises perceived *physical threats* rather than *emotional needs*. He described dreaming as an evolved, adaptive process that simulates real-life threats so we can rehearse avoidance measures for survival. Revonsuo argued: *"Empirical evidence from normative dream content, children's dreams, recurrent dreams, nightmares, post traumatic dreams, and the dreams of hunter-gatherers indicates that our dream-production mechanisms are in fact specialized in the simulation of threatening events, and thus provides support to the threat simulation hypothesis of the function of dreaming."*

To test this Threat Simulation Theory (TST), Revonsuo and co-researchers at the University of Turku in Finland carried out a study that compared dreams reported by severely traumatised refugee children to those of contemporaries brought up in non-threatening environments. They reported[824b] in 2005: *"The severely traumatized children reported a significantly greater number of dreams and their dreams included a higher number of threatening dream events. The dream threats of traumatized children were also more severe in nature than the threats of less traumatized or non-traumatized children."* Revonsuo's team subsequently developed and applied a new Dream Threat Scale (DTS) analytical tool to a wider range of subjects and obtained results[824c,d] they contended reinforced a TST function for dreams.

However, many dreams have non-threatening content that reflects problem-solving or pleasurable fantasies. As Jay Dixit, former senior editor of *Psychology Today* observed in a 2007 essay[824e]: *"Intriguing as Revonsuo's theory is, not everyone is sold on the idea that dreams are primarily a theater of threat rehearsal. Dream researchers have known for centuries that dreaming helps problem solving, for example—but they still do not know why."*

Virtual reality prepping

Neuroscientists, in particular, have been generally reluctant to endorse proposals on dream function without supporting data on *biological* mechanisms that can be empirically investigated. In 2001, American psychiatrists Robert Stickgold and J. Allan Hobson teamed up with Norwegian psychologists Roar Fosse and Magdalena Fosse, to write a special review[825a,b] on the connection between sleep, dreams and learning. The co-authors lamented that, since Freud's psychoanalytic proposals, *"there has been a frustrating dearth of scientific evidence concerning the mechanism of dream construction and its possible functions."* They urged colleagues in the neurosciences to consider a new *"multilevel system of sleep-dependent learning and memory reprocessing, wherein dreams would be the conscious manifestation of these processes."*

Hobson adopted this expansive approach in a fascinating 2009 article[825c] that suggested the onset of dreaming during REM sleep could be a hangover from early 'protoconsciousness' in the evolution of mammals and birds. In other words, dreams may be[825d] *virtual projections* by a parallel, primordial state of consciousness that's always 'switched on'; ready to 'rev up' brain neural circuits in preparation for the challenges of wakefulness. Hobson wrote:

> *"We know how, but not why, the brain is activated in sleep. I suggest that brain activation in sleep allows the development and maintenance of circuits necessary for higher brain functions, including consciousness. [....] REM sleep dreaming can be viewed as a virtual reality pattern generator used by the brain to instantiate and maintain its readiness for adaptive interaction with the world."*

G. William Domhoff likewise speculated[826a,b] in 2011 that, given the similarities with waking cognition identified in developmental and neurological studies, dreaming *"may be a subsystem of the waking default network, which is active during mind wandering, daydreaming, and simulation."*

345

According to Domhoff, such a foundational assumption grounded in *physical* neural connectivity would open the door to proper neuroscientific investigation of dreaming. As he observed: *"If this theory is correct, then dreaming may be the quintessential cognitive simulation because it is often highly complex, often includes a vivid sensory environment, unfolds over a duration of a few minutes to a half hour, and is usually experienced as real while it is happening."* He further declared in a 2019 review[826c]: *"Dreaming is an intensified and enhanced form of spontaneous thought that can be characterized as an "embodied simulation"."*

Interestingly, Chinese theorist Jie Zhang has independently developed an integrated explanatory framework for sleep, memory and dreams that also assumes the existence of an *always switched-on* primordial conscious state powered by virtual processes in the brain. In 2016, Zhang published an updated version[826d] of his ambitious 'continual activation' hypothesis that uses principles of reverse engineering to model a wide range of mental phenomena. He contended:

> *"The human heart, once it first begins beating inside the womb, needs to maintain "beating" until death. This is no different for a human brain. Once activated, it has to be continually activated all lifelong. When the brain cannot be activated externally through sensory inputs, it will activate itself from within. [...] Therefore, the existence of the continual-activation mechanisms provides a safeguard for life to go on during sleep, and is also a necessary condition for animal hibernation."*

Should experimental evidence emerge to support the idea that consciousness and brain representations are fundamental and essential virtual components of reality that continue while we're asleep (like background daemon processes in computers), it will force a paradigm shift away from long-held assumptions about the nature of life, death and the physical world we experience in between.

Non-human animal dreaming

Significantly, dreaming is not unique to humans; similar behaviour has long been observed in other animals. Over 2,300 years ago, Aristotle wrote in *History of Animals* (Book IV, 10)[827]:

> *"...it would appear that not only do men dream, but horses also, and dogs, and oxen; aye, and sheep, and goats, and all viviparous quadrupeds; and dogs show their dreaming by barking in their sleep. With regard to oviparous animals we cannot be sure that they dream, but most undoubtedly they sleep."*

Scientists now have more confidence about possible dreaming by oviparous (egg-laying) creatures. Brain wave patterns consistent with sleep states that promote dreaming have been recorded in birds (ostriches)[828a] certain reptiles (bearded dragons)[828b,c] and even some fish (zebrafish)[828d,e].

Experiments on rats since the early 2000s by neuroscientist Matthew Wilson at MIT's Picower Institute for Learning and Memory have confirmed[829a] Aristotle's intuition that lower animals also have[829b] complex dreams. Wilson and co-researchers showed[829c] that rodent dreams involve actual visual images as in human dreams; thus reinforcing[829d] the hypothesis that waking memories are reactivated for further processing during sleep. Surprisingly, waking experiences appear to be replayed[829e] in *reverse order* during dreaming.

As non-humans don't report their dreams, we can only draw conclusions[830a] about likely contents from brain activity patterns. In 2000, Daniel Margoliash and Amish Dave at University of Chicago in Illinois reported[830b] that songbirds appear to rehearse and fine-tune songs during sleep. In 2015, behavioural neuroscientists at University College London published[830c] research that indicates rats form dream representations of food placed in unexplored spaces.

Techniques used in non-human animal dream experiments are quite invasive, so this line of research remains relatively limited. But there's growing acknowledgment[831a] that *dream* deprivation might be[831b] a major factor in some of the ailments linked to sleep loss. Proposed therapies are likely to continue to differ depending[831c] on which approach – psychoanalytic or neuroscientific – is adopted in dream research.

Can dreams be hacked?

In 2012, Matthew Wilson and MIT Picower colleague Daniel Bendor reported successful manipulation[832a,b] of rat dreams by replaying task-related audio cues the rodents had been trained to recognise. The astonishing feat raised questions[832c] about the extent to which human dreams and memories could be similarly 'hacked'.

Induced dreaming

In 1913, Dutch psychiatrist and author Frederik van Eeden introduced[833a] the term 'lucid dream' to describe a peculiar mental state close to awakening in which a person becomes *aware* they're dreaming and is thought to be able to shape dream content. Although it's now recognised that dreams arise in both NREM and REM sleep phases, lucid dreaming only occurs in the latter part of REM.

British psychologist Celia Green attempted the first scientific analysis of the phenomenon in her 1968 book *Lucid Dreams*. She identified[833b] this sleep stage as a unique state of consciousness and predicted a connection with REM physiology. Green also linked the experience to *false awakenings* – realistic dreams of getting up and indulging in daily routines. However, others were sceptical[833c] that a person could become 'self-aware' while still asleep. As lucid dreams tend to occur just before waking, the experience was viewed[833d] as an interlude of *semi-wakefulness* rather than sleep dreaming.

Green had speculated[834a] that a lucid dreamer might be able to use prearranged signals to communicate with an observer. But, as muscle atonia (paralysis) is a hallmark of the REM state, it was difficult to see how this could happen. Then, in 1975, British psychologist Keith Hearne devised an 'ocular-signalling' technique that allowed[834b] lucid dreamers to signal using typical REM eye movements. American psychophysiologist Stephen LaBerge developed[834c] similar methods through independent research: in 2000 he reported[834d] a series of experiments that established lucid dreaming as a type of *conscious* experience during sleep.

LaBerge subsequently co-authored a 2006 study[835a] into *"psychophysiological correlates of lucid dreaming"* that recorded significantly heightened activity in the cortical parietal lobe – a brain zone associated with semantic understanding and self-awareness. Over a decade later, a group at University of Wisconsin (Madison) led by Giulio Tononi confirmed[835b] the link from results of a *magnetic resonance imaging* (MRI) analysis of 14 frequent lucid dreamers.

Remarkably, some people are able[836a] to initiate lucid dreaming at will and even control content and narratives. This natural or acquired attribute has motivated some therapists to investigate whether a 'dream hacking' tool can be developed to resolve sleep disorders. In 1970, American psychologist and parapsychologist Charles Tart and research associate Lois Dick published[836b] the unsettling results of an experiment in which subjects reported dream content that had been *planted* under hypnosis. The concept has received wide publicity[836c] and inspired an industry offering[836d] all sorts of aids to induce therapeutic lucid dreaming or pleasurable oneironautical 'trips'. However, a 2012 review[836e] led by Tadas Stumbrys from Heidelberg University in Germany concluded that, while some techniques were *"promising"*, they were far from being reliable or consistent.

Nonetheless, the vogue persists and gained[837a] new enthusiasts during the COVID-19 pandemic. As British parapsychologist and author Susan Blackmore remarked in a 1991 overview[837b], although the practice has become *"something of a New Age fad [...]this commercialization should not let us lose sight of the very real fascination of lucid dreaming. It forces us to ask questions about the nature of consciousness, deliberate control over our actions, and the nature of imaginary worlds."*

Consciousness transitions

Indeed, there's growing recognition[838a] that lucid dreaming may represent a 'consciousness borderland' that researchers might be able to exploit for deeper insights into human reality. In 2009, a group led by neuropsychologist Ursula Voss at Goethe University in Frankfurt, Germany published a report[838b] (co-authored by REM sleep specialist J. Allan Hobson) that concluded: *"lucid dreaming constitutes a hybrid state of consciousness with definable and measurable differences from waking and from REM sleep, particularly in frontal areas."* Three years later, another German group led by Michael Czisch at Max Planck Institute of Psychiatry in Munich reported separate research[838c] that linked lucid dreams to *"reactivation of areas which are normally deactivated during REM sleep."* Czisch suggested[838d] their results could account for the peculiar presence of *cognitive* capacity while we're still *physiologically* asleep.

The brief, semi-lucid state during sleep *onset* in NREM Stage 1 (termed *hypnagogia*)[839a] has also long been regarded as a 'consciousness tunnel' that could be explored for creative inspiration. Renowned 19th century English author Charles Dickens drew heavily[839b] on personal and reported hypnagogic experiences in his prolific writings. In her acclaimed 2001 book *The Committee of Sleep*, Harvard Medical School psychiatrist Deirdre Barrett narrated[839c] how other famous innovators like Nikola Tesla and Salvador Dali would clutch a small metal object while drifting off to sleep in the hope that the muffled noise on falling would jolt them into semi-lucidity without waking up.

Since 2017, a team at MIT's Dream Lab has been researching ways to adopt old hypnagogic techniques in a 'hacking' project[840a] that seeks to *"augment human creativity by extending, influencing, and capturing dreams in Stage 1 sleep."* The outcome so far is a hand-worn social robot dubbed *Dormio* with *"unique interactive and embodied capabilities"* for tracking sleep and using[840b] audio cues to suggestively manipulate hypnagogic dream content in subjects. In a May 2020 report[840c,d], lead co-researcher Adam Horowitz and colleagues described the extraordinary results after an initial trial test of the device on over 50 people:

> *"While dream content can predict post-sleep memory enhancement, dreaming itself remains a black box. Here, we present a novel protocol using a wearable electronic device, Dormio, to automatically generate serial auditory dream incubations at sleep onset, wherein targeted information is repeatedly presented during the hypnagogic period, enabling direct incorporation of this information into dream content, a process we call targeted dream incubation (TDI). Along with validation data, we discuss how the Dormio device and TDI protocols can serve as tools for controlled experimentation on dream content, shedding light on the role of dreams in the overnight transformation of experiences into memories."*

Dreams and reality

The striking similarities in patterns of brain cognitive activity observed in *both* waking and dream states have renewed speculation that life may be one long dream or simulated reality. In this scenario, our levels of consciousness are emergent, pre-programmed features that arise in response to environmental and interpersonal stimuli. Intriguingly, the vivid imagery and emotional anguish we recall after REM dreams is frequently embedded in memory to the *same extent* (or even more so) as waking experiences. As a significant proportion of dream content has *not* been previously experienced in real life, it raises the question just *where* such representations come from.

Dream argument

Advocates of this so-called 'dream argument' cite neurological and psychological findings[841a] that even our physical senses can mistake false dream events for reality. As Ronald Suter showed in a 1976 article[841b], variations of this worldview have been proposed by a long line of thinkers going back to the observation in Plato's dialogue *Theaetetus* (c. 369 BCE)[841c] that there's no way to be certain our waking perceptions are not, in fact, dream perceptions. Same-era Chinese philosopher Chuang Tzu (Zhuangzi) also discussed the philosophical difficulty of distinguishing dream states from waking states in his famous butterfly allegory[841d]. Zhuangzi said he dreamt (and was totally convinced while asleep) that he was a happy, carefree butterfly. However, on awakening Zhuangzi found his sense of reality had become disconcertingly blurred; he could no longer say whether he was a *man* who had dreamt of being a butterfly, or a *butterfly* now dreaming of being a man. The simple narrative is a powerful illustration of our tenuous grasp on reality.

In his 1641 work *Meditations* (Book 1)[842a], French philosopher René Descartes likewise used the dream argument to cast doubt[842b] on *all* sensory perceptions and beliefs we harbour about the world we inhabit. Although he later observed in Book 6 that dream *discontinuity* (narratives cease on awakening) might indicate falsity, his sceptical outlook continues to influence Western philosophical debate[842c] about the relationship between dream experience and waking reality.

Interestingly, the idea of 'dream time' is at the heart of cultural and existential beliefs of Australian Aborigines. They use the concept to describe an eternal universe from which human perception of time and reality emerged. It shapes their foundational worldview that all meaning in life derives from the cumulative experiences of ancestors.

However, Canadian philosopher Scott Stapleford argued reassuringly in a 2019 article[842d] that *"dreaming arguments are no cause for alarm"* about our ontological status as tangible, corporeal beings. Whatever the truth about our perception of reality, perhaps the greatest mystery is that we're able to indulge in cognitive inquiry and empirical investigation into the nature and origin of our own existence. Uniquely among organisms, these *historically recordable* endeavours survive our biological demise and serve to enlighten succeeding generations.

9. Mystery of Death

"What awaits us when we die? Unfortunately, those with enough personal insight into the matter are dead and unable to enlighten the rest of us. Whether they smile knowingly down from a heavenly perch or slip into unconscious oblivion cannot be known while on this earth."
Scott D. Smith, physician and medical scientist, in
Coping with the mystery of death (2009)[843]

When do we stop existing?

Prior to the 20th century, establishing a state of death was relatively straightforward. Humans were considered to be no longer alive if they ceased breathing, had no detectable heartbeat and proved unresponsive to external stimuli. The matter was put beyond doubt by the onset of *rigor mortis* and rapid decomposition of body tissue. 'Dead' meant fully demised – the end.

However, the advent of life support techniques and ingenious artificial organs have radically altered our traditional demarcation of life and death. Humans can now be kept going for a long time despite the failure of vital organs for self-sustenance. The increasing efficacy of medical interventions has sparked intense debate within bioethics about exactly where the borderline can be drawn in people with semi-autonomous functions that can only survive with the aid of technology. So-called *transhumans*, who have undergone 'bio-hacking' or partly replaced body parts (including brain tissue) with artificial nanomaterials, have further blurred the landscape of life.

Defining being 'alive' solely in terms of biology leads to other questions such as: do other animals *understand* or *contemplate* death? Spanish philosopher of science Susana Monsó argued in a 2021 essay[844] that a minimal concept of death as *"non-functionality and irreversibility [...] is likely to be very widespread in the animal kingdom."*

Legal death

Definition of the precise point in time at which a person becomes 'deceased' is essential for legal as well as medical considerations. Certainty is required for decisions about switching off life support machines, withdrawing medication and food, transplanting organs, releasing corpses for burial, and activation of processes like probates. Growing use of living wills (advance instructions on one's own healthcare in case of incapacitation), and continuing controversies in sensitive areas like assisted suicide or euthanasia (deliberate termination of life to end pain and suffering), has increased pressure on medical scientists for a consensus position on life-death transition.

A death certificate issued by a doctor is accepted as *prima facie* evidence of a person's demise in most jurisdictions; although surgical autopsies and judicial inquests are ordered in cases where the cause of death is unclear or there is widespread public interest. However, professional opinions on states of life and death are being increasingly challenged by relatives and advocacy groups.

Non-cognitive persons

Some patients with severe brain damage continue to display aspects of arousal, but lack cognitive ability or awareness. Unlike comatose persons that are *totally* unresponsive, PVS patients regain sufficient levels of consciousness for sleep-wake cycles and unaided breathing. The condition is technically described as loss of *behavioural function* in the cerebral cortex, while retaining *primitive reflex* and *motor functions* driven by the brainstem. This peculiar state was first identified by German psychiatrist Ernst Kretschmer in 1940, but it was Scottish surgeon Bryan Jennett and American neurologist Fred Plum who coined[845a] the term *persistent vegetative state* (PVS) in 1972 that's now widely-used to describe the condition.

PVS illustrates the legal and ethical quagmire medical decision-makers now have to navigate. Patients don't usually require life support apart from feeding and hydration (they're unable to swallow unaided), so the condition can continue for an indefinite period. Therapy is difficult, as hospitals still lack a non-invasive way to probe the exact site and extent of neural damage. The burden this impasse places on family and health care providers has prompted[845b] high-profile court cases in the UK and USA. However, the position on obligations and authority to withdraw sustenance is still unclear[845c].

PVS is part of a class of *disorders of consciousness* (DOC); a multilevel scale of cognitive disruption that continues to defy accurate diagnosis and prognosis for clear-cut medical decisions. To complicate matters, a significant number of patients have made unexpected recoveries to varying degrees. A 1993 review of 43 PVS cases by British brain damage specialist Keith Andrews revealed that[846a,b] 11 patients (25 percent) had regained awareness after more than *4 months*. In 2006, a German-Israeli team led by Boris Kotchoubey from University of Tubingen reported the case[846c,d] of a 28-year-old patient who emerged from PVS after an astonishing *20 months*.

Cognitive neuroscientist Adrian Owen has pioneered[847a] advanced brain imaging techniques at University of Western Ontario in Canada that uncovered[847b] unexpected mental capacity for communication in PVS patients judged to be clinically 'unaware'. The research has shown that some patients are not really in an *irreversible* 'vegetative' brain state, but have suffered *reversible*, trauma-induced *cognitive motor dissociation* (CMD)[847c]. Following several incidents[848a,b] of 'miraculous' PVS recoveries since 2010, Owen teamed up with bioethicists Andrew Peterson and Jason Karlawish (OPK) to co-author *Alive inside* (2019) – a compelling review[848c] that called for mandatory use of neuroimaging to assess the true state of brain-damaged patients.

OPK argued that, despite *"issues of false hope, patient suffering, and cost"*, it was ethically incumbent on clinicians to use *all* investigatory tools available to identify CMD cases with potential for recovery. Judging by the response, colleagues agree. As Oxford University philosopher and bioethicist Mackenzie Graham wrote in a passionate December 2021 analysis[848d]:

> *"The discovery of consciousness in these patients raises difficult questions about their well-being, and it has been argued that it would be better for these patients if they were allowed to die. Conversely, I argue that CMD patients may have a much higher level of well-being than is generally acknowledged. It is far from clear that their lives are not worth living, because there are still significant gaps in our understanding of how these patients experience the world."*

The challenge[849a] to distinguish[849b] CMD patients, and others in a *minimally conscious state* (MCS) with a chance[849c] of cognitive recovery, is now a major area of research. Unsurprisingly, given the continued confusion over a medical definition of consciousness, the task is fraught with diagnostic[849d] and prognostic[849e] problems. However, in January 2022, cases were reported in Russia[849f] and Switzerland[849g] where novel techniques successfully detected 'covert consciousness'.

Controversy has been further stoked by the unexpected result of experimental nerve therapy in a long-term French PVS case. In 2017, cognitive neuroscientist Angela Sirigu and a team centred at the French National Center for Scientific Research (CNRS) reported[850a] that *electrical stimulation* of the vagus nerve had partially revived a male car crash victim who had been unresponsive for *15 years*. The extraordinary outcome rekindled debate[850b] about the legal status and rights of PVS patients. Also, as Michael Price discussed in a feature article[850c], the possibility of even *minimal* recovery exacerbates already contentious issues of care costs and insurance coverage.

357

Clinical death

The traditional test for death – cessation of respiratory and blood circulation – is still the accepted clinical standard. However, life processes are so complex that this approach is far from infallible. History abounds with anecdotal and documented reports[851a] of people being declared dead and even interred erroneously; *taphophobia* (fear of being buried alive) is not as irrational as one might think. Public concern was so high in the 18th and 19th centuries that special coffins with escape hatches and alarm bells were designed and patented in case a buried person 'awoke'. While the risk has declined with advances in medical science, troubling reports persist of misdiagnoses of death with horrifying consequences.

As recently as 2017, a 24-year-old man in Peru[851b] and a teenager in India[851c] were reported to have started showing signs of life while being conveyed to their own funerals. Traumatic as these experiences must have been, the victims were at least spared the ordeal of a Venezuelan[851d] who was aroused by sharp pain from a knife incision at his 'autopsy' in 2007, and an American[851e] who narrowly escaped confinement in a freezing morgue in 2015 after being wrongly declared clinically dead.

A woman in Bogota, Columbia was even luckier in 2010: the undertaker at a funeral home was just about[851f] to inject deadly embalming fluid into her leg when he detected movement. Sadly, another unfortunate woman in Austria, who was wrongly declared dead from a heart attack in 2011, eventually died from shock after waking up[851g] to find mourners filing past her open coffin.

Since 1982, medical researchers have been aware of a so-called 'Lazarus syndrome'[852a]; people thought dead after failed attempts at *cardiopulmonary resuscitation* (CPR) suddenly self-revive[852b] and regain circulatory functions. In medical terms, the phenomenon is known as 'autoresuscitation' or *delayed return of spontaneous circulation* (ROSC)[852c].

A British review[852d] identified 38 ROSC incidents as at 2007. The authors re-emphasised the need for patients to be monitored for a reasonable period after unsuccessful CPR before certifying death:

> *"It is important to realize that death is not an event, but a process. The conference of Medical Royal Colleges in the UK advocated that death is a process during which various organs supporting the continuation of life fail. Cessation of circulation and respiration is such an example. The physical findings to support this—absence of heartbeat and respiration—are the traditional and the most widely used criteria to certify death. Since these findings alone are not a sign of definitive death, it is quite possible to declare death in the interval between cessation of CPR and delayed ROSC. [.....] Death should not be certified in any patient immediately after stopping CPR, and one should wait at least 10 minutes, if not longer, to verify and confirm death beyond doubt."*

However, there is no consensus on just how long should be allowed for passive monitoring. An extensive Canadian review published[852e] in 2010 uncovered reports of autoresuscitation from a few seconds up to *33 minutes* after failed CPR – although monitoring in some cases was considered substandard. The authors called for more studies to clarify the issue, stressing that *"existing evidence is limited and is consequently insufficient to support or refute the recommended waiting period to determine death after a cardiac arrest."*

Meanwhile, hospitals struggling to allocate scarce resources must make difficult decisions. In 2016, a probe was launched in KwaZulu-Natal, South Africa after a 28-year-old car accident victim was found alive[853a] in a morgue over *24 hours* after being declared dead. He was returned to hospital and revived, but, sadly, passed away[853b] shortly after. Hospital staff claimed he had failed to respond over a 5-hour period of CPR and other resuscitation efforts.

Morticians in most countries are now experienced enough to guard against the calamity of being actually *buried* alive after a mistaken death diagnosis. Nonetheless, the risk is still real in societies with a tradition of quick burials.

In 2014, cemetery visitors in Perraia, Greece reported[854a] hearing cries for help and banging from a grave where a woman had just been buried. Gravediggers hurriedly dug up the coffin, but medics could find no sign of life in the exhumed body. Distraught family members hired a lawyer; they were adamant the victim had suffocated to death after waking up underground. The following year, relatives of a Honduran teenager smashed a concrete tomb to retrieve her coffin after similar reports[854b] of muffled banging and screaming at the site. Witnesses reported apparent signs of a struggle to escape (smashed coffin viewing window, forehead scratches and bruised fingertips).

In a truly bizarre case reported[854c] in 2018, a police investigation was launched after several eye-witnesses claimed a woman certified dead from cardiac arrest had revived after *11 days* and tried to fight her way out of her coffin at a cemetery in Riachao das Neves, Brazil. Relatives alerted by nearby residents claimed her exhumed body was *warm*, with new hand and face injuries that were absent at burial.

British mortuary technician Carla Valentine reassured in a 2014 article[854d] that mistaken burials are unlikely in societies with access to sophisticated medical facilities – but admitted the tragedy is not totally inconceivable if signs of life are missed in the morgue. As she remarked wryly, *"But then again, we wouldn't know about those unfortunate people, would we?"* Indeed. The dead tell no tales.

Despite the controversies[854e], traditional clinical death tests are still the most widely-employed by busy physicians. But medical scientists have now developed more sophisticated definitions of death.

Brain death

Since the 1960s, permanent loss of *brain function* has been promoted as a better indicator of death than cessation of breathing and heartbeat. Brain cells (neurons) need oxygen and nutrients conveyed in blood flow to generate regulatory electrochemical signals for life-sustaining physiological functions. Hence, disruption of respiratory and blood circulation leads to rapid and irreversible termination of all activity in the brain.

In 1968, a report[855a] by an *ad hoc* committee convened at Harvard Medical School proposed a new definition of death as a state of *"irreversible coma"* where patients have *"no discernible central nervous system activity."* Thus, death was redefined as the complete absence of electrical signals in the brain or brain stem – formally termed *death by neurologic criteria* (DNC). The authors explained:

> *"Our primary purpose is to define irreversible coma as a new criterion for death. There are two reasons why there is need for a definition: (1) Improvements in resuscitative and supportive measures have led to increased efforts to save those who are desperately injured. Sometimes these efforts have only partial success so that the result is an individual whose heart continues to beat but whose brain is irreversibly damaged. [...] (2) Obsolete criteria for the definition of death can lead to controversy in obtaining organs for transplantation."*

The Harvard criterion was adopted as the standard neurological test for cessation of life in the USA. However, as an Indian review[855b,c] discussed in 2009, declaration of death on the basis of brain function (*even though* the body retains capacity for other functions) is problematic; especially for lay people and cultures that have long defined death by absence of *heartbeat* and onset of *rigor mortis*. A widely-reported 2013 case in Oakland, California showed that[855d,e], even in the USA, the brain death concept still lacks clarity.

Interpretation issues

Critical care guidelines[856a] for brain death list irreversible damage to *cerebral hemispheres*, absence of *brain stem reflexes* (eye movement and involuntary motor response to stimuli) and *apnoea* (inability to breathe). Non-mandatory technical tests like EEG, angiogram, or MRI scans may also be used. But there are protocol differences: 'brainstem death'[856b] alone is acceptable[856c] in the UK, while the USA insists[856d] on 'whole-brain death'[856e] of *both* the cerebral cortex and brainstem. Variants of these criteria have been adopted[856f] in Asia.

Furthermore, like clinical death, brain death is a *process* in which different neural areas 'shut down' over time (albeit rapidly). As D. John Doyle – an American anaesthesiologist and philosopher of science – explained in a 2011 analysis[857a], this poses fresh challenges since recommended tests are essentially *external* observations that can't precisely reveal *internal* states of neurons in the brain. These complexities, and lack of international consensus on the exact meaning of '*death by neurologic criteria*', continue to fuel confusion. Fellow philosopher and neuroethicist L. Syd Johnson summed up the several vexing issues in a 2016 essay[857b]:

> *"Brain death is counterintuitive. The brain dead 'corpse' remains warm, moves spontaneously, and retains many essential biological functions, including heartbeat and circulation, digestion, excretion, homeostasis, thermoregulation and hormonal and immunological functions. Lengthy 'survivals' of the brain dead have been documented. [...]*

> *"In a pluralistic, multicultural society there are diverse viewpoints on contentious and deeply important matters, and few aspects of human existence have the cultural, social, spiritual and personal gravity of death. There is no single, unifying definition of death that can handle all cases where there is a need to determine death in technologically advanced societies."*

Organ donation controversy

Increased global demand for oxygenated organs for transplant — life-saving items that brain dead patients with 'beating hearts' are best-placed to supply — has exacerbated tensions over death definition. To allay fears that doctors anxious to preserve transplantable organs may be tempted to make premature death declarations, an implicit *dead donor rule* (DDR)[858a] is observed which states that organs should only be taken from persons that are *certifiably* dead. However, the confusion over criteria for brain death leaves a loophole that can be exploited to harvest organs that are still in optimum, functioning condition.

Leading American bioethicist Franklin Miller and colleague Robert Truog highlighted the ethical fog around brain death and DDR in a 2008 perspective article[858b,c]:

"The arguments about why these patients should be considered dead have never been fully convincing. The definition of brain death requires the complete absence of all functions of the entire brain, yet many of these patients retain essential neurologic function, such as the regulated secretion of hypothalamic hormones. Some have argued that these patients are dead because they are permanently unconscious (which is true), but if this is the justification, then patients in a permanent vegetative state, who breathe spontaneously, should also be diagnosed as dead, a characterization that most regard as implausible. Others have claimed that "brain-dead" patients are dead because their brain damage has led to the "permanent cessation of functioning of the organism as a whole." Yet evidence shows that if these patients are supported beyond the acute phase of their illness (which is rarely done), they can survive for many years. The uncomfortable conclusion to be drawn from this literature is that although it may be perfectly ethical to remove vital organs for transplantation from patients who satisfy the diagnostic criteria of brain death, the reason it is ethical cannot be that we are convinced they are really dead."

Miller declared forthrightly in a follow-up paper[858d] that *"The practice of transplantation of vital organs from "brain-dead" donors is in a state of theoretical disarray."* He cited the warnings of philosopher and theologian Hans Jonas in the late 1960s that adopting brain death as a standard for organ donation was a slippery slope that invited malpractice. Others have expressed similar concerns: in 2009, bioethicist Joseph Verheijde joined critical care specialist Mohamed Rady and philosopher Joan McGregor in a strong critique[858e] of the Harvard criteria for brain death that greatly influenced the Uniform Determination of Death Act (UDDA) in the USA. The trio charged:

"The scientific uncertainty of defining and determining states of impaired consciousness including brain death have been neither disclosed to the general public nor broadly debated by the medical community or by legal and religious scholars. Heart-beating or non-heart-beating organ procurement from patients with impaired consciousness is de facto a concealed practice of physician-assisted death, and therefore, violates both criminal law and the central tenet of medicine not to do harm to patients. Society must decide if physician-assisted death is permissible and desirable to resolve the conflict about procuring organs from patients with impaired consciousness within the context of the perceived need to enhance the supply of transplantable organs."

Leading British neuroanaesthesia and neurocritical care specialist Martin Smith acknowledged[859a] the unsatisfactory position in 2012 and called for international consensus on guidelines. Some jurisdictions have intervened and imposed legal regulations to retain public trust – measures some practitioners fear could unnecessarily hinder medical discretion. While Canadian bioethicists largely supported[859b] Human Tissue Gift laws that forbid physicians who participate in brain death declarations from any involvement with organ transplants from patients, German intensive care specialists criticised[859c] a Supreme Court ruling[859d] that, in the absence of living wills, decisions should be guided by 'common values' and the overriding principle of *in dubio pro vita* (in doubt, favour life).

However, in a 2016 commentary[860a,b], haematopathologist and moral theologian Doyen Nguyen dismissed concerns that oversight could be counterproductive. She insisted that using brain death as currently formulated to justify organ harvesting violates the medical ethos of *primum non nocere* (first, do no harm) implied in the Hippocratic Oath.

Hence, even where patients have *explicitly permitted* removal of organs if judged brain dead in legal documents like a living will, most physicians prefer to observe the dead donor rule and refrain from any such action until life actually ceases and death is certified. Of course, as Robert Sade[860c] and Franklin Miller[860d] discussed in presentations to the Annual Meeting of the Society of Thoracic Surgeons in 2013, this creates a conflict with the obligation to honour last wishes.

Finally, a large collaboration of neuroscientists and critical care specialists launched a consultative World Brain Death Project (WBDP). The effort yielded several wide-ranging recommendations that appeared in an August 2020 report[861a] with the caveat: *"Because of the lack of high-quality data from randomized clinical trials or large observational studies, recommendations were formulated based on consensus of contributors and medical societies that represented relevant disciplines, including critical care, neurology, and neurosurgery."*

Despite being more of an opinion rather than empirical findings, the WBDP report is definitely a major step forward towards the goal of consistency in clinical decisions on life and death. Although it lacks the weight of an international legal protocol, the statement was welcomed and endorsed[861b] by several world federations and medical societies. However, absence of input[861c] from patient advocacy groups and other lay stakeholders make it unlikely[861d] that WBDP will end litigations over clinical decisions to withdraw life sustenance.

American medical anthropologist Sharon Kaufman discussed the enduring social frictions in a February 2020 essay[862a]. She observed:

"Brain death, which bucks millennia of belief, is not an obvious concept; and medicine's knowledge cannot encompass the meaning that a family imparts to the consciousness, heartbeat, personhood and life of a loved one. [....] It seems impossible, now, to settle on what death is. I've watched brain death evolve, and consider it one of medicine's most thorny notions. Its definition and criteria continue to be debated, even as new imaging technologies emerge."

Renowned neurologists Nathaniel Robbins and James Bernat acknowledged the brain death (BD) clinical dilemma in a December 2020 article[862b]. They explained: *"One reason for the mismatch between medical and legal standards for determining BD is that accepted medical standards cannot determine irreversible cessation.[...] Although broad religious, ethical, clinical, and legal consensus exists that death is irreversible and final, in practice, recognizing exactly when life transitions to death is not so easy."* Robbins and Bernat suggested four possible solutions, but admitted physicians *"can only imperfectly approximate"* time of brain death.

Phased dying

In the 1940s, Brazilian biologist Aristides Leão published results from animal experiments that revealed[863a] a striking 'spreading depression' of neurons as electrical impulses ceased in a wave-like manner across the dying brain. The startling implication is that[863b] silencing of neuronal networks is *progressive* and not instantaneous.

Over 70 years after Leão's pioneering work, researchers at Germany's Charité–Universitätsmedizin Berlin (CUB) and Ohio's University of Cincinnati Medical Center (UCMC) were permitted by family members and ethics overseers to monitor dying brain cells in patients with already implanted electrodes for the first time ever.

366

In 2018, the CUB-UCMC collaboration reported[863c] results that showed cessation of brain activity after fuel-rich blood flow is cut off actually occurs[863d] over *two phases*: an initial *reversible* fall-off as neurons go into spontaneous brain-wide 'hibernation' to save energy, followed by *irreversible* dying-off as neurons gradually exhaust their stored, battery-like electrical charge – the 'spreading depression' wave Leão observed in non-human animals seven decades earlier.

Medical scientists have therefore sought to extend neuronal life while attempts to revive the heart and blood flow continue. American physician and resuscitation specialist Lance Becker has spent over 30 years investigating the relationship between cardio-respiratory cessation (clinical death) and neurological silencing (brain death). Surveys of CPR outcomes[864a], and reviews of other resuscitation techniques like defibrillation, convinced[864b] Becker that the critical interval between heart failure and brain death can be extended greatly with better understanding of how energy generation in cellular mitochondria is disrupted during *ischaemia* (interrupted flow of oxygenated blood to the brain and other orgens). Becker shared his vision in a 2015 interview[864c] with Katlyn Nemani for the American College of Cardiology. He subsequently co-authored a journal editorial[864d] that discussed a call from the US Institute of Medicine (IOM) for a new, systemic approach based on eight strategies to improve chances of survival after cardiac arrest.

However, unlike heart tissue which is capable of retaining electrical *action potential* that allows cardiac pumping to be 'shocked' into restarting, brain cells leak their stored electrical charge rapidly and are rarely able to retain fresh energy inflows after successful CPR. It's thought disruption of normal electrochemical processing of calcium ions may cause rapid 'calcification' of our fragile brain tissue beyond repair. But research indicates neurons are more likely to recharge if the brain is cooled immediately after blood flow is cut off.

In 2014, a team centred at Alfred Hospital in Melbourne, Australia published[865a] a multipronged trial treatment dubbed CHEER (combination of mechanical CPR with 'therapeutic hypothermia' and allied techniques) that significantly increased survival rates in cardiac arrest patients who had failed to respond to CPR for *over 30 minutes*. The remarkable Australian report – and others like a 2015 Danish presentation[865b] on positive outcomes in almost 4,000 patients when brain cells are kept going – underlined the importance of continuing CPR in even seemingly hopeless cases if there is a possibility of sophisticated neural interventions.

Can brain cells be replaced?

Humans have long marvelled at the capacity for regeneration of body parts (including nerve systems) in animals like *urodeles* (salamanders, newts), *planarians* (flatworms) and *echinoderms* (sea stars, sea urchins, sea cucumbers). Zebrafish, in particular, have been widely studied[866a,b] for their remarkable ability to regenerate completely new hearts. By contrast, humans and most other mammals can only manage regeneration in embryos: once they reach adulthood, the ability to reconvert tissue cells into *blastema* (multipotent stem cells) for 'epimorphic'[866c] regeneration is lost – except for limited regrowth in liver, kidney, skin, digit-tips (fingers and toes), and other areas that retain somatic stem cells. Nonetheless, a vibrant field[866d] of regenerative medicine has emerged that explores potential use of stem cell technology and tissue engineering to replace or regenerate[866e] human tissues and organs with restored function.

In 2013, Tal Shomrat and Michael Levin at Tufts University in Maryland, USA reported a study[866f] that showed decapitated planarian flatworms are able to retain *old memories* after regenerating a new head. Apart from intriguing possibilities of epigenetic encoding of memory *outside* the brain, the Tufts result suggested that biological memory data can be retrieved and stored in *substituted* brain cells.

368

Inspired by these developments, Bioquark Inc, a US-based biotech company which had been researching tools for regeneration of human tissues and organs since 2007, teamed up with Indian-based Revita Life Sciences in 2016 to advance an audacious plan to regrow and reanimate entire populations of fresh neurons *in vivo* for experimental reversal of brain death. The controversial Reanima Project[867a] – involving stem cell and peptide injections, nerve stimulation, laser therapy and other techniques – was registered[867b] in the USA as a clinical trial and gained approval[867c] from the Institutional Review Board (IRB) in India for a pilot study on 20 legally brain dead subjects. It appeared medical science was on the verge of another extraordinary breakthrough.

However, the Indian Council of Medical Research (ICMR) subsequently identified 'procedural lapses' and derailed[868a] the project – perhaps prompted by vigorous local and international opposition from both fellow scientists and philosophical moralists. Indian science writer Sandhya Srinivasan and legal analyst Veena Johari published a scathing critique[868b] expressing alarm at the *"disturbing"* silence of authorities *"even when they know that such an unscientific, unethical and illegal trial is being undertaken in this country."* American neurocritical care specialist Ariane Lewis and medical ethicist Arthur Caplan issued a similar strong denunciation[868c] accusing Reanima proposers of taking advantage of poor public understanding of death by neurologic criteria (DNC) to create *"a cruel, false hope for recovery."* Lewis and Caplan warned:

> *"Because this trial borders on quackery yet has been well-publicized, it is the responsibility of the academic community to facilitate a public dialogue about its scientific and ethical shortcomings. Dead means dead. Proposing that DNC may not be final openly challenges the medical-legal definition of death, creates room for the exploitation of grieving family and friends and falsely suggests science where none exists."*

Bioquark CEO Ira Pastor responded with a robust rebuttal[868d]. He chided critics for ignoring *"key learnings from both recent biomedical history and parallel research disciplines within the life sciences"*, and showing *"intransigence in an era of novel clinical development models, emerging legislative initiatives regarding no-option patients, and regulatory advantages brought about by the globalization of health care."* Pastor argued:

"There have been dozens of reported cases in the literature violating the irreversibility label of the 1968 Harvard ad-hoc brain death criteria, primarily in young subjects who most likely retain some neurogenic niche. Although controversial and resulting in poor outcomes, such cases highlight that things are not always black or white in our understanding of the severe disorders of consciousness. [....]

""False hope" is unfortunately created by a global medical establishment that the public sees generating $7 trillion annually, yet provides no cures for most of the chronic degenerative diseases responsible for human suffering and death. Exploratory research programs of this nature are not false hope. They are a glimmer of hope."

Revita lead surgeon Himanshu Bansal also defended[869a] the Reanima project as a valuable contribution that will provide insights into brain death and degenerative nervous diseases. He cited recent successful results with transplanted[869b] human stem cells in stroke-damaged[869c] mice brains, and nerve stimulation[869d] in comatose patients. However, none of these cases involved *completely* brain dead subjects. Doubts have also been expressed[870a] about underlying scientific assumptions – the cephalic regeneration observed in adult flatworms is only possible because pluripotent stem cells are distributed[870b] *throughout* their bodies. As Ryan King and Phillip Newmark from University of Illinois at Urbana-Champaign showed in a 2012 review[870c], scientists are still a long way from understanding the cellular mechanisms behind tissue regeneration in animals.

In addition to feasibility doubts, critics raised the issue of responsibility for expensive long-term care if subjects are successfully revived but remain in permanent coma or minimally conscious states. The ethical aspects and funding implications appear to have been overlooked by Reanima sponsors. Apart from fresh emotional turmoil and upheavals for families of subjects, they could end up facing huge financial burdens if adequate insurance is not in place to underwrite such outcomes. However, Pastor dismissed such concerns as *"ludicrous"* in a 2017 feature article[871a]. He remarked: *"to think that if we succeed at such a monumental scientific transition, that we would actually then stop, and not try to continue on with patients through the disorders of consciousness spectrum to an eventual state of wakefulness, is just silly."*

Pastor's strong convictions have kept the Reanima vision alive. In 2017, media reports[871b] emerged that Bioquark planned to move the trial to an undisclosed Latin American country if Indian objections persist. According to a July 2019 update[871c], patients have been enrolled in India, Mexico, and Albania with the approval of relevant regulatory bodies. Whatever the fate of the venture, it's unlikely to be the last challenge to neuroscientific dogma that physical brain death is irreversible – the assumption that continues to provide ethical cover for withdrawal of sustenance from patients. Even the slightest hint of successful human neuro-regeneration and neuro-reanimation will reignite the contentious debate on organ harvesting from donors.

Brain transplant dream

In addition to improbable *in vivo* neuronal regeneration in brain dead patients, there's also debate whether a full brain transplant can ever be a viable proposition for humans. While, of course, it's hard to envisage a healthy, functioning brain becoming available for donation, the prospect of a lab-grown 'brain in a vat' is no longer mere philosophical speculation or science fiction.

In 2013, a European team of biotechnologists, geneticists and clinicians led by Juergen Knoblich and Madeline Lancaster from the Austrian Academy of Sciences in Vienna announced that they had successfully grown[872a,b] 'cerebral organoids' *in vitro* that share uncanny similarities with a human brain. Remarkably, the structures cultured from pluripotent stem cells mimicked[872c] several aspects of early brain development (embryonic neurogenesis)[872d]; including differentiation into various types of neurons and glia that then self-organise into rudiments of key brain regions like the prefrontal cortex and hippocampus. The absence of normal blood flow and nutrients restricted growth, but the miniature structures displayed enough cerebral features and longevity to give researchers an unprecedented opportunity for a close, 12-month study of conditions like microcephaly (arrested brain development).

The remarkable news of 'live' lab-grown cerebral organoids generated[873a] a ripple of excitement across the neuroscience community. Developmental biologist and stem cell specialist Lorenz Studer co-authored an assessment[873b] of prospects for 'build-a-brain' models that concluded: *"While there is still a long road ahead, the study by Lancaster et al. (2013) suggests that efforts aimed at creating a "brain in a dish" could become a valuable tool in understanding human brain function."* Arnold Kriegstein, director of regeneration medicine and stem cell research at University of California (San Francisco), and colleague Marina Bershteyn also discussed rapidly advancing techniques for cerebral synthesis and implications for medical science in a commentary[873c] that concluded with this summary:

"In time, the ability to create more complete cerebral organoids in a dish may come closer to reality. When that happens, besides having the convenience of in vitro models of brain development and disease, there will be a whole new set of ethical and philosophical issues to contemplate."

The bioethics dilemma predicted by Kriegstein and Bershteyn was closer than imagined. Just five years later (2018), researchers at The Salk Institute for Biological Studies at La Jolla, California led by Fred H. Gage reported[874a] that they had overcome the structural and functional limitations of human brain organoids grown *in vitro* by subsequent transplantation of grafts into a *live* mouse brain. Intriguingly, the Salk team subsequently observed[874b] not just *"progressive neuronal differentiation and maturation, gliogenesis, integration of microglia, and growth of axons to multiple regions of the host brain"*, but also *"functional neuronal networks and blood vessels"* as well as *"intragraft neuronal activity and suggested graft-to-host functional synaptic connectivity."*

Suddenly, the idea of partial cerebral transplants to replace dysfunctional or damaged brain tissue was no longer far-fetched science fiction. Brain organoid pioneer Madeline Lancaster welcomed the Salk report and acknowledged[874c] that 'vascularization' for blood flow was an immense step forward in the quest for replacement brains. The technique was voted[875a] 'Method of the Year 2017' by the influential publication *Nature Methods* – a special edition (Vol. 15, January 2018) featured an overview[875b] and articles that explored opportunities for cultivating[875c] sophisticated organoids for probing with technologies that normally would be ethically unacceptable[875d], and highlighted promises and challenges[875e] of the new field.

However, amidst the optimistic reviews, a parallel development emerged that cast doubt on the assumption that cerebral organoids lack 'consciousness' and can therefore be experimented on without the bioethical concerns that limit physical probes of the human brain. At a meeting convened by the US National Institutes of Health (NIH) in March 2018 to discuss ethical issues arising from novel brain research, Yale University neuroscientist Nenad Sestan disclosed[876a] that his team had managed to reanimate the brains of over 100 decapitated pigs and keep them alive for up to 36 hours.

The pigs had been dead[876b] for *four hours* at a slaughterhouse before the Yale team restored circulation with a complex system that pumped synthetic blood through the severed heads. Sestan revealed to a stunned audience that *billions* of individual brain cells had retained capacity for physiological activity – an unexpected discovery he described[876c] as *"mind-boggling"*. However, the Yale researcher insisted there was no sign of *conscious awareness* in the revived brains; an ethical and legal concern that scotches[876d] any similar efforts to reanimate a human brain or extract it for possible transplant.

Nevertheless, the ensuing debate prompted Sestan and 16 other leading neuroscientists and bioethicists to issue[876e] a call for clear guidelines on *in vitro* experimentation with brain tissue in laboratories. They highlighted the increasing complexity of brain organoids and pondered: *"If researchers could create brain tissue in the laboratory that might appear to have conscious experiences or subjective phenomenal states, would that tissue deserve any of the protections routinely given to human or animal research subjects?"* This scenario, they said, was no longer just a hypothetical question. The co-authors explained further:

> *"As brain surrogates become larger and more sophisticated, the possibility of them having capabilities akin to human sentience might become less remote. Such capacities could include being able to feel (to some degree) pleasure, pain or distress; being able to store and retrieve memories; or perhaps even having some perception of agency or awareness of self.*

> *"Could studies involving brain tissue that has been removed from a living person or corpse provide information about the person's memories, say? Could organisms that aren't 'biologically human' ever warrant some degree of quasi-human or human moral status?"*

Other issues highlighted for discussion include the inadequacy of tools for measuring sentient capabilities, ethics of human-animal chimaeras, and new challenges for brain death declarations.

How about a whole new head?

Human brain regeneration or neural transplants may or may not become reality. However, these prospects are hardly as fanciful as *complete severance* and transplantation of one's head to a new body. Incredible as this may sound, that's exactly what veteran Italian neurosurgeon Sergio Canavero proposed in a 2013 scientific paper[877a] termed *Head Anastomosis Venture* (HEAVEN) – an outline plan to effect *"the first human head transplantation with spinal linkage."* Canavero had been working on the idea since 1982 at the University Hospital in Turin, where he served as director of the Advanced Neuromodulation Group until 2015 (the ghoulish proposal attracted so much adverse publicity[877b] that his position became untenable).

The idea of head transplants is not new. Experimental procedures have been carried out[877c] on a range of animals from dogs to primates for over a century, but subjects only ever regained minimal motor functions and did not survive for long. Challenges have included maintenance of anastomosis (open vessel connections) for blood flow to a severed head, and efficient fusion of the transected spinal cords of two different creatures. However, Canavero contended that new technologies now exist to overcome past hurdles. He cited controversial work[877d] on rhesus monkeys in the 1970s by eminent American neurosurgeon Robert J. White, but acknowledged in his seminal paper that *"The greatest technical hurdle to such endeavor is of course the reconnection of the donor (D)'s and recipient (R)'s spinal cords."*

Canavero's solution is a GEMINI[878a] protocol that combines[878b] White's hypothermic techniques with 'sharp severance' for minimal damage to tissues; use of *polyethylene glycol* (PEG) as a fusogen to reconnect[878c] intricate spinal cord tubular nerve bundles and support cells; and electrical stimulation of the 'joint' to restore tissue and reactivate neurotransmission of brain signals.

To realize his vision, Canavero teamed up with Chinese orthopaedic surgeon Xiaoping Ren who was part of the University of Louisville team involved in the first-ever American hand transplant in 1999. Ren went on to pioneer experimental head transplants on mice at Harbin Medical University in Nangang, China. In 2014, Ren's lab developed[879a] a new severance procedure that retained the brain stem of a donor mouse body; thus preserving breathing ability and other reflex motor functions after transplantation of a recipient head. The following year, the Chinese team published[879b] another novel protocol that allowed crucial cross-circulation between donor and recipient during the procedure. Working independently, a German team, led by neurobiologists at Heinrich-Heine-University Medical Center in Düsseldorf, also developed[879c] a biomatrix approach that successfully regenerated axons and restored some locomotive function in rats after using PEG as a fusogen to reconnect fully severed spinal cords. Ren and Canavero cite these (and other) innovations in support of their claim that human head transplants are feasible.

Unsurprisingly, the HEAVEN proposal was received with much scepticism and unease. Could a human really be decapitated without succumbing to brain death? Even if *physiological* function was miraculously restored, how would *mental continuity* and consciousness be sustained during the hugely complex procedure? Colleagues had barely absorbed the implications when then 30-year-old Russian software entrepreneur Valery Spiridonov – a victim of Werdnig-Hoffman disease (a rare genetic disorder that gradually wastes away muscles and kills motor neurons) – was announced[880a] as the first volunteer. Crippled from childhood, and having already exceeded typical life expectancy for the condition, Spiridonov reckoned[880b] he had nothing to lose by taking a chance on a procedure that promised a healthy new body; however risky and untested. The prospect of an imminent *experimental* human head transplant galvanised[880c] the medical community into fierce public condemnation.

Eminent American neurological surgeon Hunt Batjer described[881a] the proposed procedure as *"worse than death"* while New York University medical ethicist Arthur Caplan warned[881b] that, even if it were successful, Spiridonov might, literally, *"go crazy"* from the confluence of unique biochemical pathways and neural correlates developed from birth by donor and recipient. A decade earlier, Robert White's experiments[881c] on primates had raised similar hopes for rehabilitation of neuromotor-impaired cosmologist Stephen Hawking and actor Christopher Reeve, but contemporaries had dismissed[881d] the idea as 'Monkey business'. Reaction to the planned Canavero-Ren operation on Spiridonov was equally scathing – neurologist Jerry Silver, who worked with White in the 1970s, called[881e] the proposal a *"complete fantasy"* and hoped such *"bad science"* would never take place.

In a 2015 essay[882a], Irish molecular biologist and neuroscientist Darren Ó hAilín identified still-existing gaps in scientific and technical knowledge needed for successful tissue reconnection and revival of function in a fully severed human head. He cited several reports of immune system attacks on transplanted hands – a tendency that would be catastrophic if a transplanted head was similarly rejected by a donor body. A companion article[882b] by University of Warwick philosopher Quassim Cassam examined related philosophical and ethical issues: he questioned *"whether a living person with Spridinov's head and someone else's body would be the same person as Spridinov."* Cassam pointed out that continuity of personal identity is very much a matter of *unbroken consciousness;* a state of 'being' that's still largely thought to exist independently of the body. Hence, Spridinov could be *"signing his own death warrant"* since he might cease to exist as the 'I' known before the operation – no one could tell if the entity emerging from a HEAVEN procedure would be the *head* donor, *body* donor, or a completely new person with no memories.

The issues raised by Ó hAilín and Cassam were echoed in a 2016 historical review[882c] of non-human head transplant experiments co-authored by Dutch neurosurgeon Marike Broekman and colleagues Nayan Lamba and Daniel Holsgrove. They listed several unresolved issues, including how *"patients who emerge from such a life-changing procedure react to having a new body to control and associate with their identity"*, that warrant *"elaborate further exploration before we should even consider offering humans this procedure."*

However, Ren and Canavero were undeterred. In a spirited article[883a], they defended HEAVEN and dismissed critics as short-sighted naysayers guilty of *"stifling scientific innovation"*. The mavericks referred sceptics to updated strategies[883b] for brain protection during the procedure and new proposals[883c] for virtual reality training to prepare candidates psychologically. They urged doubters to shed 'prejudices' and argued:

"Medical history shows us that many of the "quantum leaps" almost always fly in the face of conventional wisdom. Today's standard of care was yesterday's experimental treatment, and before that, in many cases, it was one man's visionary idea. The history of medicine includes many examples of ideas that were initially ridiculed or rejected by the medical establishment but that later became widely adopted, thanks to the courage of researchers and clinicians who stood by their ideas, often in the face of withering criticism from their colleagues."

In 2017, Ren and Canavero published[884a] a new scientific paper describing improved techniques for transplantation of rat heads. British neuroscientist and author Dean Burnett acknowledged the advance, but cautioned[884b] that human head transplants are a vastly different proposition. Burnett cited research[884c] that shows we develop[884d] unique brain-body interfaces from birth that give us *"neuroanatomical differences in visual, motor, and language cortices."* Thus, certain skills like musical proficiency are 'non transferable'[884e].

378

Eventually, widespread and sustained opposition (plus failure to generate the estimated cost of around US$15 million) forced Canavero to put the project on hold. He announced[885a] that the first head transplant would now take place in China on a local citizen rather than on Spiridonov who had endured a two-year wait. Spiridonov expressed[885b] a mixture of relief and disappointment at the decision, but graciously wished the pioneers success with a new patient. However, Chinese professionals were reported[885c] to have raised similar doubts and concerns expressed by Western colleagues.

In recognition of the profundity of issues and importance of the debate for medical science, the respected *American Journal of Bioethics Neuroscience* (AJOB) organised a special issue[886a] featuring 'for and against' articles with Ren and Canavero making their case[886b] alongside a counter-argument[886c] by eminent medical scientist and editor-in-chief Paul Root Wolpe, and commentaries by other colleagues. However, even this tentative initiative proved controversial. In their contribution, Canadian neuroscientist Patrick McDonald and neurologist Judy Illes (an AJOB senior editor) voiced doubts about the wisdom of discussing the merits of HEAVEN in a high-profile journal. McDonald and Illes wrote[886d]:

> *"The claims made by Canavero and Ren could not stand up to the rigors of a scientific peer review, and while we hope that the AJOB Neuroscience publication shines a light on the questionable science and ethics underpinning the proposed procedure in order to help ensure it never occurs, we fear that the authors will use its publication in such a reputable journal as a badge of legitimacy and as further justification to proceed with what can only turn out to be a medically sanctioned execution. Ongoing discussion of this topic gives undeserved credibility to those who advocate for this procedure and the claim that they will soon do it. They should not do it, and we should not talk about it any more."*

Nevertheless, Wolpe emphasised that the matter should not be censored but aired so *all* implications can be fully analysed. As he explained in a subsequent article[887a], even if Canavero and Ren do not succeed in attempting a live head transplant at this point in time, nothing prevents the procedure in theory so there are bound to be further attempts in future. Neuroethicists Zaev Suskin and James Giordan agreed in a detailed 2018 discussion[887b] of ethical and legal issues that matters arising needed *"thorough consideration, appropriate concern [....] and not simply condemnation or laissez faire concession."*

Indeed, Bruce Mathew, a former lead neurosurgeon at a UK university teaching hospital assessed[887c] in December 2019 that the technology to carry out a human head transplant might become available within a decade; although he dismissed the HEAVEN-GEMINI proposal as *"utterly ridiculous."* According to Mathew, the brain and spinal cord would need[887d] to be kept intact (along with the protective membrane) and transferred together to a new donor body.

Respected German software pioneer and philosopher Kai Krause confessed in a 2016 essay[887e] that, despite intuitive revulsion, he had an ambivalent attitude to the fascinating prospect of a human head transplant. He nominated the HEAVEN controversy as the *"most interesting"* recent scientific news and recalled heart transplant pioneer Christiaan Barnard's reply in the 1960s when challenged about the appropriateness and ethics of such a risky procedure:

"For a dying person, a transplant is not a difficult decision. If a lion chases you to a river filled with crocodiles, you will leap into the water convinced you have a chance to swim to the other side. But you would never accept such odds if there were no lion."

The moral, Krause concluded, is that one should never judge medical choices made by desperate patients or rule out what might be achieved in future decades.

Personhood death

Inability to determine exactly how and when consciousness commences and ends in humans has led to calls for a common sense approach that doesn't require tests for signals in *all* brain cells, or subjective judgements about the presence or absence of a functioning mind. Philosophical definition of death emphasises[88a] irreversible cessation of 'integrated functioning' that confers personal identity.

Renowned American medical ethicist Robert Veatch long argued that brain death (whole or otherwise) is a misguided definition for cessation of life. In a seminal 1975 paper[888b,c], Veatch expressed dismay that new *"death-assaulting technologies"* had given rise to an *"inhuman form of existence"* which could be appropriately called *"human corpses."* Humans, he contended, should be declared dead once it's determined that irreversible loss of function had occurred in those parts of the brain (cerebral hemispheres) thought to give rise to critical cognitive functions like memory and personality that allow individuals to interact *meaningfully* with others – a condition he succinctly described as *"the irreversible loss of that which is essentially significant to the nature of man."* Veatch revisited his arguments in a 1993 article[888d]. He predicted that the 'whole-brain death' definition for cessation of life would soon be replaced by a more coherent 'higher brain' standard based on extinguished personhood.

Veatch's approach was eventually adopted by other thinkers. Oxford University moral philosopher Jeff McMahan wrote in a 1995 paper[889a,b]: *"I argue that no single criterion of death captures the importance we attribute both to the loss of the capacity for consciousness and to the loss of functioning of the organism as a whole. This is because the person or self is one thing and the human organism is another. We require a separate account of death for each. Only if we systematically distinguish between persons and human organisms will we be able to provide plausible accounts both of the conditions of our ceasing to exist and of when it is that we begin to exist."*

381

However, formulating a definition of 'personhood death' that can be usefully applied in medical science is easier said than done. In 2006, McMahan published a new paper[889c,d] that sketched *"an alternative account of human death that distinguishes between the biological death of a human organism and the death or ceasing to exist of a person."* He used a hypothetical case of brain (cerebrum) transplantation and instances of dicephalic twinning (born with two heads on the same torso) to argue that humans are not defined by our organic bodies but by our 'embodied minds'. McMahan concluded:

"An organism dies in the biological sense when it loses the capacity for integrated functioning. The best criterion for when this happens is probably a circulatory-respiratory criterion. There is bound to be considerable indeterminacy about how much functional integration is required for life in an organism. But if we are not organisms, this is of little consequence. What it is important to be able to determine is when we die in the nonbiological sense – that is, when we cease to exist. If we are embodied minds, we die or cease to exist when we irreversibly lose the capacity for consciousness – or, to be more precise, when there is irreversible loss of function in those areas of the brain in which consciousness is realized."

The idea that humans can *"cease to exist"* while still having some capacity for biological functioning is highly controversial; given the many[889e] ethical and legal implications. McMahan accepted that his approach leads to the conclusion that embryos are mere organisms with no personhood, and that patients in a persistent vegetative state (PVS) who have lost 'higher-brain' function are effectively dead. But he argued[889f] this is a legitimate view because *"our concept of death allows for the possibility that death is not always a biological event, and thus that it does not always involve the cessation of integrated biological functioning."* In support, he cited religious belief in a soul that continues to exist after physical death and 'born again' states of unicellular organisms like amoebas after replicative binary fission.

British reductionist philosopher Derek Parfit used similar reasoning in a provocative 2012 article[890a] titled *We Are Not Human Beings*. McMahan's and Parfit's redefinition of *biological* 'humans' as *philosophical* 'persons' is interesting. However, their arguments were challenged by Australian health law specialist Andrew McGee in a 2016 response[890b,c] appropriately titled *We Are Human Beings*. He called denials of our biological status *"faulty metaphysical thinking"* and contended that neither McMahan nor Parfit had provided sufficient ethical or moral justification for *"permissibility of embryonic stem cell research and organ procurement from PVS patients"* that they claimed were no longer 'persons'. McGee's rebuttal echoed points made 15 years earlier by American neurologist and paediatrician D. Alan Shewmon. In a 2001 paper[890d], Shewmon rejected the assertion that brain death signals the end of human integrated existence. He argued:

> *"The mainstream rationale for equating "brain death" (BD) with death is that the brain confers integrative unity upon the body, transforming it from a mere collection of organs and tissues to an "organism as a whole." In support of this conclusion, the impressive list of the brain's myriad integrative functions is often cited. [....] Integrative unity of a complex organism is an inherently nonlocalizable, holistic feature involving the mutual interaction among all the parts, not a top-down coordination imposed by one part upon a passive multiplicity of other parts. Loss of somatic integrative unity is not a physiologically tenable rationale for equating BD with death of the organism as a whole."*

American philosopher Michael Potts agreed that personhood death can be construed from loss of capacity for integrated functioning. But he took issue with the contention that either state (cessation of personal identity or loss of integrated functioning) can be inferred *exclusively* from brain death *even though* other body parts clearly retain and exhibit capacity for life.

In response to a 2001 review[890e] of related ethical, cultural, religious and legal issues led by Canadian medical bioethicist Neil Lazar, Potts stated[890f]:

> *"I will not argue with the view that personhood is lost when the integrated unity of the human organism is lost (as opposed to a consciousness-based conception of personhood). I am sympathetic with that position myself, and a number of philosophers have made a good case for that view. The claim which has clearly become problematic since the President's Commission Report is that so-called whole brain death marks the end of integrated organic unity in a human being. Machine-dependence does not imply the loss of integrated organic unity; a number of individuals who are clearly alive (and even conscious) depend on machines in order to live, ranging from individuals who are dependent on cardiac pacemakers to individuals who are ventilator dependent. In addition, there have been a number of cases of long term survival of brain dead patients."*

Evolving boundaries

Australian pharmacist and priest Theodore Gillian pointed out in another 2001 paper[891a,b] that identifying an *"exact moment of death"* requires psychological clarity about *"the necessary substratum that actually is the human person."* He cited Cuban neurologist Calixto Machado's separation of *capacity* for consciousness (arousal) from *experience* of things and events (awareness) – an important distinction Machado complained was ignored by advocates of personhood death. However, the long-established philosophical concept of *eternal oblivion* (permanent cessation of consciousness) does not distinguish between aspects of consciousness; it simply lumps them together as 'brain functions' which end concurrently at death. Despite these conceptual difficulties, the new emphasis on personhood has become influential. As Austrian philosopher Josef Seifert observed in a 2004 compendium paper[891c]: *"The arguments in favor of equating brain death with actual human death have shifted from medicine and biology to philosophy."*

The shift has reignited an even older debate: ambiguity about what exactly *constitutes* consciousness makes it difficult to frame philosophical personhood death in practical terms for societal needs. The dilemma has been exacerbated by emerging technologies for transhumanist transformations. Legal philosopher Ben Sarbey pointed out in a 2016 essay[892a] that *both* 'whole-brain' and 'higher-brain' definitions of death will be rendered defunct if it becomes possible in future to replace damaged brain tissue, or use computers to replicate *"encoded memories, links between memories, predispositions, and even consciousness and pain—all the things that make us persons."* Sarbey noted that while our current state of medical technology compels us to adopt pragmatic *"death criteria trifecta"*, loss of *"what we value in persons"* may ultimately become the definition for death.

Whatever the accepted standard, medical determination and certification of death on the basis of *irretrievable personhood* will remain[892b] controversial. Hence, British philosopher Stephen Holland advocated[892c] in 2010 that the best way to balance growing demand for organ transplants with moral rights of potential donors is to shift emphasis from death definition to promotion of living wills. He updated and summarised his arguments thus in a 2016 essay[892d]: *"Basing treatment decisions on the ontological status of patients is inescapably problematic, so perhaps treatment decisions should be made on quite different grounds. For example, perhaps patients should be treated according to their autonomous wishes. [....] We remain in a quandary as to how to incorporate intuitively important ontological considerations into decisions about the treatment of certain patients."*

Swedish philosopher and bioethicist Ingmar Persson contended[892e] in *The End of Life and of Consciousness* (from her 2017 book *Inclusive Ethics*) that *onset* of death is as impossible to precisely define as *inception* of life. If Persson is right, humans may never pinpoint a specific moment for life-death transition.

Information-theoretic death

The information processing (IP) concept of life – biological systems and functions driven by data flow transformations – has been adopted in yet another definition of death. As futurist Mike Walsh observed in a 2016 blog post[893a]: *"From this perspective, you can think of genetics as the software that drives our physical hardware, and in the future, gene therapy, 3D printing using stem cells, cloned organs, and the use of medical nanobots may allow us to not only patch the code, but repair broken components."* In other words, life extension enthusiasts see death as just a 'software bug' that humans may be able to remedy in future.

According to the law of information conservation in quantum physics, humans, and all other living and non-living things in our biosphere, constitute[893b] an 'isolated system' within which physical information is never 'lost' but is merely rearranged from time to time. Hence, in the context of IP, death is an *irreversible disruption* of the information content that allows an organism to exist; a hypothetical state in which the functional information embodied in a living thing becomes so disordered or fragmented that the original arrangement which gives it identity cannot be reconstituted in any meaningful way.

American cryptographer and nanotechnologist Ralph Merkle defined this so-called *information-theoretic death* (ITD) thus in 1992[893c,d]:

> *"A person is dead according to the information theoretic criterion if their memories, personality, hopes, dreams, etc. have been destroyed in the information theoretic sense. If the structures in the brain that encode memory and personality have been so disrupted that it is no longer possible in principle to recover them, then the person is dead. If they are sufficiently intact that inference of the state of memory and personality are feasible in principle, and therefore restoration to an appropriate functional state is likewise feasible in principle, then the person is not dead."*

Merkle's definition has become the standard and most widely cited description of ITD. Life extension technologist Michael Federowicz (aka Mike Darwin) analysed the issue further in response to the 2005 *Critical Care* debate question[893e] *When is dead really dead?*:

> *"The brain is a discrete pattern of atoms, each as effective as the next as long as the unique pattern of their arrangement persists. Presumably all of the attributes of personhood are encoded in this lattice. This view allows us to view the person as 'information beings', defined by the arrangement of particular atoms that comprise our brains at any moment. So long as that pattern of information can be recovered, the person is not dead. If a cookbook is ripped to pieces it is no longer functional; it is impossible to read or use. The torn pages still contain all the information required, however, to allow for the book to be pieced back together and restored to a functional, useful state. By contrast, if the book is burned and the ashes stirred, the loss is irreversible given our current understanding of physical law (the limitations imposed by both the laws of thermodynamics and information theory)."*

However, ITD, as formulated, relies heavily on the assumption that *all* cognitive attributes that define a person are embedded in the brain and can be physically mapped. Merkle cited research in support of the traditional view that human memory and personality are stored in *identifiable* changes in neurons and connecting synapses (LTP). But new findings increasingly contradict[894a] the idea of memory storage at[894b] neuron synapses, and challenge[894c] the dogma of memory formation by repeated[894d] synapse strengthening mechanisms. It's now acknowledged[894e] that neuronal architecture and pathways for information processing are far more dynamic and sophisticated[894f] than assumed in ITD. Evidence of previously undetected[895a] capacity for latent storage[895b], and the multi-dimensional mathematical model unveiled[895c] in 2017 by Henry Markram's at EPFL Switzerland, suggest[895d] critical information might exist in hidden brain cavities that our limited 4-D perception may never allow us to detect.

Nevertheless, several scholars have adopted the concept of ITD because it avoids the troublesome (and increasingly frequent) shifts in physiology-based definitions of death forced by advances in medical science. In 2016, psychiatrist and neuroscientist Michael A. Cerullo described[895e] ITD as *"the ultimate definition of death"*. Of course, like personhood, an exclusive information-based approach takes us into metaphysics; a philosophical domain that involves *analytical thought* rather than *physical determination*. Thus, beyond being an interesting theoretical concept, ITD currently offers no *practical* reference point for cessation of life that medical and legal practitioners can apply to resolve pressing controversies like organ transplantation.

Chances of techno-resurrection

Conceiving death in terms of *information disruption* and rearrangement (rather than irreversible biological failure) allows theorists to argue that, in the distant future, advanced scientific techniques may emerge for resuscitation of our physical remains including the brain – provided these are properly preserved. Ralph Merkle speculated in an updated commentary[896a] that the information which defines a person may survive death for a significant period:

> *"The ability to identify synapses, neurons, and other structures critical to brain function for several hours following cessation of heart beat, blood flow and breathing suggests that information-theoretic death also does not occur for at least several hours following, for example, a massive heart attack that promptly caused legal and clinical death. This suggests that medical technology will eventually be able to revive individuals who have suffered multiple hours of ischemia. This idea is gaining traction in today's medical community."*

Based on such premises, Michael Cerullo contended in his 2016 exposition[896b] that long-term brain preservation should be viewed as *"a life-saving medical procedure."* Thus, life extension enthusiasts are passionately advocating techniques like *cryonics* (extreme freezing) and *plastination* (chemical preservation) to forestall 'information death'.

The hope is that prompt intervention to halt degradation of body tissues will also preserve embodied information. But is full restoration and resuscitation of long-defunct biological systems a viable proposition?

Prospects for resurrection

Merkle's seminal 1992 paper[896c] explored the technical feasibility of an earthly 'day of resurrection'. While he accepted that self-repair of tissue damage from long-term preservation was unlikely, he argued that, provided an initial map of all constituent biomolecules can be ascertained, the increasing ability of nanotechnology to manipulate matter with atomic precision gives hope that organic structures can one day be restored to their original form. He suggested an 'off-board repair' protocol for revival in three steps:

"1. Determine the coordinates and orientations of all major molecules, and store this information in a data base. As a side effect, disassemble the tissue into its component molecules.

"2. Using the information stored in the data base, run a computer program which determines what changes in the existing structure should be made to restore it to a healthy state.

"3. Move the molecules to their desired locations."

In a subsequent review[896d] of possible nanotechniques for molecular brain restoration, Merkle further acknowledged that if, as ITD assumes, the complex information systems which underlie fragile human attributes like memory and identity are indeed stored in a *physical* format, then these crucial elements for personhood may not survive long-term cryopreservation. But he still argued it was *"unlikely that such structures will survive the lifetime of the individual only to be obliterated beyond recognition by freezing."* ITD, he concluded, is improbable.

Merkle points to extensive research by visionaries like nanorobotics specialist Robert Freitas Jr. into a new era of nanomedicine that involves[897a] *"the monitoring, repair, construction and control of human biological systems at the molecular level, using engineered nanodevices and nanostructures."* According to Freitas, humans are on the cusp of transformative bodily alterations that will change our worldly perceptions forever. He wrote in a 2003 article[897b]:

"Our subjective experience of reality will shift by subtle degrees. For instance, all objective information about our physical surroundings has traditionally arrived in the conscious mind via the various natural senses such as hearing, sight, and smell. In the nanomedical era, machine-mediated sensory modalities may permit direct perception of physical phenomena well removed from our bodies in both time and space, or which are qualitatively or quantitatively inaccessible to our original natural senses. Perception will gradually expand to incorporate nonphysical phenomena including abstract models of mental software, purely artificial constructs of simulated or enhanced realities, and even the mental states of others. Such new perceptions will inevitably alter the way our minds process information."

Freitas explained in a 2005 interview[897c] how *"full-immersion virtual reality"* can be achieved by implantation of billions of nanorobots in our brain to create an *"in vivo fiber network"* capable of generating the necessary bandwidth – truly extraordinary ideas he expounds on in an ongoing book series. However, this exciting promise offers no testable mechanisms for regenerating *consciousness* from frozen cerebral tissue, and does not tackle[897d] metaphysical aspects of our mental states that continue to perplex scientists and philosophers alike. Also, while proposed 'antimicrobial nanorobots' may initially reduce natural disease, there's no way to predict how hardy and adaptable bacteria and viruses might mutate to evade new barriers. Furthermore, as a Canadian-Danish report[897e] cautioned in 2017, nanoparticles have largely unexplored toxic properties that could cause irreversible harm to biological systems and the environment.

These misgivings and concerns were discussed in a comprehensive review[898a] by information scientist and ethicist Rafael Capurro. He worried that Freitas' work propagates 'utopian visions' of indefinite life extension without regard for many unknowns. Capurro explained:

"The view of the human body from a nano perspective is basically reductionist similar for instance to the view of the human brain as a computer, now a nano-computer. This reductionist view can give rise to the naturalistic fallacy, i.e., to the idea that human phenomena can be changed or influenced at the nano level without telling the manipulator what changes are more or less desirable. It enforces the misleading belief that all human diseases could eventually be treated and eliminated by advanced nanotechnology. The potential benefits of nanomedicine are wrongly extrapolated into a view of the human being as a mere composition of atoms and molecules. It is hard to believe that on the basis of manipulations at the nano level the <u>condition humaine</u> between birth and death can be changed."

Nevertheless, cryonics continues to enjoy significant minority support in academic circles. Nearly 70 scientists in related fields (including some well-known names from respected institutions) have endorsed an open letter[898b] hosted at *Biostasis* that expresses general support for cryonics as *"a legitimate science-based endeavor that seeks to preserve human beings, especially the human brain, by the best technology available"* in anticipation of future resuscitation. There's even a suggested medical protocol[898c] for placing critically ill patients in *"low-temperature metabolic arrest for future resuscitation."* The Cryonics Institute in Michigan, USA is a leading research resource and provider of cryogenic 'suspension' facilities. Norwegian philosopher and ethicist Ole Martin Moen justified this extraordinary enterprise in *The case for cryonics* (2015). He argued[898d]: *"insofar as the alternatives to cryonics are burial or cremation, and thus certain, irreversible death, even small chances for success can be sufficient to make opting for cryonics a rational choice."*

The Brain Preservation Foundation (BPF) has been promoting research and technology for long-term preservation of the human *connectome* (complete blueprint of neural wiring in the brain). The cryobiology community buzzed with excitement when BPF announced that California-based 21st Century Medicine (21CM) had won their 2016 prize for the first successful freezing of a small mammalian brain (rabbit), and the 2018 prize for similarly freezing a large mammalian brain (pig) in *"uniformly excellent"* condition. The 21CM team, led by biogerontologist Gregory Fahy and former MIT computer scientist Robert McIntyre, used a new protocol called *aldehyde-stabilized cryopreservation* (ASC)[899a] which rapidly stabilises brain ultrastructure for *"indefinite long-term storage."* Earlier, Fahy had pioneered a process of vitrification[899b] – infusion of cells with cryoprotectants for rapid cooling *without* ice formation; thus avoiding the usual damage when long-frozen organic tissues are thawed out.

However, after eyebrow-raising comments on possible indefinite preservation of memory[899c] and personality[899d] appeared in media reports, 21CM issued a clarifying statement that stressed[899e]:

"Although ASC has been discussed in the popular press and even by the Brain Preservation Foundation as a new type of cryonics, in which "revival" might be accomplished by creating a computer simulation of that brain based on the scanning of immense numbers of brain sections to create a comprehensive map of the structure of that person's brain, 21CM does not endorse these views. Others have suggested that ASC preserved brains might be revived by means of biological repairs carried out with future tools from the field of medical nanotechnology, but we do not endorse this view either. 21CM sought the prize to demonstrate the power of its vitrification technology to reach beyond conventional applications of cryobiology and provide unexpected new tools to mainstream neurobiologists. While 21CM firmly believes in personal choice and respects the views of all honest people, we are not a cryonics company and as such do not endorse any form of cryonics."

Philosopher and bioethicist Alexandre Erler also pointed out in a 2018 overview[899f] that the technique developed by 21CM involves dehydration and extensive *shrinking* of the brain; a treatment that's bound to massively disrupt the *information content* theorists speculate gives rise to our unique minds and psychological profiles. Hence, Erler argued, it was highly improbable that brains vitrified by ASC could be later 'revived' or emulated to restore personal identity.

Transcendence: Uploading the mind

One of the key transhumanist proposals for indefinite life extension is retrieval of the *entire* mental content that defines a person (memories, personality traits, conscious attributes) for transfer to a new *substrate-independent mind* (SIM) that can be stored in non-perishable media. Advocates of this concept of mind uploading[900a] argue that, given our increasingly precarious environment and growing risks of an extinction event like total nuclear war or an asteroid impact, it makes sense to research techniques for possible 'reincarnation' in a non-biological format. The hope is that, provided the necessary neuronal data can be captured with 100 percent fidelity in so-called *infomorphs* that have potential for consciousness and sentience, future quantum computers will have enough power and processing capacity to simulate original mental states for embodiment in humanoid robots or life-like holograms.

Thus, unlike cryonics which aims to repair and reanimate preserved biological systems, mind uploading envisions *complete transcendence* to a new post-humanity. According to British futurologist Ian Pearson, immortality is no longer[900b] fantasy or science fiction – he suggested[900c] in 2018 that future humans may even have the surreal experience of observing their own funerals from a new body. However, a contemporary Finnish study[900d] found that society is deeply divided with people who are anxious about death and anti-suicide, or versed in science fiction, more approving[900e] of the idea.

Techno-road to immortality

Imaginary sentient creations have long featured in tales like Mary Shelley's 1818 classic *Frankenstein*. But the idea that we could use technology to transcend biology and avoid death did not appear until the second half of the 20th century. In 1971, University of Washington biogerontologist and pathologist George Martin published a paper[901a] that discussed the potential role of technology in *"a partial and interim solution"* to what Australian neurophysiologist and philosopher Sir John Eccles had called humanity's *"heartrending"* and *"terrible problem of death awareness"*. While he dismissed prospects for an ultimate solution to death as *"pure science fiction"*, Martin predicted the advent of human-machine cyborgs *"in the not too distant future, with a potentially enormous impact upon our social, economic, religious, and political institutions."* He outlined his vision based on two 'articles of faith':

> *"The first is the perfectly reasonable proposition that science will continue to grow—if not at its present exponential rate, at least linearly. The second, requiring a good deal more optimism, is the belief that Homo sapiens, during this critical phase of his natural history, will not destroy himself and his planet. We shall assume that developments in neurobiology, bioengineering, and related disciplines, perhaps over a period of centuries, will ultimately provide suitable techniques of "read-out" of the stored information from cryobiologically preserved brains into nth. generation computers capable of vastly outdoing the dynamic patterning of operation of our cerebral neurones. We would then join a family of humanoid "postsomatic" bioelectrical hybrids, capable of contributing to cultural evolution at rates far exceeding anything now imaginable."*

Today's proliferation of cyborgs in all spheres of life (inspiring notions of cyborg anthropology) vindicates Martin's bold forecast of human-machine integrations. However, brain 'read-outs' and mind uploads remained just interesting speculations until the 21st century.

In 1993, American computer scientist and sci-fi author Vernor Vinge published[901b] an apocalyptic vision of human extinction by self-evolving superintelligent machines – a scenario he dubbed 'The Singularity'. Over a decade later, inventor and futurist Raymond Kurzweil popularised the idea in his iconic book *The Singularity is Near* (2005). He asserted[901c] at his blog:

"Within a few decades, machine intelligence will surpass human intelligence, leading to The Singularity — technological change so rapid and profound it represents a rupture in the fabric of human history. The implications include the merger of biological and nonbiological intelligence, immortal software-based humans, and ultra-high levels of intelligence that expand outward in the universe at the speed of light."

Kurzweil predicted[901d] that humans have until 2045 at best to implement technologies like mind uploading for survival (a forecast that inspired Russian media tycoon Dmitry Itskov's 2045 Initiative). To combat the alleged threat, a Singularity University (SU) – which also serves as a think tank and enterprise incubator – was launched in 2009 at Silicon Valley, California with the support of NASA, Google and other corporate tech giants (an associated Singularity Hub tracks and highlights developments). Eager to capitalise on emerging technologies, Google employed Kurzweil as director of engineering in 2012. Singularitarianism is now a recognised movement.

Dutch neuroscientist and neuroengineer Randal A. Koene has also pioneered experimental research into possible transfers of mental content to SIMs. He rebranded[902a] the proposal as *whole brain emulation* (WBE) – a designation adopted in a 2008 report[902b] authored by Anders Sandberg and Nick Bostrom at Oxford University's Future of Humanity Institute. Koene's subsequent collaboration with Vrije Universiteit Amsterdam produced[902c] *"a simulation framework, called NETMORPH, for the developmental generation of 3D large-scale neuronal networks with realistic neuron morphologies."*

In 2012, Koene followed up with two papers detailing firm proposals for informational representations[903a] of mind states and transition functions, and novel techniques to measure[903b] *in vivo* neuronal activity for WBE. Koene also set up a foundation called Carbon Copies to promote associated research. However, he acknowledged in a 2014 interview[903c] that several formidable hurdles still confront WBE/SIM researchers – he assessed that the best estimate for initial brain emulations of even the tiny fruit fly was *"15-17 years"* hence. Notwithstanding, WBE is now an established research field – a call for scientific papers was issued[903d] in 2013.

Humans as machines

With assured support[904a] from billionaires keen to achieve immortality, it would appear the only constraints to WBE and post-human SIMs are techno-ethical issues and Kurzweil's 2045 Singularity deadline. However, several scholars and cognitive scientists argue that mind uploading may not even be possible in principle; let alone in practice. They dispute the foundational assumptions that 1) the mind is a phenomenon generated *solely* by physical brain activity, and 2) neural states which give us personality and capacity for worldly experience are mere *computational* results that can be reproduced by powerful enough computers. This materialist dogma of 'mechanistic functionalism' – as defined[904b] by philosopher Gualtiero Piccinini – has been rejected[904c] by a long line of theorists including Thomas Nagel, John Searle, David Chalmers, and Colin McGinn. Apart from philosophical objections, empirical research[904d] by neuropsychologists has cast serious doubt on the claim that higher-level executive brain functions – developed over *lifetimes* and thought to involve areas of the central nervous system outside the brain – can emerge *spontaneously* in mind simulations generated from non-biological substrates long disconnected from the original biological host.

In a 2011 essay[904e], Microsoft co-founder Paul Allen and Vulcan inc. colleague Mark Greaves denied that a Singularity is imminent that will match human metacognition. They argued that predicting human behaviour requires far more than models of probable neuronal activities computed by supercomputers. They pointed out that, even if an accurate snapshot of the brain's connectome is achieved, successful mind simulation would require a comprehensive database of *all* environmental variables plus *all* possible reactions and interactions of *billions* of neurons. As they explained:

> *"Hundreds of attempts have been made (using many different organisms) to chain together simulations of different neurons along with their chemical environment. The uniform result of these attempts is that in order to create an adequate simulation of the real ongoing neural activity of an organism, you also need a vast amount of knowledge about the functional role that these neurons play, how their connection patterns evolve, how they are structured into groups to turn raw stimuli into information, and how neural information processing ultimately affects an organism's behavior. Without this information, it has proven impossible to construct effective computer-based simulation models. Especially for the cognitive neuroscience of humans, we are not close to the requisite level of functional knowledge."*

Allen and Greaves also highlighted the difficulty of creating AI systems that can match human *adaptive* cognition and experience:

> *"Why has it proven so difficult for AI researchers to build human-like intelligence, even at a small scale? One answer involves the basic scientific framework that AI researchers use. As humans grow from infants to adults, they begin by acquiring a general knowledge about the world, and then continuously augment and refine this general knowledge with specific knowledge about different areas and contexts. AI researchers have typically tried to do the opposite: they have built systems with deep knowledge of narrow areas, and tried to create a more general capability by combining these systems. This strategy has not generally been successful ..."*

Indeed, 60 years earlier, AI pioneer Alan Turing evaluated the possibility of a *"child machine"* that could be taught like humans over time. In the penultimate paragraph of his seminal 1950 paper[905a] *Computing Machinery And Intelligence*, Turing concluded it may be necessary to endow the machine with *human* sensory organs:

> *"We may hope that machines will eventually compete with men in all purely intellectual fields. But which are the best ones to start with? Even this is a difficult decision. Many people think that a very abstract activity, like the playing of chess, would be best. It can also be maintained that it is best to provide the machine with the best sense organs that money can buy, and then teach it to understand and speak English. This process could follow the normal teaching of a child. Things would be pointed out and named, etc. Again I do not know what the right answer is, but I think both approaches should be tried."*

Kurzweil dismissed[905b] the well-articulated Allen-Greaves caveats as *"scientist's pessimism"*. But other brain-machine specialists have expressed similar scepticism. A theory of 'pattern recognition' outlined in Kurzweil's 2012 book *How to Create a Mind* was labelled[905c] *"dubious"* and *"disappointing"* in a review by New York University cognitive scientist Gary Marcus: he further commented, *"Ultimately Kurzweil is humbled by a challenge that has beset many a great thinker extending far beyond his field—Kurzweil doesn't know neuroscience as well as he knows artificial intelligence, and doesn't understand psychology as well as either."* Duke University neuroscientist Miguel Nicolelis, whose team devised[905d] a brain implant in 2012 that allowed mice to sense infra-red light (an ability normally beyond mammals), dismissed[905e] the whole idea of a Singularity and mind uploading as *"a bunch of hot air"* and declared: *"You could have all the computer chips ever in the world and you won't create a consciousness"*. Nicolelis insisted that, unlike *predictable* computer algorithms, human thought is wholly *unpredictable*.

Hopes of transcendence

Despite the rebuttals by respected academics and technologists, the idea of mind uploading as a way to escape our mortality has seeped into public consciousness. The 2014 sci-fi thriller *Transcendence* featured celebrity actor Johnny Depp as a terminally-ill AI researcher who uploads his consciousness into a computer with disastrous results. A 2016 *BBC Horizon* documentary[906a] on Dmitry Itskov's 2045 Initiative attracted much interest and comment. The concept was introduced to an even bigger global audience when *Netflix* aired the 2018 television series *Altered Carbon* – the futuristic plot featured controlling alien beings that are able to decant human memory and consciousness into disk-shaped 'cortical stacks' at the back of the neck for transfer to new biological or synthetic bodies at death.

AI and nanotechnology researchers are particularly concerned that associating the field with immortality goals will harm efforts to garner resources and public support for vital 'here and now' projects. British materials physicist and nanoscientist Richard Jones has written extensively[906b] against what he calls *"the delusion of technological transcendence"*. He pointed out in a 2014 essay[906c] that, since biological information processing takes place at *molecular* rather than cellular (neuronal) scales, the computing power needed for any meaningful brain simulation will have to be several orders of magnitude greater than anything humans can hope to achieve in the foreseeable future. Jones warned[906d] in 2016 that mind uploading is the sort of misguided pursuit that *"distorts our scientific priorities and gets in the way of us making sensible choices about developing the technologies we need to solve our very real current problems."* Indeed, just a year earlier, a project led by scientists at Harvard University, that sought to map a tiny sub-volume of mouse brain, reported[906e] *"considerable technical challenges"*: the researchers questioned whether it was worth the effort and debunked claims that *"mechanistic insights"* into brain function are possible.

American theoretical neuroscientist Kenneth Miller also explained in a 2015 article[906f] why hopes of transcendent mind uploading are hopelessly unrealistic at this stage of human development. Miller commented soberly:

> *"Neuroscience is progressing rapidly, but the distance to go in understanding brain function is enormous. It will almost certainly be a very long time before we can hope to preserve a brain in sufficient detail and for sufficient time that some civilization much farther in the future, perhaps thousands or even millions of years from now, might have the technological capacity to "upload" and recreate that individual's mind.*

> *"I certainly have my own fears of annihilation. But I also know that I had no existence for the 13.8 billion years that the universe existed before my birth, and I expect the same will be true after my death. The universe is not about me or any other individual; we come and we go as part of a much larger process. More and more I am content with this awareness. We all find our own solutions to the problem death poses. For the foreseeable future, bringing your mind back to life will not be one of them."*

Religious similarities

Interesting parallels are being drawn between transhumanist visions of immortality and age-old religious expectations of an afterlife. Concepts of techno-resurrection and transcendence clearly derive from the same angst about death that has always consumed humans. In his contribution[907a] to a special Singularity feature series compiled by the Institute of Electrical and Electronics Engineers (IEEE) in 2008, veteran science commentator John Horgan remarked bluntly: *"Let's face it. The singularity is a religious rather than a scientific vision. The science-fiction writer Ken MacLeod has dubbed it "the rapture for nerds," an allusion to the end-time, when Jesus whisks the faithful to heaven and leaves us sinners behind."*

Roboticist and AI pioneer Rodney Brooks, who advocates a machine perspective for life systems, readily admitted[907b]: *"Many of the advocates of the singularity appear to the more sober observers of technology to have a messianic fervor about their predictions, an unshakable faith in the certainty of their predicted future. To an outsider, a lot of their convictions seem to have many commonalities with religious beliefs."*

Richard Jones condemned[907c] the new yearning for *"transhumanist rapture"*; a tendency he later described[907d] as a peculiar replacement of apocalyptic *religious* determinism with *technological* determinism. He explained why he found the trend so disturbing in a subsequent critique[907e]: *"Everyone at some point must fear their own mortality, and who am I to argue with the many different ways people have of dealing with those fears? But transhumanism's mixing of essentially religious ideas with scientific language matters because it distorts the way we think about technology. Transhumanism tends to see technology as a way to grant all our wishes."*

However, Singularity pioneer Vernor Vinge did not see comparisons with religion as a major issue because *"the spirituality card can be played against both skeptics and enthusiasts."* As he put it[907f]: *"For the skeptic, it's a bit like subtractive sculpture, where step-by-step, each partial success is removing more dross, closing in on the ineffable features of Mind—a rather spiritual prospect! Of course, we may remove and remove and find that ultimately we are left with nothing but a pile of sand—and devices that are everything we are, and more. If that is the outcome, then we've got the singularity."*

Ray Kurzweil similarly shrugged off allusions to the spiritual. He declared in a 2000 essay[908a]: *Evolution moves toward greater complexity, elegance, intelligence, beauty, creativity and love. And God has been called all these things, only without any limitation, infinite. While evolution never reaches an infinite level, it advances exponentially, certainly moving in that direction. Technological evolution, therefore, moves us inexorably closer to becoming like God. And the freeing of our thinking from the severe limitations of our biological form may be regarded as an essential spiritual quest."*

401

Even transhumanists who don't share the view that a Singularity is imminent now openly embrace religious connotations. Italian physicist and futurologist Giulio Prisco, a fervent advocate[908b] of technological transcendence, has co-founded organisations with exotic names like 'Society for Universal Immortalism', 'Order of Cosmic Engineers', and 'The Turing Church'. In 2008, Prisco issued this robust response[908c] to accusations of a religious tendency:

"I wish to repeat here that, if religion is defined as "seeking to find transcendence and truth, meaning and purpose", then I am ready and willing to accept the label "religious". I want to find meaning and transcendence through scientific means and, if I don't find it, I want to build it. My scientific worldview and my belief in our potential for boundless expansion make me appreciate the plausibility of, for example, omega-point-like scenarios where science and spacetime engineering permit to resurrect the dead."

Patrick Hopkins, an American philosopher and ethicist, agreed in a thought-provoking 2011 essay[908d] that transhumanism has strong theological overtones. Hopkins wrote:

"With its aims of transcendence and immortality, transhumanism does not seem just another form of secular humanism. It preaches the virtue of the ends of religion but focuses on human ingenuity and technology as the means toward those ends. This makes transhumanism an odd mixture in the eyes of religious believers—a chimera of irreligion, false religion, and quasi-religion.

"However, I want to argue that it is possible to look at transhumanism as a truly religious endeavor. I am not using the term "religious" here in an abstract way [...]. I am using the term in a simpler, more popular, and more traditional sense of believing in the superhuman agency of a God and desiring to connect with and conform to that God. However, the kind of God that I am thinking of will differ in significant and even audacious ways from the object of traditional and popular devotion."

402

The Terasem Movement, co-founded by American satellite communications and biotechnology pioneer Martine Rothblatt, is another example of a 'transreligion'[908e] grounded in technology. Terasem lists its four core beliefs as: *"Life Is Purposeful; Death Is Optional; God Is Technological; Love Is Essential."* In 2009, Rothblatt launched the blog *Mindfiles, Mindware and Mindclones* to propagate these beliefs. The associated platform *Lifenaut.com* offers the opportunity to create a 'mind file' or digital archive of media that reflects your personality, along with an *avatar* that others could interact with long after your biological demise.

Christian bioethicist Wesley Smith dismisses all such aspirations as a desperate *"wail of despair in the night"* from non-believers who crave immortality while scorning religious teachings. In a 2018 critique[909a], he cited transhumanist Zoltan Istvan's claim that the movement was a natural home for godless people and charged scathingly:

> *"Transhumanism offers adherents the comforts and promises of traditional faith — without the humility that comes from being a created creature, and with the further benefit of eschewing all worry about the eternal consequences of sin, the laws of karma, or a future reincarnation in which our condition is based directly on how we live our present life. In short, transhumanism's primary purpose is to substitute religious belief with a nonjudgmental and ironic technological echo of Christian eschatology."*

Lincoln Cannon refuted[909b] Smith's allegations and accused him of *"misrepresenting Transhumanism and its relationship with religion."* But Smith is not alone in his observations. In a 2017 article[909c], Meghan O'Gieblyn, a former evangelical Christian, chronicled her traumatic journey from loss of faith to a transhumanist vision and crushing disappointment: she described her despair on discovering the new creed was just a *"secular outgrowth of Christian eschatology."*

O'Gieblyn observed: *"What makes the transhumanist movement so seductive is that it promises to restore, through science, the transcendent hopes that science itself has obliterated."* These ironies and contradictions were highlighted in a contemporary essay[909d] by Beth Singler, a social and digital anthropologist at Cambridge University. Singler noted the use of *"eerily religious"* language by *"aggressively secular"* AI and transhumanist enthusiasts in their futuristic visions.

However, Ben Goertzel, a key AI researcher and CEO at SingularityNET, views technological aspirations as a *philosophical* rather than *religious* worldview that offers an alternative notion of existential meaning for an increasingly secular postmodernist society. In *Liberating Minds from Brains* (2002), Goertzel wrote[909e]:

> *"Life is philosophically confusing, with and without the help of advanced technology. [...] On Principia Cybernetica, a website devoted to futuristic and system-theoretic topics, it is opined that "The decline of traditional religions appealing to metaphysical immortality threatens to degrade modern society. Cybernetic immortality can take the place of metaphysical immortality to provide the ultimate goals and values for the emerging global civilization." This is a bit optimistic in my view: I'm not so sure that uploading and the ensuing virtual immortality of the mind will in itself provide new goals and values."*

Goertzel advocates a new 'practical philosophy' of *Cosmism* to fulfil *"humankind's quest to comprehend, experience and perhaps ultimately fuse with more and more of the universe."* He laid out his vision in a 2010 manifesto and explained[909f]: *"What I mean by a "practical philosophy" is, in essence, a world-view and value-system — but one that, in addition to containing abstract understanding, provides concrete guidance to the issues we face in our lives. [....] I think it will become increasingly relevant in the next years, decades and centuries as technology advances, as the "human world" we take for granted is replaced with a succession of radically different realities."*

Will an uploaded mind be 'you'?

Another debated issue is whether a disembodied reincarnation can truly reconstitute personhood. Patrick Hopkins is clear that the resultant digital copy won't be the same as the original mind generated by biological substrates. Hopkins contended in a 2012 paper[910a] that *"while the technology may be feasible, uploading will not succeed because it in fact does not "transfer" a mind at all and will not preserve personal identity."* He summarised his arguments in a lay article[910b]:

> *"What's wrong is not a mistake in the science, not a mistake in the technology, but a mistake in the metaphysics. It's a problem with understanding what is preserved when you copy something. [...] The technology of uploading could copy your brain. But the mind the new brain produces will also be a copy. It will be a real mind. It will have memories and dreams and desires and it will have exactly similar memories and dreams and desires as yours. [...] In spite of the language uploading enthusiasts use, your mind will not "travel" across the room to the computer. The reorganized computer will start producing a new mind. That mind will have exactly similar features as you, but won't be you. You will be right where you started."*

Michael Cerullo also tackled the thorny question in a 2015 paper[910c]. He argued there's a possibility personhood can continue in digital substrates if *psychological structure* is unbroken, and proposed a new theory that *"allows identity to continue in multiple selves"* and maintains *"continuity of consciousness"*. According to Cerullo, the strange behavioural symptoms associated with so-called 'split-brain syndrome'[910d] suggests a single identity can indeed branch into multiple copies of conscious observers. However, research published[910e] in 2017 by a multidisciplinary group led by psychologist Yair Pinto at the University of Amsterdam questioned[910f] the assumption that split-brain syndrome produces two separate centres of consciousness within a single brain.

In any case, the scenario of multiple uploaded copies of the same brain (or mind) poses another difficulty that science writer Amy Harmon pondered in 2015. She asked[911a]: *"What if your upload acts exactly like you, has all your memories, and says it is you? How would you tell? What if 50 copies are made of that copy of you, and they all say they are you too?"* University of Connecticut philosopher Susan Schneider made similar points in a review[911b] of *Her* (2013); a film about a man who develops a romantic relationship with a virtual AI assistant.

British computational neuroscientist Jack McKay Fletcher also noted in a 2015 paper[911c] that *"a computational mind cannot recognize an emulation of itself … for much the same reason that a set of scales cannot weigh itself."* Thus, even if it becomes possible for mind copies to be uploaded to computers with perfect fidelity, there might be no way to determine with certainty that the non-biological copies are true representations of the original source; or which (if any) aspects of personal identity have been preserved.

An allied concern is the mind-boggling complication of rights over uploaded personhood data. As Ian Pearson asked in a thought-provoking 2018 blog post[911d]: *"When you're electronically immortal, will you still own your own mind?"*. He outlined the myriad of ownership issues – from hardware to software and shared social platforms – that could ensnare unwary immortality seekers in perpetual 'cyber slavery'.

The numerous uncertainties and pitfalls have left some analysts wondering whether mind uploading has any utility for current living. Princeton University neuroscientist Michael Graziano cautioned in a 2013 essay[911e] that the promise of utopia might soon become a dystopia as *"an artificial way to preserve minds after death gradually takes on an emphasis of its own"*, and life *"shrinks in importance until it becomes a kind of larval phase."* He concluded: *"To me, this prospect is three parts intriguing and seven parts horrifying. I am genuinely glad I won't be around."*

However, computer scientist and author Keith Wiley disagrees that mind uploading lacks existential utility. He argued passionately in a 2015 article[911f] that humans have a metaphysical imperative to pursue technological immortality that goes beyond mere conquest of biological death. Wiley wrote:

"We stand at the cusp of guaranteeing the survival of fundamental purpose in the universe, reality, and existence by insuring the continuation of consciousness. This is a far grander calling than merely enabling individual life extension. Existential metaphysical purpose is our foremost responsibility as conscious beings, and computer intelligence is the method of achieving it."

Near-death experience

Reports of bizarre experiences by some resuscitated patients (having being in clinical and brain dead states with no ECG or EEG readings) have added to already substantial difficulties in defining a clear, physiological borderline between life and death. To the astonishment of medical staff, seemingly hopeless cases have regained consciousness and recalled events that occurred in their clinical environment *while* they were supposedly unconscious. Stranger still, reports include features usually associated with religious experiences. The phenomenon has added to the mystery about human beings: who or what exactly are we?

Awareness has long been linked to a live, waking, physical brain. Thus, the traditional view[912a] within mainstream neuroscience is that consciousness and all related cognitive functions are lost irretrievably at death – no mental experiences should be possible thereafter. Although history abounds with anecdotes of 'visions' by people that have had a lucky escape from life-threatening situations or recovered miraculously from severe illness, such reports were not regarded as a subject for serious scientific investigation.

Then, in 1969, Swiss-American psychiatrist Elisabeth Kübler-Ross published a landmark book *On Death and Dying* that sparked huge interest and boosted the emerging field of thanatology (scientific study of death). Subsequently, Raymond A. Moody Jr, an American philosopher, psychologist and physician, documented scores of intriguing reports from patients who had been on the threshold of life, and coined the term 'Near-death experience' (NDE) to describe unexplained features in his[912b] best-selling book *Life after Life* (1975).

Moody identified[912c] nine general elements of NDE, including a sense of being dead along with a strange buzzing or ringing sound; positive sensations of peace, well-being and painlessness; out-of-body experience (OBE) as if hovering above and observing medical staff; speedy upward movement through a dark tunnel with mixed emotions of terror and rapture; encounters with unrecognised beings that glow with inner light along the way; and sudden immersion in an ultra-bright, magnetic, golden or white light before exiting the tunnel to warm reception of love and acceptance by assembled deceased loved ones. Finally, subjects reach a boundary and are presented with a panoramic, rapid review of their life at which point they have to choose whether to return (a reluctant decision some only make at the urging of the transcendent beings). Thereafter, patients return to their body with perfect recollection of events.

The extraordinary detail provided by Moody reignited both religious and non-religious debate[912d] on the fate of consciousness at death. Other medical professionals have since ventured into NDE research. In 1978, health management consultant John Audette, psychiatrist Bruce Greyson, psychologist Kenneth Ring and cardiologist Michael Sabom teamed up with Moody to create an international group for investigation and coordination of NDE reports. This early collaboration led to the launch of the International Association for Near-Death Studies (IANDS) and peer-reviewed Journal of Near-Death Studies (JNDS) in the late 1980s.

Among numerous developments, Greyson's 1983 questionnaire-based, quantitative tool[913a] to test and validate NDE claims has become the accepted standard for investigations. A host of subsequent publications by Greyson and other pioneers have helped to establish the field as a legitimate part[913b] of consciousness studies.

One of the most striking features of NDE is the universality[913c] of reports; albeit couched in language that reflects local cultures and belief systems. Another is the deep psychological impact and worldview changes observed in those that report the experience – they become more empathic, more appreciative of life and much less afraid of death. As Greyson remarked in a 2015 interview[913d]:

"As a psychiatrist, what's much more interesting to me is not the 'knock your socks off' part of the experience, but the after-effects, the way it changes people's lives. Psychiatrists and psychologists spend a lot of hard work trying to get people to make fairly small changes, and here in the flash of a second, people are totally transformed—this is a powerful experience!"

Is it just hallucination?

The persistence of NDE reports has attracted researchers from a wide range of fields including psychology, psychiatry and neurology. However, the subject remains[914a] controversial within mainstream science because it suggests a separate mind exists *outside* the mortal brain; an idea linked to[914b] religious concepts of an immortal soul. Moreover, it implies that this incorporeal mind can continue to generate conscious experience *after* the demise of our biological brain. In 1993, Greyson published a new survey[914c] that suggested NDE may be related to *Kundalini* – an ancient Indian concept of primal energy that yoga practitioners believe can be awakened by meditating in a specific posture.

409

However, sceptics argue[914d] that NDE is nothing more than hallucinations emanating from the dying brain. In 2014, French forensic scientist and paleopathologist Philippe Charlier discovered[914e] a medical manuscript dating back to the mid-18th century that attributed similar reports to excessive blood flow to the brain while regaining consciousness. But NDE advocates dispute this explanation – they point out[914f] that hallucinations occur while subjects are *conscious*, unlike NDE which is uniquely experienced while patients are undeniably *unconscious*.

More than neurophysiology

Dutch anaesthesiologist P.R. Martens remarked in a 1994 article[915a] that it was difficult to ascertain whether NDEs were *"meaningful phenomena or just fantasy of death"* due to less-than-rigorous investigatory methods and *"interfering factors such as administration of sedatives and nonspecific stress responses."* These deficiencies were remedied in a rigorous, 8-year Dutch investigation led by cardiologist Pim van Lommel. Results reported in 2001[915,c] from the controlled study across 10 different hospitals in the Netherlands supported[915d] earlier conclusions that NDE had aspects that could not be explained within medical science. The study authors acknowledged a probable role for *physiological* processes – some elements of NDE have been reported by epileptic patients during seizures[915e] or while undergoing electrical stimulation[915f] of the brain's temporal lobe. But observed *psychological* transformations in personality could not be attributed to neurological causes alone. Also, not all resuscitated patients reported visions (as should occur with generic triggers). They queried:

"With lack of evidence for any other theories for NDE, the thus far assumed, but never proven, concept that consciousness and memories are localised in the brain should be discussed. How could a clear consciousness outside one's body be experienced at the moment that the brain no longer functions during a period of clinical death with flat EEG?"

410

However, in a detailed 2008 critique[916a], University of Birmingham cognitive neuroscientist Jason Braithwaite dismissed the notion that NDE challenged the conventional view of consciousness as *"an emergent property of the human brain in action."* He agreed the Dutch report was a *"useful contribution"* to scientific investigation of NDE, but disputed interpretations and conclusions that implied *"the mind may be separable from the brain and hence we may all survive bodily death."* Braithwaite argued that adopting this extraordinary 'survivalist' position *"would require a truly radical revision of current neuroscience and the known laws of physics"*; a seismic shift for which he claimed no factual evidence had been presented.

Nevertheless, the conclusions of van Lommel's team are shared by others like[916b] British medical scientist and resuscitation specialist Sam Parnia and neuropsychiatrist and neurophysiologist Peter Fenwick who specialises in epilepsy and end-of-life research. Both scientists actively support work at the Horizon Research Foundation to understand[916c] the conscious state of the human mind near death. Two decades of clinical experience with patients facing cessation of life convinced[916d] the duo that the mind might, indeed, be an *independent* phenomenon that lingers on after physical brain death.

Parnia and Fenwick were key participants in the largest study into NDE conducted to date: an international AWARE (AWAreness during REsuscitation) collaboration launched[917a] in 2008 by the Human Consciousness Project at University of Southampton in England. The multidisciplinary project spanned 4 years and involved over 30 investigators and 2,060 subjects across 15 medical centres in Europe and North America. Researchers used novel tests in Intensive Care Units such as ceiling-facing shelves with a variety of images that were not visible to medical staff or the clinically dead patients they were attempting to resuscitate.

Disappointingly, AWARE results[917b] did not include any NDE report with a description of the hidden images, but the investigators found[917c] enough evidence of unusual mental activity to hail the exercise as a success that merited further experimental studies. In 2014, Parnia registered a follow-up AWARE II research proposal in both the UK and USA for observational study of up to 1,500 patients experiencing cardiac arrests (CA). The envisaged duration – almost seven years – was derailed by the COVID-19 pandemic in 2020. But Parnia has provided periodic updates culminating in a preliminary November 2019 report[917d] that concluded: *"In some survivors, memories lead to greater life-meaning and a positive transformation, which contrasts with negative psychological outcomes such as PTSD. In this context, in place of NDE a more appropriate term might be transformative experience of death (TED)."*

The quest to understand NDE continues[917e]. Parnia's perseverance is driven by his conviction – outlined in a 2007 journal article[917f] – that understanding of NDE may well provide the long-sought key to solving the mystery of consciousness. As he reiterated[917g] a decade on, *"we're trying to understand the exact features that people experience when they go through death, because we understand that this is going to reflect the universal experience we're all going to have when we die."* However, there's still resistance to assertions that NDE is not wholly brain-based.

Competing hypotheses

Susan Blackmore, who had long researched borderline consciousness phenomena, expressed doubt in a 2008 commentary[918a] that projects like AWARE will ever uncover incontrovertible evidence of NDE that investigators can verify objectively. Blackmore reported a personal, drug-induced out-of-body experience (OBE) in 1970, but has since become a sceptic. Her acclaimed 1993 book *Dying to Live* offered[918b] an entirely physical[918c] 'dying brain' hypothesis.

Oxford University biomedical scientist and theologian Michael Marsh has also challenged the idea that OBEs and NDEs have other-worldly, mystical, or psychical implications. In 2010, Marsh coined[918d] the term *'extra corporeal experience'* (ECE) to cover all such phenomena. He advocated a 'reawakening brain' rather than the 'dying brain' hypothesis suggested by Blackmore.

Despite mainstream scepticism, two of the most highly-publicised accounts of life-changing NDEs have come from respected medical professionals who were lucky to regain consciousness after being given up for dead. In his book *Return from Tomorrow* (1978), prominent American psychiatrist George Ritchie chronicled[919a] his OBE as a 20-year-old after being declared dead from severe pneumonia at an army hospital in 1943. His vivid recollection of places 'visited'[919b] was one of the reports that prompted Raymond Moody to undertake an in-depth research into the phenomenon. Ritchie later detailed how his experience had transformed his life in *Ordered to Return* (1998).

Eben Alexander III, a neurosurgeon and academic researcher with over 25 years practice experience, also gave a fascinating account of his 2008 NDE in *Proof of Heaven* (2012). Alexander's evocatively-titled book recounts extraordinary mental experiences while his cerebral cortex (the brain region associated with higher executive functions and personhood) was shut down[919c] by an attack of acute meningitis that left him in a 7-day-long coma. His experience led him to shed years of physicalist assumptions and call for a reassessment about the nature of consciousness and existence in a journal article[919d]. Alexander wrote: *"My coma taught me many things. First and foremost, near-death experiences, and related mystical states of awareness, reveal crucial truths about the nature of existence. And the reductive materialist (physicalist) model, on which conventional science is based, is fundamentally flawed. At its core, it intentionally ignores what I believe is the fundament of all existence — the nature of consciousness."*

However, British neurologist Oliver Sacks dismissed Alexander's suggestion that NDE is a mystical phenomenon that affords a glimpse into an 'afterlife'. In a poignant article[919e], Sacks, who had experienced migraine-inducing hallucinations in childhood, described his later experimentation with mind-bending drugs. He narrated how these experiences had motivated a life-long quest to understand the neurochemistry behind ultimately illusory mind constructs; a pursuit that led him to conclude OBEs and NDEs stem from radically altered states of consciousness generated by the *physical* brain.

In another loaded essay[919f] titled *Seeing God in the Third Millennium*, Sacks recalled the equally fascinating experience of another neuroscientist and surgeon Tony Cicoria who was struck by lightning and had a transcendent vision while in a clinically dead state. After resuscitation, Cicoria acquired an inexplicable passion and talent for classical music but, unlike Alexander, interpreted his spiritual transformation as divine intervention in how his *physical brain* functioned; not as proof of a separate mind or supernatural domain. Sacks insisted: *"Hallucinations, whether revelatory or banal, are not of supernatural origin; they are part of the normal range of human consciousness and experience. This is not to say that they cannot play a part in the spiritual life, or have great meaning for an individual. Yet while it is understandable that one might attribute value, ground beliefs, or construct narratives from them, hallucinations cannot provide evidence for the existence of any metaphysical beings or places. They provide evidence only of the brain's power to create them."*

Retracing birth?

Some investigators have interpreted the 'dark tunnel' featured[920a] in several NDE reports as a recall of our journey from the womb down the birth canal to joyous reception in a world of bright lights. The hypothesis first emerged in *The Human Encounter with Death* (1977) co-authored[920b] by Czech psychiatrist Stanislav Grof and American psychological anthropologist Joan Halifax.

414

Grof, a respected pioneer of 'transpersonal psychology' that seeks to give spiritual experience a scientific basis, subsequently drew on Hindu concepts of *Namarupa* (spiritual essence) and *Atman* (eternal soul) to explain[920c] the sensation of rapid tunnel travel when we perceive death. He re-designated this part of NDE as *Near-birth experience* (NBE); a retracing of our rapid 'coming into being' through a spectrum of consciousness that spans several modes from the physical to the transcendent. Carl Sagan popularised the notion of NBE when he suggested[920d] in the last essay of his 1979 best-seller *Broca's Brain* that lingering memories from the birth process might be the wellspring for all religion. Barbara Honegger also linked NBE (rather than NDE) to out-of-body experience (OBE) in a 1983 compendium.

However, this 'reverse birth' NBE hypothesis is even more controversial than claims that NDE has supernatural elements. Susan Blackmore called[921a] Honegger's 1983 contribution *"unhelpful"* and dismissed[921b] the birth analogy as *"pitifully inadequate"* in a 1991 article. Other sceptics argue that infant amnesia does not allow us to retain memories from childbirth – Lawrence Patihis and Helena Younes Burton suggested in a 2015 article[921c,d] that any such recollections are almost certain to be false memories.

Nevertheless, there have been several reports of OBEs during childbirth. A rigorous review of cases by health scientists at University of Hull in England concluded[921e] in 2017 that experiences of dissociation and disembodiment were real. Interestingly, mothers who had a previous record of psychological trauma were found to be more prone to the phenomenon. The report authors urged: *"Clinicians should legitimize women's disclosure of OBEs and explore and ascertain their impact, either as a normal coping mechanism or a precursor to perinatal mental illness."*

Between life and death

A detailed analysis of subjective consciousness[922a] conducted by coma specialists and cognitive psychologists at University Hospital of Liège (UHL) in Belgium has deepened the NDE mystery. In 2013, the group published[922b] results that showed[922c] NDEs are actual perceptions stemming from *even more* vivid neurophysiologic representations than those experienced for real or imagined events. They summed up the unexpected finding thus:

> *"In conclusion, the present study shows that NDE memories have more characteristics than any kind of memory of real or imagined events and of other memories of a period of coma or impaired consciousness following an acquired severe brain dysfunction. In our opinion, the presented data demonstrate that NDEs cannot be considered as imagined events. We rather propose that the physiological origins of NDEs lead them to be really perceived although not lived in reality (i.e., being hallucination- or dream-like events), having as rich characteristics as memories of real events."*

The UHL researchers published an expanded report[922d,e] in 2017 that included an overview of global NDE findings, and the unique potential the phenomenon offers for investigating neural correlates of consciousness. Another multidisciplinary team at University of Padova (UP) in Italy has since used an integrated psychodynamic-EEG approach to trace neural markers in the brain associated with stored memories of NDE. The UP investigators reported[922f]:

> *"It is notable that the EEG pattern of correlations for NDE memory recall differed from the pattern for memories of imagined events. In conclusion, our findings suggest that, at a phenomenological level, NDE memories cannot be considered equivalent to imagined memories, and at a neural level, NDE memories are stored as episodic memories of events experienced in a peculiar state of consciousness."*

These intriguing developments suggest undefined modes of consciousness may exist between states of what scientists and philosophers currently recognise as 'life' and 'death' – it appears Grof's *transitional modes* of consciousness may actually have some neurologic foundation. In a 2012 article[923a], UP neuroscientist Enrico Facco and psychologist Christian Agrillo urged scientists to remain *"rigorously neutral"* and refrain from rejecting NDE claims merely because transcendent aspects are incompatible with traditional scientific emphasis on empirical, reproducible evidence. The duo cautioned: *"Facts can be only true or false, never paranormal. In this sense, they cannot be refused a priori even when they appear implausible with respect to our current knowledge: any other stance implies the risk of turning knowledge into dogma and the adopted paradigm into a sort of theology."*

However, as a 2016 editorial review in a special issue[923b] of *Journal of Parapsychology* (vol. 80, no. 2) themed *Do We Survive Death?* discussed, it's difficult to see how any transitional consciousness that arises – *despite* cessation of physically-detectable brain activity – can be scientifically investigated.

Holographic parallels

Certain aspects of NDE – especially out-of-body experience (OBE) and feelings of universal oneness – are strikingly similar to holographic features of *interconnectedness* and *non-localised* distribution of information. These same aspects inspired Karl Pribram's holonomic interpretation[924a] of brain function; a model[924b] in which *every bit* of our neural system would contain *all* information about 'personhood' developed from birth. Could NDE be arising from a special mode of consciousness generated from information hidden somewhere in the multiple brain dimensions[924c] modelled in 2017? Does the tunnel travel experience reflect superfast *retrieval and transmission* of memories stored in holographic format to an external, non-local node?

Interestingly, widespread and persistent *déjà* episodes (the eerie feeling that one has 'been there' or 'done that' when a new situation is encountered) have also been linked[925a,b] to a holographic model of[925c] brain processing. At some point in their lives, most humans will experience a weird sense of *déjà vu* (already seen), *déjà entendu* (already heard), *déjà parlé* (already spoken), *déjà arrivé* (already happened), *déjà vécu* (already lived), and other similar sensations. However, there's no scientific consensus[925d] on possible causes.

MIT researchers suggested[926a] in 2007 that a faulty neurological circuit for pattern recognition may be generating false *déjà* memories. However, while it's true the phenomenon is common[926b] in patients afflicted with temporal lobe epilepsy, there's no empirical evidence that these experiences arise from *physical* brain conditions. A 2013 Russian EEG study[926c] of brain activity during *déjà* episodes revealed distinctly different patterns in epileptic and non-epileptic subjects – puzzling results that indicate the phenomenon is independent of normal brain physiology. Likewise, Japanese investigators reported[926d] in 2006 that frequency of occurrence among patients with schizophrenia is actually *less* than in healthy subjects (a follow-up study confirmed[926e] *déjà* experiences are unlikely to stem from patient psychopathologies).

What, then, is the source and significance of these bizarre sensations? Research led by cognitive psychologist Akira O'Connor at University of St Andrews in Scotland suggests[927a] *déjà* events may be triggered by self-checking 'runs' by the brain to ensure stored episodic memories have actually been experienced and not falsely generated. A 2016 study by O'Connor's group found that[927b] over-prompting of subjects during investigations led to higher *déjà* and *tip-of-the-tongue* (TOT) incidences. They proposed in a 2021 review[927c] that these states are 'dissociative' outputs as the brain assesses previously stored memory for familiarity with new situations.

However, the eerie aspect of *prescience* remains largely unexplored and unexplained: how is it possible to recall memories of events that were *never before* experienced or even imagined in real life? Unnervingly, a team of biologists, electrical engineers and computer scientists at University of California, Berkeley showed[928a] in 2017 that it was possible to implant[928b] false sensations and memories with an optical 'holographic brain modulator'. Cognitive psychologist Anne Cleary has also identified[928c] parallels between *déjà* experiences and human recognition memory patterns. However, Cleary and Colorado State University (CSU) colleague Alexander Claxton stressed in a 2018 report[928d] that, although *déjà* feelings are actual mental events, these are not[928e] subconscious visions of the future – they suggested that *"Metacognitive bias brought on by the state itself may explain the peculiar association between déjà vu and the feeling of premonition."*

Out of body, Out of self

The cognitive processes that allow us to identify with the biological bodies we inhabit are complex and little understood. In 2014, psychologists Andra Smith and Claude Messier from University of Ottawa in Ontario, Canada reported[929a] the surprising case of a subject who was able to invoke *voluntary* OBE at will. They found that, during these *extra-corporeal experiences* (ECEs) of being 'outside' her physical body, her brain displayed somewhat similar activity to that of persons undergoing *involuntary* OBE induced by trauma. Neuroscientists at Sweden's Karolinska Institute (KI) also discovered in 2012 that perfectly healthy people can be tricked into 'disowning' their real body during an OBE illusion. They reported[929b]:

"We demonstrate that when healthy individuals experience that they are located in a different place from their real body, they disown this body and no longer perceive it as part of themselves. Our findings are important because they reveal a relationship between the representation of self-location in the local environment and the multisensory representation of one's own body."

419

The Karolinska researchers announced[929c] an even more astonishing achievement in 2015. They successfully used OBE illusions generated in a brain scanner to 'teleport' *static* subjects around a room. The results showed that[929d], disconcertingly, the experience of being inside a body (which we take for granted) is tenuous and easily severed. The scientists also found[929e] that neurons in the hippocampus – a brain region already linked to spatial memory and perception of location – are involved in OBE. However, underlying neural mechanisms are still far from clear.

Intriguingly, University of Barcelona psychobiologists have since discovered that OBE induced by virtual reality (VR) reduces fear of death – just as in NDE. The fascinating experiment, involving immersion of subjects in 'swopped' virtual bodies, was reported[930a] in 2017. Mel Slater, who devised and led the study, explained the unexpected finding in a media report[930b]: *"What we think is happening is that somehow your brain is learning implicitly that it's possible to separate consciousness from the body. That was my body, I'm out of it, and I still have my full consciousness. Therefore, implicitly, consciousness can be separable from the body. And if consciousness is separable from the body, then it's possible to have survival beyond the physical body."*

Predictably, the VR industry has been quick to develop applications[931a] for replacement of screen-based video games with remarkable life-like holographic 'neurogames'[931b]. As American theoretical physicist and futurist Michio Kaku discussed in an overview[931c] of prospects, technologies that allow humans to induce OBEs at will, and have *tactile* (sensation of touch) interactions with virtual objects and environments at a distance, will profoundly impact our concept of reality and day-to-day living. Already, virtual 'body-hacking'[931d] kits allow us to 'inhabit' someone else's body and 'age simulation'[931e] suits give the young a taste of impairments suffered by the elderly.

420

A tool for consciousness studies

Despite the lack of scientific consensus on NDE, there's growing acknowledgment that the phenomenon offers[932a] a unique opportunity to investigate possible neural correlates of consciousness. Psychiatrists, in particular, are keenly interested[932b] in exploration of NDE for new psychotherapies.

In 2005, the journal *Progress in Brain Research* published a compendium (volume 150) edited by Steven Laureys that explored[932c] *The Boundaries of Consciousness* within neurobiology and neuropathology. Contributions included a discussion[932d] of complexities and biological assumptions by cognitive and behavioural neurologist Adam Zeman; a description[932e] of the prevailing neuroscientific approach co-authored by pharmacologist Susan Greenfield and Oxford University colleague Toby Collins; and a sceptical review[932f] of explanations for NDE by psychologist Christopher French from Goldsmiths College, University of London.

A decade later, *Annals of The New York Academy of Sciences* (ANYAS) issued a new compilation (vol. 1330, issue 1) based on a radio discussion series titled *Rethinking Mortality: Exploring the Boundaries between Life and Death*. The edition featured a foreword[933a] by Nour Foundation program director Richard Rass, and an introduction[933b] by Steve Paulson – author and executive producer of *To The Best Of Our Knowledge* (TTBOOK). Contributions included latest views on death reversal[933c] within medical science, NDE reports[933d], dilemmas arising from life-extension technologies[933e], and culture and social impacts on our approach to mortality and death[933f]. Sam Parnia authored an overview[933g] of updated research, and University of Kentucky neurologist Kevin Nelson (who has suggested[933h] that NDEs may be a form of lucid dreams) restated[933i] physicalist, brain-based arguments.

Is there an 'afterlife'?

In 2014, NDE investigator Pim van Lommel joined other researchers from a range of scientific disciplines at a summit in Tucson, Arizona, USA to discuss prevailing mechanistic-materialist ideology on consciousness. The group issued a radical manifesto[934a] committing to *"emergence of a post-materialist paradigm."* They followed up the next year with a declaration[934b] that called for incorporation of the concept of an *immaterial,* non-local consciousness into end-of-life care strategies. Another group of 100 scientists issued a separate call[934c] in the journal *Frontiers in Human Neuroscience* for *"an open, informed study of all aspects of consciousness"* that takes unbiased account of all new findings. An annual *Beyond the Brain* conference, launched at St John's College, Cambridge University in 1995, now attracts[934d] an impressive range of speakers.

Public fascination with NDE continues as evidenced by the sizeable audiences attracted by a 2017 remake of the classic 1990 cult movie *Flatliners,* and the 2021 *Netflix* documentary series *Surviving Death* that claims[934e] scientific evidence has emerged of 'life after death'. The idea of a post-mortal state of consciousness is a persuasive secular alternative to religious notions of an immortal soul. However, NDE research is unlikely to yield firm evidence of any 'death mode' of consciousness since patients reporting the experience had no *observable* brain activity while in this grey life-death zone.

Thus, medical science has no option but to recognise death in terms of the 'switching off' of *embodied,* localised consciousness – to the extent that this is detectable in our biological bodies. Metaphysical concepts of life and death are intriguing, but have no practicable application in clinical settings. Whatever part of our being might survive to an afterlife will always be 'dead' for earthly purposes.

In his 2007 book *Consciousness Beyond Life*, Pim van Lommel expressed hope[935a] that future research will show the brain is not a *producer* but a *transmitter/receiver* and facilitator of non-local 'wave-fields' of consciousness. He wrote in a 2014 review[935b]:

"In this concept, consciousness is not rooted in the measurable domain of physics, our manifest world. This also means that the wave aspect of our indestructible consciousness in the nonlocal realm is inherently not measurable by physical means. [....]

"For this reason we should seriously consider the possibility that death, like birth, can only be a transition to another state of consciousness. According to this idea death is only the end of our physical aspects, and during life our body functions as an interface or place of resonance for our nonlocal consciousness. [....]

"It often takes an NDE to get people to think about the possibility of experiencing consciousness independently of the body and to realize that presumably consciousness always has been and always will be, that everything and everybody is connected in higher levels of our consciousness, that all of our thoughts will exist forever, and that death as such does not exist."

Terminal lucidity: Final recalls

A strange phenomenon observed in patients with severe cognitive impairment when facing death has given researchers another opportunity to gain insights into the brain's relationship with consciousness at the end of life. For centuries, physicians had recorded that mentally-ill persons who had long been incoherent (or even catatonic) would suddenly regain memories with striking mental clarity and engage in meaningful communications for up to a week before passing away. Curiously, these revivals were accompanied by sudden euphoric moods in patients. However, the incidents were not deemed significant enough to merit scientific research.

Now, associated healthcare costs[936a] and family impacts of the global exponential growth[936b] in brain degeneration and psychological disorders has prompted medical scientists to investigate whether these final 'reconnections' can help unlock the neural malfunctions that are driving this seemingly irreversible trend of mental illness.

In 2009, German biologist Michael Nahm coined[936c] the term *terminal lucidity* (TL) for the mysterious mental 'reboots' – now also termed *paradoxical lucidity* (PL) as they occur in otherwise confused or irrational patients. He subsequently co-authored a review[936d] of cases going back 250 years and expressed hope that the comprehensive information would *"encourage investigation of the mechanisms involved and possible insights into both the neuroscience of memory and cognition at the end of life and treatment of terminal illness."* Among other influential work, Nahm and University of Virginia colleague Bruce Greyson (NDE research pioneer at IANDS) issued an updated report[936e] in 2014 on the particularly curious case of Anna Katharina Ehmer; a German woman with severe mental disabilities who, according[936f] to credible professional witnesses, had *never spoken* but then suddenly broke out into dying songs for half-an-hour before her death in 1922.

Hard-pressed public health authorities are also taking an interest. In June 2018, physician and geriatrician Basil Eldadah at the US National Institute on Aging (NIA) convened[937a] an interdisciplinary workshop to evaluate available case reports and analyses, consider possible causative mechanisms, and suggest a framework for further research into possible therapies for advanced dementia. The seminal event was led by anaesthesiologist and neuroscientist George Mashour (Nahm and Greyson participated). The group's remarkable assessment, published[937b] in 2019, was that TL/PL is a neurological reversal that indicates *even a severely damaged brain* is still capable of accessing hidden functional configurations that neuroscientists might be able to model[937c] with systems and network theory.

In an accompanying perspective article[937d], Eldadah and NIA colleagues Elena Fazio and Kristina McLinden announced two lines of funding *"to establish the building blocks of such a research program."* They explored the profound implications of TL/PL and commented:

> *"These foundational outcomes could lead to further studies that may eventually point to novel mechanisms underlying cognitive decline, identify potential preventive or therapeutic approaches for individuals with dementia, offer more effective strategies for caregivers, and perhaps even expand our understanding of the nature of personhood and consciousness. [....]*

> *"Of course, available literature indicates that paradoxical lucidity is not limited to dementia and that individuals with a variety of neurological or psychiatric conditions may also have unexpectedly lucid episodes. Perhaps lucidity is a specific manifestation of a more general, although still unexpected, burst of energy often observed in end-of-life settings that hospice nurses call the 'end-of-life rally.' [....]*

> *"We look forward to the science that will emerge from this new line of research. There are obviously many more questions than answers at this point, and it is hard to say what the metaphorical road will look like, as we have hardly left our metaphorical driveway. However, as the history of science has shown, answers to vexing problems can often turn up in previously unappreciated places. Whether lucidity in dementia is one of those places will be determined in due time."*

Closing Discussion

"Of making many books there is no end, and much study wearies the body.
Now all has been heard; here is the conclusion of the matter:"
From Ecclesiates 12:12-13, NIV

Making sense of existence

Among the multitude of issues that continue to perplex humans, the question *'Why is there something rather than nothing?'* has long been the starting point for discussions about the reality we're privileged to witness. In 1959, German philosopher Martin Heidegger identified[938a] the query as the most fundamental consideration in metaphysics; he sharply criticised[938b] contemporaries who sought to dismiss or evade the topic.

Australian philosopher Arthur Witherall concluded in a 2001 review[938c,d] of many possible answers (including religious narratives) that we may never arrive at a satisfactory explanation. As he noted: *"Asking the question "Why is there something instead of nothing?" almost always inspires a reaction of awe or wonder. This emotional response is both appropriate and desirable, whether or not a legitimate answer to the question is obtainable. The question is deep, and the fact about which it asks is impossible to explain by citing some other fact or some antecedent condition."*

Aristotelian philosophers and Aquinian theologians ascribe existence to a prime mover[938e] or necessary being[938f] that theists recognise as God. But this does not explain why an *eternal immaterial* superintelligence should kick-start time and put a wondrous universe in motion that ultimately produced *temporal material* beings with free will. The question goes to the heart of human perception and understanding about life's purpose and ultimate meaning.

Does it matter?

Despite Heidegger's insistence[939a] that the issue is central to any debate about the nature of things and 'beings' we observe, atheists like Sean M. Carroll dismiss the 'why' question as a trivial matter. Carroll wrote in a 2018 paper[939b]:

> *"It seems natural to ask why the universe exists at all. Modern physics suggests that the universe can exist all by itself as a self-contained system, without anything external to create or sustain it. But there might not be an absolute answer to why it exists. I argue that any attempt to account for the existence of something rather than nothing must ultimately bottom out in a set of brute facts; the universe simply is, without ultimate cause or explanation."*

British neuroethicist David Pearce even suggested[939c] in 2014 that the answer may be that, literally, *nothing* exists. He floated a 'Zero ontology' based on the mathematical assumption in physics that all properties and processes in the universe sum up to exactly zero; *everything* is in a state of mutual cancellation. According to this view, our reality is false and nothing (in a metaphysical sense) exists that we should agonise over. However, as Pearce admitted, *"it's hard to think of any experimental tests for this speculative conjecture."*

Witherall judged[939d] that Pearce's proposal had merit and was *"compelling"* and *"interesting"* in many ways. But he reiterated *"there are problems and paradoxes lurking in the very idea that one could explain why the world exists."* He also observed that the idea of a 'Zero existence' was *"unintelligible or highly counter-intuitive from the perspective of our everyday worldview"* of things and events. Humans, noted Witherall, are unable to conceive or describe the totality of the universe since *"Such an entity is beyond our experience, and certainly beyond our powers of manipulation."* Thus, only an observer *outside* our cosmic bubble can see the overall picture and calculate whether everything within sums up to zero.

From the perspective of humans, we inhabit a substantial reality; certainly our unique metacognition *compels* us to contemplate our circumstances and seek explanations for everything we behold and experience. To navigate the increasingly turbulent waters of everyday life, we desperately need worldviews that make sense and accord with cultural and social expectations. Why do we, thinking beings, exist at this point in time? If we accept, from whatever perspective, that our existence is purposive and there's an end goal, how can we best achieve coordinated[939e] universal striving for optimal outcomes?

The human condition

Beyond the need to understand origin and purpose, our search for meaning is driven by cravings for self-esteem, self-fulfilment and personal happiness. There's also a wider societal imperative[940a] for a moral compass to preserve *order* and *stability*; essential bedrocks of civilisations that have long required subjugation of unfettered human free will to restrictive divine will, or rules and regulations imposed by civil authorities. However, these constraints are fast crumbling. In 2008, the *Centre de Cultura Contemporània de Barcelona* (CCCB) in Spain hosted a series of lectures on the human condition. The event was introduced[940b] with this sobering statement:

"For some decades now, the religious, ideological, family and work-related principles that traditionally sustained human life have been in crisis. These changes, which initially appeared as a chance for the individual to enjoy greater freedom, have opened up new domains of the unknown and, paradoxically, have generated even more uncertainty as to the future. Moreover, recent scientific research has raised doubts about previous assumptions that took for granted the superiority of humans over other living beings. The enduring presence of violence in our world and constant violations of human rights prompt us to recognise that our society is a long way from the humanist ideal. At the start of the 21st century, we are faced, more than ever before, with the need to think about the features that define us as people."

428

Bleak as this may sound, it may well be an understatement of the myriad of complex problems that now confront humanity despite our impressive technological achievements. The first half of the 20th century was plagued by the horrors of two world wars and intervening economic global depression. But after World War II, there was a determined effort to avoid similar self-inflicted catastrophes. Establishment of the United Nations – along with various universal declarations of aspirations – and agreements for a new global economic order at Bretton Woods in July 1944 renewed faith that humans were capable of minimising conflict and uplifting their own condition.

However, the sense of optimism that inspired the 'Baby Boomer' generation born over the next two decades had all but evaporated by the start of the 21st century. Self-doubt, despair and insecurity have returned to haunt populations. In particular, those born within the past 40 years – Generation Y, Millennials, Generation Z, Centennials (or whatever fancy label[940c] the media dreams up) are facing an uphill battle as they try to make sense of a society in which all the old certainties are being rapidly eroded. According to contemporary thinkers, we're at various stages of a post-work[941a], post-economic[941b], post-ideological[941c], post-liberal[941d], post-religious[941e], post-secular[941f], post-science[941g] and post-truth[941h] world. Growing perception of a rudderless ship-of-life is creating a self-centred 'post-society' in which individuals struggle to define notions of meaning and morality.

As traditional social contracts break down, many are losing faith in the ability of authorities to devise workable solutions or even address increasingly debilitating issues confronting their citizens with anything approaching candour. Dystopian writers, who would once have been dismissed as 'prophets of doom', have been gaining[941i] huge audiences with dire predictions[941j] of impending collapse. Can humanity forge new solutions to avoid self-destruction?

Ancient worldviews

Classical Greek philosophers (c. 500 - 170 BCE) are celebrated for their sophisticated expositions of existential meaning. The concept of *eudaimonia*[942a] (human flourishing for happiness) was seen as key to a fulfilled life: contemporary works explored[942b] what might be the constituents and how these may be achieved. The ideology was driven by the belief that meaning is very much a matter for humans rather than external gods, and that all tools for ultimate fulfilment lie well within our grasp.

There was much debate over the extent to which *arête* (excellence, virtuousness) and *phronesis* (exercise of practical wisdom) impacted *eudaimonia*, and whether these aspects of *ethos* (character) were evidenced by physical or mental exercise or a mixture of both. A related discussion was the extent to which *moral* attributes (in the sense of voluntary good deeds and thoughts) was a legitimate constituent over and above identified virtues like prudence, temperance, courage, justice, strength, beauty and humour. Interestingly, the modern science of positive psychology[942c] echoes ancient Greek themes of *eudaimonia*.

Aristotle is credited with the first formulation of a code known as *Nicomachean Ethics*[942d] that separates physical from moral virtues. He believed practical action was essential for *eudaimonia* and identified three strands: personal acts for pleasurable living, political acts for the common good and philosophical contemplation to guide one's judgement in executing all actions in accordance with reason. He also argued[942e] that all humans can develop the necessary ethics, but acknowledged the limitations imposed by inherited circumstances and life's fortunes. For Aristotle, human vices and immoral acts reflected absence of *phronesis* due to *akrasia* (character weaknesses and bad judgement) – not inherent 'wickedness'.

Ancient Chinese philosophies also sought meaning in human activity and separated issues of morality from existential meaning. Humans were simply expected to align their affairs with opposing and complementary *Yin-Yang*[943a] cosmic influences that keep[943b] the universe in balance. Hence, *Mohists* (c. 470 BCE) advocated[943c] impartial, unconditional caring for others within a meritocratic society[943d] that emphasised *Fa-Jia* – the rule of law and order and supremacy of the state over rights, virtues or notions of fate.

These early pragmatic approaches are markedly different to later Western theological teachings. But the belief that humans have inherent capacity to evolve high ethical values is still widespread.

Pleasure principle

Another long-standing philosophical proposal is that ultimate meaning lies in the narrow pursuit of pleasure and happiness. Several strands of this worldview, now termed hedonism[944a], emerge in ancient Greek philosophy. But the idea can be traced[944b] to ancient Babylonian and Egyptian writings.

Aristippus of Cyrene (c. 435 – 356 BCE) and his grandson of the same name are credited with founding the Cyrenaic school of thought that emphasised bodily pleasures and self-gratification over abstract mental speculations on the grounds that we can only be certain about immediate physical sensations. This extreme form of hedonism was superseded within a century by a more moderate version advocated by early materialist Epicurus (341 – 270 BCE). Epicureanism held that, while pleasure indeed represented the 'greatest good', the highest form was not unbridled physical indulgence but *ataraxia* (ultimate tranquillity); a state that is only attainable through temperate and informed living to free oneself from *aponia* (unnecessary pain and worry).

431

Hedonism was revived in 19th century Europe by the Utilitarians who held that, since happiness is a universally agreed goal, the only consideration in life ought to be the *utility* of any action. They defined this measure as the extent to which an act was likely to maximise pleasure with minimum pain for everyone involved. The approach is based on a 'principle of utility' first outlined[944c] in 1780 by English philosopher and social reformer Jeremy Bentham – he formulated a *felicific calculus* algorithm that calculates the utility of specific actions *sans* pain. But it was John Stuart Mill's essay *Utilitarianism* (1861-1863)[944d] that popularised[944e] the concept as a valid, ethical viewpoint.

In 1920, Sigmund Freud introduced a new pleasure principle[945a] that argued humans are driven by biological and psychological inclinations to seek pleasure and avoid pain. He identified a 'death drive'[945b] compulsion that prevents us from achieving maximum pleasure in life. Freud proposed psychotherapies to align[945c] mental and emotional health with pleasurable desires for peace of mind and happiness. However, in *Anarchy, State, and Utopia* (1974) American philosopher Robert Nozick used a Matrix-like pleasure simulator or 'experience machine'[945d] to show that humans require[945e] far more than hedonistic gratification for happiness and well-being.

Fate and destiny

Around 300 BCE, the Cypriot Zeno of Citium (c. 334 – 262 BCE) introduced a deterministic worldview in Athens known as Stoicism[946a] that became the dominant philosophy of the Hellenistic period. Zeno's Stoics believed a universal law of fate or *Logos* governed every material thing in existence – the only factor humans have control over is our *prohairesis* or volition. They reasoned that the best policy for happiness is to train your mind to exercise good judgement in every circumstance, and seek to align one's life in accordance with the natural flow of events.

In contrast to hedonists, Stoics advocated[946b] virtuous living, strict control of emotions, and moderation of cravings for base pleasures. They argued that it is only through pursuit of knowledge and understanding of nature that humans can overcome fear of pain and death, and achieve the right frame of mind for maximum fulfilment in life. Elements of Stoic logic can be found in the ancient Chinese philosophy of *Wu wei* (path of least resistance) and the Indian Vedic concept of *karma* (self-determination of fate by behavioural choices).

Stoicism was widely adopted[946c] as a way of life during the Roman Empire. Notable adherents include statesman and dramatist Lucius Annaeus Seneca (c. 4 BCE – 65 CE) whose classic treatise *De Ira* (On Anger) is still the model for anger management, and Greek slave turned sage Epictetus (c. 55 – 135 CE) whose *Discourses* and *Enchiridion* became standard reference manuals. Emperor Marcus Aurelius (121 – 181 CE) famously compiled a classic book of Stoical *Meditations* that is still used by modern practitioners. Stoic philosophy declined after Emperor Constantine (272 – 337 CE) embraced Christianity. But it re-emerged briefly in the 16th century within a Neostoicism movement that was influenced by a series of publications from Flemish scholar Justus Lipsius who sought to combine[946d] Stoic ideas with Christianity.

Interestingly, Stoicism is again enjoying strong revival[947a]: since the late 20th century, it has been embraced[947b] by an increasingly stressed generation. Notable advocates of Modern Stoicism include[947c] philosopher of science Massimo Pigliucci and[947d] well-being researcher Jules Evans. Annual Stoic Week events have been organised since 2012. This enduring doctrine of discipline, self-help, social responsibility and rationalism has even spawned a novel *cognitive behavioural therapy* (CBT) within psychology. However, as Pigliucci admitted[947e] in a 2015 'testimony', the movement is struggling to reconcile original beliefs with contemporary secularism.

Divine providence

Theistic philosophers have long argued that, regardless of disputes over religious revelations and scripture, existence can only have meaning when viewed from the perspective of a benign divinity. Belief systems that acknowledge a transcendent first cause tend to have three themes on meaning: 1) the wondrous things we perceive bear witness to an omnipotent, omniscient creator; 2) humans are uniquely endowed to perceive this creation, and experience the awe that moves us to render homage and worship; 3) our life experience affords the opportunity to prove ourselves worthy of sharing in the creator's eternal glory by adhering to rules of conduct and observing prescribed rituals (with the overhanging threat of eternal damnation should we stray from stipulated pathways). The Christian Bible contains many verses on these themes:

> *"The heavens declare the glory of God;*
> *the skies proclaim the work of his hands.*
> *Day after day they pour forth speech;*
> *night after night they reveal knowledge."*
> (Psalm 19:1-2, NIV)

> *"Lord, our Lord, how majestic is your name in all the earth!*
> *You have set your glory in the heavens.*
> *Through the praise of children and infants ..."*
> (Psalm 8:1-2, NIV)

> *"Lord, who may dwell in your sacred tent?*
> *Who may live on your holy mountain?*
> *The one whose walk is blameless*
> *and who does what is righteous,*
> *who speaks the truth from their heart;"*
> (Psalm 15:1-2, NIV)

434

Explanations of meaning based on divine providence continue to have global appeal because they provide intelligible (though not empirically ascertainable) answers to most of our big questions: primordial causation, consciousness, senses, aesthetic awareness, music, free will, morality, worldly tribulations and ultimate fate. Belief that all circumstances in life flow from divine will provides a mental and emotional bar on which people of faith can hang life's fortunes and misfortunes. Significantly, both believers and non-believers tend to invoke supernatural agency automatically when overwhelmed (*Oh my God!*, *God help us* etc.) – it appears to be an evolved reaction to feelings of awe or dread.

However, while awareness that human destiny is not totally under our control provides some recourse and may help to reduce apprehension, life is prone to capricious vicissitudes that can lead to despair and desolation. The seeming futility of our condition was reputedly lamented by Solomon, king of ancient Israel (c. 970 to 931 BCE) in this Bible text:

> *"Meaningless! Meaningless!"*
>   *says the Teacher.*
> *"Utterly meaningless!*
>   *Everything is meaningless."*
> (Ecclesiates 1:2, NIV)

But, despite declaring that all activity and striving is like *"chasing after wind"*, the author rationalised that humans can still find meaning and fulfilment in altruism, simple pleasures and work:

> *"I know that there is nothing better for people than to be happy and do good while they live. That each of them may eat and drink, and find satisfaction in all their toil —this is the gift of God."*
> (Ecclesiates 3:12-13, NIV)

Another difficulty is that we have no experience of an 'afterlife'; the idea of a 'soul' that survives our perishable physical bodies to be rewarded or punished thereafter is entirely based on faith. No one (except Jesus Christ who Christians acknowledge as God in mortal form) has ever returned to report on post-death events. Thus, earthly adversities can lead to loss of faith even in ardent believers.

Non-divine agency

In the 19th century, some European scholars revived the ancient idea that mortals (rather than supernatural beings) bear responsibility for assigning meaning to their own lives. This concept of *existentialism* can be traced to the writings of Danish philosopher Søren Kierkegaard (early 1800s) and German philosopher Friedrich Nietzsche (late 1800s). Both these thinkers argued that human free will allows us to define our own existence for good or ill. But whereas Kierkegaard regarded[948a] God as an inspiration for 'will to meaning' and believed we can attain fulfilment by becoming 'knights of faith' able to 'leap' beyond negative experiences, Nietzsche emphasised[948b] that the euphoric 'God is dead' mood and rejection of religious authority ushered in by the European Enlightenment meant people now had to quickly evolve into *Übermensch* (superhumans) capable of creating their own moral standards and promoting inner 'will to power' to the fullest. He warned[948c] failure could result in nihilism.

These ideas of self-sufficiency were expanded and refined[948d] over the 20th century; notably in Martin Heidegger's *Being and Time* (1927), Jean-Paul Sartre's *Being and Nothingness* (1943), and Viktor Frankl's *Man's Search for Meaning* (1943). Satre argued[948e] that *"existence precedes essence"*; humans are not born with a 'life script' but have to forge their own path to meaning and fulfilment – a claim that contradicted the long-held dogma that a thing is defined by its *inherent essence,* a quality already present when it 'came into being'.

Frankl adopted Kierkegaard's 'will to meaning' to develop a psychological approach called *logotherapy* that emphasises[948f] human ability to thrive and triumph – even in[948g] circumstances of extreme adversity. Nonetheless, modern existentialists acknowledge (as Nietzsche predicted) that rejection of divine providence[948h] invokes feelings of angst and dread at the weight of responsibility humans must then assume in a world that offers no intrinsic meaning.

The consequence of living without hope of God's direction or intervention is explored in allied concepts like *abandonment*[949a] by Satre, and *absurdism*[949b] by contemporary French philosopher Albert Camus. Disillusioned by the massive destruction and loss of life wrought by World War II, Camus authored[949c] several influential works that examined the meaninglessness and absurdity of a wholly secular life in an incomprehensible universe. His iconic 1942 essay *The Myth of Sisyphus* (1942) compared[949d] our plight to the mythological Greek character who was condemned to the eternal, repetitive task of pushing an immense boulder up a mountain only for it to roll down again and again. Likewise, Irish playwright Samuel Beckett brilliantly portrayed the absurdity of expecting relief from an external agency in *Waiting for Godot* (1953) – a minimalist stage play that features[949e] two characters engaged in meaningless discussions[949f] while awaiting the arrival of a 'Godot' who never shows up.

However, as British philosopher Alison Stone argued[950a] in 2013, atheistic attempts to substitute existentialism for divine providence – as in Satre's *Existentialism Is a Humanism* (1946) – are incoherent because the 'secular' ethics envisaged are still largely derived from Judeo-Christian scriptural rules. To overcome the pervasive gloom, a spin-off Humanist movement emerged that stressed[950b] *collective* responsibility for assigning meaning to life through global moral values based on universal standards of fairness and justice.

Non-religious proposals for egalitarian principles of altruism, empathy and mutual respect across humanity mirror ancient Greek principles of *philanthrôpía* and Roman orator/politician Cicero's philosophy of *humanitas* based on a law of reciprocity (also known as the Golden Rule). However, Nietzsche was highly sceptical[950c] of a communal approach to morality – he argued that aspiration to a 'common good' is fantasy since ideas of good and bad are *relative* to culture and experience. Nietzsche also controversially equated a global standard to 'slave morality' which he asserted[950d] could weaken a society and render it vulnerable to predator cultures.

Existing in limbo

Clearly, the quest to reconcile humanity's privileged position in nature with our helplessness and fragility has barely progressed beyond the insights that inspired William Shakespeare. His tragedy *Macbeth* contains one of the gloomiest verdicts on life ever recorded:

> *"To-morrow, and to-morrow, and to-morrow,*
> *Creeps in this petty pace from day to day,*
> *To the last syllable of recorded time;*
> *And all our yesterdays have lighted fools*
> *The way to dusty death. Out, out, brief candle!*
> *Life's but a walking shadow, a poor player*
> *That struts and frets his hour upon the stage*
> *And then is heard no more. It is a tale*
> *Told by an idiot, full of sound and fury*
> *Signifying nothing."*
> (Macbeth 5:5:17-28)

Despite its nihilistic overtones, the play is actually a warning about the pitfalls of excessive vanity and the calamities which follow deeds that offend against God's laws – in Macbeth's case the treacherous murder of a king endowed with 'divine right' to rule.

As the doctor comments after observing Lady Macbeth's disturbed utterances while sleepwalking:

> *"Foul whisperings are abroad: unnatural deeds*
> *Do breed unnatural troubles: infected minds*
> *To their deaf pillows will discharge their secrets:*
> *More needs she the divine than the physician.*
> *God, God forgive us all!"*
> (Macbeth 5:1:79-83)

In contrast to the fear of divine retribution that haunted Shakespearean society, modern Western philosophy lacks a definitive rationale for self-restraint. Prominent 20th century atheist Sir Julian Huxley famously declared in *The New Divinity* (1964) that *"God is a hypothesis constructed by man to help him understand what existence is all about."* At the same time, Huxley, an evolutionary biologist, conceded that divinity is an *embedded* and essential component of our consciousness that promotes morality and provides a reference point for human values and identity. He therefore advocated[950e]:

> *"Today the god hypothesis has ceased to be scientifically tenable, has lost its explanatory value and is becoming an intellectual and moral burden to our thought. It no longer convinces or comforts, and its abandonment often brings a deep sence of relief. Many people assert that this abandonment of the god hypothesis means the abandonment of all religion and all moral sanctions. This is simply not true. But it does mean, once our relief at jettisoning an outdated piece of ideological furniture is over, that we must construct some thing to take its place."*

However, the new ideologies that have emerged have done little to assuage the growing existential crisis that now haunts modern society. But non-believers still argue that belief in God is not a rational strategy for successful surfing of life's turbulent waves.

A hidden divinity

Theologians have long grappled with the dilemma of belief in a personal, loving God who is transcendent and not physically accessible for the sort of interactive reciprocity that humans associate with intimate relationships. The Bible records many examples of anguished doubt and faith struggles occasioned by God's 'hiddenness'; such as:

> *"Why, Lord, do you stand far off?*
> *Why do you hide yourself in times of trouble?"*
> (Psalm 10:1)

> *"My soul thirsts for God, for the living God.*
> *When can I go and meet with God?*
> *My tears have been my food*
> *day and night,*
> *while people say to me all day long,*
> *"Where is your God?""*
> (Psalm 42:2-3)

These laments take on accusatory tones in some instances:

> *"Look down from heaven and see,*
> *from your lofty throne, holy and glorious.*
> *Where are your zeal and your might?*
> *Your tenderness and compassion are withheld from us. [.....]*

> *"Why, Lord, do you make us wander from your ways*
> *and harden our hearts so we do not revere you?*
> *Return for the sake of your servants,*
> *the tribes that are your inheritance."*
> (Isaiah 63:15,17)

The classic theistic explanation for divine hiddenness is that human sin has created an epistemic gulf from God. However, atheists argue that this state of affairs is actually *counterproductive* since it hampers conversion of non-believers that are otherwise receptive to the goal of human evolution to divine standards of perfection. Indeed, subsequent verses from Isaiah remind God that He had created humans with all our vices and frailties:

> *"No one calls on your name*
> *or strives to lay hold of you;*
> *for you have hidden your face from us*
> *and have given us over to our sins.*
>
> *"Yet you, Lord, are our Father.*
> *We are the clay, you are the potter;*
> *we are all the work of your hand."*
> (Isaiah 64:7-8)

Of course, the Christian perspective is that God *has* responded by laying down a path to salvation through Jesus Christ. Still, there's the problem of individuals who are *not* stubbornly resistant to belief, but are unable to 'find' God because of spiritual blindness that stems from[951a] involuntary neurological or psychological factors.

Canadian analytical philosopher John Schellenberg used this loophole of 'blameless unbelief' to construct a new argument[951b,c] against God's existence in his 1993 book *Divine Hiddenness and Human Reason*. Schellenberg complained[951d] in a 2015 update that God's hiddenness creates considerable room for doubt in reasonable humans (like himself) who are not dogmatic atheists. He argued that continued absence of even weak physical evidence amounts to a good *prima facie* case that a theistic God, who is perfectly loving and open to a personal relationship with every human being, does not exist.

In a 1995 review[952a], Irish philosopher of religion Robert McKim acknowledged that Schellenberg had produced a *"carefully argued, well constructed, clearly written, and original book"* on philosophical issues raised by continued divine hiddenness. However, he outlined four main objections to the thesis: (1) the claim that non-belief is rational because of God's remoteness is dubious because proximity and intimacy are not always required for personal relationships – indeed these aspects do not feature at all in some theistic religions; (2) the claim that even weak evidence for God is absent is contradicted by Schellenberg's own description of a 'still small voice' reported by many believers – perhaps unbelievers fail to hear this modest signal or choose to ignore it; (3) even if the ultimate divine plan hinges on a personal relationship with all humans, it may be that this is impossible at this point in time because we're not yet ready for such a relationship and are still evolving the necessary attributes and capacity; and (4) humans lack the cognitive and experiential capacity to determine exactly *why* God might be remaining hidden and permitting unbelief in agnostics – unknown goods may accrue in a wider context that we're incapable of perceiving or comprehending.

American philosopher of religion Daniel Howard-Snyder also authored[952b] a review that emphasised the need for mutual respect and freedom to choose in any relationship built on love and trust:

> *"Would an explicit, reciprocal personal relationship with God enhance our well-being? It seems so. [...] Moreover, the best love wants a personal relationship not simply for the sake of the beloved but for its own sake as well. So, God would want to develop a personal relationship with us. [...] But this needs qualification. The best love respects the choices of its objects. If we reject God's overtures, His desire to relate personally to us might be overriden by proper respect for our freedom. In general, if we culpably put ourselves in a contrary position, we should not expect to be able to relate personally to God if we choose."*

Other critics of Schellenberg's argument point out[952c] that human expectation of 'divine love' may be misguided: God is transcendent and beyond *physical* and *emotional* notions of love. In 2017, Oxford University philosopher Luke Teeninga revisited and restated[952d] McKim's caution against human presumptions about God:

"I argue that if there are valuable goods brought about by God's hiddenness, then even if each of those goods might obtain without hiddenness, God would have a sufficient reason for remaining hidden so long as enough of those goods would be made sufficiently more valuable because of God's hiddenness. If this is the case, then the existence of 'nonresistant nonbelievers' in the actual world does not entail that God does not exist."

Interestingly, there are verses in Isaiah that support these purely philosophical assessments:

""For my thoughts are not your thoughts,
neither are your ways my ways,"
declares the Lord.
As the heavens are higher than the earth,
so are my ways higher than your ways
and my thoughts than your thoughts."
(Isaiah 55:8-9)

""I revealed myself to those who did not ask for me;
I was found by those who did not seek me.
To a nation that did not call on my name,
I said, 'Here am I, here am I.'

""All day long I have held out my hands
to an obstinate people,
who walk in ways not good,
pursuing their own imaginations — "
(Isaiah 65:1-2)

443

Why so much evil?

The most potent argument atheists use to justify unbelief is the 'argument from evil' – the contention that an omnipotent, omniscient, and omnibenevolent God is wholly and intuitively incompatible with the existence of evil and consequential harm. Non-believers cite the appalling abundance of evil in the world as evidence that God, as posited by theists, does not exist since it's inconceivable that an all-knowing, all-powerful, and perfectly good deity would allow pain and suffering to exist and flourish.

There are two strands to the argument that scholars now call *The Problem of Evil* (TPoE): (1) the logical[953a] contradiction of an all-powerful and perfectly good God coexisting with evil; and (2) the abundant evidence[953b] of gratuitous evil that *appears* to make it highly unlikely such a being exists that humans can look to as a reference point of ultimate perfection. Ancient Greek philosopher Epicurus (341- 270 BC) is credited with one of the earliest statements of the paradoxes posed by TPoE:

> *Is God willing to prevent evil, but not able?*
> *Then he is not omnipotent.*
> *Is he able, but not willing?*
> *Then he is malevolent.*
> *Is he both able and willing?*
> *Then, whence cometh evil?*
> *Is he neither able nor willing?*
> *Then why call him God?*

Actually, Epicurus did not deny the existence of a god or gods. He merely reasoned that whatever gods there may be are unconcerned with events in the natural world, and thus insisted human beings are ultimately responsible for their condition and should live their lives free from expectation of reward or punishment by deities.

444

TPoE has spawned a huge amount of literature and debate within the fields of theology and philosophy of religion. Eminent American philosopher and metaphysician Michael Tooley analysed the myriad of issues involved in a detailed *Stanford Encyclopedia of Philosophy* (SEP) contribution[953c]. He explained why TPoE continues to resonate not just as an argument against religious worship, but also against looking to a non-human agency for fulfilment of *"desires that good will triumph, that justice be done, and that the world not be one where death marks the end of the individual's existence."* As he put it:

> *"What properties must something have if it is to be an appropriate object of worship, and if it is to provide reason for thinking that there is a reasonable chance that the fundamental human desires just mentioned will be fulfilled? A natural answer is that God must be a person who, at the very least, is very powerful, very knowledgeable, and morally very good. But if such a being exists, then it seems initially puzzling why various evils exist. For many of the very undesirable states of affairs that the world contains are such as could be eliminated, or prevented, by a being who was only moderately powerful, while, given that humans are aware of such evils, a being only as knowledgeable as humans would be aware of their existence. Finally, even a moderately good human being, given the power to do so, would eliminate those evils. Why, then, do such undesirable states of affairs exist, if there is a being who is very powerful, very knowledgeable, and very good?"*

Tooley discussed typical responses to TPoE: *Refutations* reject any association of God with evil on the grounds that humans don't know enough about the nature or totality of our reality to form an opinion about what's 'good' or 'bad' in the overall context of things; *Vindications* either seek to justify God's tolerance of evidential evil, or shift responsibility to rebellious demons and corrupted humans; *Defences* do not attempt a justification but merely argue that the existence of evil is a logical consequence of God allowing the world to unfold according to natural laws and human free will.

Tooley revisited the many strands, aspects and contentions in a 2019 publication[953d] that formed part of the series *Elements in the Philosophy of Religion* compiled by Cambridge University Press.

Evil for whom?

The concept of 'evil' is central to the TPoE debate, but philosophers and theologians disagree over its exact definition and whether worldly states of affairs and the nature of things should be viewed exclusively from a human standpoint. As Eve Garrard from Keele University, Newcastle, England noted in *Evil as an Explanatory Concept* (2002)[954a], the term is used in several different ways: *"Sometimes we use it to mean everything adverse in human lives, embracing moral evils such as wars and massacres and natural evils such as drought and plague."*

American moral philosopher Marcus Singer attempted a narrower definition in *The Concept of Evil* (2004)[954b]: *"Though 'evil' is often used loosely as merely the generic opposite of 'morally good', used precisely it is the worst possible term of opprobrium available. [...] An evil action is one so horrendously bad that no ordinary decent human being can conceive of doing it, and an evil person is one who knowingly wills or orders such actions."*

Clearly, while humans undeniably have proximate responsibility for *moral* evil (that resulting from our actions or omissions such as wars and poverty) we can legitimately claim to have no power over *natural* evil (that resulting from naturally occurring catastrophes such as incurable diseases, earthquakes, floods, hurricanes, tornadoes etc.). But, from the viewpoint of other creatures (with the possible exception of domesticated pets that bond with humans, obey rules, and are rewarded with love and care), our activities, whether undertaken for survival or leisure, must seem like wanton acts that are very much part of a naturally hostile environment.

The question then becomes one of *ultimate causation* – the extent to which God, recognised by theists as first cause and prime mover of all we perceive, can be reasonably blamed or excused for the existence of various evils that exist in our world.

In a 2018 article[954c], Cambridge University theologian Ian McFarland discussed some uncomfortable issues that arise from human definitions of evil and our presumptions about the scope of God's universal plan:

> *"If evil is defined as that which is against the good, and the good is identified with God's will, then the use of "evil" should be restricted to those actions of free creatures that <u>oppose</u> the divine will. The classic understanding of evil as a <u>privation</u> of good will therefore be rejected, on the grounds that it depends on an expectation that the good of individual creatures should conform to a general type. It follows that instances of what is traditionally termed "natural evil" are not properly categorized either as evil or as good, but rather as occasions for the discernment of how God's will for creaturely flourishing is to be realised in a particular context."*

Nevertheless, regardless of how evil is defined and the source thereof, it's hard to reconcile pain and suffering with any notion of 'good' in a moral or ethical sense that can be used to defend belief in an omnibenevolent deity that's also omniscient and omnipotent. This dilemma of evidential harm, as *actually experienced* by subjects of God's creation, hampers attempts to justify the existence of evil for any wider purpose.

Which entity?

In a much-cited 1979 paper[955a], philosopher of religion William Rowe distinguished between 'broad' atheism that denies the existence of *any* sort of deity, and 'narrow' atheism that merely challenges belief in an all-knowing, all-powerful and perfectly good God.

However, Graham Oppy, a self-described 'broad' atheist from Monash University in Victoria, Australia, dismissed such distinctions as superfluous to the central issue of faith. Oppy wrote in *Arguing about Gods* (2006)[955b]:

> *"At best, arguments from evil create problems for the hypothesis that there is a perfect being, that is, a being that is omnipotent, omniscient, and perfectly good. It is a controversial question whether all orthodoxly conceived monotheistic gods have these properties; at the very least, there is clearly a case to be made for the contention that the monotheistic gods that are described in the scriptures of the major monotheistic religions fall far short of perfect goodness. But, in any case, I think that there are no supernatural beings of any kind; and, moreover, I do not think that I need to have special reasons for supposing that there is no omnipotent, omniscient, and perfectly good supernatural being; my reasons for supposing that there are no supernatural beings are, in themselves, good reasons for supposing that there is no omnipotent, omniscient, and perfectly good supernatural being."*

Nevertheless, other scholars argue that, while evil may be incompatible with the concept of an omnipotent and omnibenevolent God, this does not give grounds for denying that a well-meaning, divine creator might exist outside our reality – *along with* other powerful entities that are (as Epicurus conjectured) indifferent or outright malevolent. As H. J. McCloskey put it in a 1962 paper[955c]: *"The fact of the existence of evil entails several alternatives: Either there is no God, i.e., no perfect being; or he is not all-powerful; or he is not good; or there are two or more powers, of which at least one is evil and neither or none is omnipotent."*

Indeed, some ancient traditions have long used a foundational good-evil cosmology to resolve TPoE contradictions. Persian Zoroastrianism and Chinese Taoism invoke two mighty but equal forces of good and evil that exist in perpetual opposition.

448

This approach of duality was adopted by the Gnostics – an early Church movement that spread around Mediterranean lands from the 1st to 2nd centuries CE. Adherents viewed the physical world as *inherently* evil and denied it was created by the supreme God or *Monad*. Gnostics saw the Jewish *Yaweh* as a Platonic artisan *Demiurge* that emanated from the Monad but had 'gone rogue' and unilaterally created a material world of darkness that 'trapped' humans in a bodily prison. According to Gnostics, the Demiurge creator is assisted in these nefarious activities by a host of servant *archons* (similar to biblical demons). But the Monad has also emanated good *aeons* (similar to biblical angels) led by Jesus Christ to point the way back to the *pleroma* or spiritual realm of light. Unsurprisingly, early Christians condemned Gnostic views as heresy.

French philosopher and mathematician René Descartes also famously pondered whether everything we perceive is a cruel illusion. In his seminal *Meditations on First Philosophy* (1641), Descartes suggested[955d] that a powerful, clever and deceitful 'malicious demon' may have constructed a mirage of beneficial existence to mislead human beings. Although he does not explicitly conflate this negative concept with God, Descartes was accused of blasphemy for implying God was a malevolent *deus deceptor*. The matter is still debated among philosophers and theologians.

In 2010, Stephen Law, a philosopher at the University of London, adopted Descartes' imagery in a provocative challenge to theists. Law wrote[955e]: *"The challenge is to explain why the hypothesis that there exists an omnipotent, omniscient and all-good god should be considered significantly more reasonable than the hypothesis that there exists an omnipotent, omniscient and all-evil god. Theists typically dismiss the evil-god hypothesis out of hand because of the problem of good – there is surely too much good in the world for it to be the creation of such a being. But then why doesn't the problem of evil provide equally good grounds for dismissing belief in a good god?"*

Law's bold, juxtaposed arguments attracted much attention and several responses. He subsequently clarified (in a 2016 blog post[955f]) that he did not really contend that we're governed by a malicious being: *"If there were an evil god, the world would surely look far more horrific. While there's suffering, there is also much good—some of which is surely be gratuitous from the point of view of an evil god. [...] we can pretty conclusively rule out an evil god on the basis of observation of the world around us."* But he reiterated that, even if gratuitous evil is the price for 'greater goods' outside our comprehension, a wholly benevolent and omnipotent god would never permit the extent of suffering we're witnessing.

As at 2019, John Collins from East Carolina University in Greenville, USA, concluded in an update[955g] that Law's challenge had not been met. Of course, the existence of evil is not a problem for polytheists – they simply ascribe bad events to mischievous or malevolent beings within a pantheon of deities. But it has proved more difficult[955h] for monotheists that only recognise a singular God to get around TPoE.

Augustine's original sin doctrine

For early theologians, TPoE was not an issue that cast doubt on God's existence *per se* (the matter was thought to be beyond dispute). Debate centred on narratives called *theodicies* that sought to justify[956a] the existence of evidential evil alongside an omnibenevolent and omnipotent creator. This type of response acknowledges that evil is incompatible with the concept of a wholly good, monotheistic deity, but denies that suffering is part of God's original plan or that harm is a gratuitous infliction on His creation. The first theodicy is traced to St. Augustine (354-430 CE), a philosopher and theologian who served as bishop in the Roman diocese of Hippo Regius – modern Annaba (formerly Bône) in Algeria, northern Africa.

Aurelius Augustinus, as he was then known, developed[956b] the argument that God is indeed perfectly good and could not have created evil. Paradise existed on earth until the original sin of Adam and Eve birthed evil; a self-inflicted state of affairs that humans continue to propagate by misusing our God-given free will for ill-doing rather than for good. According to Augustine, humans were once perfect (having been created in God's image) but are now under the malign influence of Satan and his legion of fallen angels. Thus, he contended, we're incapable of casting off the yoke of evil *except* by acceptance of the path to redemption through Christ offered by God as a mark of His grace and goodness.

Interestingly, as Charles Natoli, a philosopher and classical historian at St. John Fisher College in New York, discussed in a 2009 essay[956c], Augustine started out as an adherent of Manichaeism; a 'religion of light' founded by the Mesopotamian prophet Mani which described a perpetual struggle between good and evil in a dualist universe consisting of a *spiritual* world of light led by God, and a *material* world of darkness headed by Satan – both with co-equal powers and a plethora of subservient, lesser deities that use the world and humans as a battleground (beliefs adopted from Gnosticism).

Augustine later recounted in Book V[956d] of his epic *Confessions* (autobiography written circa 397–401 CE) how he came to reject Manichaean doctrine because it rationalises the existence of evil alongside a good God. Apart from disparities between espoused cosmological beliefs and actual observations of astronomers, he became disenchanted with the hypocrisy of Manichaean leaders whose salacious lifestyle did not match their teachings of ascetic abstinence. After his stay in Milan under the patronage of the bishop St. Ambrose, he switched to an allegorical (rather than a literalist) view of biblical scripture and concluded there must have been a *single good creation* that became corrupted by human sin.

Augustine's new view that human free will is independent *and* contrary to divine will was challenged in a 392 CE public disputation[956e] with Fortunatus, a Manichaean elder. Fortunatus argued that ascribing the origin of evil to humans fails to exonerate God because, as the all-knowing creator who had granted us free will, God must (or should) have foreseen that it would be misused for evil. Augustine reiterated his position on original sin and the doctrine of grace, but the question remains whether humans can be held morally responsible for evil if, indeed, we are *predisposed* to sin. The same issue continues to fuel scientific disputes[956f] over the extent to which free will is governed by auto-neurobiology.

Augustinian theodicy was endorsed and reaffirmed[957a] by St. Thomas Aquinas nearly 900 years later. The emphasis on sin as the source of evil has spawned entire subfields of theological study called *hamartiology* (from the Greek *hamartia* for sin or immoral behaviour) and *soteriology* (from the Greek *soteria* for salvation or preservation). In a 2018 paper[957b] titled *Bound Over to Satan's Tyranny*, Philip Ziegler from the University of Aberdeen in Scotland discussed new attempts to reconcile doctrines of sin and salvation within a *"three agent drama"* involving God, humans, and a mythical Satan. Ziegler pondered:

> *"Is it essential that we think and speak of Satan if we are to think and speak of sin in accordance with the demands of the gospel? Does interest in the figure of Satan in Christian soteriology reflect a properly dogmatic imperative? Or is it symptomatic of mere obscurantism, or perhaps more generously, of a persistent psychological and rhetorical reflex to want to represent important "spiritual ideas in drastic allegories"?"*

However, apart from questionable use of a symbolic Satan to deflect blame for evil and counter Fortunatus' point about misplaced free will, theodicy sceptics argue that evil can't possibly be self-inflicted fruits of sin because it befalls the *innocent* as well as the guilty.

American Humanist David McCalmont once observed[957c]:

> *"Sometimes the people killed or maimed by an accident or natural disaster turn out to have been criminals. When this happens, believers happily proclaim that their misfortune was arranged by god as a punishment – even though millions of other evil-doers escape such godly retribution. On the other hand, if some of the victims turn out to have been persons of admirable character, believers then assert that they died because they were SO good that god desired their company up in Heaven!"*

This perplexing dilemma was brilliantly portrayed by 19th century Russian author Fyodor Mikhailovich Dostoevski in *Rebellion*, a poignant chapter[957d] in his 1880 masterpiece *The Brothers Karamazov*:

> *"Listen! If all must suffer to pay for the eternal harmony, what have children to do with it, tell me, please? It's beyond all comprehension why they should suffer, and why they should pay for the harmony. [...] I understand solidarity in sin among men. I understand solidarity in retribution, too; but there can be no such solidarity with children. And if it is really true that they must share responsibility for all their fathers' crimes, such a truth is not of this world and is beyond my comprehension. [...]*

> *"It's not God that I don't accept, Alyosha [...] Imagine that you are creating a fabric of human destiny with the object of making men happy in the end, giving them peace and rest at last, but that it was essential and inevitable to torture to death only one tiny creature - that little child beating its breast with its fist, for instance - and to found that edifice on its unavenged tears, would you consent to be the architect on those conditions? Tell me, and tell the truth."* (Book 5, Ch. 4)

Thus, Christian scholars have sought to refine Augustine's exoneration of God to explain visitations of evil on perfectly innocent creatures.

Irenaean theodicy

In his 1966 classic[958a,b] *Evil and the God of Love*, English philosophical theologian John Hick identified a different form of theodicy he ascribed to Greek theology pioneer St. Irenaeus (c. 130 – 202 CE). According to Hick, Irenaeus, who served as bishop of Lugdunum (present-day Lyon in the south of France), did not seek to exonerate God but explained[958c] that the divine creation is as yet incomplete and unfinished: humans have been made in God's image but still need experience of evil and suffering to achieve God's likeness. Origen of Alexandria (c. 184 –253 CE) likewise presented[958d] our imperfect world as a 'tough love' educational arena that humans must graduate from before ascension to heaven. Hick described[958e] this conception as 'soul making' for development of beings that are spiritually and morally fit to share in God's glory.

A committed religious pluralist, Hick refused[958f] to accept that non-Christians who had lived virtuous lives would be denied reconciliation with God. He argued that the Irenaean approach did away with the need for reliance on cumbersome doctrines of original sin and salvation solely through Christ: *every* human being, he insisted, was free to embrace good or evil in a worldly arena designed to facilitate moral progress to God-like perfection – regardless of their particular faith.

Hick's 'universalist' approach was highly controversial[958g] among fellow theologians. But he passionately defended the concept as a better explanation of God's tolerance of evil than Augustinian theodicy. In contrast to the position of prominent contemporaries like Oxford University's Richard Swinburne, Hick rejected Christian doctrine that all those who die 'unsaved' will be eternally damned in hell since this fate is incompatible with the notion of an omnibenevolent, forgiving God (another key criticism by atheists).

Apart from doctrinal disputes, Church of England priest and philosopher Keith Ward argued in a 1969 critique[959a] that it was *"incoherent"* to contend it was necessary for God to place humans at an 'epistemic distance' to achieve beings that had utmost freedom to evolve morally. Roman Catholic priest and philosopher Brian Davies also admitted in a 1976 article[959b] that Hick's interpretation of Irenaean theodicy was *"difficult to accept"*. These problems (and more) led Nick Trakakis, a philosopher and bioethicist at Monash University in Australia, to conclude in a 2008 article[959c] that theodices *reinforced* rather than resolved TPoE. Trakakis wrote:

> *"Theodicy, the enterprise of searching for greater goods that might plausibly justify God's permission of evil, is often criticized on the grounds that the project has systematically failed to unearth any such goods. But theodicists also face a deeper challenge, one that places under question the very attempt to look for any morally sufficient reasons God might have for creating a world littered with evil. This 'anti-theodical' view argues that theists (and non-theists) ought to reject, primarily for moral reasons, the project of 'justifying the ways of God to men'."*

Best of all possible worlds?

The term 'theodicy' was introduced into the debate on TPoE by Gottfried Leibniz in his 1710 work *Essais de Théodicée sur la bonté de Dieu, la liberté de l'homme et l'origine du mal* (*Essays of Theodicy on the Goodness of God, the Freedom of Man and the Origin of Evil*). Leibniz, a brilliant mathematician and philosopher, penned *Théodicée* in response to a series of publications by controversial French Calvinist Protestant Pierre Bayle who had fled to the then Dutch Republic in 1681 to escape[960a] persistent persecution by the Catholic establishment and monarchy in France. The appalling treatment of his Huguenot faith group left Bayle highly sceptical[960b] of Christian teachings about the origin and causes of evil.

455

In 1697, Bayle published *Dictionnaire Historique et Critique* (Historical and Critical Dictionary); a huge encyclopaedic work with articles criticising all known theodices as unworkable and contrary to scripture which, he noted, depict *coexistence* of God and evil. Bayle argued that there was simply no rational explanation for God's tolerance of evil and dismissed as mere 'opinions' all authoritarian tenets that emphasised goodness, justice, and divine intervention in worldly affairs. These radical assertions influenced the emerging deist movement and alarmed Church authorities.

Concerned by erosion of faith in traditional Christology, Leibniz advanced new logical arguments in *Théodicée* to refute claims that TPoE detracts from God's status as the ultimate standard of goodness and perfection. He drew on his acclaimed *Principle of Sufficient Reason* (PSR)[960c] to insist there must be a rational basis – fully consistent with God's nature – for the state of affairs that exists in our world. Remarkably, he was able to use mathematical calculus and optimisation formulations to show that, out of a continuum of scenarios with differing levels of moral and natural evil, God had created the 'best of all possible worlds'.

Leibniz posited at least two metaphysical considerations that would likely feature in calculations for a 'best world' model: (1) maximisation of the *essence* that gives all entities substance and identity, and (2) maximisation of *conditions* for natural emergence of the widest range and variety of phenomena possible from the simplest set of laws. He argued[960d] that tweaking any known or unknown variable to improve the human condition may well precipitate *greater* evils – a necessary balancing of maxima and minima input values familiar to all theorists and architects tasked with designing social, economic or construction models. However, this clever and persuasive exposition was challenged by a shocking natural evil that occurred in Europe that same century.

In November 1755, a catastrophic earthquake completely destroyed Lisbon, the capital city of Portugal. Contemporary French philosopher François-Marie Arouet (pen name 'Voltaire') savagely criticised Leibniz's 'philosophical optimism' in his *Poème sur le désastre de Lisbonne* (Poem on the Lisbon disaster) [961a]. He lamented the loss of tens of thousands of lives and noted that such capricious events were a reminder we don't inhabit a 'best of all possible worlds'. The disaster strengthened Voltaire's deistic view that it was futile to expect beneficial divine intervention – any improvement in the human condition for security and well-being would have to be self-developed. He continued this pessimistic theme in his classic 1759 satire *Candide, ou l'Optimisme* (Candide, or All for the Best) [961b] – a tale of a young man who starts out infused with optimism by his mentor, 'Professor Pangloss' (a parody of Leibniz and like-minded philosophers) only to become progressively disillusioned as his comfortable lifestyle evaporates and hard realities of life set in.

Nevertheless, Leibniz's logical version of theodicy has endured. American philosopher Michael J. Murray explained in a *Stanford Encyclopedia of Philosophy* essay (2016 edition) [961c] that Voltaire appears to have misunderstood or misinterpreted Leibniz's exposition. He commented: *"Leibniz does not believe that each individual event is the best possible event, and he does not think that it is possible for finite minds to demonstrate that every individual event must be a part of the best possible world: rather, he believes that the world as a whole is the best possible world."*

No-choice defence

Despite the power and appeal of Leibniz's mathematical formulation, atheists continue to use TPoE to deny the existence of God. Australian philosopher John Mackie revived the controversy in *Evil and Omnipotence* (1955) [962a] : an essay questioning *rationality* of belief in the coexistence of an all-powerful, benevolent God alongside evil.

Mackie wrote: *"Here it can be shown, not that religious beliefs lack rational support, but that they are positively irrational, that the several parts of the essential theological doctrine are inconsistent with one another, so that the theologian can maintain his position as a whole only by a much more extreme rejection of reason than in the former case."* He accepted that TPoE was an issue *"only for someone who believes there is a God who is both omnipotent and wholly good."* But, in *Theism and Utopia* (1962)[962b], he still insisted that *all* theistic worldviews (like Christianity) are incoherent.

In response, Alvin Plantinga developed a new Free Will Defence (FWD)[962c] in *The Nature of Necessity* (1974) which he later expanded in *God, Freedom, and Evil* (1977). Using his expertise in analytical philosophy and modal logic, Plantinga showed that, contrary to Mackie's claims, the existence of evil alongside an omnipotent and omnibenevolent God was neither 'illogical' nor 'irrational'. He argued it's possible that God had *no choice* but to create an imperfect world in which creatures with free will could choose between good and evil.

According to Plantinga, libertarian free will is an indispensable component of *any* creation that has a 'greater good' goal of moral evolution of conscious beings with independent capacity to reject evil. Crucially, he showed that gradations of permissible evil in a range of possible worlds (as Leibniz had suggested) was irrelevant to the project – as long as free will is open to humans, we would *always* tend towards what he called 'transworld depravity'[962d]. Thus, God could not eliminate or minimise evil without doing away *completely* with the 'greater good' goal for humans; it was not just a case of maxima and minima parameters for a best model of creation. Platinga also used Anselm's ontological argument to show that TPoE has no bearing[962e] on the core question of God's existence.

Eventually, Mackie gracefully conceded in *The Miracle of Theism* (1982)[963a] that Platinga had shown belief in an all-powerful and morally good God was not illogical *per se*.

458

However, Mackie still questioned[963b] why it was necessary to permit the existence of so much *natural* evil over which we have little or no control if the goal is really to allow humans free will to choose. This troubling issue (unaddressed by Platinga's FWD) was also highlighted by William Rowe in his 1979 paper – he queried how the extensive and arbitrary suffering of *non-human* animals relates to any 'greater good' goal for humanity. Rowe wrote[963c]: *"In some distant forest lightning strikes a dead tree, resulting in a forest fire. In the fire a fawn is trapped, horribly burned, and lies in terrible agony for several days before death relieves its suffering."* Clearly, such a distressing scenario cannot be justified as a test of human free will.

It appears humans may never agree on an answer to TPoE. Perhaps we're too emotionally invested in the drama of life to view the issue objectively. Or it may be that, as so-called 'sceptical theists'[963d] contend, our biologically-limited cognition is simply incapable of comprehending the role of evil in the greater scheme of things. If, indeed, we inhabit a teleologically programmed universe, chances of a change of script are as slim as reversal of time flow. However, it's clearly in our individual and collective interest to strive to reduce moral evil at every level. An inclusive and equitable society, in which *everyone* believes they're a stakeholder, will add value and meaning to life, strengthen the bonds of our humanity, and drastically reduce chances of global conflict that could result in self-annihilation.

What, then, is the best route to self-fulfilment in an indeterminate world in which evil appears to be a metaphysical component? According to quantum physics, we create our own reality so experiences are intimately personal and there's no universal prescription. But it helps to remember that nature is a matrix of *probabilities;* whatever our circumstances, things are liable to change *at any time* in wholly unexpected directions.

Thus, conscious positivity and sheer willpower can influence the course of events in ways we still don't understand. This makes stoic equanimity and faith in a benevolent creation not just contemplative worldviews, but also *practical* psychological aids for weathering inevitable dark interludes in life. We may not be the scriptwriter or cast director in this mysterious existential show, but we're certainly central characters with almost unlimited capacity to improvise on stage. Hence, we can choose to put on a performance that will merit thunderous applause (from both producer and audience) when the curtain falls and the light of consciousness is finally extinguished.

Should we bio-enhance morality?

Given the seemingly unstoppable advance of physical and cognitive enhancement of humans, some ethicists are campaigning for parallel research into *moral* bioenhancement. Advocates are keen to explore possible use of biomedical technologies to influence human morality for the better. However, sociologist Gabriel Abend is sceptical[964a] that morality is reducible to a *physical* concept that can be scientifically manipulated.

Bioethicists Julian Savulescu and Ingmar Persson have pioneered research into 'engineered morality' at the Oxford Uehiro Centre for Practical Ethics. In 2008, they issued a manifesto[964b] titled *The Perils of Cognitive Enhancement and the Urgent Imperative to Enhance the Moral Character of Humanity*. They argued:

> *"As history shows, some human beings are capable of acting very immorally. Technological advance and consequent exponential growth in cognitive power means that even rare evil individuals can act with catastrophic effect. [...]*
>
> *"We argue that this is a reason which speaks against the desirability of cognitive enhancement, and the consequent speedier growth of knowledge, if it is not accompanied by an extensive moral enhancement of humankind."*

460

Savulescu and Persson further contended[964c] in their 2012 book *Unfit for the Future* that:

> *"Modern technology provides us with many means to cause our downfall, and our natural moral psychology does not provide us with the means to prevent it. The moral enhancement of humankind is necessary for there to be a way out of this predicament. If we are to avoid catastrophe by misguided employment of our power, we need to be morally motivated to a higher degree (as well as adequately informed about relevant facts). A stronger focus on moral education could go some way to achieving this, but as already remarked, this method has had only modest success during the last couple of millennia. Our growing knowledge of biology, especially genetics and neurobiology, could deliver additional moral enhancement, such as drugs or genetic modifications, or devices to augment moral education."*

Bioethicist and sociologist James Hughes – a former Buddhist monk – also sees a role for biotechnologies in shaping human morality. In a series of 2014 essays[964d] on *Enhancing Virtues*, he discussed possible *"nuanced neurotechnological intervention"* with drugs, electromagnetic stimulation, and implanted nano-neural devices to engineer increased human empathy. Hughes justified such extreme measures as necessary to forestall calamities that could be unleashed by enhanced human cyborgs still prone to immoral 'cavemen' instincts. He asked in a 2016 podcast[964e]: *"how do we make human beings smarter and more capable, so that we are the drivers of technological innovation instead of being victims of it in some apocalyptic scenario?"*

However, fellow bioethicist John Harris of the University of Manchester (who supports[965a] *physical* bioenhancement in principle) disagrees that scientific bioenhancement of morality is a viable or desirable endeavour. In *Moral Enhancement and Freedom* (2010)[965b], Harris discussed gaping flaws in contemporary assumptions and explained why all such proposals were doomed to fail.

Harris argued: *"so far from being susceptible to new forms of high tech manipulation, either genetic, chemical, surgical or neurological, the only reliable methods of moral enhancement, either now or for the foreseeable future, are either those that have been in human and animal use for millennia, namely socialization, education and parental supervision or those high tech methods that are general in their application."* He noted drily that *"God had important things to say on the subject of moral enhancement"* and cited 17th century English poet John Milton's interpretation of God's view of human moral obligations in his epic poem *Paradise Lost* (1667). According to Harris, Milton's point was that we have been bequeathed both *cognitive ability* to discern between good and evil, and *free will* to direct our actions accordingly. Thus, attempts to impose morality by technology, rather than by evolved personal responsibility, are an unwarranted reversal of our natural freedoms. Harris warned that *"the idea of moral enhancement is being fundamentally misunderstood by many of those interested in further research in this field"*, and that *"mistakes about the nature of both the opportunities it offers and the very nature of 'right conduct' are presenting dangers for the present and the future of humanity."*

The God machine

Savulescu and Persson countered in a robust 2012 response[965c,d] to Harris' critique that it was *"extreme, perhaps hyperbolic"* to claim that *"moral enhancement is wrong because it restricts the freedom to do wrong and undermines autonomy."* In any case, they remarked, such a development might not be a bad thing for humanity – a highly controversial view that suggests *individual* free will is a barrier to evolution of *collective* higher morality.

Provocatively, Savulescu and Persson went on to outline a futuristic scenario where all humans are remotely connected to a 'God Machine' that automatically stops manifestation of immoral thoughts which could cause extreme harm.

They fantasised:

"The Great Moral Project was completed in 2045. This involved construction of the most powerful, self-learning, self-developing bioquantum computer ever constructed called the God Machine. The God Machine would monitor the thoughts, beliefs, desires and intentions of every human being. It was capable of modifying these within nanoseconds, without the conscious recognition by any human subjects.

"The God Machine was designed to give human beings near complete freedom. It only ever intervened in human action to prevent great harm, injustice or other deeply immoral behaviour from occurring. For example, murder of innocent people no longer occurred. As soon as a person formed the intention to murder, and it became inevitable that this person would act to kill, the God Machine would intervene. The would-be murderer would 'change his mind.' The God Machine would not intervene in trivial immoral acts, like minor instances of lying or cheating. It was only when a threshold insult to some sentient being's interests was crossed would the God Machine exercise its almighty power."

Richard Weikart, historian at California State University-Stanislaus and author of several books on the perils of Social Darwinism, cautioned[965e] in 2016 that such ideas were dangerously ill-conceived:

"As noble as it may initially sound, Savulescu's project of moral enhancement faces a number of serious problems. The genetic determinism on which it is based is shaky, both scientifically and philosophically. Even in the abstract, the concept of "moral enhancement" is fundamentally in conflict with Savulescu's view that morality is the product of mindless evolutionary processes. Savulescu has no objective grounds for choosing which specific behaviors to favor, and his vision of human nature makes it difficult to see how we could ever improve ourselves. If humans are so morally deficient that we need moral enhancement, how can we be trusted to make wise choices that will foster moral enhancement and not debasement?"

463

To be, or not to be?

In a famous soliloquy, Shakespeare's Prince Hamlet ponders whether dying is preferable to living. The Danish royal is mindful that death is an unknown void that may harbour even worse evils:

> *"To be, or not to be, that is the question:*
> *Whether 'tis nobler in the mind to suffer*
> *The slings and arrows of outrageous fortune,*
> *Or to take arms against a sea of troubles*
> *And by opposing end them. To die—to sleep,*
> *No more; and by a sleep to say we end*
> *The heart-ache and the thousand natural shocks*
> *That flesh is heir to: 'tis a consummation*
> *Devoutly to be wish'd. To die, to sleep;*
> *To sleep, perchance to dream—ay, there's the rub:*
> *For in that sleep of death what dreams may come,*
> *When we have shuffled off this mortal coil,*
> *Must give us pause—there's the respect*
> *That makes calamity of so long life."*
> (Hamlet 3:1)

Against life

Hamlet's sober thoughts are hardly as troubling as suggestions that, maybe, it would be better *not* to have been born at all. Proponents of this nihilist defeatism argue[966a] it's *morally wrong* to continue procreating beings that are destined to experience harm and suffering. South African philosopher David Benatar is credited[966b] with coining the term 'anti-natalism' for this worldview in his 2006 book *Better Never to Have Been*. But similar sentiments are found[966c] in ancient Greek and Buddhist texts, and 19th century German 'philosopher of pessimism'[966d] Arthur Schopenhauer queried[966e] the wisdom of imposing a *"burden of existence"* on new generations.

Norwegian metaphysician Peter Wessel Zapffe revived modern debate about the utility and value of being born in his essay *The Last Messiah* (1933)[967a]. Zapffe lamented that our cognitive over-endowment has led to perpetual existential angst that we're not equipped to resolve. We were, he declared, *"A breach in the very unity of life, a biological paradox, an abomination, an absurdity, an exaggeration of disastrous nature."* He argued that the ability to ponder our own mortality had burdened us with such mental anguish that we're only able to cope with the resultant *"feeling of cosmic panic"* by actively suppressing our excessive consciousness through *"isolation"* (repression of existential doubts), *"anchoring"* (attachment to specific values and ideals), *"distraction"* (focusing on divertive impressions), and *"sublimation"* (redirecting negative energies to harmonious pursuits like music, art and literature).

Zapffe closed his bleak essay with the warning that humans are deluded in our belief that we're *"biologically fated for triumph"*, and forecasted that our condition is destined to get worse as technology reduces the need for human work and creates more time for *"rising spiritual unemployment."* Controversially, he asserted that human dreams of *"salvation and affirmation"* will end in crushing disappointment when the Last Messiah appears and declares scornfully: *"Know yourselves – be infertile and let the earth be silent after ye."* He developed this dark vision further in *On the Tragic* (1941).

In a 2004 commentary[967b], Gisle Tangenes from the University of Oslo (translator of Zapffe's essays into English) called his views *"an original brand of existentialist thought"* that espoused a 'zero sum' existence – he cited Zapffe's assertion in a 1990 letter that *"The human race come from Nothing and go to Nothing. Above that, there is Nothing."* Tangenes noted some similarities between this worldview and rejection of the material world by first century Gnostics who regarded mortal existence as a cruel deception by an evil demiurge.

Worryingly, anti-natalism is gaining[967c] new adherents. A 2021 study reported[967d] by Philipp Schönegger from the University of St Andrews in Scotland found a strong association between *"dark triad personality traits of Machiavellianism and psychopathy"* and anti-natalist views. Understandably, those who reject faith in divine providence and lack a viable alternative are more prone[967e] to existential angst. But does this mean their life is not worth conceiving or living?

Beyond human significance

Guy Kahane argued forcefully in *Our Cosmic Insignificance* (2013)[968a] that pessimism about our cosmic significance is misplaced. The question, he said, is better framed as: *To whom or what might life have significance?* He pointed out that personal considerations are hardly the same as those of our neighbourhood – much less the world. Kahane reasoned that our unlikely existence indicates we might have immense *custodial significance* for our habitat. He wrote:

> *"If we are the most significant, this isn't because we are so great. It is not so impressive to be the best when this just means being better than cosmic dust, or narrowly edging the apes. (And consider this: in a universe otherwise devoid of consciousness, even a glimmer of snail-like sentience would be precious.) [...]*

> *"If anything, this should be sobering. It is not a cause for elation, but a burden, a great responsibility. If we are alone in the universe, the only thing of value, then this gives our continuing existence, and our efforts to avert disaster, a cosmic urgency, on top of whatever self-interested, anthropocentric reasons we have to stay around. That is to say, we might be far more important than we take ourselves to be. We humans are after all careless in numerous familiar ways, we fail to safeguard the future, or kick off pernicious habits. From a cosmic point of view, the problem wouldn't be that we suffer from an inflated sense of importance. It is that that we don't take our existence seriously enough."*

Kahane further cautioned in *If Nothing Matters* (2016)[968b] that it's self-defeating and dangerous to become overwhelmed by despair and nihilism. As he pointed out, even if feelings of abject hopelessness don't lead to suicide, embracing a 'meaningless universe' worldview will reduce humans to a zombie-like death state:

> *"If we believe that nothing matters, then we no longer believe that any thing matters, or that we have any practical reasons. And this means that all the motivation, affect, intention or action that was causally sustained by such beliefs will be gone too. You come to believe that nothing matters, and practical reason just stops—it's as if the normative electricity has been shut off. [....]*

> *"And whether or not the result would be complete paralysis, or mere animal-like striving, the outcome would be something very close to personal death. Although we would still be alive, our mental lives will have undergone a radical transformation. Our concern for the personal projects that gave sense to our lives will almost certainly dry out, and the psychological continuity that sustains prudential concern would be lost. And on views that identify the self with reason or rational agency, or with endorsement of values, even our selves won't survive this upheaval."*

However, Irish philosopher Nick Hughes opined in a 2017 overview[968c] that Kahane had misdiagnosed the problem. According to Hughes, general pessimism about life arises from the fact that, regardless of what relative value it may hold, we're *causally* insignificant within the wider universe. He explained:

> *"Those of us who are thoroughly disenchanted know that almost all of space is completely beyond our control, and that, living on no more than a mote of dust, we will be borne away by the slightest breeze that happens to drift our way. Worse still, we know that once we have been snuffed out, the Universe will continue to roll on as though nothing had happened. Causally speaking, we really are insignificant from the point of view of the whole Universe."*

Nonetheless, Hughes, like Kahane, concluded that life is still worth living despite our 'cosmic insignificance'. He agreed descent into nihilism and despair is *"merely a form of narcissism"* since plenty of pathways to a meaningful existence are still open to us:

> *"Some of the things that we care about – happiness and human flourishing, for example – are intrinsically valuable to us. That is to say, we find them to be valuable in themselves. That doesn't necessarily mean that they're objectively valuable. Maybe they are, maybe they're not [.....]. What it does mean, however, is that we value them for their own sake."*

American philosopher and theologian Galen Guengerich also takes the view that we need to abandon a purely human-centred definition of existential value and adopt a holistic view that takes account of the environment that sustains us. In a 2014 article[968d], Guengerich cites Eastern philosophy specialist Alan Watts who argued that modern tendency to see meaning as something independent of nature is the root cause of our existential confusion. Guengerich recalled that Watts advocated an approach which acknowledges we're part and parcel of nature and will only grasp the full picture when we view existence as a *network of interdependent entities.*

However, as award-winning writer Emily Fox Gordon observed in a contemporary article[968e], natural emotions make it difficult to look beyond 'self' and our immediate circumstances. For humans, fulfilment is very much a matter of *personal* and *social* expectations; a hazy concept that changes over time. As she explained: *"Fulfillment is a dubious gift because you receive it only when you're approaching the end. You can't consider your life fulfilled until you're fairly sure of its temporal shape, and you can't get a view of that until you're well past its midpoint. The realization that one's life has been fulfilled is a good thing, but freighted with the weight of many days and the apprehension of death."*

Restoring hope

Sadly, for the majority of earth's inhabitants, the fulfilment described by Fox Gordon never arrives – regardless how hard they strive. According to statistics compiled by[969a] Oxford University's *Our World in Data* (OWD) group, most people were living in poverty as at 2015 with an estimated 10 percent (736 million) subsisting below the 'extreme' benchmark of US$1.90 per day. Although financial security and material comfort are not[969b] the only measures of life satisfaction and well-being, a parallel World Happiness Report (criticised[969c] for its choice of value measures) showed that[969d] assigned scores for countries still struggling with basic needs were far lower than those in societies where people could afford to indulge in existential anxieties[969e] and Schopenhauer pessimism[969f].

In 2015, the United Nations adopted Sustainable Development Goals (SDGs) – a programme of action to uplift living conditions for the most vulnerable. However, as the Secretary-General António Guterres noted[970a] in the foreword to the 2020 progress report: *"As Member States recognized at the SDG Summit held last September, global efforts to date have been insufficient to deliver the change we need, jeopardizing the Agenda's promise to current and future generations. Now, due to COVID-19, an unprecedented health, economic and social crisis is threatening lives and livelihoods, making the achievement of Goals even more challenging."*

Despite the gloomy picture, the anti-natalist views expressed by Zapffe and Benatar do not resonate in our poorest and most deprived societies – religious belief, stoicism and fierce commitment to reproductive rights[970b] continue to prevail. In April 2020, Kenyans were shocked by the viral video of a widowed mother of eight in Mombasa who resorted to[970c] boiling *stones* to fool her crying children that food was on the way. Tellingly, the response was not condemnation for birthing an unsustainable family but generous donations that allowed her to upgrade[970d] her living conditions.

However, not all distress signals or cries for help are detected in time to forestall calamity: records show[971a] nearly 800,000 people commit suicide *every year*. Alarmingly, this figure now includes[971b] an increasing number of 15-29 year-olds; making the tragic trend one of the leading causes of death among the young in 2019. Clearly, urgent action is needed to reassure the generation burdened[971c] with carrying and keeping alight the torch of humanity that life is worth living[971d].

Dealing with our mortality

Keen awareness of our ultimate demise is perhaps the most profound and troubling aspect of human existential angst. While we acknowledge cessation of life as the fate of all biological organisms, we continue to devote enormous resources to staving off (or even trying to reverse) the end of an existence we know is transient. At the same time, we studiously avoid the subject in conversation and express surprise or grief when the inevitable occurs.

Sigmund Freud assessed[972a] this ambivalent and contradictory attitude thus in his 1918 book *Reflections on War and Death*:

> *"We cannot, indeed, imagine our own death; whenever we try to do so we find that we survive ourselves as spectators. The school of psychoanalysis could thus assert that at bottom no one believes in his own death, which amounts to saying: in the unconscious every one of us is convinced of his immortality."*

According to Freud, spiritual perceptions arose from our refusal to accept death as a natural process: it became necessary to invoke supernatural beings as the agents responsible for disruption of an otherwise immortal existence. To give meaning to the 'here and now', early civilisations rationalised death as a necessary *transition* and not finality of existence. Hence, the famous mummification ritual[972b] by ancient Egyptians for safe passage to the underworld and reunion with the soul in an eternal afterlife – *if* found worthy by the gods.

American cultural anthropologist Ernest Becker took Freud's psychoanalysis much further. In his Pulitzer Prize-winning book[972c] *The Denial of Death* (1973), Becker argued[972d] that *all* of human behaviour and societal interaction is motivated by the biological need to control anxieties about our mortality and terror of death. He claimed[972e] this innate and all-consuming fear is the subconscious driver for emergence of 'immortality projects' like religion to shield us from the reality of our transient condition. According to this hypothesis, evolved cultural systems provide a rationale for day-to-day functioning while humans continue to aspire to perceived 'higher purposes' to fill in an otherwise meaningless existence.

Sadly, Becker died from cancer in March 1974 aged just 49. However, he remains a widely influential figure: the Ernest Becker Foundation (EBF) was established in 1993 to further promote his work. Social psychologists Jeff Greenberg, Sheldon Solomon and Tom Pyszczynski adapted Becker's ideas to formulate a Terror Management Theory (TMT) in their acclaimed 2015 book *The Worm at the Core: On the Role of Death in Life*; a culmination[973a] of 25 years of empirical research and experiments that revealed[973b] the surprising influence of attitudes to mortality on everyday life. The trio explored the relevance of TMT for understanding the impact of COVID-19 in a 2020 article[973c] co-written with clinical psychologist McKenzie Lockett. EBF also re-emphasised human fragility in a special pandemic issue titled *This Mortal Life* – the editors observed[973d]:

> *"Not only are we reminded of mortality itself, but a break in our normal routines is also a break in our shared reality; it is a stark reminder of how much of the time, we live under an illusion of safety. Our cultural safety nets provide a sense of security and protect us from our mortality; however, at any given time we are susceptible to their unraveling, and to the raw terror of human vulnerability that such unraveling will expose."*

Evolving perspectives

In *Western Attitudes Toward Death* (1974), French historian Philippe Ariès examined[974a] changes in perspective that have occurred since the Middle Ages. He identified[974b] distinct attitudes over four periods that he labelled *Tamed Death, One's Own Death, Thy Death,* and *Forbidden Death.* According to Ariès, the 'Tamed' period, which lasted up to the 11th or 12th century, was marked by passive acceptance and conscious preparation. Death was regarded as a normal, everyday event and people dying from natural causes would pass away openly in their homes surrounded by family (including children) and friends. Beyond a wish to be buried in a spiritual environment like a churchyard, the fate of earthly remains was of little concern since belief was strong in resurrection on a final Day of Judgement.

Ariès found that a more private 'One's Own' attitude emerged from the 12th to the 17th century due to new concerns that deeds and utterings immediately prior to one's demise might influence chances of being welcomed to heaven for everlasting life, or consigned to oblivion in hell. Thus, this second period is marked by increased deathbed angst as awareness dawned that a person's earthly existence might be all there is. This increased fear of death gave rise to prolific artwork depicting corpses and skeletons, as well as elaborate tombs with prayers for favourable reception of departed souls.

Beyond the 17th century, Ariès detected a dramatic shift away from death as an event witnessed calmly by family and friends to a more public 'Thy' period marked by open displays of grief and prolonged mourning. Acceptance is replaced by a reluctance to let go, and emphasis shifts from the fate of the departed to loss being experienced by the *survivors.* Death becomes an unpleasant topic with almost fetishist connotations that should be avoided for fear of causing offence or distress.

From the late 19th century, wrote Ariès, the attitude to death as a 'Forbidden' and unwarranted intrusion into human existence became firmly entrenched in Western society. Heightened expectations of material entitlement and personal happiness (ushered in by the preceding Age of Enlightenment) led to banishment of death from even our subconscious to a surreal realm. Cremation in place of burial became an accepted practice. Ariès concluded that these social changes, cemented over the 20th century, have made death even more taboo than sex in polite conversation. Rather than the medieval family gatherings to 'see off' the dying, close survivors are more often than not *shielded* from the event to spare them mental anguish – children are rarely informed or prepared for death's finality. Anyone broaching the subject is considered morbid or mentally disturbed.

Significantly, Iranian medical ethicist Kiarash Aramesh identified two periods which roughly correspond to Ariès' findings in a 2016 comparative study[974c] of Western and Persian historical attitudes to death. Aramesh reported some fascinating similarities such as: *"The concepts of after-death judgment and redemption/downfall dichotomy and practices like deathbed rituals and their evolution after enlightenment and modernity are almost common between the above two broad traditions."*

New pragmatism

Interestingly, the 21st century is witnessing renewed willingness to confront death; albeit with materialist determination to transcend our physical demise, rather than with mere hopes of a spiritual afterlife. While morbid connotations persist, scientific studies are helping to combat modern reticence about death. In 2004, psychologists Robert Neimeyer and Joachim Wittkowsk teamed up with behavioural scientist Richard Moser to publish a review[975a] of *"the large and multifaceted literature on death anxiety, fear, threat and acceptance"* – especially regarding attitudes among health professionals and patient groups.

473

After a decade-long investigation of death rituals and treatment of human remains across cultures, American art historian Paul Koudounaris authored two works – *The Empire of Death* (2011)[975b] and *Heavenly Bodies* (2013)[975c] – that were critically acclaimed[975d], despite the macabre contents and graphic depictions[975e].

Open discussion of our inevitable demise is no longer taboo: informal 'Death Cafés' pioneered by[976a] Swiss sociologist and anthropologist Bernard Crettaz have sprung up[976b] around the world and are proving surprisingly popular. In 2011, American mortician Caitlin Doughty founded *The Order of the Good Death* (TOGD)[976c]; a movement dedicated to *"exploring ways to prepare a death phobic culture for their inevitable mortality."* She subsequently launched a 'progressive' funeral service called Clarity that offers bereaved families the opportunity for greater involvement in burial preparation processes; including extended time at home with the corpse of a loved one (as in medieval times). Suzette Sherman has likewise founded SevenPonds[976d]; a consultancy that *"promotes a healthy attitude towards the process of death"* and offers a planning guide *"for those who wish to celebrate memory and personalize the end-of-life."*

Ironically, the shift back to pragmatic attitudes has come at a time when proximity to patients and interaction with corpses is not always possible due to public health restrictions. The high risk of infection from contagious diseases like Ebola and COVID-19 is imposing unexpected barriers to indulging our rediscovered desire for intimacy.

Virtual legacies

Apart from mortal remains, social media is generating a huge amount of personal data that is ending up as 'digital remains' of unclear status. Research by a team at Oxford University's Internet Institute (OII) has revealed as many as *4.9 billion* such deposits may arise on Facebook alone before the end of the current century.

474

In April 2019, OII published a report[977a] that warned *"an exclusively commercial approach to data preservation"* posed *"important ethical and political risks that demand urgent consideration."* Lead author Carl Öhman highlighted the implications in a press release[977b]:

> *"These statistics give rise to new and difficult questions around who has the right to all this data, how should it be managed in the best interests of the families and friends of the deceased and its use by future historians to understand the past. On a societal level, we have just begun asking these questions and we have a long way to go. The management of our digital remains will eventually affect everyone who uses social media, since all of us will one day pass away and leave our data behind. But the totality of the deceased user profiles also amounts to something larger than the sum of its parts. It is, or will at least become, part of our global digital heritage."*

British sociologist Tony Walter has written extensively on the need for new strategies to deal with aspects of death in modern society. Walter's candid and thought-provoking expositions[978a] in *The Revival of Death* (1994), *Social Death* (2016), *What death means now* (2017) and numerous other publications have made him a pre-eminent authority on death studies. The University of Bath's Centre for Death & Society (CDAS) – which Walter headed until 2015 – has undertaken several interesting projects[978b], including a 'Future Cemetery' collaboration[978c] that experimented with cutting-edge digital, audio-visual and augmented reality techniques to create an *"immersive"* experience at burial grounds involving both corporeal and virtual remains of loved ones. In a 2017 article[978d], Walter and Swedish sociologist Annika Jonsson discussed how *"continuing bonds with a deceased person can be rooted in a particular place or places"* – interviews with survivors revealed that specific locations arouse warm thoughts and images of a deceased person *"performing characteristic actions"* as if they were still around.

The so-called *DeathTech Research Team* (DTRT) based at University of Melbourne in Australia has also spent over a decade exploring new digital and online avenues for grieving and memorials. Projects so far include[979a] research into alternatives for disposal of mortal remains; a study of social and cultural implications of virtual commemorative rituals; and a Future Cemetery with broader objectives than the CDAS initiative[979b] in England. DTRT has produced several important reports, including a 2015 paper[979c] on *"prominent ways that digital media can extend one's personhood following death"* and a 2017 overview[979d] of shifting patterns in the way people *"mourn, commemorate and interact with the dead through digital media."* However, there's awareness that technologies likewise have a shelf life – they can 'die'[979e] and become obsolete.

Holographic resurrection

Another fascinating development is the 'resurrection' of deceased persons as holographic simulations. The trend of projecting virtual forms of dead music artists for 'live' performances on stage has become fashionable. In 2012, fans at the Coachella festival in Indio, California were pleasantly surprised when a life-like projection of rapper Tupac Shakur (who died in 1996) appeared[980a] on stage to 'perform' alongside a very much alive Snoop Dogg. Media reports described[980b,c] Tupac's apparition as a 3-D 'hologram'; but it was actually[980d] a modern version of the old 2-D Pepper's ghost theatrical illusion previously used to feature[980e] long-departed 'King of Rock and Roll' Elvis Presley alongside Celine Dion in a 2007 performance. In October 2018, Base Hologram productions announced[981a] that a hologram of singer Amy Winehouse, who died tragically in July 2011, would embark on a worldwide concert tour in 2019 – complete with a live band and backing singers. Eventually, the Winehouse project was postponed[981b] due to 'unique sensitivities' and concerns about prior lack of consent[981c] by the departed artiste.

A similar hologram tour of late superstar Whitney Houston kicked off[982a] in the UK in February 2020; eight years after her[982b] untimely death. Music critic Dave Simpson panned[982c] the show as a deeply unsettling *"ghoulish cash-in"*; an assessment shared by Will Gompertz who described[982d] Whitney's 'performance' as a *"technically excellent"* but *"creepily detached"* production that some might find macabre and exploitative. Gompertz asked plaintively in his review: *"Whatever happened to the notion of Rest in Peace?"*. However, for Sateena Dosanjh, Houston's reincarnation was an unforgettable experience – as she reported[982e]: *"The hologram looked so real I could have sworn she was really there. [...] She was life-sized, dancing seamlessly, talking and singing smoothly. Her gestures weren't glitchy and sim-like, they were graceful and perfect. Her facial expressions weren't robotic, they were absolutely genuine and beautiful."*

PORTL Inc, a tech innovator based in Los Angeles, California, has come up with a phone booth-sized 'holoportation' machine that can beam live holograms anywhere for real-time communication with audiences. Remarkably, there's also a facility for life-like interaction with pre-recorded holograms of historical figures or deceased relatives. The company expects[983a] the price of the machine to drop to affordable levels within a few years; just as happened with personal computers and smartphones. Other production outfits like Kaleida and Artistry In Motion are cashing-in on the expanding market: in October 2020, Kaleida surprised media celebrity Kim Kardashian with a holographic resurrection[983b] of her late father Robert as a birthday treat[983c] arranged by her then husband Kanye West.

It seems opportunities for a 'virtual afterlife' are set to expand significantly. But there is a caveat: religious prophesies of an end-time Judgment Day will take on a whole new meaning should future generations decide to summon advanced simulations of long-dead ancestors to give an account of their biological lives. Given current trends, the possibility is not as far-fetched as it might sound.

Neo- immortality

Meanwhile, the focus is very much on life extension and even possible immortality. The *Epic of Gilgamesh* (c. 2100 BCE) records a Mesopotamian king's quest for the secret of eternal life. Ancient Egyptian queen Cleopatra believed bathing in the milk of asses would keep her rejuvenated, and 16th century Hungarian countess Elizabeth Báthory was accused of slaughtering and bathing in the blood of hundreds of virgins to stay youthful.

Alas, our organic bodies are destined to age and perish. But post-humanists now sense new opportunities to transition to techno-immortality. Robin Hanson's provocative *The Age of Em* (2016) explored[984a] a world where emulated robotic and virtual posthumans (*Ems*) with uploaded minds become the majority, while residual humans become marginalised. Despite Hanson's generally upbeat assessment[984b] of projected outcomes, Steven Poole described[984c] the book's bleak scenarios and stark socio-economic implications as an *"eschatological vision"* of a *"hellish cyberworld"* which borders on a virtual dystopia. Existential risk specialist Seth Baum also concluded in a scientific review[984d] that Hanson's argument in favour of a 'pro-em' world was *"unpersuasive."*

The trend represents yet another change in attitude from denial of death to a defiant quest to transcend our biological cage; a *"rebellion against human existence as it has been given"*, as Mark O'Connell aptly notes[985a] in his travelogue-style book *To Be A Machine* (2017). O'Connell's report on interactions with transhumanists determined to solve *"the modest problem of death"* stimulated much debate on the efficacy and desirability[985b] of proposed techniques. However, as philosopher Francesca Minerva and ethics scholar Adrian Rorheim noted in a contemporary essay[985c], *"the prospect of being freed from our mortal shackles is undeniably alluring – and if it's ever an option, one way or another, many people will probably conclude that it outweighs the dangers."*

Indeed, the notion of eternal existence is still deeply embedded in our psyche – it has featured in science fiction since the mid-20th century. Terry Bisson's iconic short story[985d] *They're Made Out of Meat* (1990) describes the outcome when two superluminal (faster-than-light) celestials are sent to *"contact, welcome and log in any and all sentient races or multibeings in this quadrant of the Universe, without prejudice, fear or favour."* One of the envoys struggles to convince an increasingly incredulous partner that space-probing radio signals from our sector were sent by short-lived, intelligent beings that are entirely biological – complete with degradable brains. The cosmic explorers express bemusement that such *"thinking meat"* should imagine other sentient beings in the universe would find them worthy of contact and dialogue. Despite their obligation not to discriminate, they decide our carbon-based life is just too weird and insignificant to interact with and agree to *"erase the records and forget the whole thing."* Sadly, our sector is then marked *"unoccupied."*

Bisson's humorous piece is a reflection on the pathos of human mortality and our longing for transcendence. But, as Shakespeare's Hamlet mused, immortality may well bring a fresh set of existential dilemmas that any posthuman successors might find as difficult to deal with as we are with biological mortality.

Accepting death

Rather than attempting to ignore[986a] our mortality, embracing[986b] the inevitability of demise may provide a better psychological shield from angst about death. As American philosopher James Baillie counselled in 2019, the sooner we come to terms with what he called[986c] the *"existential shock"* of realising we will one day cease to exist, the better for our mental well-being. A July 2021 report[986d] by Spanish healthcare professionals also stressed the importance of wider social acceptance of death for end-of-life coping strategies.

In *Julius Caesar* (another famous Shakespearean tragedy), the Roman leader's wife Calpurnia implores him to stay at home after experiencing nightmarish dreams overnight as the Ides of March (15th) dawned; the date a soothsayer had portended tragedy. However, Caesar responded with typical bravado:

> *"Cowards die many times before their deaths;*
> *The valiant never taste of death but once.*
> *Of all the wonders that I yet have heard.*
> *It seems to me most strange that men should fear;*
> *Seeing that death, a necessary end,*
> *Will come when it will come."*
> (Julius Caesar 2:2: 32-37)

This type of fatalism[987a] is often touted as an antidote to death denial – Australian sociologist Alex Broom argued[987b] in 2014 that pervasive reluctance to accept our inevitable demise has become a *"major barrier to ensuring that a life otherwise well-lived ends with a good enough death."* But some philosophers contend[987c] that fatalism can also lead to surrendering of free will, and suppression of the human urge to strive for survival.

Ancient thinkers understood the need for a balanced approach. In a 2018 essay[987d], psychotherapist and author Antonia Macaro discussed how Buddhist and Stoic teachers had placed reflection on our mortality at the heart of their traditions:

> *"For both, the starting point is the fact that our normal perceptions of value are deeply flawed, as we are constantly craving or loathing things that in reality are unimportant. The Buddhist texts offer a neat list of these: gain and loss, fame and disrepute, praise and blame, pleasure and pain. The Stoics had a word for them, which translates as 'indifferents'.*

"The things that we are so keen to pursue — wealth, material possessions, sense pleasures, comfort, success, people's approval, romantic love and so on — are bound to disappoint and distract us from what really matters, which is our ethical and spiritual progress. [....] By highlighting the fact that time is short, death meditation can help us to put things in perspective and appreciate the present more."

Nevertheless, mental health professionals caution against becoming overly obsessed with dying. Although meditating on our mortality may help to combat denial and give meaning to existence, allowing this to become our main focus in life could become detrimental to well-being. Thus, while Macaro cited the advice of ancient Greek sage Epicetus that *"Day by day you must keep before your eyes death and exile, and everything that seems terrible, but death above all; and then you will never have any abject thought, or desire anything beyond due measure"*, she also recalled the admonition of 16th century French philosopher Michel de Montaigne that preoccupation with thoughts of our demise is akin to *"putting on a fur coat in summer because we'll need it at Christmas."* De Montaigne argued in 1580 (Book 3, Ch. XII of his famous *Essays*) that knowing how to *live* is far more important because this, in itself, allows us to know how to die. As he put it[987e]:

"We trouble life by the care of death, and death by the care of life: the one torments, the other frights us. It is not against death that we prepare, that is too momentary a thing; a quarter of an hour's suffering, without consequence and without damage, does not deserve especial precepts: to say the truth, we prepare ourselves against the preparations of death. Philosophy ordains that we should always have death before our eyes, to see and consider it before the time, and then gives us rules and precautions to provide that this foresight and thought do us no harm; [......] If we have not known how to live, 'tis injustice to teach us how to die, and make the end difform from all the rest; if we have known how to live firmly and quietly, we shall know how to die so too."

Going forward: A new humanity

Humans have arrived at a critical juncture of our history. Apart from growing threats[988a] to the capacity of our biosphere to sustain complex life, massive technology transformations are driving profound shifts[988b] in the way societies and individual lives have been traditionally organised for meaningful existence. Everyday *physical* interactions are being rapidly replaced[988c] by *virtual* exchanges across social media, and humans are being substituted by AI robots in both work[988d] and domestic[988e] settings. These changes are creating fresh angst[988f] about the value and utility of life.

What's to be done?

While there's general acknowledgment that we desperately need new paradigms in every sphere of life, consensus is sorely lacking on the way forward. British economist Guy Standing's 2011 book *The Precariat: The New Dangerous Class* focussed minds[989a] with his stark description of an emerging underclass that's barely existing in a 'gig economy'[989b] without the securities, rewards and leisure time we've come to expect as a matter of human rights. Proposals for restoring social equity include *Universal Basic Income* (UBI)[989c], *Universal Basic Services* (UBS)[989d], and adoption of *Modern Monetary Theory* (MMT)[989e] that will allow governments to cease borrowing and simply print money to fund the needs of citizens. Dutch historian Rutger Bregman made a powerful case[989f] for these radical measures in his 2017 book *Utopia for Realists*.

However, there's fierce resistance to a fully egalitarian socio-economic approach. Opponents fear such schemes (however well-meaning) will foster[990a] new 'ant and grasshopper' moral hazards that could diminish[990b] zest for enterprise, destroy the value of money as a means of exchange, and allow authorities to escape[990c] responsibility for financial prudence and proper planning.

Moreover, we have long derived self-esteem from personal ability *to earn* a living and pay our way. Indefinite subsistence allowance from the public purse is unlikely to replace the sense of self-worth work provides[990d] – a key factor for satisfaction in life. Renowned public policy consultant Richard Reeves warned[990e] in 2018 that there's already a *"respect deficit"* for 'blue collar' workers providing essential manual services. A new class of non-workers may well be perceived as 'scroungers' that deserve no respect at all.

Another troubling issue is the rapid loss of basic skills as we delegate simple tasks to machines and become ever more reliant on computer algorithms for problem-solving and decision-making. American technology historian Jonathan Coopersmith cautioned[991a] in 2016 that our growing dependence on 'blackboxes' may lead to serious disaster in the event of technology failures. In recognition of the danger, a new field of chaos engineering[991b] has emerged to monitor systems for early signs of AI outages[991c]. If all fails, we might well need a non-digital copy of Lewis Dartnell's *The Knowledge: How to Rebuild our World from Scratch* (2014) to 'reboot'[991d] civilisation.

Zero to infinity

The continuing devastating impact of the COVID-19 pandemic is a stark reminder that humans are far from able to fully predict and control how the many interconnected systems which underpin our existence will behave over time. Complexity scientists have renewed arguments that we should admit nature – a huge complex of quantised probabilities – will always spring surprises no matter what we do. Thus, our focus should be on *flexibility* and *response strategies* for universal relief. As David Krakauer and Geoffrey West wrote in July 2020[992a], *"A key insight from complexity science is that complex systems function by the continuous tradeoff between robustness and evolvability. [...] Just as biological systems pay a cost ... foregoing efficiency for long-term persistence, so too should we demand this of our institutions."*

483

Jessica Flack and Melanie Mitchell likewise highlighted the need for a paradigm shift in a contemporary essay[992b]: *"In complex systems, the last thing that happened is almost never informative about what's coming next. The world is always changing – partly due to factors outside our control and partly due to our own interventions. [...] But an inability to predict the future doesn't preclude the possibility of security and quality of life."* They suggested: *"Nature, after all, is full of collective, coupled systems with the same properties of nonlinearity and nonstationarity. We should therefore look to the way biological systems cope, adapt and even thrive under such conditions."*

Certainly, we need to rely less on rigid models and emphasise flexible adaptation to cope with life's unpredictability – we can't hope to pre-empt all negative events. But the deeper insight from studies across the sciences and humanities (including theology) is that nature is a massive *collaboration*. No living thing can exist without the selfless, coordinated work of trillions of diverse biomolecules – *plus* tailored assistance from trillions more cohabiting microbes. Likewise, non-living matter is an *aggregate* of innumerable subatomic particles that appear to be guided by hidden quantum 'superpartners' that might even exist *outside* our cosmic bubble. Underlying it all is a sea of consciousness and mysterious meta-programming that makes it difficult to properly distinguish[992c] the 'living' from 'non-living'.

It is therefore foolish and delusional to imagine that the sophisticated societies we have been privileged to develop can be anything but dysfunctional if we stray from this universal model of cooperative, interdependent existence. Clearly, we come from literally *nothing*. Humans can strive to nourish and sustain every part of the holographic fabric from which we spring so that it flourishes and expands onward to infinity, or we can continue to wallow in selfish individuality and collapse back to nothingness sooner than might be teleologically destined. This is not idle speculation; it is a well-founded mathematical probability[992d].

Nature's caretakers

As we continue our knowledge odyssey, the ultimate question remains just *why* humans (essentially a part of nature) are programmed for cognitive reflection and technological advancement. Perhaps, after nearly 14 billion years of labour, God is taking a well-earned rest and we, mortal proxies, have been equipped and tasked to keep watch in self-reproducing, revolving teams. Several parts of the existential puzzle have already been revealed to us. But, just as we only retain and continue to train those interns and apprentices that exhibit commitment and ability to assume further responsibilities, maybe we're meant to evolve much higher levels of *morality* and *altruism* before the final bits of the big picture are unveiled – our current tendency to misuse key information about the inner workings of nature must surely give cause for concern to any external observer.

Although research indicates there are built-it constraints to keep the marvellous meta-project we inhabit from crashing before its runtime expires, we can't be certain the plan includes any sort of divine intervention to keep humans from self-destructing. What we can surmise from cosmic and evolutionary history is that the universe will not wait on us forever – civilisations that lacked requisite knowledge, or chose to violate natural laws which keep everything in balance, simply ceased to exist.

The clock is ticking.

References

1. (a) A. Latham, How 3 prior pandemics triggered massive societal shifts. The Conversation,Oct. 1, 2020
    (b) Rose, P.I.; Frank M. Snowden, Epidemics and Society: From the Black Death to the Present. Society 57, 478–480 (2020)

2. WHO Director-General's opening remarks at the media briefing on COVID-19 - 11 Mar 2020

3. (a) Merlin Crossley, Explainer: what is RNA? The Conversation, Jun 26, 2013
    (b) Michael Dhar, What is RNA? Live Science, Oct.15, 2020

4. (a) Pardi, N., Hogan, M., Porter, F. et al.; mRNA vaccines – a new era in vaccinology. Nature Reviews Drug Discovery 17, 261–279 (2018)
    (b) Damian Garde, Jonathan Saltzman. Special Report, The story of mRNA: How a once-dismissed idea became a leading technology in the Covid vaccine race. STAT, Nov.10, 2020

5. The Human Cell Atlas website, https://www.humancellatlas.org/

6. (a) Blanco-Melo, D., Nilsson-Payant, B.E, Wen-Chun, L. et. al; Imbalanced Host Response to SARS-CoV-2 Drives Development of COVID-19. Cell 181:5, 1036-1045.e9 (2020); BioRxiv 2020.03.24.004655
    (b) Abby Olena. "Cells' Response to SARS-CoV-2 Different from Flu, RSV". The Scientist, Mar 31, 2020

7. Li, R., Pei, S., Chen, B. et al.; Substantial undocumented infection facilitates the rapid dissemination of novel coronavirus (SARS-CoV-2). Science 368: 6490, 489-493 (2020)

8. Wölfel, R., Corman, V.M., Guggemos, W. et al. Virological assessment of hospitalized patients with COVID-2019. Nature 581, 465–469 (2020)

9. He, X., Lau, E.H.Y., Wu, P. et al. Temporal dynamics in viral shedding and transmissibility of COVID-19. Nature Medicine 26, 672–675 (2020)

10. (a) Martin Kulldorff, Sunetra Gupta, Jay Bhattacharya et al.; Great Barrington Declaration, Oct.4, 2020
    (b) Rockefeller University, "Immune system mounts a lasting defense after recovery from COVID-19, researchers find." Science Daily, 21 Jan 2021

11. Lucy Selman, How coronavirus has transformed the grieving process. The Conversation, Apr 17, 2020

12. Heather Conway, Coronavirus is changing funerals and how we deal with the dead. The Conversation, Mar 30, 2020

13. Tamara Kohn, Hannah Gould et al.; Small funerals, online memorials and grieving from afar: the coronavirus is changing how we care for the dead. The Conversation, Mar 26, 2020

14. Yalda Safai, COVID-19 deaths may lead to prolonged grief disorder. ABC News, 9 July 2020

15. Yusen Zhai, Xue Du; Loss and grief amidst COVID-19: A path to adaptation and resilience. Brain, Behavior, and Immunity 87, 80-81(2020)

16. Matt Swayne, Penn. State University. Grief from COVID-19 impact may trigger secondary health and mental health crisis. Medical Express, Apr 13, 2020

17. Verdery, A.M., Smith-Greenaway, E., Margolis, R. & Daw, J.; Tracking the reach of COVID-19 kin loss with a bereavement multiplier applied to the United States. PNAS 117:30, 17695-17701 (2020)

18. Marla Milling, Coronavirus Ripple Effect: Study Shows 9 Family Members Suffer Grief From Every Covid-19 Death. Forbes, Jul 14, 2020

19. Jenesse Miller, University of Southern California. 'Tsunami of grief' as millions of Americans could lose a parent or grandparent to COVID-19. Medical Express, Apr 6, 2020

20. Wallace, C.L., Wladkowski, S.P., Gibson, A., White, P. (2020); Grief During the COVID-19 Pandemic: Considerations for Palliative Care Providers. Journal of Pain and Symptom Management, 60:1, e70-e76

21. Bilimoria Purushottama, Hindu Response to Dying and Death in the Time of COVID-19. Frontiers in Psychology, 12, 249 (2021)

22. Coppola Ilaria, Rania Nadia, Parisi Rosa, Lagomarsino Francesca, Spiritual Well-Being and Mental Health During the COVID-19 Pandemic in Italy. Frontiers in Psychiatry 12, 296 (2021)

23. Fatima, H., Oyetunji, T.P., Mishra, S. et al.; Religious coping in the time of COVID-19 Pandemic in India and Nigeria: Finding of a cross-national community survey. Int J of Social Psychiatry 62:2, 309-315 (2022)

24. White F.J., Personhood: An Essential Characteristic of the Human Species. Linacre Qtr 80:1, 74-97(2013)

25. McKee, M. & Stuckler, D.; If the world fails to protect the economy, COVID-19 will damage health not just now but also in the future. Nature Medicine 26, 640–642 (2020)

26. Larry Elliott, Gordon Brown calls for global government to tackle coronavirus. The Guardian, 26Mar2020

27. Nicky Phillips, The coronavirus is here to stay — here's what that means. Nature 590, 382-384 (2021)

28. Megan Scudellari, How the pandemic might play out in 2021 and beyond. Nature 584, 22-25 (2020)

29. Delanty, Gerard (ed), Pandemics, Politics, and Society: Critical Perspectives on the Covid-19 Crisis. 2021.

30. Samuel P. Veissière, Some Positive News About the Coronavirus Response. Psych. Today, Mar 17, 2020.

31. Norman Lewis, Humanity will win the fight against Covid-19. Spiked, 20 April 2020.

32. University of S. California, 'Thirst For Knowledge' May Be Opium Craving. Science Daily, 20 Jun 2006.

33. Xie K., Fox G.E., Liu J. et al.;. Brain Computation Is Organized via Power-of-Two-Based Permutation Logic. Frontiers in Systems Neuroscience 10, 95 (2016)

34. Medical College of Georgia at Augusta University. "Our brains have a basic algorithm that enables our intelligence." Science Daily, 21 Nov 2016

35. Ormerod, R.J., The history and ideas of critical rationalism: the philosophy of Karl Popper and its implications for OR, Journal of the Operational Research Society 60:4, 441-460 (2009)

36. Gregg Easterbrook, Really, really big questions. Reuters, Dec 23, 2011 (updated May 27, 2014)

37. Jim Baggott, How physics went down a post-empirical dead end. Prospect, Aug 9, 2019

38. Ethan Siegel, It takes 26 fundamental constants to give us our known Universe, and even with them, they still don't give us everything. Forbes, Aug 22, 2015 (updated Nov 16, 2018).

39. (a) Saint-Léger, A., Bello, C., Dans, P.D. et al.; Saturation of recognition elements blocks evolution of new tRNA identities. Science Advances 2:4, e1501860 (2016)

    (b) Institute for Research in Biomedicine (IRB Barcelona). "Discovery of a fundamental limit to the evolution of the genetic code." Science Daily, 2 May 2016.

40. Freeman Dyson, Life: What A Concept! An Edge Special Event at Eastover Farm. Edge, 27 Aug, 2007

41. Wolchover, Natalie, A trek through the probable universe. Book review, Philip Ball's Beyond Weird. Books and Arts. Nature 555, 440-441 (2018)

42. Adesso Gerardo, Franco Rosario Lo and Parigi Valentina; Foundations of quantum mechanics and their impact on contemporary society. Phil. Trans. R. Soc. A.376201801122 (2018)

43. (a) McGinn, C. The problem of philosophy. Philos Stud 76, 133–156 (1994).

    (b) ibid. Full paper and pdf download available online.

44. (a) Chalmers, D., Why Isn't There More Progress in Philosophy? Philosophy 90(1), 3-31 (2015)

    (b) ibid. Full paper and pdf download available online.

45. Frank, Philipp, Book Review: The Nature of Physical Reality. A Philosophy of Modern Physics by Henry Margenau (1950). Physics Today 4, 1, 24 (1951)

46. (a) Macintosh, David, Plato: A Theory of Forms. Philosopy Now, Issue 90 (2012)

    (b) Vienna University of Technology, "Is the universe a hologram?." ScienceDaily, 27 Apr 2015

    (c) Skibba, Ramin, "Einstein, Bohr and the war over Quantum Theory. A history of unresolved questions beyond the Copenhagen interpretation". Books and Arts, Nature 555, 582-584 (2018)

47. Klima, G., "The Medieval Problem of Universals", Stanford Encyclopedia of Philosophy (Winter2017 Ed)

48. Berkeley, George (1685-1753). A Treatise Concerning the Principles of Human Knowledge. Project Gutenberg online library.

49. Faye, Jan, "Copenhagen Interpretation of Quantum Mechanics", The Stanford Encyclopedia of Philosophy (Winter 2019 Edition), Edward N. Zalta (ed.)

50. Inamori, Hitoshi (2018), The issue with the initial state in quantum mechanics. arXiv:1810.11516

51. Singh, Virendra (2005), Einstein and the Quantum. arXiv:quant-ph/0510180 [quant-ph]

52. (a) Paty, M. The nature of Einstein's objections to the Copenhagen interpretation of quantum mechanics. Foundations of Physics 25, 183–204 (1995).

    (b) ibid. Full paper and pdf download available online.

53. Scott Bembenek, Einstein and the Quantum. Scientific American, Mar 27, 2018.

54. Song, D. (2013), Einstein's Moon. arXiv:1008.2892v2 [physics.gen-ph]

55. Peter Byrne, The Many Mice Theory of Quantum Mechanics. Nautilus, Jan. 2017.

56. Weizmann Institute Of Science. "Quantum Theory Demonstrated: Observation Affects Reality." Science Daily, 27 Feb 1998.

57. Nicola Jenner, Five Practical Uses for "Spooky" Quantum Mechanics. Smithsonian, Dec 1, 2014.

58. Kurizki, Gershon and Gordon, Goren (2020). Book review - The Quantum Matrix: Henry Bar's Perilous Struggle for Quantum Coherence. Oxford Scholarship Online. ISBN-13: 9780198787464

59. Philip Ball, Quantum Common Sense. Aeon, 21 Jun, 2017

60. Wallace, David, Quantum foundations still not cemented. Book review - What Is Real? The Unfinished Quest for the Meaning of Quantum Physics by Adam Becker. Physics Today 71, 11, 51 (2018)

61. Melinda Baldwin, Q&A: Adam Becker on unanswered quantum questions. Physics Today, 30 Nov 2018

62. Myrvold, Wayne, "Philosophical Issues in Quantum Theory", Stanford Encyclopedia of Philosophy (Fall 2018 Edition), Edward N. Zalta (ed.)

63. Gordon Kane, Are virtual particles really constantly popping in and out of existence? Or are they merely a mathematical bookkeeping device for quantum mechanics? Scientific American, Oct 9, 2006.

64. (a) Paul Sutter, String theory vs. M-theory: A showdown to explain our universe. Space.com, 11 Mar 2020
    (b) Natalie Wolchover, Why Is M-Theory the Leading Candidate for Theory of Everything? Quanta, Dec 18, 2017

65. Natalie Wolchover, Is Nature Unnatural? Decades of confounding experiments have physicists considering a startling possibility: The universe might not make sense. Quanta, May 24, 2013

66. Stanford University. "Universe Offers 'Eternal Feast,' Cosmologist Says." Science Daily, 22 Feb 2007.

67. Roger Trigg, Why Science Needs Metaphysics. Nautilus, Oct 1, 2015.

68. Paul Davies, Reality in the melting pot. According to 'multiverse' theorists, life as we know it could be nothing but a Matrix-style simulation. The Guardian, Tue 23 Sep 2003.

69. Paul Davies, A Brief History of the Multiverse. New York Times, April 12, 2003

70. James Gleick, What Does Quantum Physics Actually Tell Us About the World? Book review - What Is Real? by Adam Becker. New York Times, May 8, 2018.

71. Cowen, Ron, Simulations back up theory that Universe is a hologram. A ten-dimensional theory of gravity makes the same predictions as standard quantum physics in fewer dimensions. Nature News, 10 Dec 2013

72. Sedley, David N. (1984), Empedocles' Theory of Vision and Theophrastus' De sensibus. Chapter, Routledge eBook ISBN 9781351316569.

73. Plato (ca. 427-ca. 347 BC). Wolfram Research.

74. Zubairy M.S. (2016) A Very Brief History of Light. In: Al-Amri M., El-Gomati M., Zubairy M. (eds) Optics in Our Time. Springer, Cham.

75. Aristotle, On the Soul (c. 350 BCE). Trans. by J. A. Smith. Internet Classics Archive.

76. Sambursky, S., Philoponus' Interpretation of Aristotle's Theory of Light. Osiris vol 13, 1958.

77. Ashley P. Taylor, Newton's Color Theory, ca. 1665. The Scientist, Mar 1, 2017

78. Young, Thomas, II. The Bakerian Lecture. On the theory of light and colours.
    Philosophical Transactions of the Royal Society of London 92: 12–48 (1802)

79. Kipnis, Nahum (1991), History of the Principle of Interference of Light. Birkhäuser Verlag, Basel, eBook ISBN 978-3-0348-8652-9.

80. (a) Jim Baggott, The myth of Michael Faraday. New Scientist, 21 Sep 1991
    (b) About Michael Faraday. The Faraday Institute for Science and Religion..

81. Maxwell, James Clerk 1865 VIII. A dynamical theory of the electromagnetic field.
    Philosophical Transactions of the Royal Society of London 155: 459–512 (1865)

82. Hertz, H.G. & Doncel, M.G.; Heinrich Hertz's laboratory notes of 1887. Archive for History of Exact Sciences 49, 197–270 (1995)

83. Gearhart, C., "Planck, the Quantum, and the Historians". Physics in Perspective 4, 170–215 (2002)

84. Helge Kragh, Max Planck: the reluctant revolutionary. Physics World, 01 Dec 2000

85. Ibid. 51

86. Richard Harris, Albert Einstein's Year of Miracles: Light Theory. NPR, March 17, 2005

87. Stepansky, Barbara K., Ambiguity: Aspects of the Wave-Particle Duality. British Journal for the History of Science 30, 375-385 (1997)

88. Compton, Arthur H., A Quantum Theory of the Scattering of X-rays by Light Elements.
    Physical Review 21:5, 483-502 (1923)

89. Cassidy, David C., "Landmarks: Photons are Real". Physical Review Focus 13, 8 (2004)

90. De Broglie, L., Waves and Quanta. Nature 112, 540 (1923)

91. (a) Thomson, G. & Reid, A.; Diffraction of Cathode Rays by a Thin Film. Nature 119, 890 (1927)
    (b) Davisson, C.J. & Germer, L.H.; Reflection of Electrons by a Crystal of Nickel.
    PNAS 14 (4) 317-322 (1928)

92. Matt Williams, What Is The Double Slit Experiment? Universe Today, Jan 18, 2011

93. Laurance R. Doyle, Quantum Astronomy: The Double Slit Experiment. Space.com, Nov 11, 2004

94. Anil Ananthaswamy, Through two doors. Aeon, 02 Oct, 2018

95. (a) Tia Ghose, Classic Physics 'Thought' Experiment Finally Recreated. Live Science, Mar 14, 2013.
    (b) Eibenberger, S., Gerlich, S., Arndt, M. et al.; Matter–wave interference of particles selected from a molecular library with masses exceeding 10,000 amu.
    Physical Chemistry, Chemical Physics 15:35, 14696-14700 (2013)

96. Philip Ball, Quantum Physics May Be Even Spookier Than You Think. Scientific American, May 21, 2018

97. Bose, S., Planck's law and the light quantum hypothesis. J. of Astrophysics and Astronomy 15, 3–7 (1924)

98. Dick Teresi, The Vision Thing. Book review; The Fire Within The Eye by David Park.
    New York Times, Sep 28, 1997

99. Dirac, Paul Adrien Maurice 1925, The fundamental equations of quantum mechanics.
    Proceedings of the Royal Society of London A 109: 642–653 (1925)

100. Lacki, Jan, Observability, Anschaulichkeit and Abstraction: A Journey into Werner Heisenberg's Science and Philosophy. Progress of Physics 50:5-7, 440-458 (2002)

101. Aitchison, I.J.R., MacManus, D.A. & Snyder, T.M.; Understanding Heisenberg's "magical" paper of July 1925: A new look at the calculational details. American Journal of Physics 72, 1370 (2004)

102. Schrödinger, E., An Undulatory Theory of the Mechanics of Atoms and Molecules. Physical Review 28:6, 1049-1070 (1926)

103. Pais, A., Max Born's Statistical Interpretation of Quantum Mechanics. Science 218:4578, 1193-1198 (1982)

104. Philip Ball, Mysterious Quantum Rule Reconstructed From Scratch. Quanta, Feb 13, 2019

105. Max Born – Nobel Lecture. NobelPrize.org. Nobel Media AB 2021

106. (a) Dirac, Paul Adrien Maurice, The physical interpretation of the quantum dynamics. Proceedings of the Royal Society of London A 113: 621–641 (1927)
(b) Dirac, Paul Adrien Maurice, The quantum theory of the emission and absorption of radiation. Proceedings of the Royal Society of London A 114: 243–265 (1927)

107. Dirac, Paul Adrien Maurice, The quantum theory of the electron. Proceedings of the Royal Society A. 117 (778): 610–624 (1928)

108. Dirac, Paul Adrien Maurice, A theory of electrons and protons. Proceedings of the Royal Society A. 126 (801): 360–365 (1930)

109. Anderson, Carl D., The Positive Electron. Physical Review 43:6, 491-494 (1933)

110. Feynman, R., The theory of positrons. Physical Review 76:6, 749–759 (1949)

111. (a) Ivan Noble, More clues on matter. BBC Online, Mon 9 Jul, 2001
(b) R. Michael Barnett & Helen Quinn; What is antimatter? Scientific American, Jan 24, 2002

112. Glenn Starkman, The Standard Model of particle physics: The absolutely amazing theory of almost everything. The Conversation, May 23, 2018

113. Inamori, H. (2018), The issue with the initial state in quantum mechanics. arXiv:1810.11516 [quant-ph]

114. Koch, Christof, Is Consciousness Universal? Scientific American Mind 25:1, 26-29 (2014)

115. (a) Amanda Macias, The world's brightest scientific minds posed for this 1927 photo after historic debates about quantum mechanics. Business Insider, Apr 22, 2016
(b) Elizabeth Ashworth, Is this the greatest meeting of minds ever? Einstein and Curie among SEVENTEEN nobel prize winners at historic conference. Daily Mail, 16 Jun 2011

116. Frederica Russo & Phyllis Illari, Why causality now? Philosophical Theory meets Scientific Practice. Oxford University Press, Jan 18, 2015

117. Renn, J. & Hoffmann, D.; 1905—A miraculous year. Journal of Physics B: Atomic, Molecular and Optical Physics 38:9, S437 (2005)

118. Elizabeth Howell, Einstein's Theory of Special Relativity. Space.com, Mar 30, 2017

119. (a) Wynne Parry, Why The Speed of Light Matters. Live Science, Sep 26, 2011
(b) James Dacey, Doubts grow over superluminal-neutrino result. Physics World, 23 Feb 2012

120. (a) Lorek, Krzysztof, Louko, Jorma & Dragan, Andrzej; Ideal clocks—a convenient fiction. Classical and Quantum Gravity 32:17, 175003 (2015)
(b) Faculty of Physics University of Warsaw, Perfectly accurate clocks turn out to be impossible. ScienceDaily, 7 Oct 2015

121. (a) Elizabeth Howell, NASA's Astronaut Twins: Samples from Kelly Brothers Will Take Months to Analyze. Space.com, May 18, 2016
(b) Mike Wall, Einstein's 'Time Dilation' Spread Age Gap for Astronaut Scott Kelly & His Twin. Space.com, Jul 13, 2016

122. Jesse Emspak, Chinese Scientists Just Set the Record for the Farthest Quantum Teleportation. Live Science, Jul 14, 2017

123. (a) Krauter, H., Salart, D., Muschik, C. et al.; Deterministic quantum teleportation between distant atomic objects. Nature Phys 9, 400–404 (2013)
(b) University of Copenhagen - Niels Bohr Institute. "Quantum teleportation between atomic systems **over long distances." ScienceDaily, 6 Jun 2013**

124. Dave Hall, Teleportation: will it ever be a possibility? The Guardian, 12 Jun 2018

125. (a) Zych, M., Brukner, C. Quantum formulation of the Einstein equivalence principle. Nature Physics 14, 1027–1031 (2018)
(b) University of Queensland, How Einstein's equivalence principle extends to the quantum world. Phys.org, Aug 17, 2018

126. Suvorov, S.G., Einstein: the creation of the theory of relativity and some gnosiological lessons. Soviet Physics Uspekhi 22:7, 528 (1979)

127. Bose, S., Planck's law and the light quantum hypothesis. J. of Astrophysics and Astronomy 15, 3–7 (1924)

128. Einstein, A., Podolsky, B. & Rosen, N.; Can Quantum-Mechanical Description of Physical Reality Be Considered Complete? Physical Review 47:10, 777-780 (1935)

129. D.J.P., What is spooky action at a distance? Why some things are neither here nor there. The Economist, Mar 16, 2017

130. Bohr, N., Can Quantum-Mechanical Description of Physical Reality be Considered Complete? Physical Review 48:8, 696-702 (1935)

131. Lindley, David, What's Wrong with Quantum Mechanics? Physical Review Focus 16, 10 (2005)

132. (a) Schrödinger, E., Discussion of Probability Relations between Separated Systems. Mathematical Proceedings of the Cambridge Philosophical Society 31(4), 555-563 (1935)
(b) Schrödinger, E., Probability relations between separated systems. Mathematical Proceedings of the Cambridge Philosophical Society, 32(3), 446-452 (1936)

133. Trimmer, John D., "The Present Situation in Quantum Mechanics: A Translation of Schrödinger's 'Cat Paradox' Paper." Proceedings of the American Philosophical Society 124:5, 323–338 (1980)

134. Stapp, Henry (2001), Quantum theory and the role of mind in nature. arXiv:quant-ph/0103043

135. Wigner, Eugene P., The Problem of Measurement. American Journal of Physics 31, 6 (1963)

136. (a) Mehta, N., Mind-body dualism: A Critique from a Health Perspective. In: Brain, Mind and Consciousness: An International, Interdisciplinary Perspective (A.R. Singh & S.A. Singh eds.) Mens Sana Monographs 9(1), 202-209 (2011)
(b) ibid. Full paper and pdf download available online.

137. (a) E.P. Wigner (1961), Remarks on the mind-body question. In: The Scientist Speculates (I.J. Good ed.)
(b) Stapp H. (2009), Wigner's Friend. In: Compendium of Quantum Physics (Greenberger D., Hentschel K., Weinert F. eds.) Springer, Berlin, Heidelberg

138. (a) Frauchiger, D. & Renner, R.; Quantum theory cannot consistently describe the use of itself. Nature Communications 9, 3711 (2018)
(b) Castelvecchi, Davide, Reimagining of Schrödinger's cat breaks quantum mechanics — and stumps physicists. Nature News 561, 446-447 (2018)
(c) Pusey, M.F., An inconsistent friend. Nature Physics 14, 977–978 (2018)
(d) ETH Zurich. "Searching for errors in the quantum world." ScienceDaily, 18 Sep 2018

139. Chad Orzel, Three Ways Quantum Physics Affects Your Daily Life. Forbes, Dec 4, 2018

140. (a) Pokorny, F., Zhang, C., Higgins, G. et al.; "Tracking the Dynamics of an Ideal Quantum Measurement". Physical Review Letters 124:8, 401 (2020)
(b) Edwin Cartlidge, Physicists take snapshots of quantum measurement. Physics World, 07 Mar 2020
(c) Stockholm University, Scientists 'film' a quantum measurement. Phys.org, Feb 26, 2020

141. (a) Bong, K.W., Utreras-Alarcón, A., Ghafari, F. et al.; A strong no-go theorem on the Wigner's friend paradox. Nat. Phys. 16, 1199–1205 (2020)
(b) Brukner, C., Facts are relative. Nat. Phys. 16, 1172–1174 (2020)

142. Hesse, Mary B., Action at a Distance in Classical Physics. J. of the History of Science Society 46, 4 (1955)

143. Bohm, David, A Suggested Interpretation of the Quantum Theory in Terms of 'Hidden Variables' I". Physical Review 85(2): 166–179 (1952)

144. Goldstein, Sheldon, "Bohmian Mechanics", Stanford Encyclopedia of Philosophy (Summer 2017 Ed.)

145. John Horgan, "David Bohm, Quantum Mechanics and Enlightenment" Scientific American, Jul 23, 2018

146. Bohm, D. & Aharonov, Y.; Discussion of Experimental Proof for the Paradox of Einstein, Rosen, and Podolsky. Physical Review 108:4, 1070–1076 (1957)

147. Matt Williams, How Does Light Travel? Universe Today, May 19, 2016

148. (a) Pribram, Karl H., Quantum holography: Is it relevant to brain function? Information Sciences 115:1–4, 97-102 (1999)
(b) Pribram, Karl H. & Meade, Shelli D.; Conscious awareness: processing in the synaptodendritic web. New Ideas in Psychology 17:3, 205-214 (1999)

149. The David Bohm Society

150. Bohm, David, Wholeness and the Implicate Order (1980). Routledge, ISBN: 9780203995150

151. Bohm, David & Hiley, Basil; The Undivided Universe: An Ontological Interpretation of Quantum Theory. Routledge, ISBNs: 9780415121859 /9780415065887 /9780203980385

152. Goldstein, Sheldon; Review -The Undivided Universe: An Ontological Interpretation of Quantum Theory by David Bohm & Basil Hiley. Physics Today 47: 9, 90 (1994)

153. Englert, Berthold-Georg, Scully, Marian O., Süssmann, Georg & Walther, Herbert; "Surrealistic Bohm Trajectories". Zeitschrift für Naturforschung A, 47:12, 1175-1186 (1992)

154. (a) Kocsis, S., Braverman, B., Ravets, S. et al.; Observing the Average Trajectories of Single Photons in a Two-Slit Interferometer. Science 332:6034, 1170-1173 (2011)
(b) Cartlidge, E., A quantum take on certainty. Nature News (2011)

155. Mahler, Dylan H., Rozema, Lee, Fisher, Kent et al.; Experimental nonlocal and surreal Bohmian trajectories. Science Advances 2:2, e1501466 (2016)

156. (a) Dan Falk, New Support for Alternative Quantum View. Quanta, May 16, 2016

(b) Michael A. Gottlieb & Rudolf Pfeiffer, "Quantum Behavior", Richard Feynman Lectures (1965, 2006 &2013). California Institute of Technology.

157. (a) Henderson, L. & Vedral, V., Classical, quantum and total correlations. Journal of Physics A: Mathematical and General 34:35, 6899 (2001)

(b) Ollivier, Harold & Zurek, Wojciech H., Quantum Discord: A Measure of the Quantumness of Correlations. Physical Review Letters 88, 1, (2001)

(c) Zurek, Wojciech H., Quantum discord and Maxwell's demons. Physical Review A, 67:1, 012320 (2003)

158. Yichen, Huang, Computing quantum discord is NP-complete. New Journal of Physics, 16, 033027 (2014)

159. (a) Auccaise, R., Maziero, J., Céleri, L.C. et al.; Experimentally Witnessing the Quantumness of Correlations. Physical Review Letters 107:7, 070501 {2011)

(b) Miranda Marquit, Quantum correlations -- without entanglement. Phys.org, Aug 24, 2011

160. (a) Dieks, Dennis, Von Neumann's impossibility proof: Mathematics in the service of rhetorics. Studies in History and Philosophy of Modern Physics 60, 136-148 (2017)

(b) Bub, J. (2011). Is Von Neumann's "No Hidden Variables" Proof Silly? In H. Halvorson (Ed.), Deep Beauty: Understanding the Quantum World through Mathematical Innovation (pp. 393-408). Cambridge

161. (a) Bell, John S., On the Einstein Podolsky Rosen paradox. Physics Physique Fizika 1:3, 195–200 (1964)

(b) ibid. Full paper and pdf download available online.

162. Bell, John S., On the Problem of Hidden Variables in Quantum Mechanics. Reviews of Modern Physics 38:3, 447-452 (1966)

163. (a) Kochen, Simon B. & Specker, Ernst P., The problem of hidden variables in quantum mechanics. Journal of Mathematics and Mechanics 17(1): 59–87 (1967)

(b) Mermin, N. David, Simple unified form for the major no-hidden-variables theorems. Physical Review Letters 65:27, 3373–3376 (1990)

(c) Mermin, N. David, What's Wrong with this Pillow? Physics Today 42, 4, 9 (1989)

(d) Peres, A., Two simple proofs of the Kochen-Specker theorem. Journal of Physics A: Mathematical and General 24:4, L175–L178 (1991)

(e) Peres, A., Quantum information and general relativity. Forts.der Physik. 52 (11): 1052–1055 (2004)

164. Myrvold, Wayne, Genovese, Marco & Shimony, Abner, "Bell's Theorem", The Stanford Encyclopedia of Philosophy (Fall 2020 Edition), Edward N. Zalta (ed.)

165. Whitaker, A., John Bell and the most profound discovery of science. Physics World 11:12, 29–34 (1998)

166. (a) Aspect, Alain, Dalibard, Jean & Roger, Gérard; Experimental Test of Bell's Inequalities Using Time-Varying Analyzers. Physical Review Letters 49:25, 1804-1807 (1982)

(b) Aspect, Alain, Closing the Door on Einstein and Bohr's Quantum Debate. APS Physics 8, 123 (2015)

167. (a) Handsteiner, J., Friedman, A.S., Rauch, D. et al.; Cosmic Bell Test: Measurement Settings from Milky Way Stars. Physical Review Letters 118:6, 060401 (2017)

(b) Wright, Katherine, "Cosmic Test of Quantum Mechanics". APS Physics 10, s14 (2017)

(c) Natalie Wolchover, Experiment Reaffirms Quantum Weirdness. Quanta, Feb 7, 2017

168. Rab, A.S., Polino, E., Man, Z.X. et al.; Entanglement of photons in their dual wave-particle nature. Nature Communications 8, 915 (2017)

169. (a) Ockeloen-Korppi, C.F., Damskägg, E., Pirkkalainen, J.M. et al.; Stabilized entanglement of massive mechanical oscillators. Nature 556, 478–482 (2018)

(b) Aalto University. "Einstein's 'spooky action' goes massive." ScienceDaily, 25 Apr 2018

170. (a) Kirchmair, G., Zähringer, F., Gerritsma, R. et al.; State-independent experimental test of quantum contextuality. Nature 460, 494–497 (2009)

(b) Austrian Academy of Sciences, Quantum measurements: Common sense is not enough. Phys.org, Jul 22, 2009

171. Stapp, H.P., Bell's theorem and world process. Il Nuovo Cimento B 29, 270–276 (1975)

172. Ellis, Brian, Physical Realism. Ratio 18:4, 371-384 (2005)

173. Jeremy Bernstein, reply by Lee Smolin, "Einstein: An Exchange". The New York Review, Letters, Aug 16, 2007 (In response to: The Other Einstein from Jun 14, 2007 issue)

174. (a) Ringbauer, M., Giarmatzi, C., Chaves, R. et al.; Experimental test of nonlocal causality. Science Advances 2:8, id: e1600162 (2016)

(b) Philip Ball, Quantum mechanics trumps nonlocal causality. Physics World, 18 Aug 2016

175. (a) Lemos, G., Borish, V., Cole, G. et al.; Quantum imaging with undetected photons. Nature 512, 409–412 (2014)

(b) University of Vienna, "Quantum physics enables revolutionary imaging method." ScienceDaily, 28 Aug 2014

(c) Jesse Emspak, Spooky Quantum Entanglement Gets Extra 'Twist'. Live Science, Nov 06, 2012

176. Abouraddy, Ayman F., Saleh, Bahaa E.A., Sergienko, Alexander V. & Teich, Malvin C.; Quantum holography. Optics Express 9:10, 498-505 (2001)

177. (a) Robert Workman, What is a Hologram? Live Science, May 23, 2013

(b) Gabor, D., Microscopy by reconstructed wave-fronts. Proc.R.Soc. Lond A197:1051, 454–487 (1949)

(c) Gabor, Dennis, A New Microscopic Principle. Nature 161, 777–778 (1948)

178. (a) Chrapkiewicz, R., Jachura, M., Banaszek, K. et al.; Hologram of a single photon. Nature Photon 10, 576–579 (2016)

(b) Faculty of Physics University of Warsaw. "The birth of quantum holography: Making holograms of single light particles!" ScienceDaily, 18 Jul 2016

179. Madan, I., Vanacore, G.M., Pomarico, E. et al.; Holographic imaging of electromagnetic fields via electron-light quantum interference. Science Advances 5:5, id: eaav8358 (2019)

180. (a) Moon, C., Mattos, L., Foster, B. et al.; Quantum holographic encoding in a two-dimensional electron gas. Nature Nanotech 4, 167–172 (2009)

(b) Heller, E., Quantum holography for real. Nature Nanotech 4, 141–142 (2009)

181. (a) Defienne, H., Ndagano, B., Lyons, A. et al.; Polarization entanglement-enabled quantum holography. Nature Physics 17, 591–597 (2021)

(b) Töpfer, S., Basset, M.G., Fuenzalida, J. et al.; Quantum holography with undetected light. Science Advances 8:2, eabl4301 (2022)

182. Marcer, Peter J. & Schempp, Walter; Quantum holography—the paradigm of quantum entanglement. American Institute of Physics Conference Proceedings 465:1, 461 (1999)

183. Peter Byrne, Why Science Should Stay Clear of Metaphysics. Nautilus, Sep 2016

184. Barrett, Jeffrey, "Everett's Relative-State Formulation of Quantum Mechanics", The Stanford Encyclopedia of Philosophy (Winter 2018 Edition), Edward N. Zalta (ed.)

185. Jennifer Ouellette, "Splitting Image: The Alternate Realities of the Multiverse". Nautilus, Jun 27, 2013

186. Everett III, Hugh (1956-1957), "The Theory of the Universal Wavefunction" (pdf . In: The Many-Worlds Interpretation of Quantum Mechanics, DeWitt, Bryce S. & Graham, Neill R., eds. (1973). Princeton Series in Physics. ISBN 0-691-08131-X. (Full paper and pdf download available online.)

187. Osnaghi, Stefano, Freitas, Fábio & Freire Jr., Olival; The origin of the Everettian heresy. Studies in History and Philosophy of Modern Physics. 40:2, 97-123 (2009)

188. Jaeger, G., What in the (quantum) world is macroscopic? American J. of Physics. 82:9, 896–905 (2014)

189. Peter Byrne, "The Many Worlds of Hugh Everett". Scientific American, Oct 21, 2008

190. (a) DeWitt, Bryce S., Quantum mechanics and reality. Physics Today 23: 9, 30 (1970)

(b) Peter Byrne, The Many Mice Theory of Quantum Mechanics. Nautilus, Dec 31, 2016

191. Vaidman, Lev, "Many-Worlds Interpretation of Quantum Mechanics", The Stanford Encyclopedia of Philosophy (Fall 2018 Edition), Edward N. Zalta (ed.)

192. Jason Chu, Parallel Universes and the Many-Worlds Theory. Universe Today, Aug 15, 2014

193. (a) Hall, Michael J.W., Deckert, Dirk-André & Wiseman, Howard M.; Quantum Phenomena Modeled by Interactions between Many Classical Worlds. Physical Review X 4:4, 041013 (2014)

(b) Griffith University, "Scientists propose existence and interaction of parallel worlds: Many Interacting Worlds theory challenges foundations of quantum science." ScienceDaily, 30 Oct 2014

(c) Howard Wiseman, When parallel worlds collide, quantum mechanics is born. The Conversation, Oct 24, 2014

194. (a) Natalie Wolchover, A trek through the probable universe. Book review - Philip Ball's Beyond Weird. Books and Arts, Nature 555, 440-441 (2018)

(b) Philip Ball, Why the Many-Worlds Interpretation Has Many Problems. Quanta, Oct 18, 2018

195. (a) Albert, D. & Loewer, B.; Interpreting the many worlds interpretation. Synthese 77, 195–213 (1988)

(b) Felline, Laura & Bacciagaluppi, Guido; Locality and Mentality in Everett Interpretations I: Albert and Loewer's Many Minds. Mind and Matter 11:2, 223-241 (2013). HAL Id: halshs-00995887

196. (a) Lockwood, Michael, 'Many Minds' Interpretations of Quantum Mechanics. British Journal for the Philosophy of Science 47:2, 159–188 (1996)

(b) ibid. Full paper and pdf download available online.

197. (a) Papineau, D, Many Minds are No Worse than One. British J. for the Philosophy of Science 47, 2 (1996)

(b) Papineau, David, Uncertain Decisions and The Many-Minds Interpretation of Quantum Mechanics. The Monist 80:1, 97–117 (1997)

(c) Garson, J. & Papineau, D.; Teleosemantics, selection and novel contents. Biol Philos 34, 36 (2019)

198. (a) Donald, M. J. (1997), On Many-Minds Interpretations of Quantum Theory. arXiv:quant-ph/9703008

(b) ibid, 48

(c) ibid, 198a. Full paper and pdf download available online.

199. ibid, 194b

200. (a) George Johnson, Shadow Worlds. Our universe, a physicist says, is but one of many. Book review: The Fabric of Reality by David Deutsch. New York Times, Oct 5, 1997

(b) Deutsch, David (2001), The Structure of the Multiverse. arXiv:quant-ph/0104033

(c) ibid. Full paper and pdf download available online.

201. Peach, Filiz (2001), David Deutsch Interview. Philosophy Now, Issue 30: Dec 2000/Jan 2001

202. Marcus Chown, Taming the Multiverse. New Scientist, 14 Jul 2001

203. Ibid, 199a

204. Tom Siegfried, Long Live the Multiverse! Scientific American, Dec 3, 2019

205. (a) Ellis, George F.R., Does the Multiverse Really Exist? Scientific American 305:2, 38–43 (2011)

(b) ibid. Reprinted Aug 2014.

(c) Ellis, G. & Silk, J.; Scientific method: Defend the integrity of physics. Nature 516, 321–323 (2014)

206. (a) Chris Berthelot, Does God exist in the multiverse? Grandin Media, Mar 8, 2018

(b) Dennis Prager, Why Some Scientists Embrace the 'Multiverse'. National Review, Jun 18, 2013

207. (a) Tegmark, Max, The Interpretation of Quantum Mechanics: Many Worlds or Many Words? Progress of Physics 46:6-8, 855-862 (1998)

(b) ibid. Full paper and pdf download available online.

208. Lewis, Peter J., What is it like to be Schrödinger's cat? Analysis 60:1, 22–29 (2000)

209. (a) Papineau, David, Why You Don't Want to Get in the Box with Schrödinger's Cat. Analysis 63:1, 51-58 (2003)

(b) ibid. Full paper and pdf download available online.

210. (a) Tomberlin, James E., Reviewed Work: On the Plurality of Worlds by David Lewis. Noûs 23:1, 117-125 (1989)

(b) Jane O'Grady, "David Lewis. Princeton philosopher who formulated ground-breaking theories on everything from language to identity to alternative worlds". The Guardian, 23 Oct 2001

211. (a) Lewis, David (2001, 2004) How Many Lives Has Schrödinger's Cat? Australasian Journal of Philosophy 82:1, 3-22 (2004)

(b) Aranyosi, István, Should We Fear Quantum Torment? Ratio 25:3, 249-259 (2012)

212. (a) Zeh, H.D., On the interpretation of measurement in quantum theory. Foundations of Physics 1:1, 69–76 (1970)

(b) Full paper and pdf download available online.

213. (a) Zeh, H.D. (1995-2002), Decoherence: Basic Concepts and Their Interpretation. arXiv:quant-ph/9506020

(b) ibid. Full paper and pdf download available online.

(c) Joos, Erich and Zeh, H. Dieter, Coming to terms with decoherence. Physics Today 63:7, 8 (2010)

214. (a) Joos, Erich (1999), Elements of Environmental Decoherence. arXiv:quant-ph/9908008

(b) ibid. Full paper and pdf download available online.

(c) Erich Joos, The Quantum Wave Function as a Psychological Barrier. Metanexus, Mar 11, 2003

215. (a) Seth Lloyd, The universe is a quantum computer. Review of Vlatko Vedral's Decoding Reality. New Scientist, 17 Mar 2010

(b) Aleks Krotoski, Interview: Vlatko Vedral: 'I'd like to explain the origin of God'. Guardian, 7 Mar 2010

216. (a) Zurek, Wojciech H. (2001-2003), Decoherence, einselection, and the quantum origins of the classical. arXiv:quant-ph/0105127

(b) Zurek, Wojciech H, Decoherence, einselection, and the quantum origins of the classical. Reviews of Modern Physics 75:3, 715-775 (2003)

217. (a) Zurek, Wojciech H. (2003), Quantum Darwinism and Envariance. arXiv:quant-ph/0308163

(b) Zurek, Wojciech H. (2009), Quantum Darwinism. arXiv:0903.5082 [quant-ph]

218. (a) Gamble, John (2008), Foundations of Quantum Decoherence. arXiv:0805.3178 [quant-ph]

(b) Healey, R., Quantum Decoherence in a Pragmatist View: Dispelling Feynman's Mystery. Foundations of Physics 42, 1534–1555 (2012)

(c) Philip Ball, The Universe Is Always Looking. The Atlantic, Oct 20, 2018

(d) Schlosshauer, Maximilian, "Decoherence, the measurement problem, and interpretations of quantum mechanics". Reviews of Modern Physics 76:4, 1267-1305 (2005)

219. (a) Ghirardi, G.C., Rimini, A. & Weber, T.; Unified dynamics for microscopic and macroscopic systems. Physical Review D 34:2, 470-491 (1986)

494

(b) Bassi, A. & Ghirardi, G.; Dynamical Reduction Models. Physics Reports 379:5–6, 257-426 (2003)

(c) Frigg, Roman (2009), GRW Theory (Ghirardi, Rimini, Weber Model of Quantum Mechanics). In: Compendium of Quantum Physics, pp. 266-270, Greenberger D., Hentschel K., Weinert F. (eds), Springer

220. Joos, Erich, Comment on 'Unified dynamics for microscopic and macroscopic systems'. Physical Review D 36:10, 3285-3286 (1987)

221. (a) Penrose, Roger, On Gravity's role in Quantum State Reduction. Gen Relat Gravit 28, 581–600 (1996)

(b) Penrose, Roger, Quantum computation, entanglement and state reduction. Philosophical Transactions of the Royal Society A, 356:1743, 1927–1939 (1998)

(c) Penrose, Roger, On the Gravitization of Quantum Mechanics 1: Quantum State Reduction. Foundations of Physics 44:5, 557–575 (2014)

222. (a) Oniga, Teodora & Wang, Charles H.-T.; Quantum gravitational decoherence of light and matter. Physical Review D 93:4, 044027 (2016)

(b) Charlie Wood, What Is Quantum Gravity? Space.com, Aug 27, 2019

223. Ghirardi, Grlo & Bassi, A., "Collapse Theories", Stanford Encyclopedia of Philosophy (Summer 2020 Ed.)

224. (a) Adler, Stephen L., Why decoherence has not solved the measurement problem: a response to P.W. Anderson. Studies in History and Philosophy of Modern Physics 34:1, 135-142 (2003)

(b) ibid. Full paper and pdf download available online.

225. Leggett, A.J., Realism and the physical world. Reports on Progress in Physics 71:2, 022001 (2008)

226. (a) Leggett, A.J. & Garg, Anupam.; Quantum mechanics versus macroscopic realism: Is the flux there when nobody looks? Physical Review Letters 54:9, 857-860 (1985)

(b) Leggett, A.J., Testing the limits of quantum mechanics: motivation, state of play, prospects. Journal of Physics: Condensed Matter, 14:15, R415-R451 (2002)

227. (a) Emary, C., Lambert, N. & Nori, F.; Leggett-Garg Inequalities. Rep. Prog. Phys. 77:1, 016001 (2013)

(b) Robens, C., Alt, W., Meschede, D. et al.; Ideal Negative Measurements in Quantum Walks Disprove Theories Based on Classical Trajectories. Physical Review X, 5:1, 011003 (2015)

(c) Knee, George C., Do Quantum Superpositions Have a Size Limit? Physics 8, 6 (2015)

228. Ingólfsson H.I., Lopez C.A., Uusitalo J.J. et al.; The power of coarse graining in biomolecular simulations. WIREs Computational Molecular Science 4:3, 225–248 (2014)

229. (a) Kofler, Johannes & Brukner, Caslav; Classical World Arising out of Quantum Physics under the Restriction of Coarse-Grained Measurements. Physical Review Letters 99:18, 180403 (2007)

(b) ibid. Full paper and pdf download available online.

230. (a) Kofler, Johannes & Brukner, Caslav; Conditions for Quantum Violation of Macroscopic Realism. Physical Review Letters 101:9, 090403 (2008)

(b) ibid. Full paper and pdf download available online

231. (a) Raeisi, S., Sekatski, P. & Simon, C.; Coarse Graining Makes It Hard to See Micro-Macro Entanglement. Physical Review Letters 107:25, 250401 (2011)

(b) ibid. Full paper and pdf download available online.

(c) University of Calgary, "Quantum cats are hard to see: Researchers explain the difficulty of detecting quantum effects." ScienceDaily, 22 Dec 2011

232. (a) Cárdenas-López, F., Allende, S. & Retamal, J.; Sudden Transition between Classical to Quantum Decoherence in bipartite correlated Qutrit Systems. Sci Rep 7, 44654 (2017)

(b) Feldman, Marc J. & Bocko, Mark F.; A realistic experiment to demonstrate macroscopic quantum coherence. Physica C: Superconductivity, 350:3–4, 171-176 (2001)

(c) Tanisha Bassan, Decoherence: Quantum Computer's Greatest Obstacle. Hackernoon, Jun 01, 2018

233. Vlatko Vedral, Living in a Quantum World. Scientific American, Jun 2011

234. Atmanspacher, Harald, "Quantum Approaches to Consciousness", The Stanford Encyclopedia of Philosophy (Summer 2020 Edition), Edward N. Zalta (ed.)

235. (a) Filip, Radim (2001), Phase-selective reversible quantum decoherence in cavity QED experiment. arXiv:quant-ph/0108115

(b) Zurek, Wojciech H., Quantum reversibility is relative, or does a quantum measurement reset initial conditions? Philosophical Transactions of the Royal Society A, 376:2123, 20170315 (2018)

(c) Sellier, J.M., Nedjalkov, M., Dimov, I. & Selberherr, S.; Decoherence and time reversibility: The role of randomness at interfaces. Journal of Applied Physics 114, 174902 (2013)

236. (a) Joyce, James, "Bayes' Theorem", The Stanford Encyclopedia of Philosophy (Spring 2019 Ed.)

(b) Bayes, Thomas, LII, An essay towards solving a problem in the doctrine of chances. By the late Rev. Mr. Bayes, F.R.S. communicated by Mr. Price, in a letter to John Canton, A.M.F.R.S. Philosophical Transactions of the Royal Society 53:370–418 (1763)

237. John A. Paulos, Book review: "The Mathematics of Changing Your Mind by Sharon Bertsch McGrayne". New York Times, 5 Aug 2011

238. (a) Caves, Carlton M., Fuchs, Christopher A. & Schack, Rüdiger; Quantum probabilities as Bayesian probabilities. Physical Review A, 65:21, 022305 (2002)

(b) ibid. Full paper and pdf download available online.

239. Fuchs, C. A. (2010), QBism, the Perimeter of Quantum Bayesianism. arXiv:1003.5209 [quant-ph]

240. (a) Fuchs, Christopher A., Mermin, N. David & Schack, Rüdiger; An introduction to QBism with an application to the locality of quantum mechanics. American Journal of Physics 82, 749 (2014)

(b) ibid. Full paper and pdf download available online.

241. Mermin, N. David, Commentary: Quantum mechanics: Fixing the shifty split. Phys Today 65, 7, 8 (2012)

242. (a) Fuchs, Christopher A. & Schack, Rüdiger; QBism and the Greeks: why a quantum state does not represent an element of physical reality*. Physica Scripta 90:1, 015104 (2014)

(b) ibid. Full paper and pdf download available online.

243. (a) Nauenberg, Michael, QBism And Locality In Quantum Mechanics. Am. J. of Physics 83, 197 (2015)

(b) Fuchs, C. A., Mermin, N. David & Schack, R.; Reply to Nauenberg. Am. J. of Physics 83, 198 (2015)

244. Amanda Gefter, A Private View of Quantum Reality. Interview with C. Fuchs. Quanta, Jun 4, 2015

245. (a) Holborow, Les (1974), The 'Prejudice in Favour of Psychophysical Parallelism'. In: Understanding Wittgenstein. Royal Institute of Philosophy Lectures. Palgrave Macmillan, London.

(b) Mehlberg, H. & Cohen, .R. S. (1980), Conceptual Analysis of Psychophysical Parallelism. In: Cohen R.S. (eds) Time, Causality, and the Quantum Theory. Boston Studies in the Philosophy of Science, 19-1.

246. Betony Adams, Francesco Petruccione; Do quantum effects play a role in consciousness? Physics World, 26 Jan 2021

247. (a) Gurney, R., Condon, E.; Wave Mechanics and Radioactive Disintegration. Nature 122, 439 (1928)

(b) Hartman, Thomas E., Tunneling of a Wave Packet. Journal of Applied Physics 33, 3427 (1962)

(c) Hauge, E.H. & Støvneng, J.A.; Tunneling times: a critical review. Rev. Mod. Phys. 61:4, 917-936 (1989)

248. (a) Enders,A. &Nimtz, G.; On superluminal barrier traversal. J.de Physique I France, 2:9,1693-1698 (1992)

(b) Enders, Achim & Nimtz, Günter; Evanescent-mode propagation and quantum tunneling. Physical Review E 48:1, 632-634 (1993)

(c) Nimtz, Günter, Tunneling Confronts Special Relativity. Foundations of Physics 41, 1193–1199 (2011)

249. Jon Butterworth, Understanding quantum tunnelling. The Guardian, 19 Oct 2014

250. (a) Winful, Herbert G., Energy storage in superluminal barrier tunneling: Origin of the "Hartman effect". Optics Express 10:25, 1491-1496 (2002)

(b) Winful, Herbert G., Delay Time and the Hartman Effect in Quantum Tunneling. Physical Review Letters 91:26, 260401 (2003)

(c) Winful, Herbert G., Tunneling time, the Hartman effect, and superluminality: A proposed resolution of an old paradox. Physics Reports 436:1–2, 1-69 (2006)

(d) Winful, Herbert G., The meaning of delay in barrier tunnelling: a re-examination of superluminal group velocities. New Journal of Physics 8:6, 101-101 (2006)

251. (a) Camus, N., Yakaboylu, E., Fechner, L. et al.; Experimental Evidence for Quantum Tunneling Time. Physical Review Letters 119:2, 023201 (2017)

(b) Michael Irving, Does quantum tunneling take time or is it instantaneous? New Atlas, Aug 07, 2017

(c) Nimtz, Günter & Aichmann, Horst; Zero-Time Tunneling – Revisited. Zeitschrift für Naturforschung A, 72:9, 881-884 (2017)

(d) Davies, Paul C.W., Quantum tunneling time. American Journal of Physics 73, 23 (2005)

252. (a) U. Satya Sainadh, We did a breakthrough 'speed test' in quantum tunnelling, and here's why that's exciting. The Conversation, Mar 19, 2019

(b) Sainadh, U.S., Xu, H., Wang, X. et al.; Attosecond angular streaking and tunnelling time in atomic hydrogen. Nature 568, 75–77 (2019)

253. (a) Ramos, R., Spierings, D., Racicot, I. & Steinberg, A.M.; Measurement of the time spent by a tunneling atom within the barrier region. Nature 583, 529–532 (2020)

(b) Philip Ball, Quantum-tunnelling time is measured using ultracold atoms. Physics World, 22 Jul 2020

(c) Dumont, Randall S., Rivlin, Tom & Pollak, Eli; The relativistic tunneling flight time may be superluminal, but it does not imply superluminal signaling. New Journal of Physics 22:9, 093060 (2020)

(d) Natalie Wolchover, Quantum Tunnels Show How Particles Can Break the Speed of Light. Quanta, Oct 20, 2020

254. (a) Gisin, Nicolas (2005), Can relativity be considered complete? From Newtonian nonlocality to quantum nonlocality and beyond. arXiv:quant-ph/0512168

(b) ibid. Full paper and pdf download available online.

255. (a) Bancal,J. D., Pironio, S., Acín, A. et al.; Quantum non-locality based on finite-speed causal influences leads to superluminal signalling. Nature Physics 8, 867–870 (2012)

(b) National University of Singapore, Looking beyond space and time to cope with quantum theory. ScienceDaily, 28 Oct 2012

256. Dennis Gabor (1971), Nobel Lecture, NobelPrize.org. Lectures, Physics 1971-1980, Stig Lundqvist ed.

257. (a) Piet Hut (2000), There Are No Things. Response to the Edge.org 2000 question

(b) Bernard d'Espagnat, Quantum weirdness: What we call 'reality' is just a state of mind. The Guardian, 20 Mar 2009

(c) Anton Zeilinger (2016), Quantum Entanglement Is Independent Of Space And Time. Response to the Edge.org 2016 question

(d) Unruh William G., Locality and quantum mechanics. Phil. Trans. R. Soc. A.376:2123, 20170320 (2018)

258. Trixler, Frank, Quantum Tunnelling to the Origin and Evolution of Life. Current Organic Chemistry 17:16, 1758-1770 (2013)

259. (a) Stuart, T.E., Slater, J.A., Colbeck, R. et al.; Experimental Bound on the Maximum Predictive Power of Physical Theories. Physical Review Letters 109;2, 020402 (2012)

(b) University of Calgary, "A roll of the dice: Quantum mechanics researchers show that nature is unpredictable." ScienceDaily, 9 Jul 2012

260. (a) Cubitt, T., Perez-Garcia, D. & Wolf, M.; Undecidability of the spectral gap. Nat 528, 207–211 (2015)

(b) University College London, "Quantum physics problem proved unsolvable: Gödel and Turing enter quantum physics." ScienceDaily, 9 Dec 2015

261. (a) Kant, Immanuel, Critique of Pure Reason (1st ed. 1781, 2nd ed. 1787). Project Gutenberg online

(b) Grier, M., "Kant's Critique of Metaphysics", Stanford Encyclopedia of Philosophy (Summer 2018 Ed.)

262. Lederman, Leon with Dick Teresi (1993); The Invisible Soccer Ball (chap. 1) in The God Particle: If the Universe is the Answer, What is the Question? (p.1), Boston: Houghton Mifflin Co.

263. (a) Nola Taylor Redd, Milky Way Galaxy: Facts About Our Galactic Home. Space.com, Nov 14, 2017

(b) Michael Schirber, What Is Relativity? Live Science, Jul 02, 2019

(c) Elizabeth Howell, How Many Galaxies Are There? Space.com, Mar 20, 2018

264. (a) Belenkiy, Ari, Alexander Friedmann and the origins of modern cosmology. Phy Today 65:10, 38 (2012)

(b) Ethan Siegel, The Most Important Equation In The Universe. Forbes, Apr 17, 2018

(c) Lemaître, G., "A Homogeneous Universe of Constant Mass and Increasing Radius accounting for the Radial Velocity of Extra-galactic Nebulæ". Monthly Notices of the Royal Astr Soc 91:5, 483–490 (1931)

265. Nussbaumer, H., Einstein's conversion from his static to an expanding universe. EPJ H 39, 37–62 (2014)

266. (a) Lemaître, Georges, The Beginning of the World from the Point of View of Quantum Theory. Nature 127, 706 (1931)

(b) Kragh, Helge, "Georges Lemaître, Pioneer of Modern Theoretical Cosmology". Foundations of Physics 48:10, 1333–1348 (2018)

(c) Kirshner, Robert P., Book Review, The Atom of the Universe: The Life and Work of Georges Lemaître by Dominique Lambert. Physics Today 69:7, 60 (2016)

(d) Midbon, Mark, 'A Day Without Yesterday': Georges Lemaitre & the Big Bang. Commonweal Magazine 127: 6, 18-19 (2000). Reprint, Catholic Education Resource Center

267. (a) Berger, A.L. (1984), ed., The Big Bang and Georges Lemaître. Springer, Netherlands.

(b) New Scientist, The Genesis Problem. Magazine issue 2847, 14 Jan 2012

(c) 'Big Bang' astronomer dies. Obituary: Sir Fred Hoyle. BBC online, 22 Aug 2001

268. (a) O'Raifeartaigh, Cormac & Mitton, Simon (2015), A new perspective on steady-state cosmology: from Einstein to Hoyle. arXiv:1506.01651 [physics.hist-ph]

(b) Bondi, Hermann & Gold, Thomas; The Steady-State Theory of the Expanding Universe. Monthly Notices of the Royal Astronomical Society 108:3, 252–270 (1948)

(c) Hoyle, Fred, A New Model for the Expanding Universe. M. N. of R Astr Soc 108:5, 372–382 (1948)

(d) Matt Williams, What is the Steady State Hypothesis? Universe Today, Mar 1, 2020

269. (a) Penzias, Arno A. & Wilson, Robert W.; A Measurement of Excess Antenna Temperature at 4080 Mc/s. Astrophysical Journal, 142, 419-421 (1965)

(b) Riess, Adam G. et al., Observational Evidence from Supernovae for an Accelerating Universe and a Cosmological Constant. The Astronomical Journal 116:3, 1009 (1998)

270. (a) Chelsea Gohd, Astronomers reevaluate the age of the universe. Space.com, Jan 08, 2021

(b) Lakhal, B.S. & Guezmir, A.; The Horizon Problem. J. of Physics: Conf. Series 1269, 012017 (2019)

(c) Helbig, Phillip, Is there a flatness problem in classical cosmology? Monthly Notices of the Royal Astronomical Society 421:1, 561–569 (2012)

271. (a) Carter, Brandon, Republication of: Large number coincidences and the anthropic principle in cosmology. General Relativity and Gravitation 43, 3225 (2011)

(b) Ellis, George F.R., Editorial note to: Brandon Carter, Large number coincidences and the anthropic principle in cosmology. General Relativity and Gravitation 43, 3213 (2011)

272. (a) Craig, William Lane, Book Review, The Anthropic Cosmological Principle by John D. Barrow and Frank J. Tipler. International Philosophical Quarterly 27:4, 437-447 (1987)

(b) Cloud, Preston, Book Review, The Anthropic Cosmological Principle by John D. Barrow and Frank J. Tipler. The Quarterly Review of Biology 62:1 (1987)

(c) Tipler, Frank J., Intelligent life in cosmology. International Journal of Astrobiology 2:2, 141-148 (2003)

(d) Timothy Ferris, "I Think, Therefore The Universe Is". Review of Barrow & Tipler's Anthropic Cosmological Principle. New York Times, Feb 16, 1986

273. (a) Paul Davies, The Goldilocks Enigma (extracts). BBC Newsnight book club, 9 Oct 2006

(b) Guth, Alan H., Inflationary universe: A possible solution to the horizon and flatness problems. Physical Review D 23:2, 347-356 (1981)

(c) Lindley, David, Landmarks: The Inflationary Universe. Physical Review Focus 27, 12 (2011)

274. (a) Nanopoulos, D.V., Olive, K.A. & Srednicki M.; After primordial inflation. Physics Letters B, 127:1–2, 30-34 (1983)

(b) Linde, Andrei D., A new inflationary universe scenario: A possible solution of the horizon, flatness, homogeneity, isotropy and primordial monopole problems. Physics Letters B, 108:6, 389-393 (1982)

(c) Albrecht, Andreas & Steinhardt, Paul J.; Cosmology for Grand Unified Theories with Radiatively Induced Symmetry Breaking. Physical Review Letters 48:17, 1220-1223 (1982)

275. (a) Bardeen, J.M., Steinhardt, P.J. & Turner, M.S.; Spontaneous creation of almost scale-free density perturbations in an inflationary universe. Physical Review D 28:4, 679-693 (1983)

(b) Vilenkin, Alexander, Birth of inflationary universes. Physical Review D 27:12, 2848-2855 (1983)

(c) Linde, Andrei D., Eternally existing self-reproducing chaotic inflanationary universe. Physics Letters B, 175:4, 395-400 (1986)

276. (a) White, Roger, Fine-Tuning and Multiple Universes. Nous 34:2, 260-276 (2000)

(b) Natalie Wolchover & Peter Byrne, In a Multiverse, What Are the Odds? Quanta, Nov 3, 2014

277. (a) Dicke, R.H., Peebles, P.J.E., Roll, P.G. & Wilkinson, D.T.; Cosmic Black-Body Radiation. Astrophysical Journal 142, 414-419 (1965)

(b) Khoury, J., Ovrut, B.A., Steinhardt, P.J. & Turok, N.; Ekpyrotic universe: Colliding branes and the origin of the hot big bang. Physical Review D 64:12, 123522 (2001)

(c) Steinhardt, Paul J. & Turok, Neil; A Cyclic Model of the Universe. Science 296:5572, 1436-1439 (2002)

(d) Ijjas, Anna & Steinhardt, Paul; A new kind of cyclic universe. Physics Letters B, 795, 666-672 (2019)

278. (a) John Horgan, Physicist Slams Cosmic Theory He Helped Conceive. Scientific American, Dec 1, 2014

(b) Maggie McKee, Yvonne Bang; Ingenious: Paul J. Steinhardt. Nautilus, Sep 2, 2014

(c) Natalie Wolchover, How the Universe Got Its Bounce Back. Quanta, Jan 31, 2018

(d) Novello, M. & Perez-Bergliaffa, S.E; Bouncing cosmologies. Physics Reports 463:4, 127-213 (2008)

279. (a) Graham, P. W., Kaplan, D.E. & Rajendran, S.; "Born again universe". Phy Rev D 97:4, 044003 (2018)

(b) Barbour, Julian, Koslowski, Tim & Mercati, Flavio; Identification of a Gravitational Arrow of Time. Physical Review Letters 113:18, 181101 (2014)

(c) Carlip, Steven, Arrow of Time Emerges in a Gravitational System. Viewpoint, Physics 7, 111 (2014)

280. (a) Kaloper, Nemanja & Padilla, Antonio; Sequestering the Standard Model Vacuum Energy. Physical Review Letters 112:9, 091304 (2014)

(b) Schirber, Michael, Cosmological Constant Redefined. Synopsis, Physics 7, s29 (2014)

281. (a) Guth, Alan H., Eternal inflation and its implications. Journal of Physics A: Mathematical and Theoretical 40:25,6811 (2007)

(b) Philip Goff, Our Improbable Existence Is No Evidence for a Multiverse. Sci. American, Jan 10, 2021

(c) J. Richard Gott, Universe in a bubble. Aeon, 05 Oct, 2017.

282. (a) Cameron, R., "Infinite Regress Arguments", The Stanford Encyclopedia of Philosophy (Fall 2018 Ed.)

(b) Wieland, J.W. Infinite Regress Arguments. Acta Analytica 28, 95–109 (2013)

283. (a) Bodnar, I., "Aristotle's Natural Philosophy", Stanford Encyclopedia of Philosophy (Spring 2018 Ed.)

(b) Cohoe, Caleb, There must be a First: Why Thomas Aquinas Rejects Infinite, Essentially Ordered, Causal Series. British Journal for the History of Philosophy 21:5, 838-856 (2013)

(c) Reichenbach, B., "Cosmological Argument", Stanford Encyclopedia of Philosophy (Spring 2021 Ed.)

284. (a) Erika Duncan, A Mathematician Who Asks Questions Without Answers (Arvind Borde profile). New York Times, Apr 20, 1997

(b) Borde, Arvind, Guth, Alan H. & Vilenkin, Alexander; Inflationary Spacetimes Are Incomplete in Past Directions. Physical Review Letters 90:15, 151301 (2003)

285. (a) Carroll, Sean M. & Chen, Jennifer (2004), Spontaneous Inflation and the Origin of the Arrow of Time. arXiv:hep-th/0410270

(b) Vilenkin, A., Arrows of time and the beginning of the universe. Physical Review D, 88:4, 043516 (2013)

(c) Mithani, A. & Vilenkin, A. (2012), Did the universe have a beginning? arXiv:1204.4658 [hep-th]

(d) Jacqueline Mitchell, In the Beginning Was the Beginning. Tufts University, May 29, 2012

286. (a) Paul Davies, Yes, the universe looks like a fix. But that doesn't mean that a god fixed it. The Guardian, 26 Jun 2007

(b) Paul Halpern, The Big Bang's Identity Crisis. PBS Nova, May 30, 2014

(c) Paul Davies, A Brief History of the Multiverse. New York Times, Apr 12, 2003

287. (a) Momen, Arshad & Rahman, Rakibur (2011), Spacetime Dimensionality from de Sitter Entropy. arXiv:1106.4548 [hep-th]

(b) Pourhasan, R., Afshordi, N. & Mann, R.B.; Out of the White Hole: A Holographic Origin for the Big Bang. Journal of Cosmology and Astroparticle Physics 04, 005 (2014)

288. (a) University of Cambridge, Taming the multiverse: Stephen Hawking's final theory about the big bang. Cambridge Research News, 2 May 2018

(b) Hawking, S. W. & Hertog, T.; A smooth exit from eternal inflation? J of H E Physics, 2018, 147 (2018)

289. (a) Avery Thompson, In 1928, One Physicist Accidentally Predicted Antimatter. Popular Mechanics, Jun 23, 2017

(b) R. Michael Barnett & Helen Quinn; What is antimatter? Scientific American, Jan 24, 2002

(c) Lisa Zyga, Antimatter gravity could explain Universe's expansion. Phys.org, Apr 13, 2011

290. (a) Kapteyn, Jacobus C., First Attempt at a Theory of the Arrangement and Motion of the Sidereal System. Astrophysical Journal, 55, 302 (1922)

(b) Oort, Jan H., The force exerted by the stellar system in the direction perpendicular to the galactic plane and some related problems. Bulletin of the Astronomical Institutes of the Netherlands, 6, 249 (1932)

(c) ibid. Full paper and pdf download available online.

(d) Zwicky, Fritz, On the Masses of Nebulae and of Clusters of Nebulae. Astrophysical J., 86, .217 (1937)

291. Trimble, Virginia, Existence and Nature of Dark Matter in the Universe. Annual Review of Astronomy and Astrophysics, 25, 425-472 (1987)

292. (a) Rubin, Vera C. & Ford, W. Kent, Jr., Rotation of the Andromeda Nebula from a Spectroscopic Survey of Emission Regions. Astrophysical Journal, 159, 379–403 (1970)

(b) Freeman, K.C., On the Disks of Spiral and S0 Galaxies. Astrophysical Journal, 160, 811 (1970)

(c) de Swart, J., Bertone, G. & van Dongen, J.; How dark matter came to matter. Nat Astr 1, 0059 (2017)

293. Einstein, Albert, Lens-Like Action Of A Star By The Deviation Of Light In The Gravitational Field. Science 84:2188, 506-507 (1936)

294. (a) Walsh, D., Carswell, R. & Weymann, R.; "0957 + 561 A, B: twin quasistellar objects or gravitational lens?". Nature 279, 381–384 (1979)

(b) Scranton, R., Ménard, B. et al; Detection of Cosmic Magnification with the Sloan Digital Sky Survey. The Astrophysical Journal, 633:2, 589-602 (2005)

(c) Michael Schirber, Seeing the Universe with Einstein's Glasses. Space.com, May 03, 2005

(d) Sloan Digital Sky Survey. "SDSS Uses 200,000 Quasars to Confirm Einstein's Prediction of Cosmic Magnification." ScienceDaily, 18 May 2005

295. (a) Garrett, K. & Duda, G.; "Dark Matter: A Primer". Adv. in Astronomy, 2011, article ID 968283 (2011)

(b) Randall, Lisa, What Is Dark Matter? Nature 557, S6-S7 (2018)

(c) Duffy, L.D. & van Bibber, K..; Axions as dark matter particles. New J. of Physics, 11, 105008 (2009)

(d) Kamionkowski, Marc (1997), WIMP and Axion Dark Matter. arXiv:hep-ph/9710467

296. (a) Brown University. "Dark matter search: New calibration confirms LUX dark matter results." ScienceDaily, 20 Feb 2014

(b) Ian Sample, Dark matter stays hidden as detector fails to see a single particle. The Guardian, Wed 30 Oct 2013

(c) University of California, Los Angeles. "Possible evidence for dark matter particle presented at UCLA physics symposium." ScienceDaily, 10 Mar 2014

297. (a) Liz Kruesi, The Case for Complex Dark Matter. James Bullock interview. Quanta, Aug 20, 2015

(b) Wechsler, Risa H. & Tinker, Jeremy L.; The Connection Between Galaxies and Their Dark Matter Halos. Annual Review of Astronomy and Astrophysics 56:1, 435-487 (2018)

(c) Karukes, E.V. & Salucci, P.; The universal rotation curve of dwarf disc galaxies. Monthly Notices of the Royal Astronomical Society 465:4, 4703–4722 (2017)

(d) Sissa Medialab. "Beyond the standard model through 'mini spirals'." ScienceDaily, 15 Dec 2016

298. (a) Bœhm, C., Schewtschenko, J.A.. et al.; Using the Milky Way satellites to study interactions between cold dark matter and radiation. Monthly Notices of the Royal Astr Soc: Letters 445:1, L31–L35 (2014)

(b) Royal Astronomical Society, "Interactions between Cold Dark Matter and Radiation Leads to a Dramatic Reduction in Satellite Galaxies". SciTechDaily, Sep 9, 2014

299. (a) Milgrom, Mordehai, A modification of the Newtonian dynamics as a possible alternative to the hidden mass hypothesis. Astrophysical Journal, 270, 365-370 (1983)

(b) Milgrom, Mordehai, A modification of the Newtonian dynamics - Implications for galaxies. Astrophysical Journal, 270, 371-383 (1983)

(c) Milgrom, Mordehai, A modification of the Newtonian dynamics: implications for galaxy systems. Astrophysical Journal, 270, 384-389 (1983)

300. (a) Famaey, Benoit & Binney, James; Modified Newtonian dynamics in the Milky Way. Monthly Notices of the Royal Astronomical Society 363:2, 603–608 (2005)

(b) Kravtsov, Andrey V. & Borgani, Stefano; Formation of Galaxy Clusters. Annual Review of Astronomy and Astrophysics 50:1, 353-409 (2012)

(c) Bautz, L.P. & Morgan, W.W.; On the Classification of the Forms of Clusters of Galaxies. Astrophysical Journal, 162, L149 (1970)

301. (a) Bekenstein, Jacob & Milgrom, Mordehai; Does the missing mass problem signal the breakdown of Newtonian gravity? Astrophysical Journal Part 1 (ISSN 0004-637X), 286, 7-14 (1984)

(b) Bekenstein, Jacob D., Relativistic gravitation theory for the modified Newtonian dynamics paradigm. Physical Review D 70:8, 083509 (2004)

(c) Nieuwenhuizen, Theodorus M., How Zwicky already ruled out modified gravity theories without dark matter. Fortschritte der Physik (Progress of Physics) 65:6-8, 1600050 (2017)

302. (a) McGaugh, Stacy S. and de Blok, W.J.G.; Testing the Hypothesis of Modified Dynamics with Low Surface Brightness Galaxies and Other Evidence. The Astrophysical Journal 499:1, 66 (1998)

(b) McGaugh, Stacy S., Milky Way Mass Models and MOND. The Astrophysical Journal 683:1, 137 (2008)

(c) McGaugh, Stacy S., Novel Test of Modified Newtonian Dynamics with Gas Rich Galaxies. Physical Review Letters 106:12, 121303 (2011)

(d) McGaugh, Stacy S., A tale of two paradigms: the mutual incommensurability of LCDM and MOND. Canadian Journal of Physics,. 93:2, 250-259 (2015)

(e) Sanders, Robert H., A historical perspective on modified Newtonian dynamics. Canadian Journal of Physics 93:2, 126-138 (2015)

303. (a) McGaugh, Stacy S., Lelli, Federico & Schombert, James M.; Radial Acceleration Relation in Rotationally Supported Galaxies. Physical Review Letters 117:20, 201101 (2016)

(b) Kosowsky, Arthur, Connecting the Bright and Dark Sides of Galaxies. Viewpoint, Physics 9, 130 (2016)

(c) Case Western Reserve University. "In rotating galaxies, distribution of normal matter precisely determines gravitational acceleration." ScienceDaily, 21 Sep 2016

304. (a) Markevitch, M., Gonzalez, A.H., Clowe, D. et al.; Direct Constraints on the Dark Matter Self-Interaction Cross Section from the Merging Galaxy Cluster 1E 0657–56. Astrophy J. 606:2, 819-824 (2004)

(b) Clowe, D., Gonzalez, A. & Markevitch, M.; Weak-Lensing Mass Reconstruction of the Interacting Cluster 1E 0657–558: Direct Evidence for the Existence of Dark Matter*. Astrophy J. 604:2, 596-603 (2004)

(c) Robert Roy Britt, Colossal Cosmic Collision Reveals Mysterious Dark Matter. Space.com, Aug 21, 2006

305. (a) Moffat, John W., Scalar–tensor–vector gravity theory. J of Cos and Astr Physics 2006:3, 004 (2006)

(b) Brownstein, J.R. and Moffat, J.W.; The Bullet Cluster 1E0657-558 evidence shows modified gravity in the absence of dark matter. Monthly Notices of the Royal Astronomical Society 382:1, 29–47 (2007)

(c) Ker Than, Scientists Say Dark Matter Doesn't Exist. Space.com, Oct 29, 2007

(d) Pavel Kroupa, Has dogma derailed the scientific search for dark matter? Aeon, 25 Nov 2016

306. (a) Landauer, Rolf, Irreversibility and Heat Generation in the Computing Process. IBM Journal of Research and Development 5:3, 183-191 (1961)

(b) Bennett, Charles H., Notes on Landauer's principle, reversible computation, and Maxwell's Demon. Studies in History and Philosophy of Modern Physics 34:3, 501-510 (2003)

(c) Vaccaro, Joan A. & Barnett, Stephen M.; Information erasure without an energy cost. Proceedings of the Royal Society A 467:2130, 1770–1778 (2011)

307. (a) Bérut, A., Arakelyan, A., Petrosyan, A. et al.; Experimental verification of Landauer's principle linking information and thermodynamics. Nature 483, 187–189 (2012)

(b) Bérut, A., Petrosyan, A. & Ciliberto, S.; Information and thermodynamics: experimental verification of Landauer's Erasure principle. J. of Statistical Mechanics: Theory and Experiment 2015:6, P06015 (2015)

308. (a) López-Suárez, M., Neri, I. & Gammaitoni, L.; Sub-kBT micro-electromechanical irreversible logic gate. Nature Communications 7, 12068 (2016)

(b) University of Perugia, Computing study refutes famous claim that 'information is physical'. Phys.org, Jul 11, 2016

(c) Peterson J.P.S., Sarthour R.S., Souza A.M. et al.; Experimental demonstration of information to energy conversion in a quantum system at the Landauer limit. Proc of the Royal Soc A 472:2188, 20150813 (2016)

(d) Emily Conover, Information is physical, even in quantum systems, study suggests. Erasing information in qubits produces heat, as predicted by Landauer's principle. ScienceNews, Apr 19, 2016

309. (a) Yan, L.L., Xiong, T.P., Rehan, K. et al.; Single-Atom Demonstration of the Quantum Landauer Principle. Physical Review Letters 120:21, 210601 (2018)

(b) Esposito, M., Landauer Principle Stands up to Quantum Test. Viewpoint, Physics 11, 49 (2018)

310. (a) Frank, Michael P., Throwing computing into reverse. IEEE Spectrum 54:9, 32-37 (2017)

(b) ibid. Full paper and pdf download available online.

311. (a) Vopson, M.M., The mass-energy-information equivalence principle. AIP Advances 9:9, 095206 (2019)

(b) P. Perry, There is no dark matter. Instead, information has mass, physicist says. Big Think, 21 Jan, 2020

(c) Gough, M. Paul, Information Equation of State. Entropy 10:3, 150-159 (2008)

(d) Clara Moskowitz, What's 96 Percent of the Universe Made Of? Astronomers Don't Know. Space.com, May 12, 2011

312. (a) Astier, Pierre and Pain, Reynald; Observational evidence of the accelerated expansion of the Universe. Comptes Rendus Physique 13:6-7, 521–538 (2012)

(b) Huterer, Dragan & Turner, Michael S.; Prospects for probing the dark energy via supernova distance measurements. Physical Review D 60:8, 081301 (1999)

(c) Adam Mann, What Is Dark Energy? Live Science, Aug 21, 2019

(d) Albrecht, A., Bernstein, G., Cahn, R. et al. (2006); Report of the Dark Energy Task Force. arXiv:astro-ph/0609591

313. Kragh, Helge, Preludes to dark energy: zero-point energy and vacuum speculations. Archive for History of Exact Sciences 66:3, 199–240 (2012)

314. (a) Peebles, P.J.E. & Ratra, Bharat; The cosmological constant and dark energy. Reviews of Modern Physics 75:2, 559–606 (2003)

(b) Adam Mann, What is the cosmological constant? Live Science, Feb 16, 2021

(c) University of Arizona, "Dark energy alternatives to Einstein are running out of room." ScienceDaily, 9 Jan 2013

(d) Martel, Hugo, Shapiro, Paul R. & Weinberg, Steven; Likely Values of the Cosmological Constant. The Astrophysical Journal 492:1, 29-40 (1998)

315. (a) Mattsson, Teppo, Dark energy as a mirage. General Relativity and Gravitation 42:3, 567–599 (2010)

(b) Ishak, Mustapha, Peel, Austin & Troxel, M.A.; Stringent Restriction from the Growth of Large-Scale Structure on Apparent Acceleration in Inhomogeneous Cosmological Models. Physical Review Letters 111:25, 251302 (2013)

(c) Schirber, Michael, Lumpy Universe Called into Question. Synopsis: Physics 6, s160 (2013)

(d) Amanda Siegfried, Study finds 'lumpy' universe cannot explain cosmic acceleration. University of Texas at Dallas via Phys.org, Jun 19, 2014

316. (a) Space Telescope Science Institute (STScI), "The universe is expanding even faster than expected." ScienceDaily, 2 Jun 2016

(b) Johns Hopkins University, "New Hubble measurements confirm universe is expanding faster than expected." ScienceDaily, 25 Apr 2019

317. (a) Carroll, Sean M., Quintessence and the Rest of the World: Suppressing Long-Range Interactions. Physical Review Letters 81:15, 3067–3070 (1998)

(b) Jean Tate, Quintessence. Universe Today, Nov 24, 2009

(c) Basilakos, Spyros & Solà, Joan; Effective equation of state for running vacuum: 'mirage' quintessence and phantom dark energy. Monthly Notices of the Royal Astronomical Society 437:4, 3331–3342 (2014)

(d) Plataforma SINC, "Dark energy hides behind phantom fields". ScienceDaily, 26 Mar 2014

318. (a) Royal Astronomical Society (RAS), "Dark energy is real, say astronomers". ScienceDaily, 12 Sep 2012

(b) Gregg Easterbrook, The Revolutionary Ideas of Nobelist Adam Riess. The Atlantic, Oct 4 2011

319. (a) Arbey, Alexandre (2005), Is it possible to consider Dark Energy and Dark Matter as a same and unique Dark Fluid? arXiv:astro-ph/0506732

(b) Arbey, Alexandre, Dark Fluid: a complex scalar field to unify dark energy and dark matter. Physical Review D 74:4, 043516 (2006)

(c) Arbey, Alexandre, Cosmological constraints on unifying Dark Fluid models.
The Open Astronomy Journal 8:1, 27-38 (2008)

(d) Michael Schirber, New Cosmic Theory Unites Dark Forces. Space.com, Feb 11, 2008

320. (a) Science and Technology Facilities Council, "Dark Fluid: Dark Matter And Dark Energy May Be Two Faces Of Same Coin." ScienceDaily, 01 Feb 2008

(b) Gentile, G., Famaey, B., Zhao, H. et al.; Universality of galactic surface densities within one dark halo scale-length. Nature 461, 627–628 (2009)

(c) University of St. Andrews, "Is Unknown Force In Universe Acting On Dark Matter?" ScienceDaily, 23 Oct 2009

321. (a) Farnes, Jamie S., A unifying theory of dark energy and dark matter: Negative masses and matter creation within a modified ΛCDM framework. Astronomy & Astrophysics 620, A92 (2018)

(b) University of Oxford, "Bringing balance to the universe: New theory could explain missing 95 percent of the cosmos." ScienceDaily, 5 Dec 2018

322. (a) Maeder, Andre, Dynamical Effects of the Scale Invariance of the Empty Space: The Fall of Dark Matter? The Astrophysical Journal 849:2, 158 (2017)

(b) Université de Genève, "Dark matter and dark energy: Do they really exist?." ScienceDaily, 22 Nov 2017

323. (a) Hal Hodson, Chameleons and holograms: Dark energy hunt gets weird. New Scientist, 3 Sep 2014

(b) Ahmed, Nasr & Kamel, Tarek M.; Note on dark energy and cosmic transit in a scale-invariance cosmology. International Journal of Geometric Methods in Modern Physics 18:5, 2150070 (2021)

324. (a) Max Planck Society, Black holes theorized in the 18th century. Phys.org, Apr 11, 2017

(b) Nola Taylor Redd & Meghan Bartels, Einstein's theory of general relativity. Space.com, Jun 04, 2021

(c) Schwarzschild, Karl, On the gravitational field of a mass point according to Einstein's theory (1916). Prussian Academy of Sciences Berlin (Math.Phys.), 189-196. arXiv:physics/9905030

(d) Schwarzschild, Karl, On the gravitational field of a sphere of incompressible fluid according to Einstein's theory (1916). Prussian Acad of Sciences Berlin (Math.Phys.), 424-434. arXiv:physics/9912033

325. (a) Nola Taylor Redd, White dwarfs: Compact corpses of stars. Space.com, Oct 11, 2018

(b) Chandrasekhar, S., The Highly Collapsed Configurations of a Stellar Mass (Second Paper). Monthly Notices of the Royal Astronomical Society 95:3, 207–225 (1935)

(c) Arthur I Miller, "S Chandrasekhar: the student who took on the world's top astrophysicist". The Guardian, 19 Oct 2017

(d) Brian Resnick, Subrahmanyan Chandrasekhar explained what happens when humongous stars die. Vox, Oct 19, 2017

(e) Nola Taylor Redd, What Are Black Holes? Space.com, Jul 11, 2019

326. (a) Charles Q. Choi, What Exactly Is a Black Hole Event Horizon (and What Happens There)? Space.com, Apr 09, 2019

(b) Paul Sutter, Black holes: The darkest objects in the universe. Live Science, Apr 08, 2021

(c) Almheiri, A., Marolf, D., Polchinski, J. & Sully, J. (2012); Black Holes: Complementarity or Firewalls? arXiv:1207.3123 [hep-th]

327. (a) Goss, W.M., Brown, R.L. & Lo, K.Y.; The Discovery of Sgr A*. Astro. Notes 324:S1, 497-504 (2003)

(b) Clara Moskowitz, Scientists Closing in on Black Hole at Center of Our Galaxy. Space.com, Apr 05, 2012

(c) Diane Lincoln, Our galaxy's supermassive black hole is closer to Earth than we thought. Live Science, Dec 20, 2020

(d) Charles Q. Choi, The strangest black holes in the universe. Space.com, Jul 08, 2013

328. (a) Pilbratt, G.L., Riedinger, J.R., Passvogel, T. et al; Herschel Space Observatory - An ESA facility for far-infrared and submillimetre astronomy. Astronomy & Astrophysics 518, L1 (2010)

(b) Natalie Wolchover, 'Infinity Symbol' Found at Center of Milky Way. Space.com, Jul 26, 2011

(c) Carole Mundell, Astronomers to peer into a black hole for first time with new Event Horizon Telescope. The Conversation, Mar 17, 2017

(d) Doris Elin Urrutia, The Event Horizon Telescope Is Trying to Take the First-Ever Photo of a Black Hole. Space.com, Apr 08, 2019

329. (a) The Event Horizon Telescope Collaboration et al., First M87 Event Horizon Telescope Results. I. The Shadow of the Supermassive Black Hole. The Astrophysical Journal Letters 875, L1 (2019)

(b) Clery, D., Cho, A. & Normile, D.; For the first time, you can see what a black hole looks like. Science, Apr 10, 2019

(c) Massachusetts Institute of Technology. "Working together as a 'virtual telescope,' observatories around the world produce first direct images of a black hole: Images reveal supermassive black hole at the heart of the Messier 87 galaxy.." ScienceDaily, 10 Apr 2019

(d) Alister Graham, Black holes are even stranger than you can imagine. The Conversation, Feb 10, 2017

330. (a) Curiel, Erik, The many definitions of a black hole. Nature Astronomy 3, 27–34 (2019)

(b) Cho, Adrian, After decades of effort, scientists are finally seeing black holes—or are they? Science, Jan 7, 2021

(c) Curiel, Erik, "Singularities and Black Holes", Stanford Encyclopedia of Philosophy (Spring 2021 Ed.)

(d) Zoë Macintosh, What's at the Center of Black Holes? Live Science, Jun 22, 2010

331. (a) Plato, A.D.K., Hughes, C.N. & Kim, M.S.; Gravitational effects in quantum mechanics. Contemporary Physics 57:4, 477-495 (2016)

(b) Charlie Wood, What Is Quantum Gravity? Space.com, Aug 27, 2019

(c) Clara Moskowitz, Black Holes: Everything You Think You Know Is Wrong. Space.com, Aug 02, 2012

(d) Natalie Wolchover, Have Three Little Photons Broken Theoretical Physics? Live Science, Aug 30, 2012

332. (a) Ashtekar, Abhay & Bianchi, Eugenio; A short review of loop quantum gravity. Reports on Progress in Physics 84:4, 042001 (2021)

(b) Bianconi, Ginestra & Rahmede, Christoph; Complex Quantum Network Manifolds in Dimension d>2 are Scale-Free. Scientific Reports 5, 13979 (2015)

(c) Queen Mary, University of London, "Understanding of complex networks could help unify gravity and quantum mechanics: When the understanding of complex networks such as the brain or the Internet is applied to geometry the results match up with quantum behavior." ScienceDaily, 10 Sep 2015

(d) Ashtekar, Abhay, Gravity and the quantum. New Journal of Physics 7, 198 (2005)

333. (a) Gambini, Rodolfo and Pullin, Jorge; Loop Quantization of the Schwarzschild Black Hole. Physical Review Letters 110:21, 211301 (2013)

(b) Clara Moskowitz, Space-Time Loops May Explain Black Holes. Space.com, Jul 10, 2013

334. (a) Gambini, Rodolfo & Pullin, Jorge (2020), Loop Quantum Gravity for Everyone. World Scientific, ISBN: 978-981-121-196-6

(b) Max Planck Society, Black holes theorized in the 18th century. Phys.org, Apr 11, 2017

(c) Nikitin, Igor (2021), On dark stars, Planck cores and the nature of dark matter. arXiv:2102.07769

335. (a) Mike Wall, Scientists Find 13 Mysterious Deep-Space Flashes, Including 2nd Known 'Repeater'. Space.com, Jan 09, 2019

(b) Tim Childers, Black Holes May Not Be Black. Or Even Holes. Their true nature could finally explain the origins of dark matter and fast radio bursts. Popular Mechanics, Mar 18, 2021

336. (a) Bañados, E., Venemans, B., Mazzucchelli, C. et al. An 800-million-solar-mass black hole in a significantly neutral Universe at a redshift of 7.5. Nature 553, 473–476 (2018)

(b) Glikman, Eliat, A beacon at the dawn of the Universe. Nature 553, 410-411 (2018)

(c) Charles Q. Choi, Oldest Monster Black Hole Ever Found Is 800 Million Times More Massive Than the Sun. Space.com, Dec 06, 2017

337. (a) Chesler, Paul M., Narayan, Ramesh & Curiel, Erik (2019), Singularities in Reissner-Nordström black holes. arXiv:1902.08323 [gr-qc]

(b) Steve Nadis, Black Hole Singularities Are as Inescapable as Expected. Quanta, Dec 2, 2019

338. (a) Wilkins, D.R., Gallo, L.C., Costantini, E. et al. Light bending and X-ray echoes from behind a supermassive black hole. Nature 595, 657–660 (2021)

(b) Ben Turner, Light from behind a black hole spotted for 1st time, proving Einstein right. Live Science, 29 Jul 2021

(c) Stanford University, "First detection of light from behind a black hole." ScienceDaily, 28 Jul 2021

339. (a) Bill Andrews, White holes: Do black holes have mirror images? Astronomy, Jun 28, 2019

(b) Charlie Wood, White Holes: Black Holes' Neglected Twins. Space.com, Jun 10, 2019

(c) M.Francis, "White Holes" Could Exist—But That Doesn't Mean They Do. Nautilus, May 2, 2014

340. (a) Andreea Font, Wormholes may be lurking in the universe – and new studies are proposing ways of finding them. The Conversation, Jan 13, 2021

(b) Einstein, Albert and Rosen, Nathan; The Particle Problem in the General Theory of Relativity. Physical Review 48:1,73-77 (1935)

(c) Poplawski, N.J., Radial motion into an Einstein–Rosen bridge. Physics Letters B 687:2–3, 110-113 (2010)

(d) Charles Q. Choi, Our Universe Was Born in a Black Hole, Theory Says. Space.com, Apr 27, 2010

(e) Poplawski, Nikodem J., Cosmology with torsion: An alternative to cosmic inflation. Physics Letters B 694:3, 181-185 (2010)

341. (a) Retter, A. & Heller, S.; The revival of White Holes as Small Bangs. New Astronomy 17:2, 73-75 (2012)

(b) Haggard, Hal M. & Rovelli, Carlo; Quantum-gravity effects outside the horizon spark black to white hole tunneling. Physical Review D 92:10, 104020 (2015)

(c) Charles Q. Choi, 'White Holes' May Be the Secret Ingredient in Mysterious Dark Matter. Space.com, Apr 27, 2018

(d) Bardeen, James M. (2018), Models for the nonsingular transition of an evaporating black hole into a white hole. arXiv:1811.06683 [gr-qc]

342. (a) Hoefer, Carl, "Causal Determinism", Stanford Encyclopedia of Philosophy (Spring 2016 Ed.)

(b) 't Hooft, Gerard (2001), How Does God Play Dice? (Pre-)Determinism at the Planck Scale. arXiv:hep-th/0104219

343. (a) Senovilla, José M.M. & Garfinkle, David; The 1965 Penrose singularity theorem. Classical and Quantum Gravity 32:12, 124008 (2015)

(b) Natalie Wolchover, Where Gravity Is Weak and Naked Singularities Are Verboten. Quanta, Jun 20, 2017

(c) Hawking, Stephen William and Penrose, Roger; The singularities of gravitational collapse and cosmology. Proceedings of The Royal Society of London A, 314:1519, 529–548 (1970)

(d) Landsman, Klaas, Singularities, Black Holes, and Cosmic Censorship: A Tribute to Roger Penrose. Foundations of Physics 51, 42, (2021)

344. (a) Klainerman, S., Rodnianski, I. & Szeftel, J.; The bounded L2 curvature conjecture. Inventiones Mathematicae 202, 91–216 (2015)

(b) CNRS, "A breakthrough on the mathematical understanding of Einstein's equations." ScienceDaily, 14 Oct 2015

345. (a) Israel, W., Event Horizons in Static Vacuum Space-Times. Physical Review 164:5, 1776-1779 (1967)

(b) Hamish Johnston, Black hole is hairless, reveals analysis of gravitational waves. Physics World, 17 Sep 2019

346. (a) Bekenstein, Jacob D., Black holes and the second law. Lettere al Nuovo Cimento 4, 737–740 (1972)

(b). ibid. Full paper and pdf download available online

(c) Bekenstein, Jacob D., Black Holes and Entropy. Physical Review D 7:8, 2333-2346 (1973).

347. (a) Jennifer Ouellette, In Memoriam: Jacob Bekenstein (1947–2015) and Black Hole Entropy. Scientific American, Aug 17, 2015

(b) Marianne Freiberger, The limits of information. University of Cambridge Plus Magazine, Nov 3, 2014

(c) Bousso, Raphael (2018), Black hole entropy and the Bekenstein bound. arXiv:1810.01880 [hep-th]

348. (a) Zel'dovich, Yakov B. (1974), Creation of particles in cosmology. In: Confrontation of cosmological theories with observational data; Proc. of the Symposium, Krakow, Poland, Sep 1973. (A75-21826 08-90)

(b) ibid. Full paper and pdf download available online.

349. (a) Hawking, Stephen W., Black hole explosions? Nature 248, 30–31 (1974)

(b) Hawking, Stephen W., Particle creation by black holes. Comm. in Math. Physics 43:3, 199–220 (1975)

(c) Traschen, Jennie (2000), An Introduction to Black Hole Evaporation. arXiv:gr-qc/0010055

(d) Carlip, S., Black hole thermodynamics. International J. of Modern Physics D 23:11, 1430023 (2014)

350. (a) Paul Sutter, What Is the Black Hole Information Paradox? Space.com, Jun 06, 2019

(b) Dennis Overbye, Hawking's Breakthrough Is Still an Enigma. New York Times, Jan 22, 2002

(c) 't Hooft, Gerard, On the quantum structure of a black hole. Nuclear Physics B, 256, 727-745 (1985)

(d) Susskind, Leonard, Black Holes and the Information Paradox. Scientific American 276:4, 52-57 (1997)

351. (a) John Preskill, Black hole information bet with Stephen Hawking and Kip Thorne. Caltech, 6 Feb 1997

(b) Hawking, Stephen W., Information Loss in Black Holes. Physical Review D 72:8, 084013 (2005)

(c) Charles Seife, Cosmic Wager Conceded. Stephen Hawking now says that information swallowed by black holes can get spit back out. Science Magazine, Jul 21, 2004

(d) Jennifer Ouellette, Why Stephen Hawking's Black Hole Puzzle Keeps Puzzling. Quanta, Mar 14, 2018

352. (a) Preskill, John (1992), Do Black Holes Destroy Information? arXiv:hep-th/9209058

(b) Natalie Wolchover, Why Black Hole Interiors Grow (Almost) Forever. Quanta, Dec 6, 2018

(c) Barbón, J.L.F., Black holes, information and holography. J of Physics: Conf. Series 171, 012009 (2009)

353. (a) Paul Rincon, "Hawking: Black holes store information". BBC News, 26 Aug 2015

(b) Stephens, C.R., 't Hooft, G. & Whiting, B.F.; Black hole evaporation without information loss. Classical and Quantum Gravity 11:3, 621-647 (1994)

(c) Susskind, Leonard, The World as a Hologram. Journal of Maths and Physics 36, 6377 (1995)

(d) Gogberashvili, M. & Midodashvili, P.; Localization of fields on a brane in six dimensions. Europhysics Letters (EPL) 61:3, 308-313 (2003)

354. (a) Maldacena, J.; The Large-N Limit of Superconformal Field Theories and Supergravity. International Journal of Theoretical Physics 38, 1113–1133 (1999)

(b) Natalie Wolchover, Why Is M-Theory the Leading Candidate for Theory of Everything? Quanta, Dec 18, 2017

(c) Bekenstein, Jacob D., Information in the Holographic Universe. Sci. Am.. special ed. 17, 66-73 (2007)

(d) Jaime Trosper, The Holographic Universe Principle. Futurism, 13 Dec 2013

355. (a) Caldarelli, M.M., Camps, J., Goutéraux, B. & Skenderis, K.; AdS/Ricci-flat correspondence and the Gregory-Laflamme instability. Physical Review D 87:6, 061502 (2013)

(b) University of Southampton, "New mathematical model links space-time theories." ScienceDaily, 30 May 2013

356. (a) Hyakutake, Yoshifumi, Quantum near-horizon geometry of a black 0-brane. Progress of Theoretical and Experimental Physics 2014:3, 033B04 (2014)

(b) Hanada, M., Hyakutake, Y., Ishiki, G. & Nishimura, Jun; Holographic description of quantum black hole on a computer. Science 344:6186, 882-885 (2014)

(c) Maldacena, J, Testing gauge/gravity duality on a quantum black hole. Science 344:6186, 806-807 (2014)

(d) Cowen, Ron, Simulations back up theory that Universe is a hologram. Nature (2013)

357. (a) Almheiri, A., Mahajan, R., Maldacena, J. & Zhao, Y. The Page curve of Hawking radiation from semiclassical geometry. Journal of High Energy Physics 2020, 149 (2020)

(b) Charlie Wood, Hologram Within a Hologram Hints at Fate of Black Holes. Quanta, Nov 19, 2019

358. (a) Verlinde, E., On the origin of gravity and the laws of Newton. J of High Energy Physics 2011, 29 (2011)

(b) Verlinde, Erik, Emergent Gravity and the Dark Universe. SciPost Physics 2:3, 016 (2017)

(c) Universiteit van Amsterdam (UVA), "New theory of gravity might explain dark matter." ScienceDaily, 8 Nov 2016

359. (a) Natalie Wolchover, The Case Against Dark Matter. Quanta, Nov 29, 2016

(b) Brouwer, M. M., Visser, M.R., Dvornik, A. et al.; First test of Verlinde's theory of emergent gravity using weak gravitational lensing measurements. M.N. of the Royal Astro. Soc . 466:3, 2547–2559 (2017)

(c) Hees, Aurélien, Famaey, Benoit & Bertone, Gianfranco; Emergent gravity in galaxies and in the Solar System. Physical Review D 95:6, 064019 (2017)

(d) Sabine Hossenfelder, Recent Claims Invalid: Emergent Gravity Might Deliver A Universe Without Dark Matter. Forbes, Feb 28, 2017

360. (a) Merali, Zeeya, Theoretical physics: The origins of space and time. Nature 500, 516–519 (2013)

(b) Afshordi, N., Corianò, C., Delle Rose, L. et al.; From Planck Data to Planck Era: Observational Tests of Holographic Cosmology. Physical Review Letters 118:4, 041301 (2017)

(c) Afshordi, Niayesh, Gould, Elizabeth & Skenderis, Kostas; Constraining holographic cosmology using Planck data. Physical Review D 95:12, 123505 (2017)

(d) University of Southampton, Study reveals substantial evidence of holographic universe. Phys.org, Jan 30, 2017

361. (a) Uffink, Jos, "Boltzmann's Work in Statistical Physics", The Stanford Encyclopedia of Philosophy (Spring 2017 Edition), Edward N. Zalta(ed.)

(b) Lebowitz, Joel L. (2008), Time's arrow and Boltzmann's entropy. Scholarpedia 3(4):3448

(c) Goldstein, Sheldon (2001), Boltzmann's Approach to Statistical Mechanics. arXiv:cond-mat/0105242

362. (a) Falcioni, Massimo & Vulpiani, Angelo; "Ludwig Boltzmann: a tribute on his 170th birthday". Lettera Matematica 2, 171–183 (2015)

(b) Albrecht, A. & Sorbo, L.; Can the universe afford inflation? Physical Review D 70:6, 063528 (2004)

(c) Amelia Settembre, Is The Boltzmann Brain Theory Plausible? Medium, Jan 19, 2020

363. (a) Paul Ratner, Are you a Boltzmann Brain? Why nothing in the Universe may be real. Big Think, 21 Oct, 2018

(b) Marianne Freiberger, Dreaming the dream. University of Cambridge Plus Magazine, Sep 24, 2014

(c) Nomura, Yasunori, A note on Boltzmann brains. Physics Letters B 749, 514-518 (2015)

(d) Olum, Ken D., Upadhyay, Param & Vilenkin, Alexander; Black holes and uptunneling suppress Boltzmann brains. Physical Review D 104:2, 023528 (2021)

364. (a) Amir Aczel, "The Higgs, Boltzmann Brains, and Monkeys Typing Hamlet". Discover, Oct 31, 2012

(b) Sean Carroll, On Templeton [Foundation]. Science and Religion Can't Be Reconciled. Preposterous Universe, May 08, 2013

(c) Sean Carroll, Boltzmann's Anthropic Brain. Preposterous Universe, Aug 01, 2006

365. (a) Carroll, Sean M. (2017), Why Boltzmann Brains Are Bad. arXiv:1702.00850 [hep-th]

(b) Anil Ananthaswamy, Universes that spawn 'cosmic brains' should go on the scrapheap. New Scientist, 15 Feb 2017

(c) Boddy, Kimberly K., Carroll, Sean M. & Pollack, Jason (2014); De Sitter Space Without Dynamical Quantum Fluctuations. arXiv:1405.0298 [hep-th]

(d) Sean Carroll, Squelching Boltzmann Brains (And Maybe Eternal Inflation). Preposterous Universe, May 05, 2014

(e) B. Koberlein, Can Many-Worlds Theory Rescue Us From Boltzmann Brains? Nautilus, Mar 05, 2018

366. (a) Berryman, Sylvia, "Ancient Atomism", The Stanford Encyclopedia of Philosophy (Winter 2016 Ed.)
   (b) Inwood, Brad, "Anaxagoras and Infinite Divisibility". Illinois Classical Studies 11:1-2, 17-33 (1986)
   (c) Emma Woolerton, Lucretius, Part 1: A poem to explain the entire world around us.
   The Guardian, 21 Jan 2013

367. (a) Thomson, John J., M.A. F.R.S., XL. Cathode Rays. The London, Edinburgh, and Dublin Philosophical
   Magazine and Journal of Science 5, 44:269, 293-316 (1897)
   (b) Strutt, R.J., "Joseph John Thomson, 1856 - 1940". Obituary Notices of F. Royal Soc 3, 587–609 (1941)

368. (a) Rutherford, E., F.R.S., "The scattering of a and ß particles by matter and the structure of the atom".
   The London, Edinburgh, and Dublin Philosophical Magazine and J of Science 6, 21:125, 669-688 (1911)
   (b) Geiger, Hans & Marsden, Ernest; The laws of deflexion of a particles through large angles.
   The London, Edinburgh, and Dublin Philosophical Magazine and J. of Science 6, 25:148, 604-623 (1913)

369. (a) Aston, Francis W., XLIV. The constitution of atmospheric neon. The London, Edinburgh, and Dublin
   Philosophical Magazine and Journal of Science 6, 39:232, 449-455 (1920)
   (b) Chadwick, James, Possible Existence of a Neutron. Nature 129, 312 (1932)
   (c) James Chadwick (1935), The Neutron and Its Properties. Nobel Prize in Physics Lecture, Dec 12, 1935

370. (a) Adam Mann, What Are Elementary Particles? Live Science, May 07, 2019
   (b) University of Cincinnati, "Fermions to bosons, bosons to fermions: Physicists develop formula that
   contradicts decades of published research." ScienceDaily, 14 Mar 2016
   (c) Jerald Pinson, Hundreds of hadrons. Symmetry (Fermilab/SLAC), Jun 30, 2020
   (d) Ball, Philip, Splitting the quark. Nature (2007)

371. (a) Rothman, Tony & Boughn, Stephen; Can Gravitons be Detected?.
   Foundations of Physics 36:12, 1801–1825 (2006)
   (b) Arizona State University, "Researchers propose a new way to detect the elusive graviton."
   ScienceDaily, 4 Mar 2014

372. (a) Friedrich, Bretislav & Herschbach, Dudley; "Stern and Gerlach: How a Bad Cigar Helped Reorient
   Atomic Physics". Physics Today 56:12, 53 (2003)
   (b) Paul Sutter, The Weird Quantum Property of 'Spin'. Space.com, Dec 19, 2017
   (c) Oscar Miyamoto Gomez, Nature through the looking glass. Symmetry (Fermilab/SLAC), Sep 22, 2020
   (d) Deepa, S., Bhargava Ram, B.S. & Senthilkumaran, P.; Helicity dependent diffraction by angular
   momentum transfer. Scientific Reports 9, 12491 (2019)

373. (a) Rafelski, Johann, Connecting QGP-Heavy Ion Physics to the Early Universe.
   Nuclear Physics B - Proceedings Supplements 243–244, 155-162 (2013)
   (b) Bengt Nagel, Award ceremony speech, The Nobel Prize in Physics 1979 (shared between Sheldon
   Glashow, Abdus Salam and Steven Weinberg). NobelPrize.org
   (c) Jonathan Carroll, Explainer: Standard Model of Particle Physics. The Conversation, Aug 25, 2011
   (d) Higgs, Peter, Prehistory of the Higgs boson. Comptes Rendus Physique 8:9, 970-972 (2007)

374. (a) Higgs, P.W., Broken Symmetries and the Masses of Gauge Bosons. Phy Rev Ltrs 13:16, 508-509 (1964)
   (b) Englert, François & Brout, Robert; Broken Symmetry and the Mass of Gauge Vector Mesons.
   Physical Review Letters 13:9,321-323 (1964)
   (c) Anna Phan, Explainer: the Higgs boson particle. The Conversation, Apr 14, 2011
   (d) Natalie Wolchover, Samuel Velasco & Lucy Reading-Ikkanda. A New Map of All the Particles and
   Forces. Quanta, Oct 22, 2020

375. (a) Ian Sample, "Father of the God particle: Portrait of Peter Higgs unveiled". The Guardian, 03 Mar 2009
   (b) Jakobs, Karl and Seez, Chris (2015), The Higgs Boson discovery. Scholarpedia 10(9):32413
   (c) Alekhin, S., Djouadi, A. & Moch, S.; The top quark and Higgs boson masses and the stability of the
   electroweak vacuum. Physics Letters B 716:1, 214-219 (2012)

376. (a) Sarah Charley, When was the Higgs actually discovered? Symmetry (Fermilab/SLAC), Jul 03, 2017
   (b) Brian Greene, How the Higgs Boson Was Found. Smithsonian Magazine, Jul 2013
   (c) University of S. Denmark. "Maybe it wasn't the Higgs particle after all." ScienceDaily, 07 Nov 2014
   (d) Gianotti F. & Virdee T. S.; The discovery and measurements of a Higgs boson.
   Philosophical Transactions of The Royal Society A, 373:2032, 03842014 (2015)
   (e) Louise Mayor, Why converge? Physicists meet to discuss lack of experimental support for the Standard
   Model of particle physics. Physics World, Jun 22, 2015

377. (a) Oscar Miyamoto Gomez, Five mysteries the Standard Model can't explain.
   Symmetry (Fermilab/SLAC), Oct 18, 2018
   (b) Fairbairn, Malcolm & Hogan, Robert; Electroweak Vacuum Stability in Light of BICEP2.
   Physical Review Letters 112:20, 201801 (2014)

(c) Royal Astronomical Society, "Should the Higgs boson have caused our Universe to collapse?" Phys.org, Jun 24, 2014

(d) Madeleine O'Keefe, Fine-tuning versus naturalness. Symmetry (Fermilab/SLAC), Jan 28, 2020

(e) Natalie Wolchover, Is Nature Unnatural? Quanta, May 24, 2013

378. (a) Matthew R. Francis, The mystery of particle generations. Why are there three almost identical copies of each particle of matter? Symmetry (Fermilab/SLAC), Aug 05, 2015

(b) Goldhaber, Maurice, A closer look at the elementary fermions. PNAS 99:1, 33-36 (2002)

(c) Karlsruhe Institute of Technology, "12 matter particles suffice in nature: Limited number of fermions in standard model, physicists say." ScienceDaily, 13 Dec 2012

(d) Ibe, M., Kusenko, A. & Yanagid, T.T.; Why three generations? Physics Letters B 758, 365-369 (2016)

379. (a) Weinberg, Steven, Models of lepton and quark masses. Physical Review D, 101:3, 035020 (2020)

(b) C. Wood, Why Do Matter Particles Come in Threes? A Physics Titan Weighs In. Quanta, Mar 30, 2020

380. (a) Ethan Siegel, The Greatest Unsolved Problem In Theoretical Physics. Medium, Dec 19, 2015

(b) Martin, S.P. (1998), A Supersymmetry Primer. Perspectives on Supersymmetry,. 1-98, ed. GL Kane

(c) Paul Sutter, Supersymmetry is super-awesome. Here's what it means for particle physics. Space.com, Feb 14, 2020

381. (a) Adam Mann, What Is the Large Hadron Collider? Live Science, Jan 29, 2019

(b) Natalie Wolchover, As Supersymmetry Fails Tests, Physicists Seek New Ideas. Quanta, Nov 20, 2012

(c) Ethan Siegel, Why Supersymmetry May Be The Greatest Failed Prediction In Particle Physics History. Forbes, Feb 12, 2019

(d) Paul Sutter, From squarks to gluinos: It's not looking good for supersymmetry. The future of the theory is in serious doubt. Space.com, Jan 07, 2021

(e) The ATLAS collaboration. Aad, G., Abbott, B. et al.; Search for squarks and gluinos in final states with jets and missing transverse momentum using 139 fb-1 of sv = 13 TeV pp collision data with the ATLAS detector. Journal of High Energy Physics 2021, 143 (2021)

382. (a) John H. Schwarz, String theory. According to string theory, matter is made up of strings. Symmetry (Fermilab/SLAC), May 01, 2007

(b) Ethan Siegel, What Every Layperson Should Know About String Theory. Forbes, Nov 25, 2016

(c) T.Ghose, Beyond Higgs: 5 Elusive Particles That May Lurk in the Universe. Live Science, Mar 22, 2013

(d) Charlie Wood, What Is String Theory? Space.com, Jul 11, 2019

(e) P. Sutter, Can M-theory bring the various string-theory candidates together? Space.com, 28 May 2020

(f) Natalie Wolchover, Why Is M-Theory the Leading Candidate for Theory of Everything? Quanta, Dec 18, 2017

383. (a) Margaret Wertheim, Radical dimensions. Relativity says we live in four dimensions. String theory says it's 10. What are 'dimensions' and how do they affect reality? Aeon, 10 Jan 2018

(b) Csáki, C. & Tanedo, P. (2015), Beyond the Standard Model. Proc. of European School of High-Energy Physics, Paradfurdo, Hungary, 5-18 Jun 2013. M. Mulders, G. Perez ed., CERN-2015-004

(c) Bars, Itzhak & Rychkov, Dmitry; Is string interaction the origin of quantum mechanics? Physics Letters B 739, 451-456 (2014)

(d) University of Southern California, "String field theory could be the foundation of quantum mechanics: Connection could be huge boost to string theory." ScienceDaily, 3 Nov 2014

384. (a) Glenn Starkman, The Standard Model of particle physics: The absolutely amazing theory of almost everything. The Conversation, May 23, 2018

(b) Sabine Hossenfelder, Is the Standard Model of Physics Now Broken? Scientific American, Apr 7, 2021

385. (a) John Emsley, Period drama: the story of the periodic table. The Guardian, 01 May 2008

(b) Szuromi, Phillip, Setting the table. Introduction to Special Issue: Periodic Table Turns 150. Science 363:6426, 464-465 (2019)

(c) Goudsmit, S.A. & Richards, Paul I.; The Order Of Electron Shells In Ionized Atoms. Proceedings of the National Academy of Sciences (PNAS) 51:4, 664-671 (1964)

386. (a) Rogers, Nala, Four new elements complete the seventh row of the periodic table. Science News (2016)

(b) Scerri, Eric, "Mendeleev's Periodic Table Is Finally Completed and What To Do about Group 3?" Chemistry International 34:4, 28-31 (2012)

(c) Helen Briggs, 150 years of the periodic table: Test your knowledge. BBC News, 29 Jan 2019

387. (a) Maddie Stone, There Is Growing Evidence that Our Universe Is a Giant Hologram. Vice, May 5, 2015

(b) The 2016 Isaac Asimov Memorial Debate: Is the Universe a Simulation? AMNH, 05 Apr 2016

(c) Clara Moskowitz, Are We Living in a Computer Simulation? Scientific American, Apr7, 2016

(d) Clara Moskowitz, Higgs Boson Particle May Spell Doom For the Universe. Live Science, Feb 19, 2013

388. (a) Kevin Loria, Neil deGrasse Tyson thinks there's a 'very high' chance the universe is just a simulation. Business Insider, Apr 21, 2016

(b) K. Loria, Why it's impossible to prove that we don't live in a simulation. Business Insider, Apr 08, 2016

389. (a) Ezra Klein, Elon Musk believes we are probably characters in some advanced civilization's video game. Vox, Jun 02, 2016

(b) Anna Maria Tremonti and Kristin Nelson, Are we living in a computer simulation? It's more likely than you might think, scientist argues. CBC Canada, The Current, Mar 26, 2018

(c) Rob Waugh, This is the clue that shows we are living in The Matrix, according to NASA scientist. Metro UK, 12 Oct 2016

(d) Olivia Solon, Is our world a simulation? Why some scientists say it's more likely than not. The Guardian, 11 Oct 2016

(e) Sam Kriss, Tech Billionaires Want to Destroy the Universe. Seriously. The Atlantic, Oct 13, 2016

390. (a) Neil deGrasse Tyson Explains the Simulation Hypothesis (video). Startalk, 17 Mar 2020

(b) Mark Harris, Inside the First Church of Artificial Intelligence. Wired, Nov 15, 2017

(c) Kirsten Korosec, Anthony Levandowski closes his Church of AI. TechCrunch, Feb 18, 2021

391. (a) Nicholson, Arwen & Forgan, Duncan. Slingshot dynamics for self-replicating probes and the effect on exploration timescales. International Journal of Astrobiology 12:4, 337-344 (2013)

(b) Lin Edwards, Self-replicating alien probes could already be here. Phys.org, Jul 19, 2013

(c) Benford, J., Looking for Lurkers: Co-orbiters as SETI Observables. Astronomical J 158:4, 150 (2019)

(d) Stephanie Pappas, Could E.T. Have Bugged a Space Rock to Listen In on Earthlings? Live Science, Sep 30, 2019

392. (a) Colombano, Silvano P. (2018), New Assumptions To Guide SETI Research. NASA Ames Research Center Moffett Field, CA, USA. SETI Decoding Alien Intelligence report no.ARC-E-DAA-TN53461

(b) "Undetectable" –NASA Suggests We May Be Blind to Signs of Alien Technologies'. The Daily Galaxy, Mar 23, 2019

(c) Caleb Scharf, Is Physical Law an Alien Intelligence? Nautilus, Nov 17, 2016

393. (a) Michael Segalov, Helen Sharman: 'There's no greater beauty than seeing the Earth from up high'. The Observer, 05 Jan 2020

(b) Samantha Rolfe, Could invisible aliens really exist among us? An astrobiologist explains. The Conversation, Jan 10, 2020

394. (a) Mindy Weisberger, Are UFOs a threat? We need to investigate, says former head of secret US program. Live Science, 11 Jul 2020

(b) D. Strauss, Pentagon releases three UFO videos taken by US Navy pilots. The Guardian, 28 Apr 2020

(c) Jonathan Marcus, Pentagon releases UFO videos for the record. BBC News, 28 Apr 2020

395. (a) Glattfelder, James B. (2019), A Universe Built of Information. In: Information-Consciousness-Reality (pp 473-514). The Frontiers Collection. Springer, Cham.

(b) Boston University College of Arts & Sciences, "Even professional scientists are compelled to see purpose in nature, psychologists find." ScienceDaily, 17 Oct 2012

(c) Hoyle, Fred, The Universe: Past and Present Reflections. Ann. Rev. Astro Astrophys 20:1, 1-36 (1982)

396. Saint Augustine, Bishop of Hippo, "The Confessions of Saint Augustine", Book XI (401 CE)

397. (a) Springer, "Timeless thoughts on the definition of time: On the evolution of how we have defined time, time interval and frequency since antiquity." ScienceDaily, 24 Mar 2016

(b) University of Helsinki, "What is time?." ScienceDaily, 15 Apr 2005

398. (a) Matt Williams, What is Absolute Space? Universe Today, Jul 4, 2011

(b) Rynasiewicz, Robert, "Newton's Views on Space, Time, and Motion", The Stanford Encyclopedia of Philosophy (Summer 2014 Edition), Edward N. Zalta (ed.)

(c) Dieks D. (1988), Newton's Conception of Time in Modern Physics and Philosophy. In: Scheurer P.B., Debrock G. (eds), Newton's Scientific and Philosophical Legacy pp. 151-159

(d) Valente, Mario Bacelar (2013), The flow of time in the theory of relativity. arXiv:1312.6653

399. (a) Proceedings of the Study Week on Cosmology and Fundamental Physics Sep 28 - Oct 2, 1981. Pontifical Academy of Sciences, Vatican City. H.A. Bruck, G.V. Coyne & M.S. Longair (eds).

(b) Hartle, J.B. & Hawking, S.W.; Wave function of the Universe. Phys Rev D 28:12, 2960--2975 (1983)

(c) Brandon Specktor, Stephen Hawking Says He Knows What Happened Before the Big Bang. Live Science, Mar 02, 2018

(d) Stephen W. Hawking (1996), The Beginning of Time. Lecture, Stephen Hawking Foundation

400. (a) Bojowald, Martin, Quantum cosmology: a review. Reports on Progress in Physics 78:2, 023901 (2015)

(b) Veneziano, G., The Myth Of The Beginning Of Time. Sci. American, Special ed., 16, 72-81 (2006)

(c) Page, Don N., Susskind's challenge to the Hartle–Hawking no-boundary proposal and possible resolutions. Journal of Cosmology and Astroparticle Physics 2007:01, 004 (2007)

    (d) Natalie Wolchover, Physicists Debate Hawking's Idea That the Universe Had No Beginning. Quanta, Jun 6, 2019

    (e) Stephen W. Hawking (2016), The Origin of Time. Presentation at the Vatican's Conference on Science and Sustainability, Nov 2016. Pontifical Academy of Sciences, Vatican City

401. (a) Graham, Daniel W., "Heraclitus", The Stanford Encyclopedia of Philosophy (Summer 2021 Ed.)

    (b) Palmer, John, "Parmenides", The Stanford Encyclopedia of Philosophy (Winter 2020 Ed.)

    (c) Mermin, N. David, Commentary: What I think about Now. Physics Today 67:3, (2014)

    (d) Brian Koberlein, The Emperor's New Clothes. Blog post, 06 Dec 2014

    (e) Brian Koberlein, Private Time. Blog post, 01 Feb 2013

402. (a) McTaggart, John M. Ellis, The Unreality of Time. Mind 17:4, 457–474 (1908)

    (b) Freeman, E., On Mctaggart's Theory Of Time. History of Philosophy Quarterly 27:4, 389-401 (2010)

    (c) McDaniel, Kris, "John M. E. McTaggart", Stanford Encyclopedia of Philosophy (Summer 2020 Ed.)

403. (a) Dan Falk, A Debate Over the Physics of Time. Quanta, Jul 19, 2016

    (b) Butterfield, J. (2002), Critical Notice: Book review, "The End of Time: The Next Revolution in Our Understanding of the Universe" by Julian Barbour. British J for the Phil. of Science 53:2, 289-330 (2002)

    (c) John Brockman, The End Of Time: A Talk With Julian Barbour. Edge, Aug 15, 1999

404. (a) Michael Brooks, The Country Gentleman of Physics. Nautilus, May 12, 2021

    (b) Jaffe, Andrew, The illusion of time. Book review, Carlo Rovelli's 'The Order of Time'. Books and Arts, Nature 556, 304-305 (2018)

    (c) Tim Radford, The Order of Time by Carlo Rovelli – no difference between past and future. The Guardian, 05 May 2018

405. (a) Lee Smolin (1995), A Theory Of The Whole Universe. Chap. 17 in The Third Culture by John Brockman. Edge, May 02, 1996

    (b) Lee Smolin and Stuart A. Kauffman (1997), A Possible Solution For The Problem Of Time In Quantum Cosmology (with an Introduction by John Brockman). Edge, April 06, 1997

    (c) Smolin, Lee (2013), Temporal naturalism. arXiv:1310.8539 [physics.hist-ph]

    (d) Clara Moskowitz, Controversially, Physicist Argues Time Is Real. Live Science, Apr 26, 2013

    (e) Zych, Magdalena, Costa, Fabio, Pikovski, Igor & Brukner, Caslav; Bell's theorem for temporal order. Nature Communications 10, 3772 (2019)

406. (a) A.Azvolinsky, Profile: Dean Buonomano Studies How the Brain Encodes Time. Scientist, Sep 1, 2016

    (b) Klopper, Abigail, The eternal question. Book review, "Your Brain Is a Time Machine: The Neuroscience and Physics of Time" by Dean Buonomano. Nature Physics 13, 621 (2017)

    (c) Thomas MacMillan, The Human Brain Is a Time Machine. Interview with Dean Buonomano. The Cut, Vox Media, Apr 25, 2017

    (d) Siegfried, Tom (2019), A quantum origin for spacetime. Knowable Magazine, Ann Rev, May 04, 2019

407. (a) Eddington, Arthur Stanley Sir (1928), The Nature of the Physical World. Open Library OL15026629M

    (b) Fernando Gallardo, The Arrow of Time. Medium, Jul 24, 2019

    (c) Gross, David J., The role of symmetry in fundamental physics. PNAS 93:25, 14256-14259 (1996)

    (d) Ebadi, Behrooz, Arrow of time: A physical concept with philosophical roots. International Journal of Fundamental Physical Sciences 9:3, 37-40 (2019)

    (e) Price, Huw (2013), Time's Arrow and Eddington's Challenge. In: Duplantier B. (ed), Progress in Mathematical Physics, vol 63, chapter, Time pp 187-215. Birkhäuser, Basel

408. (a) Tom Siegfried, Law & Disorder. Physicists keep trying to explain why time flows one way. Science News, Jun 4, 2010

    (b) Natalie Wolchover, Time's Arrow Traced to Quantum Source. Quanta, Apr 16, 2014

    (c) Bacciagaluppi, Guido (2007), Probability, Arrow of Time and Decoherence. arXiv:quant-ph/0701225

409. (a) Frank Wilczek, Time's (Almost) Reversible Arrow. Quanta, Jan 07, 2016

    (b) Oreshkov, Ognyan & Cerf, Nicolas; Operational formulation of time reversal in quantum theory. Nature Physics 11, 853–858 (2015)

    (c) Libre de Bruxelles, Université, "Arrow of time: New understanding of causality, free choice, and why we remember the past but not the future." ScienceDaily, 28 Jul 2015

410. (a) Vaccaro, Joan A., Quantum asymmetry between time and space. Proc. R. Soc A 472:2185, 0670 (2016)

    (b) Griffith University, "How we escaped the Big Bang: New theory on moving through time." ScienceDaily, 17 Aug 2016

411. (a) Peres, Asher, Delayed choice for entanglement swapping. J. of Modern Optics 47:2-3, 139-143 (2000)

(b) Ma, Xs., Zotter, S., Kofler, J. et al. Experimental delayed-choice entanglement swapping. Nature Physics 8, 479–484 (2012)

(c) University of Vienna. "Can future actions influence past events? Experiment mimics quantum physics 'spooky action into the past'." ScienceDaily, 23 Apr 2012

412. (a) Megidish, E., Halevy, A., Shacham, T. et al.; Entanglement Swapping between Photons that have Never Coexisted. Physical Review Letters 110:21, 210403 (2013)

(b) Elise Crull, You thought quantum mechanics was weird: check out entangled time. Aeon, 02 Feb 2018

(c) Frederica Russo and Phyllis Illari, Why causality now? Philosophical Theory meets Scientific Practice. Oxford University Press, Jan 18, 2015

413. (a) Zeeya Merali, Back From the Future. A series of quantum experiments shows that measurements performed in the future can influence the present. Discover, Aug 26, 2010

(b) Perlman, Mark, The Modern Philosophical Resurrection of Teleology. The Monist 87:1, 3-51 (2004)

(c) ibid. Full paper and pdf download available online

(d) Brian Koberlein, At Least There Is Symmetry. Blog post, 11 Jun 2015

(e) Brian Koberlein, Could The Present Ever Change The Past? Forbes, Jul 16, 2018

414. (a) Rachel Gutman, Could Quantum Computing Be the End of Free Will? The Atlantic, Jun 30, 2018

(b) George Ellis, From chaos to free will. Aeon, 09 Jun, 2020

415. (a) 't Hooft, Gerard (2014), The Cellular Automaton Interpretation of Quantum Mechanics. arXiv:1405.1548 [quant-ph]

(b) Forte, Stefano, The Cellular Automaton Interpretation of Quantum Mechanics. Book review. Physics Today 70:7, 60 (2017)

(c) 't Hooft, Gerard (2016), Interpreting Quantum Mechanics. In: The Cellular Automaton Interpretation of Quantum Mechanics. Fundamental Theories of Physics, vol 185. Springer, Cham

416. (a) Norsen, Travis & Price, Huw (2021), Lapsing Quickly into Fatalism: Bell on Backward Causation. arXiv:2102.02392 [quant-ph]

(b) Hossenfelder, Sabine & Palmer, Tim; Rethinking Superdeterminism. Frontiers in Physics 8, 139 (2020)

(c) Sabine Hossenfelder & Tim Palmer, How to Make Sense of Quantum Physics. Nautilus, Mar 12, 2020

417. (a) Michael Brooks, Is everything predetermined? Why physicists are reviving a taboo idea. New Scientist, 12 May 2021

(b) Hossenfelder, S. (2020), Superdeterminism: A Guide for the Perplexed. arXiv:2010.01324 [quant-ph]

(c) Yurchenko, S.B., The Importance of Randomness in the Universe: Superdeterminism and Free Will. Axiomathes 31: 453–478 (2021)

418. (a) Price, Huw, Does time-symmetry imply retrocausality? How the quantum world says "Maybe"? Studies in History and Philosophy of Modern Physics 43:2, 75-83 (2012)

(b) Leifer, Matthew S. & Pusey, Matthew F.; Is a time symmetric interpretation of quantum theory possible without retrocausality? Proceedings of The Royal Society A, 473:2202, 0607 (2017)

(c) Lisa Zyga, Physicists provide support for retrocausal quantum theory, in which the future influences the past. Phys.org, Jul 5, 2017

(d) Taming the quantum spooks. Reconciling Einstein with quantum mechanics may require abandoning the notion that cause always precedes effect. Aeon, 14 Sep 2016

419. (a) Yuan, X., Assad, S., Thompson, J. et al.; Replicating the benefits of Deutschian closed timelike curves without breaking causality. npj Quantum Information 1, 15007 (2015)

(b) National University of Singapore, "Computing with time travel?" ScienceDaily, 9 Dec 2015

420. (a) Page, Don N. & Wootters, William K.; Evolution without evolution: Dynamics described by stationary observables. Physical Review D, 27:12, 2885-2892 (1983)

(b) Marletto, Chiara & Vedral, Vlatko; Evolution without evolution and without ambiguities. Physical Review D, 95:4, 043510 (2017)

(c) Moreva, E., Brida, G., Gramegna, M. et al.; Time from quantum entanglement: An experimental illustration. Physical Review A, 89:5, 052122 (2014)

421. (a) The Physics arXiv Blog, "Quantum Experiment Shows How Time 'Emerges' from Entanglement". Medium, Oct 23, 2013

(b) Zeeya Merali, In Search of Time's Origin. Nautilus, Jan 9, 2014

(c) Merali, Zeeya, Theoretical physics: The origins of space and time. Nature 500, 516–519 (2013)

422. (a) Seth Lloyd, One Hundred Years Of Failure. Response to 2016 Edge question

(b) Time in Cosmology conference, Perimeter Institute for Theoretical Physics, Waterloo, Canada. Convened Jun 2016 by M. Cortes, L. Smolin & R.M. Unger. Sponsored by The Templeton Foundation.

(c) Dan Falk, A Debate Over the Physics of Time. Quanta, Jul 19, 2016

423. (a) Eugene Tracy, A science without time. Aeon, 25 Apr 2016

510

(b) Hayflick L., Moorhead P.S.; The serial cultivation of human diploid cell strains. Experimental Cell Research 25:3, 585-621, (1961)

(c) Sahl, S.J., Hell, S.W. & Jakobs, S.; Fluorescence nanoscopy in cell biology. Nature Reviews, Molecular Cell Biology 18, 685–701 (2017)

424. (a) Olovnikov, Alexey M., A theory of marginotomy: The incomplete copying of template margin in enzymic synthesis of polynucleotides and biological significance of the phenomenon. Journal of Theoretical Biology 41:1, 181-190 (1973)

(b) Li, J.S.Z., Fusté, J.M., Simavorian, T. et al.; TZAP: A telomere-associated protein involved in telomere length control. Science 355: 6325, 638-641 (2017)

(c) Scripps Research Institute, "Master regulator of cellular aging discovered." ScienceDaily, 12 Jan 2017

(d) Chen, Y., Podlevsky, J.D., Logeswaran, D. & Chen, J.J-L; A single nucleotide incorporation step limits human telomerase repeat addition activity. EMBO 37:6, e97953 (2018)

(e) Arizona State University, "Hidden secret of immortality enzyme telomerase: Can we stay young forever, or even recapture lost youth?" ScienceDaily, 27 Feb 2018

425. (a) Dorado-Correa, A.M., Zollinger, S., Heidinger, B. et al.; Timing matters: traffic noise accelerates telomere loss rate differently across developmental stages. Frontiers in Zoology, 15, 29 (2018)

(b) BioMed Central, "Traffic noise may make birds age faster." ScienceDaily, 28 Aug 2018

426. (a) Moore, Lisa D., Le, Thuc & Fan, Guoping; DNA Methylation and Its Basic Function. Neuropsychopharmacology 38, 23–38 (2013)

(b) Hannum, G., Guinney, J., Zhao, L. et al.; Genome-wide Methylation Profiles Reveal Quantitative Views of Human Aging Rates. Molecular Cell 49:2, 359-367 (2013)

(c) Horvath, Steve, DNA methylation age of human tissues and cell types. Genome Biol. 14, 3156 (2013)

(d) UCLA, Health Sciences, "Scientist uncovers internal clock able to measure age of most human tissues; Women's breast tissue ages faster than rest of body." ScienceDaily, 20 Oct 2013

427. (a) Gibbs, W. Wayt, Biomarkers and ageing: The clock-watcher. Nature 508, 168–170 (2014)

(b) Chen, B.H., Marioni, R.E., Colicino, E. et al.; DNA methylation-based measures of biological age: meta-analysis predicting time to death. Aging (Albany NY) 8:9, 1844—1865 (2016)

(c) Horvath, Steve, Gurven, Michael, Levine, Morgan E. et al.; An epigenetic clock analysis of race/ethnicity, sex, and coronary heart disease. Genome Biology 17, 171 (2016)

428. (a) de Magalhães, João Pedro, The Scientific Quest for Lasting Youth: Prospects for Curing Aging. Rejuvenation Research 17:5, 458-467 (2014)

(b) Abbott, Alison, First hint that body's 'biological age' can be reversed. Nature 573, 173 (2019)

(c) van Deursen, Jan M., The role of senescent cells in ageing. Nature 509, 439–446 (2014)

429. (a) Zhu, Y., Tchkonia, T., Pirtskhalava, T. et al.; The Achilles' heel of senescent cells: from transcriptome to senolytic drugs. Aging Cell 14:4, 644–658 (2015)

(b) Hickson, L.J., Langhi P., Larissa G.P. et al; Senolytics decrease senescent cells in humans: Preliminary report from a clinical trial of Dasatinib plus Quercetin in individuals with diabetic kidney disease. EBioMedicine (a journal of The Lancet), 47 446-456 (2019)

(c) Iske, J., Seyda, M., Heinbokel, T. et al; Senolytics prevent mt-DNA-induced inflammation and promote the survival of aged organs following transplantation. Nature Communications 11, 4289 (2020)

(d) Nathaniel Scharping, Senolytics: A New Weapon in the War on Aging. Discover, Aug 11, 2020

430. (a) Perls, T. T., Anti-Aging Medicine: The Legal Issues: Anti-Aging Quackery: Human Growth Hormone and Tricks of the Trade—More Dangerous Than Ever. J. of Geron.: Series A, 59:7, B682–B691 (2004)

(b) Gretchen Voss, The Risks of Anti-Aging Medicine. CNN (Health.com), Dec 14, 2016

(c) Olshansky, S. Jay, Hayflick, Leonard & Carnes, Bruce A.; Position Statement on Human Aging. The Journals of Gerontology: Series A, 57:8, B292–B297 (2002)

(d) Binstock, Robert H., The War on "Anti-Aging Medicine". The Gerontologist 43:1, 4–14 (2003)

431. (a) Zs-Nagy, Imre, The membrane hypothesis of aging: its relevance to recent progress in genetic research. Journal of Molecular Medicine 75, 703–714 (1997)

(b) Zs-Nagy, Imre, Is consensus in anti-aging medical intervention an elusive expectation or a realistic goal? Archives of Gerontology and Geriatrics 48:3, 271-275 (2009)

432. (a) Lan, J., Rollins, J.A., Zang, X. & Wu, D.; Translational Regulation of Non-autonomous Mitochondrial Stress Response Promotes Longevity. Cell Reports 28:4, 1050-1062.e6 (2019)

(b) M. D. Island Biological Lab, "Pathways that extend lifespan by 500 percent identified: Discovery of cellular mechanisms could open door to more effective anti-aging therapies." ScienceDaily, 8 Jan 2020

(c) Vaupel, James W., Biodemography of human ageing. Nature 464, 536–542 (2010)

433. (a) Dong, X., Milholland, Brandon & Vijg, Jan; Evidence for a limit to human lifespan. Nature 538, 257–259 (2016)

(b) Diana Kwon, Evidence for Human Lifespan Limit Contested. The Scientist, Jun 28, 2017

(c) The limits to human lifespan must be respected (editorial). Nature 538, 6 (2016)

434. (a) Fleming, Nic, Scientists up stakes in bet on whether humans will live to 150. Nature (2016)

(b) Olshansky, S. Jay, Measuring our narrow strip of life. Nature 538, 175–176 (2016)

(c) Charles Q. Choi, Is There a Limit to the Human Life Span? Live Science, Jun 28, 2017

(d) Geddes, Linda, Human age limit claim sparks debate. Nature (2016)

435. (a) Barbi, E., Lagona, F., Marsili, M. et al.; The plateau of human mortality: Demography of longevity pioneers. Science 360:6396, 1459-1461 (2018)

(b) Dolgin, Elie, There's no limit to longevity, says study that revives human lifespan debate. Nature 559, 14-15 (2018)

(c) Gavrilov, Leonid A. & Gavrilova, Natalia S.; Demographic Consequences of Defeating Aging. Rejuvenation Research 13:2-3, 329-334 (2010)

(d) ibid. Full paper and pdf download available online.

436. (a) Nicholas Graham, Ancient Egyptian Math Is Identical To Math Used In Modern Computers HuffPost (video), 16 Dec 2010

(b) Ossendrijver, Mathieu, Ancient Babylonian astronomers calculated Jupiter's position from the area under a time-velocity graph. Science 351:6272, 482-484 (2016)

(c) Cowen, Ron, Ancient Babylonians took first steps to calculus. Science 351:6272, 435 (2016)

(d) Rebecca Morelle, Ancient Babylonians 'first to use geometry'. BBC News, 29 Jan 2016

(e) Ball, Philip, Babylonian astronomers used geometry to track Jupiter. Nature (2016)

437. (a) Kavli Foundation, "The universe or the brain: Where does math originate?" ScienceDaily, 15 Jul 2013

(b) CEA, Identification of a network of brain regions involved in mathematics. ScienceDaily, 13May 2016

(c) Leibovich, T., Katzin, N., Harel, M. & Henik, A.; From "sense of number" to "sense of magnitude": The role of continuous magnitudes in numerical cognition. Behavioral and Brain Sciences 40, E164 (2017)

(d) American Associates, Ben-Gurion University of the Negev, "New theory debunks consensus that math abilities are innate." ScienceDaily, 1 Nov 2016

438. (a) Max Tegmark, Everything in the Universe Is Made of Math – Including You. Discover, Nov 04, 2013

(b) Max Tegmark, Can the Meaning of Life Be Explained by Math? Publishers Weekly, Jan 10, 2013

(c) Massimo Pigliucci, Mathematical Universe? I ain't convinced. Rationally Speaking, Dec 11, 2013

(d) Brian Rotman, Our Mathematical Universe by Max Tegmark - Review. The Guardian, 31 Jan 2014

439. (a) Keith Devlin, Love and Math: A Modern Russian's Lara Poem. HuffPost, 15 Jan 2014

(b) Jim Holt, A Mathematical Romance. Review of 'Love and Math' by Edward Frenkel. The New York Review, Dec 5, 2013

440. (a) Wigner, Eugene P., The unreasonable effectiveness of mathematics in the natural sciences. Richard Curant lecture in mathematical sciences (NYU May 11, 1959). Comm. Pure Appl. Math. 13:1, 1-14 (1960)

(b) Pradeep Mutalik, Does Natural Law Need Elegant Mathematics? Quanta, Dec 5, 2019

(c) Adam Becker, What is good science? Demanding that a theory is falsifiable or observable, without any subtlety, will hold science back. Aeon, 05 Apr 2018

441. (a) Fractal Foundation, Albuquerque, New Mexico, USA. Online resource

(b) Gabrielle Lipton, The fractal nature of almost all things. Landscape News, 20 Mar 2020

(c) Costanzo, M., Vandersluis, B., Koch, E.N. et al.; A global genetic interaction network maps a wiring diagram of cellular function. Science 353:6306, aaf1420 (2016)

(d) Enright, Matthew B. & Leitner, David M.; Mass fractal dimension and the compactness of proteins. Physical Review E 71:1, 011912 (2005)

442. (a) Michael Rose, Explainer: what are fractals? The Conversation, Dec 11, 2012

(b) Weisstein, Eric W., "Chaos Game." From MathWorld, a Wolfram Web Resource

(c) Jeffrey, H. Joel, Chaos game visualization of sequences. Computers & Graphics 16:1, 25-33 (1992)

443. (a) Thompson, D'Arcy Wentworth (1917), On Growth and Form. Open Library. OL6604798M

(b) McMurrich, J.P. (2017), Book Review; On Growth and Form by D'Arcy Wentworth Thompson, Cambridge University Press (1917). Science 46:1195, 513-514

(c) Ball, Philip, In retrospect: On Growth and Form. Nature 494, 32–33 (2013)

(d) Turing, Alan M., The chemical basis of morphogenesis. Phil Trans Royal Soc B, 237:641, 37–72 (1952)

444. (a) Economou, A., Ohazama, A., Porntaveetus, T. et al.; Periodic stripe formation by a Turing mechanism operating at growth zones in the mammalian palate. Nature Genetics 44, 348–351 (2012)

(b) King's College London, "How the tiger got its stripes: Proving Turing's tiger stripe theory." ScienceDaily, 19 Feb 2012

(c) Cooper, R.L., Thiery, A.P., Fletcher, A.G. et al.; An ancient Turing-like patterning mechanism regulates skin denticle development in sharks. Science Advances 4:11, eaau5484 (2018)

(d) University of Sheffield, "Codebreaker Turing's theory explains how shark scales are patterned." ScienceDaily, 7 Nov 2018

445. (a) Sheth, R., Marcon, L., Bastida, M.F. et al.; Hox Genes Regulate Digit Patterning by Controlling the Wavelength of a Turing-Type Mechanism. Science 338:6113, 1476-1480 (2012)

(b) Institut de recherches cliniques de Montreal, "What mechanism generates our fingers and toes? Genetic studies confirm a mathematical model." ScienceDaily, 14 Dec 2012

(c) Vogel, Gretchen, Turing Pattern Fingered for Digit Formation. Science 338:6113, 1406 (2012)

(d) Tompkins, N., Li, N., Girabawe, C. et al.; Testing Turing's theory of morphogenesis. PNAS 111:12, 4397-4402 (2014)

446. (a) Volkening, Alexandria & Sandstede, Björn.; Iridophores as a source of robustness in zebrafish stripes and variability in Danio patterns. Nature Communications 9, 3231 (2018)

(b) Patterson, L.B. & Parichy, D.M.; Interactions with Iridophores and the Tissue Environment Required for Patterning Melanophores and Xanthophores during Zebrafish Adult Pigment Stripe Formation. PLoS Genetics 9:5, e1003561 (2013)

(c) Ohio State University, "Why zebrafish (almost) always have stripes: Mathematical model helps explain key role of one pigment cell." ScienceDaily, 13 Aug 2018

447. (a) John, Grace P., Scoffoni, Christine & Sack, Lawren; Allometry of cells and tissues within leaves. American Journal of Botany 100:10, 1936-1948 (2013)

(b) University of California - Los Angeles, "The secret math of plants: Biologists uncover rules that govern leaf design." ScienceDaily, 30 Oct 2013

448. (a) Mannige, R.V., Haxton, T.K., Proulx, C. et al.; Peptoid nanosheets exhibit a new secondary-structure motif. Nature 526, 415–420 (2015)

(b) Lawrence Berkeley Nat Lab, "Newly discovered 'design rule' brings nature-inspired nanostructures one step closer: First atomic-resolution structure of a peptoid nanosheet." ScienceDaily, 07 Oct 2015

(c) Patel, N., White, S.J. et al.; HBV RNA pre-genome encodes specific motifs that mediate interactions with the viral core protein that promote nucleocapsid assembly. Nature Microbiology 2, 17098 (2017)

(d) Jordana Cepelewicz, The Illuminating Geometry of Viruses. Quanta, Jul 19, 2017

449. (a) Srinivasan, Shyam & Stevens, Charles F.; Scaling Principles of Distributed Circuits. Current Biology 29:15, 2533-2540.e7 (2019)

(b) Salk Institute, How mammals' brains evolved to distinguish odors is nothing to sniff at: Study finds that the relationship of 'distributed circuit' components scales across species. ScienceDaily, 18 Jul 2019

450. (a) Iyer-Biswas, S., Wright, C.S., Henry, J.T. et al.; Scaling laws governing stochastic growth and division of single bacterial cells. PNAS 111:45, 15912-15917 (2014)

(b) Taheri-Araghi, S., Bradde, S. Sauls, J.T. et al.; Cell-Size Control and Homeostasis in Bacteria. Current Biology 25:3, 385-391 (2015)

(c) Si, F., Le Treut, G., Sauls, J.T. et al.; Mechanistic Origin of Cell-Size Control and Homeostasis in Bacteria. Current Biology 29:11, 1760-1770.e7 (2019)

(d) UCSD, "Researchers unravel mechanisms that control cell size: Team of biologists, engineers and physicists uncover origins of precise cellular reproduction". ScienceDaily, 17 May 2019

451. (a) Gómez-Gálvez, P., Vicente-Munuera, P., Tagua, A. et al; Scutoids are a geometrical solution to three-dimensional packing of epithelia. Nature Communications 9, 2960 (2018)

(b) Lehigh University, "New geometric shape used by nature to pack cells efficiently." ScienceDaily, 28 Jul 2018

(c) Yasemin Saplakoglu, Geometry Has a New Shape. Meet the 'Scutoid.' Live Science, Jul 30, 2018

452. (a) Fei, C., Mao, S., Yan, J. et al.; Nonuniform growth and surface friction determine bacterial biofilm morphology on soft substrates. PNAS 117:14, 7622-7632 (2020)

(b) Princeton University, Engineering School, "Mechanical forces shape bacterial biofilms' puzzling patterns." ScienceDaily, 24 Mar 2020

453. (a) Markowsky, George, Misconceptions about the Golden Ratio. The College Maths. J. 23:1, 2-19 (1992)

(b) Adam Mann, Phi: The Golden Ratio. Live Science, Nov 25, 2019

(c) Tia Ghose, What Is the Fibonacci Sequence? Live Science, Oct 24, 2018

(d) Lee Reich, Nature follows a number pattern called Fibonacci. Phys.org, Feb 20, 2013

454. (a) Gautam Nag, What Is So Special About The Number 1.61803? Medium, May 5, 2019

(b) Kuhlemeier, Cris,"Phyllotaxis". Current Biology 27:17, R882-R887 (2017)

(c) Ron Knott, Fibonacci Numbers and the Golden Section. Online resource hosted by the Mathematics Department of the University of Surrey, UK.

455. (a) Chris Budd, Myths of maths: The golden ratio. University of Cambridge Plus Magazine, Feb 23, 2020
    (b) Shelley Esaak, How the Golden Ratio Relates to Art. ThoughtCo, Nov 13, 2019
    (c) Mario Livio, The golden ratio and aesthetics. University of Cambridge Plus Magazine, Nov 1, 2002

456. (a) Boeyens, Jan C.A. & Thackeray, J. Francis; Number theory and the unity of science.
    South African Journal of Science 110, 11/12 (2014)
    (b) Wits University, Golden Ratio offers unity of science. Phys.org, Nov 27, 2014
    (c) Vaezi, Abolhassan & Barkeshli, Maissam; Fibonacci Anyons From Abelian Bilayer Quantum Hall States. Physical Review Letters 113:23, 236804 (2014)
    (d) L.Zyga, 'Fibonacci quasiparticle' could form basis of future quantum computers. Phys.org, Dec 15, 2014

457. Herrmann, Burghard, Visibility in a pure model of golden spiral phyllotaxis.
    Mathematical Biosciences 301, 185-189 (2018)

458. (a) Kragh, Helge (2015), On Arthur Eddington's Theory of Everything. arXiv:1510.04046 [physics.hist-ph]
    (b) Dirac, Paul, The Cosmological Constants. Nature 139, p. 323 (1937)
    (c) Parker, R.H., Yu, C., Zhong, W. et al.; Measurement of the fine-structure constant as a test of the Standard Model. Science 360:6385, 191-195 (2018)
    (d) Morel, L., Yao, Z., Cladé, P. & Guellati-Khélifa, S.; Determination of the fine-structure constant with an accuracy of 81 parts per trillion. Nature 588, 61–65 (2020)

459. Kragh, Helge, Magic Number: A Partial History of the Fine-Structure Constant.
    Archive for History of Exact Sciences 57, 395–431 (2003)

460. (a) Pauli, Wolfgang (1994), Exclusion Principle and Quantum Mechanics. In: Enz C.P., von Meyenn K. (eds) Writings on Physics and Philosophy, pp 165-181, Springer, Berlin, Heidelberg
    (b) Wolfgang Pauli (1946), Exclusion Principle and Quantum Mechanics. Nobel Lecture, NobelPrize.org
    (c) Arthur Miller (2009), The Strange Friendship of Pauli and Jung – When Physics Met Psychology
    (d) Paul Ratner, Why the number 137 is one of the greatest mysteries in physics. Big Think, Oct 31, 2018

461. (a) Dudley, J.M. & Kwan, A.M.; Richard Feynman's popular lectures on quantum electrodynamics:
    The 1979 Robb lectures at Auckland University. American Journal of Physics 64:6, 694 (1996)
    (b) The Mysterious 137, Richard Feynman's conjecture.

462. (a) Webb, J.K., King, J.A., Murphy, M.T. et al.; Indications of a Spatial Variation of the Fine Structure Constant. Physical Review Letters 107:19, 191101 (2011)
    (b) Lisa Zyga, Variations in fine-structure constant suggest laws of physics not the same everywhere.
    Phys.org, Sep 6, 2010
    (c) Paul Davies, The number that fascinates physicists. The fine-structure constant denoted by the Greek letter alpha. Cosmos, 28 Jan 2016

463. (a) Newcomb, Simon, Note on the Frequency of Use of the Different Digits in Natural Numbers.
    American Journal of Mathematics 4:1, 39-40 (1881)
    (b) Benford, Frank, The Law of Anomalous Numbers. Proc.of the Amer. Phil Soc 78:4, 551-572 (1938)
    (c) Formann, Anton K., The Newcomb-Benford Law in Its Relation to Some Common Distributions.
    PLoS ONE 5:5, e10541 (2010)

464. (a) Hill, Theodore P., A Note on Distributions of True versus Fabricated Data.
    Perceptual and Motor Skills 83:3, 776-778 (1996)
    (b) ibid. Full paper and pdf download available online
    (c) Deckert, Joseph; Myagkov, Mikhail & Ordeshook, Peter C.; Benford's Law and the Detection of Election Fraud. Political Analysis 19:3, 245-268 (2011)
    (d) Hill, Theodore P., The First Digit Phenomenon: A century-old observation about an unexpected pattern in many numerical tables applies to the stock market, census statistics and accounting data.
    American Scientist 86:4, 358-363 (1998)
    (e) Berger, Arno & Hill, Theodore P.; A basic theory of Benford's Law. Probab. Surveys 8, 1-126 (2011)

465. (a) Sambridge, M., Tkalcic, H. & Jackson, A.; Benford's law in the natural sciences.
    Geophysical Research Letters 37:22, L22301 (2010)
    (b) Rachel Courtland, Curious mathematical law is rife in nature. New Scientist, 13 Oct 2010
    (c) Golbeck, J., Benford's Law Applies to Online Social Networks. PLoS ONE 10:8, e0135169 (2015)

466. (a) Sambridge, Malcolm & Jackson, Andrew; National COVID numbers — Benford's law looks for errors.
    Nature 581, 384 (2020)
    (b) Kennedy, Adrian P. & Yam, Sheung C.P.; On the authenticity of COVID-19 case figures.
    PLoS ONE 15:12, e0243123 (2020)

467. (a) Bejan, Adrian, Constructal-theory network of conducting paths for cooling a heat generating volume.
    International Journal of Heat and Mass Transfer 40:4, 799-816 (1997)

514

(b) Bejan, Adrian & Marden, James H.; The constructal unification of biological and geophysical design. Physics of Life Reviews 6:2, 85-102 (2009)

(c) Duke University, "Can Living And Non-living Follow Same Rules? Unifying The Animate And Inanimate Designs Of Nature." ScienceDaily, 30 Apr 2009

(d) Bejan, Adrian & Lorente, Sylvie; The constructal law of design and evolution in nature. Philosophical Transactions of the Royal Society B, 365:1545, 1335–1347 (2010)

468. (a) Anthony Wing Kosner, There's a New Law in Physics and It Changes Everything. Interview with Adrian Bejan. Forbes, 29 Feb 2012

(b) S. Donoghue, Review; Design in Nature: How the Constructal Law Governs Evolution in Biology, Physics, Technology, and Social Organization by Adrian Bejan & J. Peder Zane. Op.Ltrs Mthly, Jan29, 2012

(c) Adrian Bejan's website on Constructal law. https://constructal.org/

469. (a) Anthony Wing Kosner, "Freedom Is Good for Design," How to Use Constructal Theory to Liberate Any Flow System. Forbes, Mar 18, 2012

(b) Duke University's Pratt School of Engineering, Book Review, "The Physics of Life: The Evolution of Everything". May 20, 2016

(c) J. Berlin, What's the Meaning of Life? A revolutionary law of physics explains it. NatGeo, May 30, 2016

(d) Lage, J.L., Anderson, R., Costa, V. et al.; In Celebration: Professor Adrian Bejan on his 60th birthday. International Journal of Heat and Mass Transfer 51:25, 5759-5761 (2008)

470. (a) Bejan, Adrian; Gunes, Umit; Errera, Marcelo R. & Sahin, Bahri; Social organization: The thermodynamic basis. International Journal of Energy Research 42:12, 3770– 3779 (2018)

(b) Duke University. "How physics explains the evolution of social organization: Constructal law reveals how people come together to have greater access to scarce resources." ScienceDaily, 20 Jun 2018

(c) Duke University. "Rolling stones, turbulence connect evolution to physics: Bigger stones last longer and roll farther, but all tumble the same number of times." ScienceDaily, 17 Feb 2016

(d) Bejan, A., Gunes, U., Charles, J.D. & Sahin, B.; The fastest animals and vehicles are neither the biggest nor the fastest over lifetime. Scientific Reports 8, 12925 (2018)

471. (a) Günaydin, M. & Gürsey, F; Quark structure and octonions. J. of Math. Phys 14:11, 1651-1667 (1973)

(b) Baez, John C. (2001), The Octonions. arXiv:math/0105155 [math.RA]

472. (a) Furey, Cohl, Unified theory of ideals. Physical Review D 86:2, 025024 (2012)

(b) Furey, Cohl, Charge quantization from a number operator. Physics Letters B 742, 195-199 (2015)

(c) Furey, Cohl (2016), Standard model physics from an algebra? arXiv:1611.09182 [hep-th]

473. (a) Furey, Cohl, SU(3)C×C×SU(2)L×U(1)Y(×U(1)X) as a symmetry of division algebraic ladder operators. The European Physical Journal C 78, 375 (2018)

(b) Natalie Wolchover, The Peculiar Math That Could Underlie the Laws of Nature. Quanta, Jul 20, 2018

(c) Ana Roldán, The Mathematics of Physics. Young Physicist Forum (YPF), Switzerland, Aug 13, 2018

(d) Kevin Hartnett, Strange Numbers Found in Particle Collisions. Quanta, Nov 15, 2016

474. (a) Natalie Wolchover, A Jewel at the Heart of Quantum Physics. The Amplituhedron, a newly discovered mathematical object resembling a multifaceted jewel in higher dimensions. Quanta, Sep 17, 2013

(b) Arkani-Hamed, N. & Trnka, J.; The Amplituhedron. Journal of High Energy Physics 2014, 30 (2014)

(c) What is an intuitive explanation of the amplituhedron? Quora forum answers (2014-2017)

(d) Karla Lant, The Geometric Structure That Is Changing Notions of Reality. Futurism, Aug 21, 2017

475. (a) Arkani-Hamed, N., Bourjaily, J.L., Cachazo, F. et al. (2012); "Scattering Amplitudes and the Positive Grassmannian". arXiv:1212.5605 [hep-th]

(b) Arkani-Hamed, N., Thomas, H. & Trnka, J. Unwinding the Amplituhedron in binary. Journal of High Energy Physics 2018, 16 (2018)

(c) Penrose, Roger, "Twistor Algebra". Journal of Mathematical Physics 8:2, 345-366 (1967)

(d) Penrose, Roger, Twistor geometry of light rays. Class.and Quantum Grav. 14:1A, A299-A323 (1997)

476. (a) Institute for Advanced Study, Princeton (2015), Nima Arkani-Hamed on the Amplituhedron

(b) S. Palus, Amplituhedron May Shape the Future of Physics and possibly also revolutionize physics. Discover, Jan 07, 2014

(c) Carlo Rovelli, When twistors met loops. CERN Courier, 26 Nov 2019

(d) Twistors and Loops Meeting, 2-6 Sep 2019 (Théorie des twisteurs et gravitation quantique à boucles). Centre for Mathematical Researches (CIRM), Campus of Luminy in Marseille, France.

477. (a) Mario Livio, Unreasonable effectiveness. University of Cambridge Plus Magazine, Dec 1, 2008

(b) Marianne Freiberger, 'Is God a mathematician?' University of Cambridge Plus Magazine, Dec 1, 2008

478. (a) Alexanderson, G.L. & Erdos, P.; "An Interview with Paul Erdos". The Two-Year College Mathematics Journal 12:4, 249-259 (1981)

    (b) Chvátal, Vašek (2021), The Discrete Mathematical Charms of Paul Erdos: A Simple Introduction. Cambridge University Press, Online ISBN: 9781108912181

    (c) Aigner, Martin & Ziegler, Günter M.(1998), Proofs from THE BOOK. Revised, 5th ed.(2014)

    (d) Erica Klarreich, In Search of God's Perfect Proofs. Quanta, Mar 19, 2018

479. Schrödinger, Erwin (1944). The Classical Physicist's Approach To The Subject. Chap. 1 in What is Life?: With Mind and Matter and Autobiographical Sketches (Canto, pp. 3-18). Cambridge University Press (1992)

480. (a) Clara Moskowitz, Bringing the Definition of 'Life' to Closure. Astrobio.net via Phys.org, Feb 11, 2010

    (b) Ramin Skibba, To find aliens, we must think of life as we don't know it. Aeon, 19 Sep 2017

481. (a) Fraser, C.M., Gocayne, J.D., White, O. et al.; The Minimal Gene Complement of Mycoplasma genitalium. Science 270:5235, 397-404 (1995)

    (b) Mushegian, Arcady R. & Koonin, Eugene V.; A minimal gene set for cellular life derived by comparison of complete bacterial genomes. PNAS 93:19, 10268-10273 (1996)

    (c) J. Craig Venter, What Is Life? A 21st Century Perspective. Edge, Jul 12, 2012

482. (a) Gibson, D.G., Benders, G.A. & Andrews-Pfannkoch, C. et al.; Complete Chemical Synthesis, Assembly, and Cloning of a Mycoplasma genitalium Genome. Science 319:5867, 1215-1220 (2008)

    (b) Gibson, D.G., Glass, J.I., Lartigue, C. et al.; Creation of a Bacterial Cell Controlled by a Chemically Synthesized Genome. Science 329:5987, 52-56 (2010)

    (c) AAAS, "Scientists 'boot up' a bacterial cell with a synthetic genome." ScienceDaily, 20 May 2010

    (d) Pennisi, E., Synthetic Genome Brings New Life to Bacterium. Science 328:5981, 958-959 (2010)

    (e) Katsnelson, Alla, Researchers start up cell with synthetic genome. Nature (2010)

483. (a) Hutchison, C.A., Chuang, R-Y., Noskov, V.N. et al.; Design and synthesis of a minimal bacterial genome. Science 351:6280, aad6253 (2016)

    (b) Emily Singer, In Newly Created Life-Form, a Major Mystery. Quanta, Mar 24, 2016

    (c) Ed Yong, The Mysterious Thing About a Marvelous New Synthetic Cell. The Atlantic, Mar 24, 2016

484. (a) Deplazes, A., Huppenbauer, M.; Synthetic organisms and living machines. Syst Synth Biol 3, 55 (2009)

    (b) Are atoms alive or dead? And, if everything is made up of atoms, what separates living beings from non living things? Quora forum (2016-2021)

    (c) de Araujo Duarte, Celso, "Quantum Mechanics and New Perspectives on the Nature of Life". The Philosopher, CIII, 1 (2015)

485. (a) Aiewsakun, Pakorn & Katzourakis, Aris; Marine origin of retroviruses in the early Palaeozoic Era. Nature Communications 8, 13954 (2017)

    (b) University of Oxford, Retroviruses 'almost half a billion years old'. ScienceDaily, 10 Jan 2017

    (c) Imai, R., Nagai, M., Oba, M. et al.; A novel defective recombinant porcine enterovirus G virus carrying a porcine torovirus papain-like cysteine protease gene and a putative anti-apoptosis gene in place of viral structural protein genes. Infection, Genetics and Evolution 75, 103975 (2019)

    (d) Tokyo University of Agriculture and Technology, "Novel virus type may shed light on viral evolution." ScienceDaily, 16 Oct 2019

    (e) Al-Shayeb, B., Sachdeva, R., Chen, L-X. et al.; Clades of huge phages from across Earth's ecosystems. Nature vol. 578, pp. 425–431 (2020)

    (f) University of California - Berkeley, "Huge bacteria-eating viruses close gap between life and non-life: Large bacteriophages carry bacterial genes, including CRISPR and ribosomal proteins." ScienceDaily, 12 Feb 2020

    (g) Didier Raoult, Viruses Reconsidered. The discovery of more and more viruses of record-breaking size calls for a reclassification of life on Earth. The Scientist, Mar 01, 2014

486. (a) Lovelock, Jame E. & Margulis, Lynn; Atmospheric homeostasis by and for the biosphere: the Gaia hypothesis. Tellus 26:1-2, 2-10 (1974)

    (b) Radford, Tim, James Lovelock at 100: the Gaia saga continues. Nature 570, 441-442 (2019)

    (c) Lovelock, James, "Gaia: The living Earth". Nature 426, 769–770 (2003)

487. (a) Onori, Luciano & Visconti, Guido; The GAIA theory: from Lovelock to Margulis. From a homeostatic to a cognitive autopoietic worldview. Rendiconti Lincei 23, 375–386 (2012)

    (b) Kirchner, James W., The Gaia Hypothesis: Fact, Theory, and Wishful Thinking. Climatic Change 52, 391–408 (2002)

    (c) Kirchner, James W., The Gaia hypothesis: Can it be tested? Rev. of Geophys. 27:2, 223-235 (1989)

    (d) Lovelock, James E., Geophysiology, the science of Gaia. Reviews of Geophysics 27:2, 215-222 (1989)

488. (a) Sagan , Lynn, On the origin of mitosing cells. J. of Theoretical Biology 14:3, 225-274, IN1-IN6 (1967)

    (b) Mann, Charles, "Lynn Margulis: Science's Unruly Earth Mother". Science 252:5004, 378-381 (1991)

    (c) John Brockman, "Lynn Margulis 1938-2011 'Gaia Is A Tough Bitch'". Edge, Nov 23, 2011

(d) David Grinspoon, It's Time to Take the Gaia Hypothesis Seriously. Nautilus, Mar 08, 2017

(e) Michael Ruse, Earth's holy fool? Some scientists think that James Lovelock's Gaia theory is nuts, but the public love it. Could both sides be right? Aeon, 14 Jan, 2013

489. (a) Lynn Rothschild, Pam Conrad & Carol Cleland. 'What is Life' debate, Astrobiology Science Conference. Space Daily. Reprinted at Phys.org, Dec 18, 2006

(b) Liebert Inc, What is life? New answers to an age-old question in astrobiology. Phys.org, Jan 13, 2011

490. (a) Hoshika, S., Leal, N.A., Kim, M-J. et al.; Hachimoji DNA and RNA: A genetic system with eight building blocks. Science 363:6429, 884-887 (2019)

(b) Ruth Williams, DNA's Coding Power Doubled. The Scientist, Feb 21, 2019

491. (a) Wagner, Ingrid & Musso, Hans; New Naturally Occurring Amino Acids. Angewandte Chemie International Edition (English), 22:11, 816-828 (1983)

(b) Salk Institute, "Pre-history of life: Elegantly simple organizing principles seen in ribosomes." ScienceDaily, 13 Apr 2010

(c) Saint-Léger, A., Bello, C., Dans, P.D. et al.; Saturation of recognition elements blocks evolution of new tRNA identities. Science Advances 2:4, e1501860 (2016)

(d) Institute for Research in Biomedicine (IRB Barcelona), "Discovery of a fundamental limit to the evolution of the genetic code". ScienceDaily, 2 May 2016

(e) Granold, M., Hajieva, P., Tosa, M.I. et al.; Modern diversification of the amino acid repertoire driven by oxygen. PNAS 115:01, 41-46 (2018)

(f) Johannes Gutenberg Universitaet Mainz, "Quantum chemistry solves mystery why there are these 20 amino acids in the genetic code: An answer to an old and fundamental question of biochemistry." ScienceDaily, 1 Feb 2018

492. (a) University of York, "Scientists discover new clue to chemical origins of life." ScienceDaily, 24 Jan 2012

(b) Cocinero, E.J., Carcabal, P., Vaden, T.D. et al.; Sensing the anomeric effect in a solvent-free environment. Nature 469, 76–79 (2011)

(c) University of Oxford, "Shape-shifting sugars pinned down." ScienceDaily, 31 Jan 2011

493. (a) Penrose, Roger (1992). Foreword to Erwin Schrödinger's What is Life? With Mind and Matter and Autobiographical Sketches (Canto). Cambridge: Cambridge University Press

(b) Matthew Cobb, What is life? The physicist who sparked a revolution in biology. Erwin Schrödinger introduced some of the most important concepts in biology. The Guardian, Thu 07 Feb 2013

(c) Chris Mckay, What is life? It's a Tricky, Often Confusing Question. Phys. org, Sep 18, 2014

494. (a) Robert Shapiro, A Simpler Origin for Life. Scientific American, Feb 12, 2007

(b) Serdiuk, T., Steudle, A., Mari, S.A. et al.; Insertion and folding pathways of single membrane proteins guided by translocases and insertases. Science Advances 5:1, eaau6824 (2019)

(c) ETH Zurich, "How proteins become embedded in a cell membrane." ScienceDaily, 14 Feb 2019

495. (a) Cavalier-Smith, Thomas; Membrane heredity and early chloroplast evolution. Trends in Plant Science 5:4, 174-182 (2000)

(b) Cavalier-Smith, Thomas; Rooting the tree of life by transition analyses. Biology Direct 1, 19 (2006)

(c) Lomize, A.L., Lomize, M.A., Krolicki, S.R., Pogozheva, I.D.; Membranome: a database for proteome-wide analysis of single-pass membrane proteins. Nucleic Acids Research 45:D1, D250–D255 (2017)

(d) Lomize, A.L., Hage, J.M. & Pogozheva, I.D.; Membranome 2.0: database for proteome-wide profiling of bitopic proteins and their dimers. Bioinformatics 34:6, 1061–1062 (2018)

(e) Ghosh, D., Beavis, R.C. & Wilkins, J.A.; The Identification and Characterization of Membranome Components. Journal of Proteome Research 7:4, 1572–1583 (2008)

496. (a) Chen, Irene A. & Szostak, Jack W.; Membrane growth can generate a transmembrane pH gradient in fatty acid vesicles. PNAS 101:21, 7965-7970 (2004)

(b) Chen, Irene A. & Szostak, Jack W.; A Kinetic Study of the Growth of Fatty Acid Vesicles. Biophysical Journal 87:2, 988-998 (2004)

(c) Chen, I.A., The Emergence of Cells During the Origin of Life. Science 314:5805, 1558-1559 (2006)

(d) Chen, Irene A. & Salehi-Ashtiani, Kourosh & Szostak, Jack W.; RNA Catalysis in Model Protocell Vesicles. Journal of the American Chemical Society 127:38, 13213–13219 (2005)

(e) Adamala, Katarzyna & Szostak, Jack W.; Nonenzymatic Template-Directed RNA Synthesis Inside Model Protocells. Science 342:6162, 1098-1100 (2013)

(f) Massachusetts General Hospital, "Researchers find missing component in effort to create primitive, synthetic cells." ScienceDaily, 28 Nov 2013

497. (a) Matosevic, S. & Paegel, B.; Layer-by-layer cell membrane assembly. Nat Chem 5, 958–963 (2013)

(b) Karzbrun, E., Tayar, A.M., Noireaux, V. & Bar-Ziv, R.H.; Programmable on-chip DNA compartments as artificial cells. Science 345:6198, 829-832 (2014)

(c) Szostak, Jack W., Attempts to define life do not help to understand the origin of life.

Journal of Biomolecular Structure & Dynamics 29:4, 599-600 (2012)

(d) ibid. Full paper and pdf download available online.

498. (a) Alenghat, Francis J. & Golan, David E.; Chap 3 - Membrane Protein Dynamics and Functional Implications in Mammalian Cells. In: Functional Organization of Vertebrate Plasma Membrane ed. by Vann Bennett. Current Topics in Membranes 72, 89-120 (2013)

(b) ibid. Full paper and pdf download available online.

(c) Sokolova, E., Spruijt, E., Hansen, M.M.K. et al.; Enhanced transcription rates in membrane-free protocells formed by coacervation of cell lysate. PNAS 110:29, 11692-11697 (2013)

(d) Radboud University Nijmegen, "Protocells may have formed in a salty soup." ScienceDaily, 2 Jul 2013

499. (a) Temple, Robert; The Prehistory of Panspermia: Astrophysical or Metaphysical? International Journal of Astrobiology 6:2, 169-180 (2007)

(b) ibid. Full paper and pdf download available online

(c) Hollinger, Maik; Life from Elsewhere – Early History of the Maverick Theory of Panspermia. Sudhoffs Archiv. 100:2, 188-205 (2016)

(d) Wainwright, Milton and Alshammari, Fawaz; The Forgotten History of Panspermia and Theories of Life From Space. Journal of Cosmology 7, 1771-1776 (2010)

500. Lord Kelvin (William Thomson, "On the Origin of Life". Excerpt from the Presidential Address to the British Association for the Advancement of Science; held at Edinburgh in August, 1871. Reprinted in Kelvin's Popular Lectures and Addresses, p. 132-205

501. (a) Arrhenius, Svante (1908), The Spreading of Life Throughout the Universe. Reprinted from: Svante Arrhenius, IV, "Worlds in the Making". Journal of Cosmology 1, 91-99 (2009)

(b) Olsson-Francis, Karen & Cockell, Charles S.; Experimental methods for studying microbial survival in extraterrestrial environments. Journal of Microbiological Methods 80:1, 1-13 (2010)

502. (a) Brig Klyce; Hoyle and Wickramasinghe's Analysis of Interstellar Dust. Cosmic Ancestry.

(b) Hoyle, Fred & Wickramasinghe, N. Chandra (1982), Proofs that Life is Cosmic. Memoirs of the Institute of Fundamental Studies, Sri Lanka, No. 1.

(c) Wickramasinghe, N. C. (1982), Introduction: Proofs that Life is Cosmic. WSP reprint, pp. 1-18 (2017)

(d) Kamminga, H., Life from space - A history of panspermia. Vistas in Astronomy 26:2, 67-86 (1982)

503. (a) Caleb A. Scharf, The Panspermia Paradox. Scientific American, Oct 15, 2012

(b) Burchell, M. J.; Panspermia today. International Journal of Astrobiology 3:2, 73-80 (2004)

(c) Horneck, Gerda & Klaus, David M. & Mancinelli, Rocco L..; "Space Microbiology". Microbiology and Molecular Biology Reviews 74:1, 121-156 (2010)

(d) Wickramasinghe, N. Chandra (2011), Viva Panspermia! arXiv:1101.4295 [astro-ph.CO]

504. (a) "DNA building blocks can be made in space, NASA evidence suggests." ScienceDaily, 9 Aug 2011

(b) Kwok, Sun and Zhang, Yong; Mixed aromatic–aliphatic organic nanoparticles as carriers of unidentified infrared emission features. Nature 479, 80–83 (2011)

(c) The University of Hong Kong, "Astronomers discover complex organic matter exists throughout the universe." ScienceDaily, 27 Oct 2011

(d) Steele, E.J., Al-Mufti, S., Augustyn, K.A. et al.; Cause of Cambrian Explosion - Terrestrial or Cosmic? Progress in Biophysics and Molecular Biology 136, 3-23 (2018)

(e) Noble, Denis; Editorial: Cause of Cambrian Explosion - Terrestrial or Cosmic? Progress in Biophysics and Molecular Biology 136, 1-2 (2018)

505. (a) Wesson, Paul S., Panspermia, Past and Present: Astrophysical and Biophysical Conditions for the Dissemination of Life in Space. Space Science Reviews 156:1-4, 239–252 (2010)

(b) Lisa Grossman, All Life on Earth Could Have Come From Alien Zombies. Wired, Nov 10, 2010

(c) ibid, 503d

(d) Secker, J., Lepock, J. & Wesson, P.; Damage due to ultraviolet and ionizing radiation during the ejection of shielded micro-organisms from the vicinity of 1M main sequence and red giant stars. Astrophysics and Space Science 219, 1–28 (1994)

(e) Žgur-Bertok, Darja; DNA Damage Repair and Bacterial Pathogens. PLoS Path. 9:11, e1003711 (2013)

(f) Lin Edwards, 'Necropanspermia' suggested as a way of seeding life on Earth. Phys.org, Nov 12, 2010

506. (a) Thiel, C.S., Tauber, S., Schütte, A. et al.; Functional Activity of Plasmid DNA after Entry into the Atmosphere of Earth Investigated by a New Biomarker Stability Assay for Ballistic Spaceflight Experiments. PLoS ONE 9:11, pp. e112979 (2014)

(b) Zurich University, DNA survives critical entry into Earth's atmosphere. ScienceDaily, 26 Nov 2014

507. (a) Crick, Francis H.C. & Orgel, Leslie E.; Directed Panspermia. Icarus 19:3, 341-346 (1973)

(b) ibid. Full paper and pdf download available online.

(c) Christian Orlic, The Origins of Directed Panspermia. Scientific American, Jan 9, 2013

(d) Ginsburg, Idan and Lingam, Manasvi; The History and Origins of Directed Panspermia. Research Notes of the AAS, 5: 6, 154 (2021)

508. (a) Carl Sagan, Is There Life Elsewhere, And Did It Come Here? New York Times, Nov 29, 1981

(b) Paul Davies, 50 Years of Eerie Silence is Not a Long Time. Big Think, Jun 29, 2013

(c) Robert Sanders (University of California - Berkeley); Search for extraterrestrial intelligence gets hearing on Hill. Phys.org, May 22, 2014

(d) CORDIS, Researcher says 'We are going to find life in space this century'. Phys.org, Mar 20, 2014

509. (a) Kara Swisher, Yuri Milner Bets $100M That 'We Are Not Alone' in the Universe. Vox, Jul 20, 2015

(b) Charles Q. Choi, Stephen Hawking Helps Launch Massive Search for E.T. Space.com, July 20, 2015

(c) NRA Observatory. "Accelerating search for intelligent life in the universe." ScienceDaily, 20 Jul 2015

(d) Calla Cofield, 'Search for Extraterrestrial Intelligence' Needs a New Name, SETI Pioneer Says. Space.com, Jan 25, 2018

510. (a) Tariq Malik, Stephen Hawking Helps Launch Project 'Starshot' for Interstellar Space Exploration. Space.com, Apr 12, 2016

(b) Jesse Emspak, No Breakthrough Yet: Stephen Hawking's Interstellar 'Starshot' Faces Challenges. Space.com, Apr 15, 2016

(c) De la Torre, Gabriel G., Toward a new cosmic consciousness: Psychoeducational aspects of contact with extraterrestrial civilizations. Acta Astronautica 94:2, 577-583 (2014)

(d) Spanish Foundation for Science and Technology (FECYT), Are we ready for contact with extraterrestrial intelligence? Phys.org, May 6, 2014

511. (a) Clara Moskowitz, If Aliens Exist,They May Come to Get Us, Stephen Hawking Says. Space.com, Apr 26, 2010

(b) Mike Wall, Stephen Hawking Is Still Afraid of Aliens. Space.com, Sep 24, 2016

(c) Seth Shostak, Why Stephen Hawking is light years from the truth about 'dangerous aliens'. The Guardian, 27 Sep 2016

(d) Lisa Grossman, It's time to start taking the search for E.T. seriously, astronomers say. Science News, Jan 28, 2019

512. (a) Institute of Physics, Widening the search for extraterrestrial intelligence. Phys.org, Mar 01, 2010

(b) shCherbak, Vladimir I. & Makukov, Maxim A.; The "Wow! signal" of the terrestrial genetic code. Icarus 224:1, 228-242 (2013)

(c) Maxim Makukov, Response to comments on 'Wow signal' detection in genetic code. Reddit r/science forum, 04 Oct 2014

(d) Budisa, Nediljko, Kubyshkin, Vladimir & Schmidt, Markus; Xenobiology: A Journey towards Parallel Life Forms. ChemBioChem 21:16, 2228-2231 (2020)

513. (a) Sleator, Roy D. & Smith, Niall; Directed panspermia: a 21st century perspective. Science Progress 100:2, 187–193 (2017)

(b) ibid. Full paper and pdf download available online.

514. (a) Mautner, Michael N., Directed panspermia. 3. Strategies and motivation for seeding star-forming clouds. Journal of the British Interplanetary Society 50:3, 93-102 (1997)

(b) ibid. Full paper and pdf download available online.

(c) Lisa Zyga, "Professor: We have a 'moral obligation' to seed universe with life". Phys.org, Feb 09, 2010

(d) Mautner, Michael N., Seeding the Universe with Life: Securing Our Cosmological Future. Journal of Cosmology 5, 982-994 (2010)

(e) Mautner, Michael N., Astroecology, cosmo-ecology, and the future of life. Acta Societatis Botanicorum Poloniae – Journal of the Polish Botanical Society, 83:4, 449-464 (2014)

(f) Liu, Y., Cockell, C.S., Wang, G. et al.; Control of Lunar and Martian Dust—Experimental Insights from Artificial and Natural Cyanobacterial and Algal Crusts in the Desert of Inner Mongolia, China. Astrobiology 8:1, 75-86 (2008)

515. (a) Lane, Nick, The unseen world: reflections on Leeuwenhoek (1677) 'Concerning little animals'. Philosophical Transactions of the Royal Society B, 370:1666, 20140344 (2015)

(b) Gest, H., The discovery of microorganisms by Robert Hooke and Antoni van Leeuwenhoek, Fellows of The Royal Society. Notes & Records, R. Soc. Lond. J of History of Science, 58:2, 187–201 (2004)

(c) Richard Gunderman, "The 17th-century cloth merchant who discovered the vast realm of tiny microbes – an appreciation of Antonie van Leeuwenhoek". The Conversation, Apr 6, 2021

516. (a) The Human Cell Atlas project website. https://www.humancellatlas.org/

(b) Villani, A-C., Satija, R., Reynolds, G. et al.; Single-cell RNA-seq reveals new types of human blood dendritic cells, monocytes, and progenitors. Science 356:6335, aah4573 (2017)

(c) Abbott, A., Scientists bust myth that our bodies have more bacteria than human cells. Nature (2016)

517. (a) Bosch, Thomas C.G. & McFall-Ngai, Margaret J.; Metaorganisms as the new frontier. Zoology 114:4, 185-190 (2011)

(b) ibid. Full paper and pdf download available online.

(c) Bordenstein, Seth R. & Theis, Kevin R.; Host Biology in Light of the Microbiome: Ten Principles of Holobionts and Hologenomes. PLOS Biology 13;8, id. e1002226 (2015)

(d) Valdes, Ana M.; Walter, Jens; Segal, Eran & Spector, Tim D.; Role of the gut microbiota in nutrition and health. British Medical Journal (BMJ), 361, id. k2179 (2018)

(e) Kamada, Nobuhiko; Seo, Sang-Uk; Chen, Grace Y. & Núñez, Gabriel; Role of the gut microbiota in immunity and inflammatory disease. Nature Reviews Immunology 13, 321–335 (2013)

(f) NYU Langone Medical Center, "Natural gut viruses join bacterial cousins in maintaining health and fighting infections." ScienceDaily, 19 Nov 2014

518. (a) Minot, S., Grunberg, S., Wu, G.D. et al.; Hypervariable loci in the human gut virome. PNAS 109:10, 3962-3966 (2012)

(b) University of Pennsylvania School of Medicine, "Genetic variation in human gut viruses could be raw material for inner evolution." ScienceDaily, 19 Mar 2012

(c) Kelly Robinson & Julie Dunning Hotopp, "Bacteria and Humans Have Been Swapping DNA for Millennia". The Scientist, Oct 1, 2016

(d) Taylor, T.B., Mulley, G., Dills, A.H. et al.; Evolutionary resurrection of flagellar motility via rewiring of the nitrogen regulation system. Science 347:6225, 1014-1017 (2015)

(e) Ruth Williams, Evolutionary Rewiring. Strong selective pressure can lead to rapid and reproducible evolution in bacteria. The Scientist, Feb 26, 2015

519. (a) Brooks, A.W., Kohl, K.D., Brucker, R.M. et al.; Phylosymbiosis: Relationships and Functional Effects of Microbial Communities across Host Evolutionary History. PLOS Biology 14:11, e2000225 (2016)

(b) Vanderbilt University, "Each animal species hosts a unique microbial community and benefits from it." ScienceDaily, 29 Nov 2016

(c) Jain, Nita, The Need for Personalized Approaches to Microbiome Modulation. Frontiers in Public Health 8, 144 (2020)

520. (a) Turnbaugh, P., Ley, R., Hamady, M. et al.; The Human Microbiome Project. Nat 449, 804–810 (2007)

(b) NIH Human Microbiome Portfolio Analysis Team. A review of 10 years of human microbiome research activities at the US Natl. Institutes of Health, Fiscal Years 2007-2016. Microbiome 7, 31 (2019)

(c) NIH/National Human Genome Research Institute, "Human microbiome project: Diversity of human microbes greater than previously predicted." ScienceDaily, 21 May 2010

(d) Nicola Davis, The human microbiome: why our microbes could be key to our health. The Guardian, 26 Mar 2018

521. (a) Roy, Dipayan; Tomo, Sojit; Purohit, Purvi & Setia, Puneet; Microbiome in Death and Beyond: Current Vistas and Future Trends. Frontiers in Ecology and Evolution 9, 75 (2021)

(b) Pechal,J.L., Schmidt,C.J., Jordan,H.R. & Benbow,M.E.; A large-scale survey of the postmortem human microbiome, and its potential to provide insight into the living health condition. Sci Repts 8, 5724 (2018)

(c) Javan, G.T., Finley, S.J., Abidin, Z. & Mulle, J.G.; The Thanatomicrobiome: A Missing Piece of the Microbial Puzzle of Death. Frontiers in Microbiology 7, 225 (2016)

(d) Can, I., Javan, G.T., Pozhitkov, A.E. & Noble, P.A.; Distinctive thanatomicrobiome signatures found in the blood and internal organs of humans. Journal of Microbiological Methods 106, 1-7 (2014)

(e) Hyde, E.R., Haarmann, D.P., Lynne, A.M. et al.; The Living Dead: Bacterial Community Structure of a Cadaver at the Onset and End of the Bloat Stage of Decomposition. PLoS One 8:10, id. e77733 (2013)

522. (a) Wioland, H., Woodhouse, F.G., Dunkel, J. & Goldstein, R.E.; Ferromagnetic and antiferromagnetic order in bacterial vortex lattices. Nature Physics 12, 341–345 (2016)

(b) MacDonald, M., Spalding, G. & Dholakia, K.; Microfluidic sorting in an optical lattice. Nature 426, 421–424 (2003)

(c) Massachusetts Institute of Technology, "Bacteria, electrons spin in similar patterns: Bacteria streaming through a lattice behave like electrons in a magnetic material." ScienceDaily, 5 Jan 2016

523. (a) Witzany, Günther (2010), Biocommunication and Natural Genome Editing. Springer Media B.V.

(b) Witzany, Guenther, What is Life? Frontiers in Astronomy and Space Sciences 7, 7 (2020)

(c) Gilbert, S.F., Sapp, J. & Tauber, A.I.; A Symbiotic View of Life: We Have Never Been Individuals. The Quarterly Review of Biology 87:4, 325-341 (2012)

524. (a) Chelsea Gohd, Astronomers reevaluate the age of the universe. Space.com, Jan 08, 2021

(b) Ohtomo, Y., Kakegawa, T., Ishida, A. et al.; Evidence for biogenic graphite in early Archaean Isua metasedimentary rocks. Nature Geoscience 7, 25–28 (2014)

525. (a) Michael Lucy, What is the Fermi Paradox? Why can't we see any sign of life elsewhere in the universe? Cosmos, 22 Oct 2017

(b) Robert H. Gray, The Fermi Paradox Is Not Fermi's, and It Is Not a Paradox. Sci Amer, Jan 29, 2016

(c) Elizabeth Howell, Fermi Paradox: Where Are the Aliens? Space.com, Apr 27, 2018

(d) Glade, Nicolas; Ballet, Pascal & Bastien, Olivier; A stochastic process approach of the drake equation parameters. International Journal of Astrobiology 11:2, 103-108 (2012)

(e) Burchell, Mark J., W(h)ither the Drake equation? International J. of Astrobiology 5:3, 243-250 (2006)

(f) Derek Thompson, But, Seriously, Where Are the Aliens? The Atlantic, Jun 22, 2018

(g) Ethan Siegel, No, We Haven't Solved The Drake Equation, The Fermi Paradox, Or Whether Humans Are Alone. Forbes, Jun 26, 2018

(h) Fraser Cain, Where Are All the Aliens? The Fermi Paradox. Universe Today, Jun 20, 2013

526. (a) Hanson, Robin (1996), The Great Filter — Are We Almost Past It? Updated version Sep 15, 1998

(b) Elizabeth Howell, How the 'Great Filter' could affect tech advances in space. Phys.org, May 14, 2014

(c) Matt Williams, Beyond "Fermi's Paradox" III: What is the Great Filter? Universe Today, Jul 23, 2020

(d) Brian Koberlein, Does A Great Filter Solve the Fermi Paradox? Futurism, Apr 30, 2015

(e) Doug Adler, The Great Filter: a possible solution to the Fermi Paradox. Astronomy, Nov 20, 2020

527. (a) Schmidt, Gavin A. & Frank, Adam; The Silurian hypothesis: would it be possible to detect an industrial civilization in the geological record? International Journal of Astrobiology 18:2, 142-150 (2019)

(b) Adam Frank, Was There a Civilization on Earth Before Humans? The Atlantic, Apr 13, 2018

(c) University of Rochester, "We think we're the first advanced earthlings -- but how do we really know?" ScienceDaily, 16 Apr 2018

(d) Michele Diodati, The Silurian Hypothesis. Medium, Jun 27, 2020

(e) Steven Ashley, Could an Industrial Prehuman Civilization Have Existed on Earth before Ours? Scientific American, Apr 23, 2018

(f) Wright, Jason T., Prior indigenous technological species. Int. J. of Astrobiology 17:1, 96-100 (2017)

528. (a) Kempes, Christopher P. & Krakauer, David C.; The Multiple Paths to Multiple Life. Journal of Molecular Evolution 89, 415–426 (2021)

(b) Santa Fe Institute, "New theory of life's multiple origins." ScienceDaily, 16 Aug 2021

(c) Joyce, Gerald F., Bit by Bit: The Darwinian Basis of Life. PLoS Biology 10:5, id: e1001323 (2012)

(d) Public Library of Science, "Is a new form of life really so alien?" ScienceDaily, 8 May 2012

(e) Budisa, Nediljko; Kubyshkin, Vladimir & Schmidt, Markus; "Xenobiology: A Journey towards Parallel Life Forms". ChemBioChem 21:16, 2228-2231 (2020)

529. (a) Sharov, Alexei A. & Gordon, Richard (2013), "Life Before Earth". arXiv:1304.3381 [physics.gen-ph]

(b) Bob Yirka, Researchers use Moore's Law to calculate that life began before Earth existed. Phys.org, Apr 18, 2013

(c) Tim Radford, What is life? The Guardian, 27 Apr 2008

530. (a) Nick Bostrom, The Simulation Argument. Online resource site.

(b) Bostrom, Nick, "Are We Living in a Computer Simulation?". The Phil Qterly 53:211, 243–255 (2003)

(c) Hanson, Robin D., "How To Live In A Simulation". Journal of Evolution and Technology, 7, (2001)

(d) Chalmers, David J. (2003), The Matrix as Metaphysics. In (Christopher Grau, ed.) Philosophers Explore the Matrix, Oxford University Press, 2005

(e) Weatherson, Brian, "Are You a Sim? The Philosophical Quarterly 53:212, 425–431 (2003)

(f) Dainton, Barry (2002), Innocence Lost: Simulation Scenarios - Prospects and Consequences.

(g) Bostrom, Nick & Kulczycki, Marcin; A Patch for the Simulation Argument. Analysis 71:1, 54-61 (2011)

531. (a) Beane, Silas R. & Davoudi, Zohreh & Savage, Martin J.; Constraints on the universe as a numerical simulation. The European Physical Journal A, 50, 148 (2014)

(b) Joshua Filmer, Are We Living in a Computer Simulated Reality? Futurism, Apr 18, 2014

(c) Emerging Technology from arXiv, "The Measurement That Would Reveal The Universe As A Computer Simulation". MIT Technology Review, Oct 10, 2012

532. (a) Mark Robert Anderson, Elon Musk says we're probably living in a computer simulation – here's the science. The Conversation, Jun 23, 2016

(b) Adam Penenberg, 'We are architects of the simulation we're living in'. Wired, 12 Nov 2013

(c) Mike Colagrossi, 3 superb arguments for why we live in a matrix – and 3 arguments that refute them. Big Think, Jan 17, 2019

(d) Campbell, T., Owhadi, H., Sauvageau, J. & Watkinson, D.(2017), On testing the simulation theory. arXiv:1703.00058 [quant-ph]

533. (a) Aristotle (350 BCE), Historia animalium (History of Animals). Trans. by Richard Cresswell.

(b) Mark Perlman, The Modern Philosophical Resurrection of Teleology. The Monist 87:1, 3–51 (2004)

534. (a) Immanuel Kant (1790), Critique Of The Teleological Judgement. Part II in The Critique of Judgement. Trans. by J.H. Bernard. Project Gutenberg online library.

(b) ibid. § 61, Of the objective purposiveness of Nature.

(c) ibid. § 64, Of the peculiar character of things as natural purposes.

(d) ibid. § 65, Things regarded as natural purposes are organised beings.

(e) ibid. § 75, The concept of an objective purposiveness of nature is a critical principle of Reason for the reflective Judgement.

535. (a) Woodford, Peter; Neo-Darwinists and Neo-Aristotelians: how to talk about natural purpose. History and Philosophy of the Life Sciences, 38, 23 (2016)

(b) Pinho A.J., Garcia S.P., Pratas D. & Ferreira P.J.S.G.; DNA Sequences at a Glance. PLOS ONE 8:11, e79922 (2013)

(c) Koonin, E.V. & Novozhilov, A.S.; Origin and evolution of the genetic code: The universal enigma. IUBMB Life, 61:2, 99-111 (2009)

(d) Brauckmann, S., "Karl Ernst von Baer (1792-1876) and Evolution". Int J Dev Biol 56, 653-660 (2012)

(e) Lennox, James G.; Darwin was a teleologist. Biology and Philosophy 8, 409–421 (1993)

536. (a) de Laguna, Grace A. The Role of Teleonomy in Evolution. Philosophy of Science 29, 2 (1962)

(b) Mayr, Ernst; Cause and Effect in Biology: Kinds of causes, predictability, and teleology are viewed by a practicing biologist. Science 134:3489, 1501-1506 (1961)

(c) Mayr, Ernst; The Idea of Teleology. Journal of the History of Ideas 53:1, 117-135 (1992)

(d) Nagel, Ernest; Goal-Directed Processes in Biology. The Journal of Philosophy 74:5, 261-279 (1977)

(e) ibid. Full paper and pdf download available online.

537. (a) Michael Ruse, Does life have a purpose? Aeon, 24 Jun 2013

(b) Allen, Colin & Jacob Neal, "Teleological Notions in Biology", Stanford Encyclopedia of Philosophy (Spring 2020 Edition), Edward N. Zalta (ed.)

(c) Midgley, Mary, "Why The Idea Of Purpose Won't Go Away". Philosophy 86:4, 545-561 (2011)

(d) Aristotle's Posterior Analytics. Trans.by E.S. Bouchier, Oxford: Blackwell 1901 (OLL)

538. Karolinska Institutet, "Learning the alphabet of gene control." ScienceDaily, 17 Jan 2013

539. Gibbons, Ann, Bonobos Join Chimps as Closest Human Relatives. Science News Feature, 13 Jun 2012

540. (a) Ivan Noble, Human genome finally complete. BBC News, 14 Apr 2003

(b) Green, E., Watson, J. & Collins, F.; Human Genome Project: Twenty-five years of big biology. Nature 526, 29–31 (2015)

541. (a) Salzberg, S.L. Open questions: How many genes do we have?. BMC Biol 16, 94 (2018)

(b) NIH, "Researchers Trim Count Of Human Genes To 20,000-25,000." ScienceDaily, 21 Oct 2004

(c) Adams. M.D, Celniker, S.E., Holt, R.A. et al.; The Genome Sequence of Drosophila melanogaster. Science 287:5461, 2185-2195 (2000)

(d) Yu, J., Hu, S., Wang, J. et al.; A Draft Sequence of the Rice Genome (Oryza sativa L. ssp. indica). Science 296:5565,79-92 (2002)

542. (a) Willyard, Cassandra, New human gene tally reignites debate. Nature 558, 354-355 (2018)

(b) Abascal, F., Juan, D., Jungreis, I. et al.; Loose ends: almost one in five human genes still have unresolved coding status. Nucleic Acids Research 46:14, 7070–7084 (2018)

(c) Centro Nacional de Investigaciones Oncológicas (CNIO). "Human genome could contain up to 20 percent fewer genes, researchers reveal." ScienceDaily, 30 Aug 2018

543. (a) The ENCODE Project Consortium. An integrated encyclopedia of DNA elements in the human genome. Nature 489, 57–74 (2012)

(b) European Molecular Biology Laboratory, "Fast forward for biomedical research: Massive DNA encyclopedia scraps the junk." ScienceDaily, 5 Sep 2012

(c) Gerstein, M., Kundaje, A., Hariharan, M. et al.; Architecture of the human regulatory network derived from ENCODE data. Nature 489, 91–100 (2012)

(d) The ENCODE Project Consortium. An integrated encyclopedia of DNA elements in the human genome. Nature 489, 57–74 (2012)

544. (a) Neph, S., Vierstra, J., Stergachis, A. et al.; An expansive human regulatory lexicon encoded in transcription factor footprints. Nature 489, 83–90 (2012)

(b) Thurman, R., Rynes, E., Humbert, R. et al.; The accessible chromatin landscape of the human genome. Nature 489, 75–82 (2012)

(c) University of Washington. "Millions of DNA switches that power human genome's operating system are discovered." ScienceDaily, 5 Sep 2012

545. Woolston, C. Furore over genome function. Nature 512, 9 (2014)

546. (a) The FANTOM Consortium and the RIKEN PMI and CLST (DGT). A promoter-level mammalian expression atlas. Nature 507, 462–470 (2014)

(b) Harvard Public Health, First comprehensive atlas of human gene activity. ScienceDaily, 26 Mar 2014

547. (a) Whyte, W.A., Orlando, D.A., Hnisz, D. et al.; Master Transcription Factors and Mediator Establish Super-Enhancers at Key Cell Identity Genes. Cell 153:2, 307-319 (2013)

(b) Lovén, J., Hoke, H.A., Lin, C.Y. et al.; Selective Inhibition of Tumor Oncogenes by Disruption of Super-Enhancers. Cell 153:2, 320-334 (2013)

(c) Eric Olson, Enhanced Enhancers. The Scientist, Nov 1, 2014

(d) Kagey, M., Newman, J., Bilodeau, S. et al. Mediator and cohesin connect gene expression and chromatin architecture. Nature 467, 430–435 (2010)

(e) ibid. Full paper and pdf download available online

(f) Nicole Giese Rura, Surprise in genome structure linked to developmental diseases. Whitehead Institute, Cambridge, MA, Aug 18, 2010

548. (a) Factor, D.C., Corradin, O., Zentner, G.E. et al.; Epigenomic Comparison Reveals Activation of "Seed" Enhancers during Transition from Naive to Primed Pluripotency. Cell Stem Cell 14:6, 854-863 (2014)

(b) Case Western Reserve University. "Stem cells hold keys to body's plan." ScienceDaily, 5 Jun 2014

(c) Whyte, W., Bilodeau, S., Orlando, D. et al.; Enhancer decommissioning by LSD1 during embryonic stem cell differentiation. Nature 482, 221–225 (2012)

(d) ibid. Full paper and pdf download available online

(e) Nicole Giese Rura, Chaos in the cell's command center. Whitehead Institute, MA, Feb 01, 2012

549. (a) Barone, V., Lang, M., Gabriel Krens, S.F. et al. An Effective Feedback Loop between Cell-Cell Contact Duration and Morphogen Signaling Determines Cell Fate. Developmental Cell 43:2, 198-211.e12 (2017)

(b) Institute of Science and Technology Austria. "Cell biology: Cell contacts in embryonic development determine cellular fate: Feedback loop between contact formation and cell fate specification discovered." ScienceDaily, 12 Oct 2017

550. (a) Center for Genomic Regulation. "How genes interact to build tissues and organisms." ScienceDaily, 7 Jun 2019

(b) Ghavi-Helm, Y., Klein, F., Pakozdi, T. et al.; Enhancer loops appear stable during development and are associated with paused polymerase. Nature 512, 96–100 (2014)

(c) European Molecular Biology Laboratory (EMBL). "Embryology: Unexpected stability and complexity in transcriptional enhancers' interactions." ScienceDaily, 3 Jul 2014

(d) Cold Spring Harbor Laboratory. "In massive genome analysis ENCODE data suggests 'gene' redefinition." ScienceDaily, 5 Sep 2012

551. (a) Emmert-Streib, F., Dehmer, M. & Haibe-Kains, B.; Gene regulatory networks and their applications: understanding biological and medical problems in terms of networks. Front. Cell Dev. Biol. 2 (2014)

(b) Costanzo, M., VanderSluis, B. & Koch, E.N.; A global genetic interaction network maps a wiring diagram of cellular function. Science 353:6306, aaf1420 (2016)

(c) Veronique Greenwood, Giant Genetic Map Shows Life's Hidden Links. Quanta, Oct 25, 2016

(d) Taylor, Peter and Richard Lewontin, "The Genotype/Phenotype Distinction", Stanford Encyclopedia of Philosophy (Summer 2021 Edition), Edward N. Zalta (ed.)

(e) Jeanette Kazmierczak, The Cell's Backup Genetic Instructions. Quanta, Oct 28, 2016

552. (a) Valverde, F., Groover, A. & Romero, J.M.; Editorial: Evolution of Gene Regulatory Networks in Plant Development. Front. Plant Sci. 8 (2017)

(b) Mehta, T.K., Koch, C., Nash, W. et al.; Evolution of regulatory networks associated with traits under selection in cichlids. Genome Biol 22, 25 (2021)

553. (a) Erdmann, V., Barciszewska, M.. et al. Regulatory RNAs. Cell. Mol. Life Sci. 58, 960–977 (2001)

(b) Whitehead Institute for Biomedical Research. "Paired genes in stem cells shed new light on gene organization and regulation." ScienceDaily, 4 Feb 2013

(c) Massachusetts Institute of Technology. "Reading DNA, backward and forward: Biologists reveal how cells control the direction in which the genome is read." ScienceDaily, 24 Jun 2013

(d) Poliseno, L., Pseudogenes: Newly Discovered Players in Human Cancer. Sci. Signal.5:242, re5 (2012)

554. (a) Miraldi, E.R., Pokrovskii, M., Watters, A. et al.; Leveraging chromatin accessibility for transcriptional regulatory network inference in T Helper 17 Cells. Genome Res. 29, 449-463 (2019)

(b) Cincinnati Children's Hospital Medical Center. "A new way to map cell regulatory networks: Tool reduces material needed to ID transcription factors regulating gene expression." ScienceDaily, 5 Mar 2019

(c) Iacono, G., Massoni-Badosa, R. & Heyn, H. Single-cell transcriptomics unveils gene regulatory network plasticity. Genome Biol. 20, 110 (2019)

(d) CGR. "How genes interact to build tissues and organisms." ScienceDaily, 7 Jun 2019

(e) Nagy-Staron, A., Tomasek, K., Carter, C.C. et al.; Local genetic context shapes the function of a gene regulatory network. eLife 2021;10:e65993

555. (a) Shulha, H.P., Crisci, J.L., Reshetov D. et al.; Human-Specific Histone Methylation Signatures at Transcription Start Sites in Prefrontal Neurons. PLOS Biology 10(11): e1001427 (2012)

(b) Public Library of Science. "Evolution of human intellect: Human-specific regulation of neuronal genes." ScienceDaily, 20 Nov 2012

(c) American Society of Human Genetics. "Humans, chimpanzees and monkeys share DNA but not gene regulatory mechanisms." ScienceDaily, 6 Nov 2012

556. (a) Khan, Z., Ford, M.J., Cusanovich, D.A. et al.; Primate Transcript and Protein Expression Levels Evolve Under Compensatory Selection Pressures. Science 342:6162, 1100-1104 (2013)

(b) ibid. Full paper and pdf download available online

(c) University of Chicago Medical Center. "Gene regulation differences between humans, chimpanzees very complex." ScienceDaily, 17 Oct 2013

557. (a) ibid, 550d

(b) Erin Wayman, The Accidental Species: Misunderstandings of Human Evolution by Henry Gee (book review). Science News, Nov 24, 2013

558. (a) Attanasio, C., Nord, A.S., Zhu, Y. et al.; Fine Tuning of Craniofacial Morphology by Distant-Acting Enhancers. Science 342:6157, 1241006 (2013)

(b) ibid. Full paper and pdf download available online.

(c) DOE/Lawrence Berkeley National Laboratory. "What is it about your face? Researchers provide new insight into why each human face is unique." ScienceDaily, 24 Oct 2013

559. (a) Galanter, J.M., Gignoux, C.R., Oh, S.S et al.; Differential methylation between ethnic sub-groups reflects the effect of genetic ancestry and environmental exposures. eLife 2017;6:e20532

(b) University of California - San Francisco. "Cultural differences may leave their mark on DNA." ScienceDaily, 10 Jan 2017

560. Katherine S. Pollard, Decoding Human Accelerated Regions. Do the portions of our genomes that set us apart from other animals hold the secret to human evolution? The Scientist, Aug 1, 2016

561. (a) Lambert, S.A., Jolma, A. et al.; The Human Transcription Factors. Cell 172:4, 650-665 (2018)

(b) Lambert, S.A., Yang, A.W.H., Sasse, A. et al.; Similarity regression predicts evolution of transcription factor sequence specificity. Nature Genetics 51, 981–989 (2019)

(c) University of Toronto. "Scientists uncover a trove of genes that could hold key to how humans evolved." ScienceDaily, 27 May 2019

562. (a) Gokhman, D., Lavi, E., Prüfer, K. et al.; Reconstructing the DNA Methylation Maps of the Neandertal and the Denisovan. Science 344:6183, 523-527 (2014)

(b) Hebrew University of Jerusalem. "How are we different and what gave us the advantage over extinct types of humans like the Neanderthals?." ScienceDaily, 22 Apr 2014

563. (a) Jolma, A., Yan, J., Whitington, T. et al.; DNA-Binding Specificities of Human Transcription Factors. Cell 152:1-2, 327-339 (2013)

(b) Karolinska Institutet. "Learning the alphabet of gene control." ScienceDaily, 17 Jan 2013

564. (a) Smith, R., Taher, L., Patwardhan, R. et al.; Massively parallel decoding of mammalian regulatory sequences supports a flexible organizational model. Nature Genetics 45, 1021–1028 (2013)

(b) University of California - San Francisco. "'Grammar' plays key role in activating genes." ScienceDaily, 12 Aug 2013

565. (a) Jolma, A., Yin, Y., Nitta, K. et al. DNA-dependent formation of transcription factor pairs alters their binding specificity. Nature 527, 384–388 (2015)

(b) Karolinska Institutet. "Complex grammar of the genomic language." ScienceDaily, 9 Nov 2015

566. (a) Stergachis, A.B., Haugen, E., Shafer, A. et al.; Exonic Transcription Factor Binding Directs Codon Choice and Affects Protein Evolution. Science 342:6164, 1367-1372 (2013)

(b) Weatheritt, R.J., Madan Babu, M., The Hidden Codes That Shape Protein Evolution. Science 342:6164, 1325-1326 (2013)

(c) Univ. of Washington. "Scientists discover double meaning in genetic code." ScienceDaily, 12 Dec 2013

567. (a) Ivan Amato, Genetic Geometry Takes Shape. Quanta, Feb. 25, 2015

(b) Stu Borman, Role Of Folded DNA Revealed. Chemical & Engineering News (C&EN), Mar 21, 2014

(c) Kerry Grens, DNA Bends Control Gene Activation. The Scientist, Mar 25, 2014

568. (a) Emily Singer, How Strange Twists in DNA Orchestrate Life. Quanta, Jan 5, 2016

(b) Wang, H., Xu, X., Nguyen, C.M. et al.; CRISPR-Mediated Programmable 3D Genome Positioning and Nuclear Organization. Cell 175:5, 1405-1417.e14 (2018)

(c) J. Cepelewicz, In the Nucleus, Genes' Activity Might Depend on Their Location. Quanta, Nov 6, 2018

569. (a) Muskhelishvili, G., Travers, A.; Integration of syntactic and semantic properties of the DNA code reveals chromosomes as thermodynamic machines converting energy into information. Cell. Mol. Life Sci. 70, 4555–4567 (2013)

(b) US NIH 4D Nucleome (4DN) program. https://www.4dnucleome.org/

570. (a) Marc Bekoff, Do Animals Know Who they Are? Psychology Today, Jul 6, 2009

(b) Duncan, M., The Self Shows Up in Experience. Rev. Phil. Psych. 10, 299–318 (2019)

(c) Wozniak, M., "I" and "Me": The Self in the Context of Consciousness. Front. Psychol., 9 (2018)

(d) Whitworth, B., The Physical World as a Virtual Reality. arXiv:0801.0337 [cs.OH]

571. (a) Slater, M., Spanlang, B., Sanchez-Vives, M.V. & Blanke O.; First Person Experience of Body Transfer in Virtual Reality. PLOS ONE 5(5): e10564 (2010)

(b) Petkova, V.I. & Ehrsson, H.H.; If I Were You: Perceptual Illusion of Body Swapping. PLOS ONE 3:12, e3832 (2008)

(c) Dobricki, M. & and Pauli, P.; Sensorimotor body-environment interaction serves to regulate emotional experience and exploratory behavior. Heliyon 2:10, e00173 (2016)

572. (a) Aghajan, Z., Acharya, L., Moore, J. et al.; Impaired spatial selectivity and intact phase precession in two-dimensional virtual reality. Nature Neuroscience 18, 121–128 (2015)

(b) University of California - Los Angeles. "How does the brain react to virtual reality? Completely different pattern of activity in brain." ScienceDaily, 24 Nov 2014

(c) Acharya, L., Aghajan, Z.M., Vuong, C. et al.; Causal Influence of Visual Cues on Hippocampal Directional Selectivity. Cell 164:1-2, 197-207 (2016)

(d) University of California, Los Angeles (UCLA), Health Sciences. "Brain's GPS depends on visual landmarks to triangulate location, researchers find." ScienceDaily, 17 Dec 2015

573. (a) Rognini, G., Petrini, F.M., Raspopovic, S. et al.; Multisensory bionic limb to achieve prosthesis embodiment and reduce distorted phantom limb perceptions. Journal of Neurology, Neurosurgery & Psychiatry 90:7, 833-836 (2019)

(b) Ecole Polytechnique Fédérale de Lausanne. "Amputees feel as though their prosthetic limb belongs to their own body." ScienceDaily, 13 Aug 2018

574. (a) Milgram, P., Takemura, H., Utsumi, A. & Kishino, F.; "Augmented Reality: A class of displays on the reality-virtuality continuum". Proc. SPIE 2351, Telemanipulator and Telepresence Technologies (1994-5)

(b) ibid. Full paper and pdf download available online.

575. (a) Parsons, T.D., Gaggioli, A. & Riva, G.; Virtual Reality for Research in Social Neuroscience. Brain Sci. 7:4, 42 (2017)

(b) Suárez, G., Jung, S. & Lindeman, R.W.; Evaluating Virtual Human Role-Players for the Practice and Development of Leadership Skills. Frontiers in Virtual Reality, 2 (2021)

(c) Nicola Davis, Long-term effects of virtual reality use need more research, say scientists. The Guardian, 19 Mar 2016

576. (a) de Borst, A.W. & de Gelder, B.; Is it the real deal? Perception of virtual characters versus humans: an affective cognitive neuroscience perspective. Frontiers in Psychology, 6 (2015)

(b) Bailey, J.O. & Bailenson, J.N.; Considering virtual reality in children's lives. Journal of Children and Media 11:1, 107-113 (2017)

(c) Angela Buckingham, Murder in virtual reality should be illegal. Aeon, 24 Nov 2016

577. (a) J.Campbell, Virtual reality boom brings giant robots, cyberpunk castles to China. Reuters, Nov24, 2017

(b) Indian Institute of Technology Bombay, 58th Convocation (Virtual Reality mode). IIT, 23 Aug 2020

(c) Anthony S. Rozario, IIT Bombay Beats COVID With Virtual Convocation, VR Campus Tour. The Quint, 24 Aug 2020

578. (a) Light Jr., D.W, The Social Construction of Reality: A Treatise in the Sociology of Knowledge. By Peter L. Berger and Thomas Luckmann. New York: Doubleday, 1966. Sociology of Religion 28:1, 55–56 (1967)

(b) Colin Fisher, Group-think: what it is and how to avoid it. The Conversation, May 27, 2021

579. (a) Morris, J., Simulacra in the Age of Social Media: Baudrillard as the Prophet of Fake News. Journal of Communication Inquiry 45:4, 319-336 (2021)

(b) Steven Poole, "Jean Baudrillard. Philosopher and sociologist who blurred the boundaries between reality and simulation". The Guardian, 07 Mar 2007

(c) RKW, Guy Debord's Society of the Spectacle. Global Media Studies, Mar 9, 2010

580. (a) Mantini, D., Corbetta, M., Romani, G.L. et al.; Evolutionarily Novel Functional Networks in the Human Brain? Journal of Neuroscience 33:8, 3259-3275 (2013)

(b) KU Leuven. "Has evolution given humans unique brain structures?." ScienceDaily, 22 Feb 2013

(c) Neubert, F.-X., Mars, R.B., Thomas, A.G. et al.; Comparison of Human Ventral Frontal Cortex Areas for Cognitive Control and Language with Areas in Monkey Frontal Cortex. Neuron 81:3, 700-713 (2014)

(d) University of Oxford. "What makes us human? Unique brain area linked to higher cognitive powers." ScienceDaily, 5 Feb 2014

(e) Boldog, E., Bakken, T.E., Hodge, R.D. et al. Transcriptomic and morphophysiological evidence for a specialized human cortical GABAergic cell type. Nature Neuroscience 21, 1185–1195 (2018)

(f) Allen Inst. "Scientists identify a new kind of human brain cell: 'Rosehip' neurons not found in rodents, may be involved in fine-level control between regions of the human brain." ScienceDaily, 27 Aug 2018

581. (a) Shanahan, M., Bingman, V.P., Shimizu, T. et al.; Large-scale network organization in the avian forebrain: a connectivity matrix and theoretical analysis. Front. Comput. Neurosci., 7(2013)

(b) Imp. College Lond., Bird brain? Birds and humans have similar brain wiring. ScienceDaily, 17 Jul 2013

(c) Gutiérrez-Ibáñez, C., Iwaniuk, A.N. & Wylie, D.R. Parrots have evolved a primate-like telencephalic-midbrain-cerebellar circuit. Scientific Reports 8, 9960 (2018)

(d) University of Alberta. "Neuroscientists uncover secret to intelligence in parrots: Study shows evidence of convergence in bird and primate evolution." ScienceDaily, 3 Jul 2018

(e) Duke University. "Ten-year project redraws the map of bird brains." ScienceDaily, 17 Sep 2013

582. (a) Fitch, W.T., de Boer, B., Mathur, N. & Ghazanfar, A.A.; Monkey vocal tracts are speech-ready. Science Advances, 2:12, e1600723 (2016)

(b) Ben Andrew Henry, Why Can't Macaques Talk Like Humans? The Scientist, Dec 12, 2016

(c) Fitch, W.T., The Biology and Evolution of Speech: A Comparative Analysis. Annual Review of Linguistics, 4, 255-279 (2018)

583. (a) Okobi, D.E., Banerjee, A., Matheson, A.M.M. et al.; Motor cortical control of vocal interaction in neotropical singing mice. Science 363:6430, 983-988 (2019)

(b) NYU Langone Health. "Study of singing mice suggests how mammalian brain achieves conversation: Research may lead to future solutions to speech problems." ScienceDaily, 28 Feb 2019

(c) Siegfried, Tom; Why speech is a human innovation. Knowable, 21 Feb. 2019

584. (a) Fedzechkina, M., Chu, B. & Florian Jaeger, T.; Human Information Processing Shapes Language Change. Psychological Science 29:1, 72-82 (2018)

(b) University of Arizona. "Why do we see similarities across languages? Human brain may be responsible." ScienceDaily, 1 Dec 2017

(c) Bohn, M., Kachel, G. & Tomasello, M.; Young children spontaneously recreate core properties of language in a new modality. PNAS 116:51, 26072-26077 (2019)

(d) Max Planck Institute for Evolutionary Anthropology. "How does language emerge? New study provides insights into the first steps." ScienceDaily, 3 Dec 2019

585. (a) Li, J., Osher, D.E., Hansen, H.A. et al. Innate connectivity patterns drive the development of the visual word form area. Scientific Reports 10, 18039 (2020)

(b) Ohio State University. Humans are born with brains 'prewired' to see words. ScienceDaily, 22 Oct 2020

586. (a) Mollica, F. & Piantadosi, S.T.; Humans store about 1.5 megabytes of information during language acquisition. Royal Society Open Science, 6:3, 181393 (2019)

(b) University of California - Berkeley. "Kids store 1.5 megabytes of information to master their native language." ScienceDaily, 27 Mar 2019

587. (a) Traxler, M.J., Boudewyn, M. & Loudermilk, J.; What's Special About Human Language? The Contents of the "Narrow Language Faculty" Revisited. Language and Linguistics Compass, 6: 611-621 (2012)

(b) ibid. Full paper and pdf download available online.

(c) Buckner, C., Rational Inference: The Lowest Bounds. Philos Phenomenol Res 98, 697-724 (2019)

588. (a) Moser, Keith; Rethinking the Essence of Human and Other-Than-Human Communication in the Anthropocene Epoch: A Biosemiotic Interpretation of E.Morin's "Complex Thought". Human. 7, (2018)

(b) Cornell University. "Psychologists solve mystery of songbird learning." ScienceDaily, 31 Jan 2019

(c) Bjorn Carey, Ant School: The First Formal Classroom Found in Nature. Live Science, Jan 11, 2006

(d) Landgraf, T., Rojas, R., Nguyen, H., Kriegel, F. & Stettin. K.; Analysis of the Waggle Dance Motion of Honeybees for the Design of a Biomimetic Honeybee Robot. PLOS ONE 6:8, e21354 (2011)

589. (a) Dan Cossins, Plant Talk. Plants communicate and interact with each other, both aboveground and below, in surprisingly subtle and sophisticated ways. The Scientist, Jan 1, 2014

(b) Gagliano, M., Renton, M. Love thy neighbour: facilitation through an alternative signalling modality in plants. BMC Ecol 13, 19 (2013)

(c) Kim, G., LeBlanc, M.L., Wafula, E.K. et al.; Genomic-scale exchange of mRNA between a parasitic plant and its hosts. Science 345:6198, 808-811 (2014)

(d) Virginia Tech. "Plants may use newly discovered molecular language to communicate." ScienceDaily, 14 Aug 2014

590. (a) Sidoli, N.C (2015).; Aristarchus (1), of Samos, Greek astronomer, mathematician, 3rd century BCE. Oxford Classical Dictionary.

(b) Hirshfeld, A.W.; The Triangles of Aristarchus. The Mathematics Teacher 97:4, 228–231 (2004)

(c) Rushkin, Ilia (2015); Optimizing the Ptolemaic Model of Planetary and Solar Motion. arXiv:1502.01967

591. Andrew Zimmerman Jones, "Copernican Principle." ThoughtCo, Aug. 25, 2020

592. (a) Gott, J., Implications of the Copernican principle for our future prospects. Nature 363, 315–319 (1993)

(b) Manuel Berdoy, Have Humans Evolved Beyond Nature—and Do We Even Need It? The Conversation, Feb 6, 2020

593. (a) Samuel Arbesman (2011), The Copernican Principle. Response to 2011 Edge.org question.

(b) Livio, Mario, Astrobiology: Cosmic prestige. Nature 512, 368–369 (2014)

594. (a) Caldwell, R.R. &Stebbins, A.; A Test of the Copernican Principle. Phy.Rev.Lett. 100:19, 191302 (2008)

(b) ibid. Full paper and pdf download available online

(c) Lisa Zyga, A Test of the Copernican Principle. Phys.org, May 22, 2008

(d) M. Gleiser, What does the Copernican principle say about life in the universe? Big Think, Sep 22, 2021

595. (a) Briefer, E.F., Haque, S., Baciadonna, L. et al.; Goats excel at learning and remembering a highly novel cognitive task. Frontiers in Zoology 11, 20 (2014)

(b) Queen Mary, University of London. "Goats are far more clever than previously thought, and have an excellent memory." ScienceDaily, 26 Mar 2014

596. (a) Fiorito, G. & Scotto, P.; Observational Learning in Octopus vulgaris. Science 256:5056, 545-547 (1992)

(b) Octopus twists for shrimps. BBC News, 25 Feb 2003

(c) Richter, J.N., Hochner, B. & Kuba, M.J. Pull or Push? Octopuses Solve a Puzzle Problem. PLOS ONE 11:3, e0152048 (2016)

597. (a) Bates, L.A., Lee, P.C., Njiraini, N. et al.; Do Elephants Show Empathy? Journal of Consciousness Studies 15:10-11, 204-225 (2008)

(b) San Diego Zoo Global. "Elephants' unique interactions with their dead: Findings reveal broad interest in deceased, even in unrelated elephants." ScienceDaily, 6 Feb 2020

(c) Don Ross, The elephant as a person. Aeon, 24 Oct 2018

598. (a) Solvi, C., Baciadonna, L. & Chittka, L.; Unexpected rewards induce dopamine-dependent positive emotion–like state changes in bumblebees. Science 353:6307, 1529-1531 (2016)

(b) University of Queen Mary London. "Good food puts bees in good mood." ScienceDaily, 29 Sep 2016

(c) Edsinger, E. & Dölen, G.; A Conserved Role for Serotonergic Neurotransmission in Mediating Social Behavior in Octopus. Current Biology 28:19, 3136-3142.e4 (2018)

(d) S. Williams, Octopuses On Ecstasy Reveal Commonalities with Humans. The Scientist, Sep 21, 2018

(e) Zer-Krispil, S., Zak, H., Shao, L. et al.; Ejaculation Induced by the Activation of Crz Neurons Is Rewarding to Drosophila Males. Current Biology 28:9, 1445-1452.e3 (2018)

(f) Lars Chittka & Catherine Wilson, Bee-brained. Are insects 'philosophical zombies' with no inner life? Aeon, 27 Nov 2018

599. (a) Richard Kerridge, The Inner Life of Animals by Peter Wohlleben (review). A revolution in how we regard other species. The Guardian, 20 Oct 2017

(b) Ramesh, S., Tyerman, S., Xu, B. et al. GABA signalling modulates plant growth by directly regulating the activity of plant-specific anion transporters. Nature Communications 6, 7879 (2015)

(c) University of Adelaide. "Stressed out plants send animal-like signals." ScienceDaily, 29 Jul 2015

600. (a) Grey, W., Anthropocentrism and deep ecology. Australasian J. of Philosophy 71:4, 463-475 (1993)

(b) Crist, E., Reimagining the human. Science 362:6420, 1242-1244 (2018)

(c) Mumby, H.S. & Plotnik, J.M.; Taking the Elephants' Perspective: Remembering Elephant Behavior, Cognition and Ecology in Human-Elephant Conflict Mitigation. Front. Ecol. Evol., 6 (2018)

(d) Watson, R.A.; A Critique of Anti-Anthropocentric Biocentrism. Environ. Ethics 5:3, 245-256 (1983)

601. (a) Swiss Federal ECNH, The Dignity of Living Beings with Regard to Plants (2008)

(b) Lloyd Alter, Swiss Government Issues Bill of Rights for Plants. Treehugger, Oct 11, 2018

(c) Lev-Yadun, S.; Bioethics: On the road to absurd land. Plant Signaling & Behavior, 3:8, 612 (2008)

(d) Koechlin, F.; The dignity of plants. Plant Signaling & Behavior, 4:1, 78-79 (2009)

602. (a) Michael Marder, The time is ripe for plant rights. Al Jazeera, 21 Jan 2013

(b) Jeremy Hance, Are plants intelligent? New book says yes. The Guardian, 4 Aug 2015

603. (a) Smith, Wesley J. (2014), The War on Humans. Discovery Institute Press, Seattle, WA 98104.

(b) Dolphins deserve same rights as humans, say scientists. BBC News, 21 Feb 2012

(c) Eric Michael Johnson, Nonhuman Personhood Rights (and Wrongs). Scientific American, Mar 9, 2012

604. (a) Abend, G., What the Science of Morality Doesn't Say About Morality. Philosophy of the Social Sciences 43:2, 157-200 (2013)

(b) Abend, G., What are neural correlates neural correlates of? BioSocieties 12, 415–438 (2017)

605. (a) A. Rutherford, The human league: what separates us from other animals? The Guardian, 21 Sep 2018

(b) Robin McKie, The Book of Humans by Adam Rutherford review – a pithy homage to our species. The Guardian, 9 Oct 2018

(c) Nicholas Maxwell, Natural philosophy redux. The great split between science and philosophy must be repaired. Aeon, 13 May 2019

606. (a) Dunbar, R., Religion, the social brain and the mystical stance. Arch. Psych. Religion 42:1, 46-62 (2020)

(b) Wesley Wildman, Religion is uniquely human, but computer simulations may help us understand religious behavior. The Conversation, Jun 11, 2018

607. (a) Prat, S., Péan, S.C., Crépin, L. et al.; The Oldest Anatomically Modern Humans from Far Southeast Europe: Direct Dating, Culture and Behavior. PLOS ONE 6:6, e20834 (2011)

(b) Jennifer Carpenter, Early human fossils unearthed in Ukraine. BBC News, 21 Jun 2011

(c) Rendu, W., Beauval, C., Crevecoeur, I. et al.; Evidence supporting an intentional Neandertal burial at La Chapelle-aux-Saints. PNAS 111:1, 81-86 (2014)

(d) New York University. "Neanderthals buried their dead, new research of remains concludes." ScienceDaily, 16 Dec 2013

(e) Robert N. McCauley , Are Modern Human Beings the Only Species with Religion? Psychology Today, Nov 4, 2018

608. (a) Ed Stourton, The decline of religion in the West. BBC News, 26 Jun 2015

(b) The Global Religious Landscape. Pew Research Center, Dec 18, 2012

(c) Amy Sawitta Lefevre, New Thai PM uses holy water, feng shui to ward off occult. Reuters, Sep 8, 2014

(d) Orion Jones, Iceland is officially worshiping Norse Gods again. Big Think, Feb 4, 2015

609. (a) Stroumsa, G.G, Robert Bellah on the origins of religion. A Critical Review. Revue de l'histoire des religions 4, 467-477 (2012)

(b) Heather Horn, Where Does Religion Come From? A conversation with Robert Bellah, author of a new book about faith's place in evolution. The Atlantic, Aug 17, 2011

(c) Robert N. Bellah, Where did religion come from? Social Science Research Council, NY, Nov 2, 2011

610. (a) Peoples, H.C. & Marlowe, F.W.; Subsistence and the Evolution of Religion. Human Nature 23, 253–269 (2012)

(b) Peoples, H.C., Duda, P. & Marlowe, F.W.; Hunter-Gatherers and the Origins of Religion. Human Nature 27, 261–282 (2016)

611. (a) Singh, M., The cultural evolution of shamanism. Behavioral and Brain Sciences 41, E66 (2018)

(b) ibid. Full paper and pdf download available online

(c) Grosman, L., Munro, N.D. & Belfer-Cohen, A.; A 12,000-year-old Shaman burial from the southern Levant (Israel). PNAS 105:46, 17665-17669 (2008)

(d) Scham, S., The World's First Temple. Archaeology 61:6 (2008)

612. (a) Henshilwood, C.S., d'Errico, F., van Niekerk, K.L. et al.; An abstract drawing from the 73,000-year-old levels at Blombos Cave, South Africa. Nature 562, 115–118 (2018)

(b) C. Henshilwood & K.L. van Niekerk, South Africa's Blombos cave is home to the earliest drawing by a human. The Conversation, Sep 12, 2018

613. (a) Ajit Varki, Dating the Origin of Us. The Scientist, Nov 1, 2013

(b) Gómez-Robles, A., de Castro, J.M.B, Arsuaga, J-L. et al.; No known hominin species matches the expected dental morphology of the last common ancestor of Neanderthals and modern humans. PNAS 110:45, 18196-18201 (2013)

(c) Indiana University. "No known hominin is common ancestor of Neanderthals and modern humans, study suggests." ScienceDaily, 21 Oct 2013

614. (a) Wilson, D.S., Green, W.S. (2011), Evolutionary Religious Studies: A Beginner's Guide. OUP, chap. 13 in: Creating Consilience: Integrating the Sciences and the Humanities ed. by E.Slingerland & M.Collard.

(b) Wilson, D.S., Whitehouse, H., Hartberg, Y. et al.; The nature of religious diversity: a cultural ecosystem approach. Religion, Brain & Behavior, 7:2, 134-153 (2017)

(c) David Sloan Wilson, Evolutionary Religious Studies Comes of Age. This View Of Life, Jun 23, 2017

(d) Sosis, R., Schjoedt, U., Bulbulia, J. & Wildma, W.J.; Wilson's 15-year-old cathedral. Religion, Brain & Behavior, 7:2, 95-97 (2017)

615. (a) Barrett, J.L. & Burdett, E.R.; The cognitive science of religion. The Psychologist, 24, 252-255 (2011)

(b) White, C. (2021), An Introduction to the Cognitive Science of Religion. Connecting Evolution, Brain, Cognition and Culture. 368 pp, Routledge (Taylor & Francis). ISBN 9781138541467.

(c) McCauley, R.N., Recent Trends In The Cognitive Science Of Religion: Neuroscience, Religious Experience, And The Confluence Of Cognitive And Evolutionary Research. Zygon®, 55: 97-124 (2020)

616. (a) Borg, J., Andrée, B., Soderstrom, H. & Farde, L.; The Serotonin System and Spiritual Experiences. American Journal of Psychiatry 160:11, 1965-1969 (2003)

(b) Borg, J., Andrée, B., Soderstrom, H. & Farde, L.; Letter to the Editor: Dr. Borg and Colleagues Reply. American Journal of Psychiatry 161:9, 1721-1721 (2004)

(c) Silveira, Linda A., Experimenting with Spirituality: Analyzing The God Gene in a Nonmajors Laboratory Course. CBE: Life Sciences Education 7:1, 132–145 (2008)

(d) Goldman, M. The God Gene: How Faith is Hardwired Into Our Genes. Nat Genet 36, 1241 (2004)

(e) Geneticist claims to have found 'God gene' in humans. The Washington Times, Nov 14, 2004

617. (a) John Cookson, The Neurological Origins of Religious Belief. Big Think, Sep 10, 2010

(b) Megan Erickson, Is The Human Brain Hardwired for God? Big Think, May 29, 2012

(c) Urgesi, C., Aglioti, S.M., Skrap, M. & Fabbro, F.; The Spiritual Brain: Selective Cortical Lesions Modulate Human Self-Transcendence. Neuron 65:3, 309-319 (2010)

(d) A. Chris Gajilan, Are humans hard-wired for faith? CNN, Apr 5, 2007

618. (a) Johnstone, B., Bodling, A. & Cohen, D. et al.; Right Parietal Lobe-Related "Selflessness" as the Neuropsychological Basis of Spiritual Transcendence. Intl J for Psych of Religion 22:4, 267-284 (2012)

(b) University of Missouri-Columbia. "Distinct 'God spot' in the brain does not exist, study shows." ScienceDaily, 19 Apr 2012

619. (a) Kapogiannis, D., Deshpande, G., Krueger,F. et al.; Brain Networks Shaping Religious Belief. Brain Connectivity 4:1, 70-79 (2014)

(b) Auburn University. "Evidence of biological basis for religion in human evolution." ScienceDaily, 17 Jan 2014

(c) Miller, L., Balodis, I.M., McClintock, C.H. et al.; Neural Correlates of Personalized Spiritual Experiences. Cerebral Cortex 29:6, 2331–2338 (2019)

(d) Yale University. "Where the brain processes spiritual experiences." ScienceDaily, 1 Jun 2018

620. (a) Yaden, D.B., Eichstaedt, J.C., Schwartz, H.A. et al.; The language of ineffability: Linguistic analysis of mystical experiences. Psychology of Religion and Spirituality 8:3, 244–252 (2016)

(b) Thomas Jefferson University. "Describing the indescribable: Underlying features of reported mystical experiences." ScienceDaily, 15 Oct 2015

(c) Ferguson, M.A., Nielsen, J.A., King, J.B. et al.; Reward, salience, and attentional networks are activated by religious experience in devout Mormons. Social Neuroscience 13:1, 104-116 (2018)

(d) University of Utah Health Sciences. "This is your brain on God: Spiritual experiences activate brain reward circuits." ScienceDaily, 29 Nov 2016

621. (a) Zuckerman, M., Silberman, J. & Hall, J.A.; The Relation Between Intelligence and Religiosity: A Meta-Analysis and Some Proposed Explanations. Personality and Social Psychology Review 17:4,325-354 (2013)

(b) Zuckerman, M., Li, C., Lin, S. & Hall, J.A.; The Negative Intelligence–Religiosity Relation: New and Confirming Evidence. Personality and Social Psychology Bulletin 46:6, 856-868 (2020)

(c) Daws, R.E. & Hampshire, A.; The Negative Relationship between Reasoning and Religiosity Is Underpinned by a Bias for Intuitive Responses Specifically When Intuition and Logic Are in Conflict. Frontiers in Psychology, 8 (2017)

622. (a) Neisser, U., Boodoo, G., Bouchard, T.J.; Intelligence: Knowns and unknowns. American Psychologist 51:2, 77–101 (1996)

(b) Nigel Barber, The Real Reason Atheists Have Higher IQs. Is atheism a sign of intelligence? Psychology Today, May 4, 2010

623. (a) Webster, G.D. & Duffy, R.D.; Losing faith in the intelligence–religiosity link: New evidence for a decline effect, spatial dependence, and mediation by education and life quality. Intellig. 55, 15-27 (2016)

(b) Warren Mansell & Vyv Huddy; There's a crisis in psychology – here's how technology could provide a solution. The Conversation, May 21, 2018

(c) Miguel Farias, Are the brains of atheists different to those of religious people? The Conversation, Jan 18, 2021

624. (a) Time to accept that atheism, not god, is odd. New Scientist, 3 Mar 2010

(b) Newberg, Andrew, "Ask the Brains". Scientific American, Mind 22, 6, 70 (2012)

625. Sharon Begley, Religion And The Brain. Newsweek, 6 May 2001

626. (a) Emmons, C.F. & Sobal, J.; Paranormal Beliefs: Functional Alternatives to Mainstream Religion? Review of Religious Research 22:4, 301-312 (1981)

(b) L.C. David, The Origins and Meanings Behind Our Most Common Superstitions. Exemplore, Jul 3, 2020

(c) Paul Kingsbury, Crop circles blur science, paranormal in X-Files culture. The Conversation, Nov 1, 2017

627. (a) Tiffanie Wen, Why Do People Believe in Ghosts? The Atlantic, Sep 5, 2014

(b) Martina Petkova, Why Do Dogs Kill Themselves at the Overtoun Bridge? Medium, Sep 23, 2020

(c) Natasha Ishak, Inside The Mystery Of Overtoun Bridge, Scotland's Dog Suicide Hotspot. All That's Interesting, Mar 28, 2019

628. Sussex Centre for Cultural Studies. Paranormal Cultures Conference, June 2010.

629. (a) Michelle Goldberg, Season of the Witch. New York Times, Nov 3, 2017

(b) Tanya Ghahremani, Astrology doesn't need to be scientifically proven to be empowering — or feminist. NBC, Dec 23, 2019

630. (a) Michael Lipka & Claire Gecewicz; More Americans now say they're spiritual but not religious. Pew Research Center, Sep 6, 2017

(b) K.Paul, Why millennials are ditching religion for witchcraft and astrology. MarketWatch, Oct. 20, 2017

(c) Corin Faife, How Witchcraft Became A Brand. BuzzFeed, Jul 26, 2017

(d) Amanda Montell, Influencer Witches of Instagram. Cosmopolitan, Oct 30, 2018

(e) Lynn Garrett, Season of the Witch: Mind-Body-Spirit Books. Publishers Weekly, Aug 02, 2019

631. (a) Susan Page, "Sally Quinn has cast 3 hexes, and worries they worked". USA Today, 9 Aug 2017

(b) Andrew Ferguson, The Ruling Classless. Sally Quinn's Finding Magic. Commentary, Nov 2017

(c) Daniel Krep, Lana Del Rey Joins Effort to Defeat Trump With Witchcraft. Rolling Stone, Feb 25, 2017

(d) Emma G. Ellis, Trump's Presidency Has Spawned a New Generation of Witches. Wired, Oct 30, 2019

632. (a) Gershman, B., Witchcraft beliefs and the erosion of social capital: Evidence from Sub-Saharan Africa and beyond. Journal of Development Economics 120, 182-208 (2016)

(b) American University. "Do witchcraft beliefs halt economic progress?" ScienceDaily, 9 May 2016

633. (a) Taliaferro, Charles, "Philosophy of Religion", Stanford Encyclopedia of Philosophy (Winter 2021 Ed.)

(b) Morley, Brian, Western Concepts of God. Internet Encyclopedia of Philosophy, ISSN 2161-0002.

634. (a) Defilippo, J.; Aristotle' identification of the Prime Mover as God. Classical Qtrly 44:2, 393-409 (1994)

(b) Tegtmeyer, H., Can Aristotle's Prime Mover Be A Physical Cause? Rivista di Filosofia Neo-Scolastica 107:4, 767-782 (2015)

(c) Lang, Helen S., Aristotle's First Movers and the Relation of Physics to Theology. The New Scholasticism 52:4, 500-517 (1978)

635. (a) Terry Eagleton, Lunging, Flailing, Mispunching. Richard Dawkins' The God Delusion. London Review of Books, 19 Oct 2006

(b) Damon Linker, Memo to atheists: God's not dead yet. The Week, Jan 10, 2015

(c) Oliver Burkeman, The one theology book all atheists really should read. The Guardian, 14 Jan 2014

636. (a) Galen Guengerich, "God, Revised: The Atheists Are Half Right". HuffPost, Jun 10, 2013

(b) God Revised: How Religion Must Evolve in a Scientific Age (2013) by Galen Guengerich. Publishers Weekly book review:

637. (a) Barry Seagren, The Case for God – a review. Evangelicals Now, Feb 2010 (reprint).

(b) Terry Gross, Karen Armstrong Builds A 'Case For God'. NPR interview, Sep 21, 2009

(c) Gregg Henriques, Toward Resolving Our God Conflict. Psychology Today, Oct 17, 2013

(d) Loftus, John (2010), The Case For God by Karen Armstrong. Philosophy Now, 81, Oct/Nov 2010

638. (a) Huxley, Julian, The New Divinity (1964). In: Essays of a Humanist, Chatto & Windus, London

(b) Phillips, P.T., One World, One Faith: The Quest for Unity in Julian Huxley's Religion of Evolutionary Humanism. Journal of the History of Ideas 68:4, 613-63 (2007)

(c) When Americans Say They Believe in God, What Do They Mean? Pew Research Center, Apr 25, 2018

(d) Harriet Sherwood, Religion: why faith is becoming more and more popular. Guardian, 27 Aug 2018

639. (a) Ursula Goodenough, Exploring The Religious Naturalist Option. NPR, Nov 23, 2014

(b) Neil deGrasse Tyson, Cosmic Perspective. Universe: The 100th Essay, Apr 2007. Nat. Hist.Magazine

(c) John Farrell, Cosmology, God And Why 'The Big Picture' Needs To Be Bigger. Forbes, Jul 10, 2016

(d) Taylor, James E., The New Atheists. Internet Encyclopedia of Philosophy, ISSN 2161-0002.

(e) Stuart A. Kauffman, Beyond Reductionism: Reinventing The Sacred. Edge, Nov 12, 2006

640. Carter, K. Codell, Godhood. The Encyclopedia of Mormonism.

641. (a) Masson, O., Turning into Gods: Transhumanist Insight on Tomorrow's Religiosity. Implicit Religion, 17:4, 443–458 (2014)

(b) Cannon, L., What is Mormon Transhumanism? Theology and Science, 13:2, 202-21 (2015)

(c) Mormon Transhumanist Association. https://transfigurism.org/

642. (a) ibid, 530b

(b) ibid, 530a

643. (a) Killian, T. (2016), An Analytical Review of Lincoln Cannon's "The New God Argument".

(b) ibid. Full article available as pdf download online.

(c) Cannon, L. (2016), Response to a New God Argument Critique by Killian (Transhumanity.net).

(d) ibid. Full article also available at Cannon's online blog.

644. (a) Sadler, Greg, Anselm of Canterbury (1033 –1109). Internet Encyclopedia of Philosophy.

(b) Williams, Thomas, "Saint Anselm", Stanford Encyclopedia of Philosophy (Winter 2020 Edition).

(c) A Reply on Behalf of the Fool by Gaunilo. In: St. Anselm's Proslogion.
University of Notre Dame Press, 1979. Project MUSE 1769151.

(d) The Author's Reply to Gaunilo. In: St. Anselm's Proslogion.
University of Notre Dame Press, 1979. Project MUSE 1769152.

645. (a) Oppy, Graham, "Ontological Arguments", Stanford Encyclopedia of Philosophy (Winter 2021 Ed.)

(b) Dore, C. (1984), A Modal Argument. In: Theism, Philosophical Studies Series in Philosophy, 30, 49-61

(c) Malcolm, N., Anselm's Ontological Arguments. The Philosophical Review 69:1, 41-62 (1960)

(d) Duthie, G.D., Book Review, Anselm's Discovery by Charles Hartshorne.
The Philosophical Quarterly 17:69, 381 (1967)

(e) Pailin, D.A. (1990), Rigor, Reason and Moderation: Hartshorne's Contribution to the Philosophy of
Religion and Philosophical Theology. In: Sia S. (eds) Charles Hartshorne's Concept of God.
Studies in Philosophy and Religion 12, 219-238. Springer, Dordrecht

(f) Plantinga, A. (1974), The Nature of Necessity. Clarendon Press, Oxford, England. OUP online.

(g) Henry, D.P., Book Reviews, The Nature of Necessity by Alvin Plantinga.
The Philosophical Quarterly 25:99, 178–180 (1975)

646. (a) Robert J. Marks, Samuel Haug, Gödel Says God Exists and Proves It. Mind Matters, Jun 7, 2021

(b) Kanckos, A. & Lethen, T.; The Development Of Gödel's Ontological Proof.
The Review of Symbolic Logic 14:4, 1011-1029 (2021)

(c) Benzmüller, C. & Paleo, B.W. (2013); Formalization, Mechanization and Automation of Gödel's Proof
of God's Existence. arXiv:1308.4526 [cs.LO]

(d) Benzmüller, C. & Paleo, B.W. (2014); Automating Gödel's Ontological Proof of God's Existence with
Higher-order Automated Theorem Provers. Frontiers in Artificial Intelligence and Apps 263, 93-98 ECAI

(e) Von David Knight, Holy Logic: Computer Scientists 'Prove' God Exists. Spiegel Intl., 23 Oct 2013

647. Chalmers, D.J., Facing Up to the Problem of Consciousness. J. Consciousness Studies 2:3, 200-219 (1995)

648. Van Gulick, Robert, "Consciousness", Stanford Encyclopedia of Philosophy (Winter 2021 Edition).

649. (a) Howell, Robert J. and Alter, Torin (2009), Hard problem of consciousness. Scholarpedia, 4(6):4948

(b) Tye, Michael, "Qualia", Stanford Encyclopedia of Philosophy (Fall 2021 Edition).

(c) Levine, J., Materialism and Qualia: The Explanatory Gap. Pacific Phil. Quarterly, 54:354-361 (1983)

(d) Oliver Burkeman, Why can't the world's greatest minds solve the mystery of consciousness?
The Guardian, 21 Jan 2015

(e) Dan Falk, The Philosopher's Zombie. Aeon, 4 Feb 2022

650. (a) Dennett, D., Facing Backwards on the Problem of Consciousness. J Consciousness Stu. 3:1, 4-6 (1996)

(b) Hacker, Peter, How not to Argue. The Philosophers' Magazine 51:4, 23-32 (2010)

(c) Pigliucci, Massimo (2013), What hard problem? Philosophy Now, 99, Nov/Dec 2013

(d) Jim Holt, Is there such a thing as the self? Prospect Magazine, Jun 23, 2014

651. (a) Marc Bekoff, After 2,500 Studies, It's Time to Declare Animal Sentience Proven (Op-Ed).
Live Science, Sep 06, 2013

(b) Margulis, L., The Conscious Cell. Annals of the New York Academy of Sciences, 929:1, 55-70 (2001)

(c) Baluška, F., Miller Jr., W.B. & Reber, A.S.; Biomolecular Basis of Cellular Consciousness via Subcellular
Nanobrains. International Journal of Molecular Sciences, 22, 2545 (2021)

652. (a) Nagel, Thomas, What Is It Like to Be a Bat? The Philosophical Review, 83:4, 435–450 (1974)

(b) ibid. Full paper and pdf download available online.

(c) Mary Bates, What It Is Like to Be a Bat? Exploring the neuroscience of animal behavior.
Psychology Today, Feb 12, 2012

(d) Cal Flyn, What it's like to be a bat. Prospect Magazine, Jan 23, 2021

653. (a) Hacker, P.M.S., Is There Anything it is Like to be a Bat? Philosophy 77:2, 157-174 (2002)

(b) Smith, David Woodruff, "Phenomenology", Stanford Encyclopedia of Philosophy (Summer 2018 Ed.)

654. (a) Skrbina, David, "Panpsychism". Internet Encyclopedia of Philosophy, ISSN 2161-0002.

(b) Clark, S., Book review: Mortal Questions by Thomas Nagel. Cambridge University Press 1979.
Scottish Journal of Theology 33:5, 475-476 (1980)

(c) Goff, Philip (2017), The Case For Panpsychism. Philosophy Now, 121, Aug/Sep 2017

(d) ibid. 114

655. (a) Tam Hunt, Could consciousness all come down to the way things vibrate?
The Conversation, Nov 9, 2018

(b) Schooler J.W., Hunt T. & Schooler J.N. (2011). Reconsidering the Metaphysics of Science from the Inside Out. In: Walach H., Schmidt S., Jonas W. (eds) Neuroscience, Consciousness and Spirituality. Studies in Neuroscience, Consciousness and Spirituality 1, Springer, Dordrecht

656. (a) Chalmers, David J., Panpsychism and Panprotopsychism. The Amherst Lecture in Phil. 8, 1–35 (2013)
(b) David J. Chalmers, reply by John R. Searle. 'Consciousness and the Philosophers': An Exchange. The New York Review, May 15, 1997.
(c) Keith Frankish, Why panpsychism fails to solve the mystery of consciousness. Aeon, 20 Sep 2016
(d) Philip Goff, Panpsychism is crazy, but it's also most probably true. Aeon, 1 Mar 2017

657. (a) Riekki, T., Lindeman, M. & Lipsanen, J.; Conceptions about the mind-body problem and their relations to afterlife beliefs, paranormal beliefs, religiosity, and ontological confusions. Advances in Cognitive Psychology 9:3, 112–120 (2013)
(b) ibid. Full paper and pdf download also available at PMC4158462.
(c) Weed, L. (2011), Philosophy of Mind: An Overview. Philosophy Now, 87, Nov/Dec 2011

658. (a) McLeod, S.A., Mind body debate. Simply Psychology, Feb 05 2018
(b) Calef, Scott, "Dualism and Mind". Internet Encyclopedia of Philosophy, ISSN 2161-0002.
(c) Osborne, C. (2007), On the Transmigration of Souls: Reincarnation Into Animal Bodies in Pythagoras, Empedocles, and Plato. Ch.3 in Dumb Beasts and Dead Philosophers: Humanity and the Humane, OUP.

659. (a) Skirry, Justin, "René Descartes: The Mind-Body Distinction". Internet Encyclopedia of Philosophy.
(b) Smart, J.J. C., The Mind/Brain Identity Theory. Stanford Encyclopedia of Philosophy (Spring2017 Ed)
(c) Thibaut, F., The mind-body Cartesian dualism and psychiatry. Dialog. Clinical Neurosci. 20:1, 3 (2018)

660. (a) Sean Robsville, Bridging the Explanatory Gap of the Hard Problem - from the Side of the Mind. Rational Buddhism blog, 28 Feb 2012
(b) ibid, 75
(c) de Spinoza, Benedict (1677), Of the Nature & Origin of the Mind. Part II of The Ethics. Trans. from the Latin by R.H.M. Elwes. Project Gutenberg online.
(d) Stubenberg, Leopold, "Neutral Monism", Stanford Encyclopedia of Philosophy (Fall 2018 Ed.)

661. (a) Robinson, William "Epiphenomenalism", Stanford Encyclopedia of Philosophy (Summer 2019 Ed.)
(b) Walter, Sven, "Epiphenomenalism". Internet Encyclopedia of Philosophy, ISSN 2161-0002.

662. (a) Chalmers, D.J. (2003). Consciousness and its Place in Nature. In: The Blackwell Guide to Philosophy of Mind (eds S.P. Stich and T.A. Warfield).
(b) ibid. Full paper and pdf download available online.

663. (a) Oppy, G. & D. Dowe "The Turing Test", Stanford Encyclopedia of Philosophy (Winter 2021 Ed.)
(b) Searle, J.R., "Minds, brains, and programs". Behavioral and Brain Sciences 3:3, 417-424 (1980)
(c) Cole, David "The Chinese Room Argument", Stanford Encyclopedia of Philosophy (Winter 2020 Ed.)

664. (a) Shane Snow, How Emotional Intelligence Separates Us From A.I. Forbes, Mar 4, 2021
(b) O. Brookhouse, Can Artificial Intelligence understand emotions? Think Big, Telefónica, 7 Feb 2022

665. (a) Smythies, J., Book review: The Rediscovery of the Mind by John R. Searle. Psychological Medicine 23:4, 1043-1046 (1993)
(b) Searle, J.R., Why I am not a property dualist. Journal of Consciousness Studies 9:12, 57-64 (2002)
(c) ibid. Full paper and pdf download available online.
(d) Searle, J. (2007, 2017). Biological Naturalism. In The Blackwell Companion to Consciousness (eds S. Schneider and M. Velmans).

666. (a) Shapiro, L.A., Multiple Realizations. The Journal of Philosophy, 97:12, 635-654 (2000)
(b) Bickle, John, "Multiple Realizability", Stanford Encyclopedia of Philosophy (Summer 2020 Ed.)

667. (a) Robbins, Philip, "Modularity of Mind", Stanford Encyclopedia of Philosophy (Winter 2017 Ed.)
(b) Fodor, J., "Searle on what only brains can do". Behavioral and Brain Sciences 3:3, 431-432 (1980)
(c) Corcoran, K., The Trouble with Searle's Biological Naturalism. Erkenntnis 55:3, 307-324 (2001)

668. (a) Tegmark, Max, Consciousness as a state of matter. Chaos, Solitons & Fractals 76, 238-270 (2015)
(b) ibid. Full paper and pdf download available at arXiv:1401.1219 [quant-ph]
(c) Why Physicists Are Saying Consciousness Is A State Of Matter, Like a Solid, A Liquid Or A Gas. Physics arXiv Blog, Medium, Jan 15, 2014

669. (a) Tononi, Giulio (2015), Integrated information theory. Scholarpedia, 10(1):4164
(b) Oizumi, M., Albantakis, L. & Tononi, G.; From the Phenomenology to the Mechanisms of Consciousness: Integrated Information Theory 3.0. PLOS Computational Biology 10:5, e1003588 (2014)
(c) ibid. 660d.

670. (a) ibid, 114.

(b) Koch, Christof, A "Complex" Theory of Consciousness. Is complexity the secret to sentience, to a panpsychic view of consciousness? Scientific American Mind 20:4, 16-19 (2009)

(c) Mørch, Hedda H. (2017), The Integrated Information Theory of Consciousness.
Philosophy Now, 121, Aug/Sep 2017

(d) Tsuchiya, N., What is it like to be a bat? — a pathway to the answer from the integrated information theory. Philosophy Compass, 12:3, e12407 (2017)

671. (a) John R. Searle, Can Information Theory Explain Consciousness? Book review: Consciousness: Confessions of a Romantic Reductionist by Christof Koch. The New York Review, Jan 10, 2013

(b) Scott Aaronson, Why I Am Not An Integrated Information Theorist (or, The Unconscious Expander). Blog post, May 21st, 2014

(c) Giulio Tononi, Why Scott should stare at a blank wall and reconsider (or, the conscious grid). Response to Scott Aaronson (2014)

(d) Scott Aaronson, "Giulio Tononi and Me: A Phi-nal Exchange". Blog post, May 30th, 2014

(e) Cerullo, M.A., The Problem with Phi: A Critique of Integrated Information Theory.
PLoS Computational Biology11:9, e1004286 (2015)

(f) Paul L. Nunez, Consciousness and Integrated Information Theory. Psychology Today, Dec 13, 2021

672. (a) John Horgan, Can Integrated Information Theory Explain Consciousness? Sci. American, Dec 1, 2015

(b) Tononi, G. & Koch, C.; Consciousness: here, there and everywhere?
Philosophical Transactions of the R. Society B, 370:1668 ,20140167 (2015)

673. (a) Jacob Sage, Mind, Brain and Consciousness. Psychology Today, Jan 31, 2011

(b) Webb, T.W. & Graziano, M.S.A, The attention schema theory: a mechanistic account of subjective awareness. Frontiers in Psychology, 6 (2015)

(c) Graziano, M.S.A., The Attention Schema Theory: A Foundation for Engineering Artificial Consciousness. Frontiers in Robotics and AI, 4 (2017)

674. (a) Escobar, W.A., Quantized visual awareness. Frontiers in Psychology, 4, (2013)

(b) W. Alex Escobar, Breaking down experiences into millions of parts may help explain consciousness. The Conversation, Sep 15, 2014

675. (a) von der Malsburg, C., The What and Why of Binding: The Modeler's Perspective.
Neuron 24:1, 95-104 (1999)

(b) Brook, Andrew & Paul Raymont, "The Unity of Consciousness". Stanford Encyclopedia of Philosophy (Summer 2021 Edition), Edward N. Zalta (ed.)

676. (a) Connors, B.W. & Regehr, W.G.; Neuronal firing: Does function follow form?
Current Biology 6:12, 1560-1562 (1996)

(b) Singer, Wolf, "Binding by synchrony". Scholarpedia, 2:12, 1657 (2007)

(c) Shadlen, M.N. & Movshon, J.A.; Synchrony Unbound: A Critical Evaluation of the Temporal Binding Hypothesis. Neuron 24:1, 67-77 (1999)

(d) Merker, B., Cortical gamma oscillations: the functional key is activation, not cognition.
Neuroscience & Biobehavioral Reviews 37:3, 401-417 (2013)

677. (a) Glyn, I.M. & Brelstaff, G.; Reviews: The Astonishing Hypothesis: The Scientific Search for the Soul. Computational Models of Visual Processing by Francis Crick. Perception 23:3, 367-370 (1994)

(b) Hopfield, J.J., Neural networks and physical systems with emergent collective computational abilities. PNAS 79:8, 2554-2558 (1982)

(c) Hopfield, J.J., An Envisioning of Consciousness. The Astonishing Hypothesis: The Scientific Search for the Soul by Francis Crick. Science 263:5147, 696-696 (1994)

(d) Treisman, A.M. & Gelade, G.; A feature-integration theory of attention. Cogn Psy 12:1, 97-136 (1980)

678. (a) Eguchi, A., Isbister, J.B., Ahmad, N. & Stringer, S.; The emergence of polychronization and feature binding in a spiking neural network model of the primate ventral visual system.
Psychological Review 125:4, 545-571 (2018)

(b) Isbister, J.B., Eguchi, A., Ahmad, N. et al.; A new approach to solving the feature-binding problem in primate vision. R. Soc. Interface Focus 8:4, 20180021 (2018)

679. (a) Godwin, D., Barry, R.L. & Marois, R.; Breakdown of the brain's functional network modularity with awareness. PNAS 112:12, 3799-3804 (2015)

(b) Network theory suggests consciousness is global in the brain. Kurzweil library online, Mar 16, 2015

680. (a) Lahav, N., Ksherim, B., Ben-Simon, E. et al.; K-shell decomposition reveals hierarchical cortical organization of the human brain. New Journal of Physics, 18, 083013 (2016)

(b) Carmi, S., Havlin, S., Kirkpatrick, S. et al.; A model of Internet topology using k-shell decomposition. PNAS 104:27, 11150-11154 (2007)

(c) Bar-Ilan University, "Where is my mind? New study looks for the cortical conscious network." ScienceDaily, 31 Oct 2016

(d) Guldenmund, P., Gantner, I.S., Baquero, K. et al.; Propofol-Induced Frontal Cortex Disconnection: A Study of Resting-State Networks, Total Brain Connectivity, and Mean BOLD Signal Oscillation Frequencies. Brain Connectivity 6:3, 225-237 (2016)

681. (a) Lovett, A., & Forbus, K.; Modeling visual problem solving as analogical reasoning. Psychological Review 124:1, 60–90 (2017)

(b) Northwestern University, "Making AI systems that see the world as humans do: Model performs at human levels on standard intelligence test." ScienceDaily, 19 Jan 2017

(c) Kwiatkowski,R. &Lipson,H.; Task-agnostic self-modeling machines. SciRobotics 4:26, eaau9354 (2019)

(d) Columbia University School of Engineering and Applied Science, "Engineers create a robot that can 'imagine' itself." ScienceDaily, 30 Jan 2019

(e) Carruthers, Peter and Rocco Gennaro, "Higher-Order Theories of Consciousness", Stanford Encyclopedia of Philosophy (Fall 2020 Edition), Edward N. Zalta (ed.).

682. (a) Ullian, J.S. (1971), Hilary Putnam. Minds and machines (ed. A.R. Anderson, Prentice-Hall Inc. NJ), 1964 pp. 72–97. Reprinted fron Dimensions of mind, A symposium, ed. S. Hook, NYU Press 1960 pp. 148–179. Journal of Symbolic Logic, 36:1, 177-177

(b) Falguera, José L., Concha Martínez-Vidal & Gideon Rosen, "Abstract Objects", Stanford Encyclopedia of Philosophy (Winter 2021 Edition), Edward N. Zalta (ed.)

(c) Reicher, Maria, "Nonexistent Objects", Stanford Encyclopedia of Philosophy (Winter 2019 Ed.)

683. (a) Edelman, Shimon, On the Nature of Minds, or: Truth and Consequences. Journal of Experimental and Theoretical AI, 20:3, 181-196 (2008)

(b). ibid. Full paper and pdf download available online.

(c) Rescorla, Michael, "The Computational Theory of Mind", Stanford Encyclopedia of Philosophy (Fall 2020 Edition), Edward N. Zalta (ed.)

(d) Schweizer, P., Triviality Arguments Reconsidered. Minds & Machines 29, 287–308 (2019)

684. (a) Blackmon, J., Searle's Wall. Erkenn 78, 109–117 (2013)

(b) J.R. Searle, 'Is Just Thinking Enough?'. In response to C. McGinn. New York Review, Feb 24, 2011

(c) Rivetti, A.T. (1990), Book reviews. Representation and reality, by Hilary Putnam, MIT Press, Cambridge, Massachusetts, 1988, 136 pp and A Cognitive Theory of Metaphor, by Earl R. MacCormac, MIT Press, Cambridge, Massachusetts, 1985, 254 pp.. Systems Research 7:3, 209-210

685. (a) Piccinini, Gualtiero & Corey Maley, "Computation in Physical Systems", Stanford Encyclopedia of Philosophy (Summer 2021 Edition), Edward N. Zalta (ed.)

(b) Piccinini, G. & Bahar, S.; Neural Computation and the Computational Theory of Cognition. Cognitive Science 37:3, 453-488 (2013)

686. (a) Rescorla, Michael, "The Language of Thought Hypothesis", Stanford Encyclopedia of Philosophy (Summer 2019 Edition), Edward N. Zalta (ed.)

(b) Tillas, A., Language as grist to the mill of cognition. CognitiveProcessing 16, 219–243 (2015)

(c) Verdejo, V., The Commitment to LOT. Dialogue 55(2), 313-341 (2016)

687. (a) Arantes, M.E. & Cendes, F.; In Search of a New Paradigm for Functional Magnetic Resonance Experimentation With Language. Frontiers in Neurology, 11 (2020)

(b) Kaye, L.J., The languages of thought. Philosophy of Science 62:1, 92-110 (1995)

(c) Woodfield, A., "Peter Carruthers, Language, Thought and Consciousness: An Essay In Philosophical Psychology". Book review. The British Journal for the Philosophy of Science 49:1, 168-174 (1998)

(d) Block, Ned, Mental Pictures and Cognitive Science. The Philosophical Review 92:4, 499–541 (1983)

(e) Dobler, T., The Occasion-Sensitivity of Thought. Topoi 39, 487–497 (2020)

688. (a) C.Hales, Learning experience: let's take consciousness in from the cold. The Conversation, May16,2012

(b) John Horgan, Mind–Body Problems: My Meta-Solution to the Mystery of Who We Really Are. Scientific American, Sep 10, 2018

(c) Tania Lombrozo (2014), The Mind Is Just The Brain. Response to the 2014 Edge.org question.

(d) Adam Frank, Minding matter. The closer you look, the more the materialist position in physics appears to rest on shaky metaphysical ground. Aeon, 13 Mar 2017

689. (a) ibid, 234.

(b) Penrose, Roger, Précis of The Emperor's New Mind: Concerning computers, minds, and the laws of physics. Behavioral and Brain Sciences 13:4, 643-655 (1990)

(c) Raatikainen, Panu, "Gödel's Incompleteness Theorems", Stanford Encyclopedia of Philosophy (Spring 2022 Edition), Edward N. Zalta (ed.)

(d) Natalie Wolchover, How Gödel's Proof Works. Quanta, Jul 14, 2020

(e) Penrose, Roger, The Emperor's New Mind. Summary. RSA Journal, 139:5420, 506–514 (1991)

690. (a) ibid, 259b

(b) ibid, 221b

691. (a) Hameroff, S.R. & Watt, R.C.; Information processing in microtubules.
Journal of Theoretical Biology 98:4, 549-561 (1982)

(b) Hameroff, S., Quantum computation in brain microtubules? The Penrose–Hameroff 'Orch OR' model of consciousness. Phil. Trans. R. Soc. A. 356:1743, 1869–1896 (1998)

(c) Julian Brown, Tell me where consciousness is bred: Shadows of the Mind by Roger Penrose, Oxford University Press, pp 320, £16.99. Book review, New Scientist, 19 Nov 1994.

692. (a) Victor Stenger, The Myth of Quantum Consciousness. First published in The Humanist in 1992. HuffPost, 27 Oct 2010

(b) Hilary Putnam, The Best of All Possible Brains? Review of Shadows of the Mind by Roger Penrose. New York Times, Nov 20, 1994

(c) Tegmark, M., Importance of quantum decoherence in brain processes. PhyRevE 61:4,4194-4206 (2000)

(d) ibid. Full paper and pdf download available at arXiv:quant-ph/9907009

(e) McKemmish, L.K., Reimers, J.R., McKenzie, R.H. et al.; Penrose-Hameroff orchestrated objective-reduction proposal for human consciousness is not biologically feasible. Phys. Rev. E 80:2, 021912 (2009)

693. (a) Sahu, S., Ghosh, S., Ghosh, B. et al.; Atomic water channel controlling remarkable properties of a single brain microtubule: Correlating single protein to its supramolecular assembly. Biosensors and Bioelectronics 47, 141-148 (2013)

(b) Emerson, D.J., Weiser, B.P., Psonis, J. et al.; Direct Modulation of Microtubule Stability Contributes to Anthracene General Anesthesia. J. Am. Chem. Soc. 135:14, 5389–5398 (2013)

694. (a) Günter, G., Schempp, H., Robert-de-Saint-Vincent, M. et al.; Observing the Dynamics of Dipole-Mediated Energy Transport by Interaction-Enhanced Imaging. Science 342:6161, 954-956 (2013)

(b) Heidelberg University. "Key processes of photosynthesis simulated on quantum level." ScienceDaily, 8 Nov 2013

(c) O'Reilly, E. & Olaya-Castro, A.; Non-classicality of the molecular vibrations assisting exciton energy transfer at room temperature. Nature Communications 5, 3012 (2014)

(d) UCL. "Quantum mechanics explains efficiency of photosynthesis." ScienceDaily, 9 Jan 2014

695. (a) Fisher, M.P.A., Quantum cognition: The possibility of processing with nuclear spins in the brain. Annals of Physics 362, 593-602 (2015)

(b) Jennifer Ouellette, A New Spin on the Quantum Brain. Quanta, Nov 2, 2016

(c) John Preskill, Wouldn't you like to know what's going on in my mind? Quantum Frontiers, Caltech, Nov 6, 2015

696. (a) Hameroff, S. & Penrose, R.; Consciousness in the universe: A review of the 'Orch OR' theory. Physics of Life Reviews 11:1, 39-78 (2014)

(b) Elsevier. "Discovery of quantum vibrations in 'microtubules' inside brain neurons supports controversial theory of consciousness." ScienceDaily, 16 Jan 2014

(c) Koch, C. & Hepp, K. Quantum mechanics in the brain. Nature 440, 611 (2006)

(d) Betony Adams & Francesco Petruccione, Do quantum effects play a role in consciousness? Physics World, 26 Jan 2021

697. (a) Dawes, Gregory W., "Ancient and Medieval Empiricism", Stanford Encyclopedia of Philosophy (Winter 2017 Edition), Edward N. Zalta (ed.)

(b) Samet, Jerry, "The Historical Controversies Surrounding Innateness", Stanford Encyclopedia of Philosophy (Summer 2019 Edition), Edward N. Zalta (ed.)

(c) Locke, John (1690), An Essay Concerning Humane Understanding, Book I. Project Gutenberg online.

698. (a) Nature vs. Nurture. Psychology Today

(b) Kimberly Powell, Nature vs. Nurture: How Are Personalities Formed? ThoughtCo, Aug 14, 2019

(c) Sravanti, Lakshmi, Nurture the nature. Indian Journal of Psychiatry 59:3, 385 (2017)

699. (a) Libet, B., Gleason, C.A., Wright, E.W. et al.; Time of conscious intention to act in relation to onset of cerebral activity (readiness-potential): The unconscious initiation of a freely voluntary act. Brain 106:3, 623-642 (1983)

(b) Soon, C., Brass, M., Heinze, HJ. et al. Unconscious determinants of free decisions in the human brain. Nature Neuroscience 11, 543–545 (2008)

700. (a) Heisenberg, M. Is free will an illusion? Nature 459, 164–165 (2009)

(b) Smith, K. Neuroscience vs philosophy: Taking aim at free will. Nature 477, 23–25 (2011)

(c) Pereboom, D. (2001). Living without Free Will. Cambridge Studies in Philosophy, CU Press.

701. (a) Trevena, J. & Miller, J.; Brain preparation before a voluntary action: Evidence against unconscious movement initiation. Consciousness and Cognition 19:1, 447-456 (2010)

(b) Schurger, A., Sitt, J.D. & Dehaene, S.; An accumulator model for spontaneous neural activity prior to self-initiated movement. PNAS 109:42, E2904-E2913 (2012)

702. (a) Denyse O'Leary, How Can We Believe in Naturalism if We Have No Choice?
Evolution News & Science Today (EN), Feb 10, 2015

(b) Kamala Kelkar, Can a brain scan uncover your morals? The Guardian, 17 Jan 2016

703. (a) Erika Engelhaupt, BOOK REVIEW: The Science of Evil: On Empathy and the Origins of Cruelty by Simon Baron-Cohen. Science News, Jul 15, 2011

(b) K. Bouton, From Hitler to Mother Teresa: 6 Degrees of Empathy. New York Times, Jun 13, 2011

(c) Ron Rosenbaum, The End of Evil? Neuroscientists suggest there is no such thing. Are they right? Slate, Sep 30, 2011

(d) Ball, P., Do flies have free will? Nature (2007)

704. (a) Libet, B., Unconscious cerebral initiative and the role of conscious will in voluntary action.
Behavioral and Brain Sciences 8:4, 529-539 (1985)

(b) Filevich, E., Kühn, S. & Haggard, P.; There Is No Free Won't: Antecedent Brain Activity Predicts Decisions to Inhibit. PLoS ONE 8:2, e53053 (2013)

(c) Schultze-Kraft, M., Birman, D., Rusconi, M. et al.; The point of no return in vetoing self-initiated movements. PNAS 113:4, 1080-1085 (2016)

(d) Charité - Universitätsmedizin Berlin. "The brain-computer duel: Do we have free will? Researchers test mechanisms involved in decision-making." ScienceDaily, 4 Jan 2016

705. (a) Scotty Hendricks, Free Will or Free Won't? Neuroscience on the Choices We Can (and Can't) Make. Big Think, Sep 30, 2016

(b) Tim A Pychyl, Free Won't: It May Be All That We Have (or Need). Psychology Today, Jun 20, 2011

(c) Deecke, L. & Soekadar, S.R.; Beyond the point of no return: Last-minute changes in human motor performance. PNAS 113:21, E2876-E2876 (2016)

706. (a) Dennett, D.C., The Self as a Responding—and Responsible—Artifact.
Annals of the New York Academy of Sciences 1001:1, 39-50 (2003)

(b) ibid. Full paper and pdf download available online

(c) K. Malik, Review of Freedom Evolves by Daniel Dennett. First pub. in New Statesman, 10 Feb 2003

707. (a) Christian Jarrett, Neuroscience and Free Will Are Rethinking Their Divorce. The Cut, Feb. 3, 2016

(b) Magda Osman, To what extent are we ruled by unconscious forces? The Conversation, May 26, 2021

708. (a) Inagaki, H.K., Chen, S., Ridder, M.C. et al.; A midbrain-thalamus-cortex circuit reorganizes cortical dynamics to initiate movement. Cell 185:6, P1065-1081.e23 (2022)

(b) Max Planck Florida Institute for Neuroscience, "Ready, set ... GO! Scientists discover a brain circuit that triggers the execution of planned movement." ScienceDaily, 14 Mar 2022

709. (a) Mcginn, Colin, Can We Solve the Mind–Body Problem? Mind 98:391, 349–366 (1989)

(b) Dennett, D.C. (1991), The Brain and its Boundaries: Review of The Problem of Consciousness by Colin McGinn. The Times Literary Supplement, May 10, 1991 (Tufts digital library ID: rv0435288)

(c) Mysterianism lite. Nature Neuroscience 3, 199 (2000)

(d) Colin McGinn, Mysterianism Revisited. Blog post, Dec 23, 2014

710. (a) Margaret Wertheim, I feel therefore I am. Aeon, 01 Dec 2015

(b) Nicholas G. Carr (2017), Mysterianism. Response to the 2017 Edge.org question.

711. (a) Ebbinghaus, H. (1885), Memory: A Contribution to Experimental Psychology.
Reprint: Annals of Neurosciences 20:4, 155-156 (2013)

(b) ibid. Full paper and pdf download available at PMC4117135.

712. (a) Jacoby, L.L. & Witherspoon, D.; Remembering without awareness.
Canadian Journal of Psychology 36:2, 300–324 (1982)

(b) Jacoby, L.L. & Dallas, M.; On the relationship between autobiographical memory and perceptual learning. Journal of Experimental Psychology: General, 110:3, 306–340 (1981)

(c) Schacter, D.L., Implicit memory: History and current status. Journal of Experimental Psychology: Learning, Memory, and Cognition, 13:3, 501–518 (1987)

(d) Loonis, R.F., Brincat, S.L., Antzoulatos, E.G. & Miller, E.K.; A Meta-Analysis Suggests Different Neural Correlates for Implicit and Explicit Learning. Neuron 96:2, 521–534.e7 (2017)

(e) Massachusetts Institute of Technology, "Brain waves reflect different types of learning." ScienceDaily, 12 Oct 2017

713. (a) Brown, R.E. Donald O. Hebb and the Organization of Behavior: 17 years in the writing.
Molecular Brain 13, 55 (2020)

(b) Shaw, G.L. (1986), Donald Hebb: The Organization of Behavior. In: Palm, G., Aertsen, A. (eds) Brain Theory pp 231–233. Springer, Berlin, Heidelberg.

(c) Löwel, S. & Singer, W.; Selection of Intrinsic Horizontal Connections in the Visual Cortex by Correlated Neuronal Activity. Science 255:5041, 209-212 (1992)

(d) Caporale, N. & Dan, Y.; Spike Timing–Dependent Plasticity: A Hebbian Learning Rule. Annual Review of Neuroscience 31:1, 25-46 (2008)

714. (a) Miller, G.A., The magical number seven, plus or minus two: Some limits on our capacity for processing information. Psychological Review 63:2, 81–97 (1956)

(b) Cowan, N. (2008), Chapter 20: What are the differences between long-term, short-term, and working memory? In Essence of Memory, Elsevier, eds. W.S. Sossin, J-C Lacaille, V.F. Castellucci, S Belleville. Progress in Brain Research 169, 323-338

(c) ibid. Full paper and pdf download available at PMC2657600.

715. (a) Squire, L.R., The legacy of patient H. M. for neuroscience. Neuron 61:1, 6–9 (2009)

(b) Erin Heaning, Henry Gustav Molaison: The Curious Case of Patient H.M. Simply Psych, Jan 13, 2022

(c) Shah, B., Pattanayak, R. & Sagar, R.; The study of patient Henry Molaison and what it taught us over past 50 years: Contributions to neuroscience. J Mental Health Hum Behav 19:2, 91-93 (2014)

716. (a) Annese, J., Schenker-Ahmed, N., Bartsch, H. et al.; Postmortem examination of patient H.M.'s brain based on histological sectioning and digital 3D reconstruction. Nature Communications 5, 3122 (2014)

(b) Squire, L.R. & Wixted, J.T.; The Cognitive Neuroscience of Human Memory Since H.M.. Annual Review of Neuroscience 34:1, 259-288 (2011)

(c) ibid. Full paper and pdf download available at PMC3192650.

717. (a) Moore, J.J., Ravassard, P.M., Ho, D. et al.; Dynamics of cortical dendritic membrane potential and spikes in freely behaving rats. Science 355:6331, eaaj1497 (2017)

(b) University of California - Los Angeles, "Brain is 10 times more active than previously measured." ScienceDaily, 9 Mar 2017

718. (a) Chen, S., Cai, D., Pearce, K. et al.; Reinstatement of long-term memory following erasure of its behavioral and synaptic expression in Aplysia. eLife 3, e03896 (2014)

(b) University of California, Los Angeles, "Lost memories might be able to be restored, suggests research into marine snail." ScienceDaily, 20 Dec 2014

(c) Ryan, T.J., Roy, D.S., Pignatelli, M., Arons, A. & Tonegawa, S.; Engram cells retain memory under retrograde amnesia. Science 348:6238, 1007-1013 (2015)

(d) Massachusetts Institute of Technology, "Scientists retrieve lost memories using optogenetics." ScienceDaily, 28 May 2015

719. (a) Dubue, J.D., McKinney, T.L., Treit, D. & Dickson, C.T.; Intrahippocampal Anisomycin Impairs Spatial Performance on the Morris Water Maze. Journal of Neuroscience 35:31, 11118-11124 (2015)

(b) University of Alberta, Consolidating consciousness: Memory permanence may be mediated by neural rehearsal following learning. Medical Xpress, Aug 4, 2015

(c) Rose, N.S., LaRocque, J.J., Riggall, A.C. et al.; Reactivation of latent working memories with transcranial magnetic stimulation. Science 354:6316, 1136-1139 (2016)

(d) Anna Azvolinsky, Retrieving Short-Term Memories. The Scientist, Dec 1, 2016

720. (a) Parthasarathy, A., Herikstad, R., Bong, J.H. et al. Mixed selectivity morphs population codes in prefrontal cortex. Nature Neuroscience 20, 1770–1779 (2017)

(b) Cavanagh, S., Towers, J., Wallis, J. et al. Reconciling persistent and dynamic hypotheses of working memory coding in prefrontal cortex. Nature Communications 9, 3498 (2018)

721. (a) Maria Cohut, Alzheimer's: 'Music may make symptoms more manageable'. Medical News Today, Apr 30, 2018

(b) Ned Dymoke, Study: Memories of music cannot be lost to Alzheimer's and dementia. Big Think, Apr 29, 2018

722. (a) Parthasarathy, A., Tang, C., Herikstad, R. et al.; Time-invariant working memory representations in the presence of code-morphing in the lateral prefrontal cortex. Nature Communications 10, 4995 (2019)

(b) National University of Singapore, "Researchers use machine learning tools to reveal how memories are coded in the brain." ScienceDaily, 27 Nov 2019

(c) Hammer, S., Monavarfeshani, A., Lemon, T. et al.; Multiple Retinal Axons Converge onto Relay Cells in the Adult Mouse Thalamus. Cell Reports 12:10, 1575-1583 (2015)

(d) Virginia Tech, "'Brainbow' reveals surprising data about visual connections in brain." ScienceDaily, 27 Aug 2015

723. (a) Reimann, M.W., Nolte, M., Scolamiero, M. et al.; Cliques of Neurons Bound into Cavities Provide a Missing Link between Structure and Function. Frontiers in Compututational Neuroscience, 11 (2017)

(b) Frontiers, "'Multi-dimensional universe' in brain networks: Using mathematics in a novel way in neuroscience, scientists demonstrate that the brain operates on many dimensions, not just the 3 dimensions that we are accustomed to." ScienceDaily, 12 Jun 2017

724. (a) van den Berg, R. & Ma, W.J.; A resource-rational theory of set size effects in human visual working memory. eLife 7, e34963 (2018)

(b) Uppsala University, "Working memory might be more flexible than previously thought." ScienceDaily, 16 Aug 2018

725. (a) Mandler, G., Recognizing: The judgment of previous occurrence. Psych. Review, 87:3, 252–271 (1980)

(b) ibid. Full paper and pdf download available online

(c) Jacoby, Larry L., A process dissociation framework: Separating automatic from intentional uses of memory. Journal of Memory and Language 30:5, 513-541 (1991)

(d) Cabeza, R., Kapur, S., Craik, F.I.M. et al.; Functional Neuroanatomy of Recall and Recognition: A PET Study of Episodic Memory. Journal of Cognitive Neuroscience 9:2, 254–265 (1997)

(e) ibid. Full paper and pdf download available online.

(f) Mandler, G., Familiarity Breeds Attempts: A Critical Review of Dual-Process Theories of Recognition. Perspectives on Psychological Science 3:5, 390-399 (2008)

726. (a) Rutishauser, U., Schuman, E.M. & Mamelak, A.N.; Activity of human hippocampal and amygdala neurons during retrieval of declarative memories. PNAS 105:1, 329-334 (2008)

(b) Hannula, D.E. & Ranganath, C.; The Eyes Have It: Hippocampal Activity Predicts Expression of Memory in Eye Movements. Neuron 63:5, 592-599 (2009)

(c) Horner, A., Bisby, J., Bush, D. et al.; Evidence for holistic episodic recollection via hippocampal pattern completion. Nature Communications 6, 7462 (2015)

(d) University College London, "How the human brain might reconstruct past events: Remembering one tidbit can reactive entire event in the brain." ScienceDaily, 2 Jul 2015

727. (a) Richter, F.R., Cooper, R.A., Bays, P.M. & Simons, J.S.; Distinct neural mechanisms underlie the success, precision, and vividness of episodic memory. eLife 5, e18260 (2016)

(b) Riès, S.K., Dhillon, R.K., Clarke, A. et al.; Spatiotemporal dynamics of word retrieval in speech production revealed by cortical high-frequency band activity. PNAS 114:23, E4530-E4538 (2017)

(c) San Diego State University, "Mapping how words leap from brain to tongue: Neuroscientist explores the complex brain connections employed during word retrieval." ScienceDaily, 19 Jun 2017

(d) Murray, J.G., Howie, C.A. & Donaldson, D.I.; The neural mechanism underlying recollection is sensitive to the quality of episodic memory: Event related potentials reveal a some-or-none threshold. NeuroImage 120, 298-308 (2015)

728. (a) Roy, D.S., Kitamura, T., Okuyama, T. et al.; Distinct Neural Circuits for the Formation and Retrieval of Episodic Memories. Cell 170:5, 1000-1012.e19 (2017)

(b) Anne Trafton, How we recall the past. Neuroscientists discover a brain circuit dedicated to retrieving memories. MIT News Office, Aug 17, 2017

(c) Ding, S., Cueva, C.J., Tsodyks, M. & Qian, N.; Visual perception as retrospective Bayesian decoding from high- to low-level features. PNAS 114:43, E9115-E9124 (2017)

(d) The Zuckerman Institute at Columbia University, "Human brain recalls visual features in reverse order than it detects them." ScienceDaily, 9 Oct 2017

729. (a) Vaz, A.P., Wittig, J.H., Inati, S.K. & Zaghloul, K.A.; Replay of cortical spiking sequences during human memory retrieval. Science 367:6482, 1131-1134 (2020)

(b) NIH/Nat Inst. of Neurological Disorders and Stroke, "Scientists monitor brains replaying memories in real time: Our brains use distinct firing patterns to store and replay memories." ScienceDaily, 5 Mar 2020

730. (a) Nairne, James S., The myth of the encoding-retrieval match. Memory 10:5-6, 389-395 (2002)

(b) Choi, H. & Smith, S.M.; Incubation and the Resolution of Tip-of-the-Tongue States. The Journal of General Psychology 132:4, 365-376 (2005)

(c) Mace, John, Priming involuntary autobiographical memories. Memory 13:8, 874-884 (2005)

(d) Krans, J., de Bree, J. & Moulds, M.L.; Involuntary Cognitions in Everyday Life: Exploration of Type, Quality, Content, and Function. Frontiers in Psychiatry, 6 (2015)

731. (a) Qasim, S.E., Miller, J., Inman, C.S. et al.; Memory retrieval modulates spatial tuning of single neurons in the human entorhinal cortex. Nature Neuroscience 22, 2078–2086 (2019)

(b) Khan, U., Liu, L., Provenzano, F. et al.; Molecular drivers and cortical spread of lateral entorhinal cortex dysfunction in preclinical Alzheimer's disease. Nature Neuroscience 17, 304–311 (2014)

(c) ibid. Full paper and pdf download available at PMC4004925.

(d) Columbia University School of Engineering and Applied Science, "Specific neurons that map memories now identified in the human brain." ScienceDaily, 12 Nov 2019

732. Barba, G.D., Brazzarola, M. et al.; A longitudinal study of confabulation. Cortex 87, 44-51 (2017)

733. (a) Coltheart, Max, Confabulation and conversation. Cortex 87, 62-68 (2017)

(b) Kopelman, M.D., Varieties of confabulation and delusion. Cogn. Neuropsychiatry 15:1-3, 14-37 (2010)

(c) Metcalf, K., Langdon, R. & Coltheart, M.; Models of confabulation: A critical review and a new framework. Cognitive Neuropsychology 24:1, 23-47 (2007)

(d) Langdon, R. & Turner, M.; Delusion and confabulation: Overlapping or distinct distortions of reality? Cognitive Neuropsychiatry 15:1-3, 1-13 (2010)

(e) Schnider, A. (2012), Confabulation and Reality Filtering. Encyclopedia of Human Behavior (2nd Ed.) 563-571, ed. V.S. Ramachandran.

734. Zagorski, N., Profile of Elizabeth F. Loftus. PNAS 102:39, 13721-13723 (2005)

735. (a) Schnider, Armin, Orbitofrontal reality filtering. Frontiers in Behavioral Neuroscience, 7 (2013)

(b) Thézé, R., Manuel, A.L., Nahum, L. et al.; Frontiers in Behavioral Neuroscience, 11 (2017)

(c) ibid, 733e

(a) Barba, G.D. & Kopelman, M.; Confabulations and related disorders: We've come a long way, but there is still a lot to do! Cortex 87, 1-4 (2017)

736. (b) Triviño, M., Ródenas, E. et al.; Effectiveness of a neuropsychological treatment for confabulations after brain injury: A clinical trial with theoretical implications. PLoS ONE 12:3, e0173166 (2017)

737. (a) Foschini, Luigi (2013), Where the "it from bit" come from? arXiv:1306.0545 [physics.hist-ph]

(b) ibid, 663c

(c) ibid, 683c

738. (a) R. Berezin, The Brain Is NOT a Computer Stuck on Top of a Body. Psychology Today, Mar 22, 2014

(b) ibid, 442(a)

(c) Gary Marcus, "Ray Kurzweil's Dubious New Theory of Mind". The New Yorker, Nov 15, 2012

(d) du Castel, B., Pattern Activation/Recognition Theory Of Mind. Front. Comput. Neurosci., 9 (2015)

739. Robert Epstein, The empty brain. Your brain does not process information, retrieve knowledge or store memories. Aeon, 18 May 2016

740. (a) Shapiro, Lawrence and Shannon Spaulding, "Embodied Cognition". Stanford Encyclopedia of Philosophy (Winter 2021 Edition), Edward N. Zalta (ed.)

(b) Ward, D., Silverman, D. & Villalobos, M.; Introduction: The Varieties of Enactivism. Topoi 36, 365–375 (2017)

(c) Samuel McNerney, A Brief Guide to Embodied Cognition: Why You Are Not Your Brain. Scientific American, Nov 4, 2011

741. (a) Zwaan, R.A., Two Challenges to "Embodied Cognition" Research And How to Overcome Them. Journal of Cognition, 4:1, 14 (2021)

(b) Wilson, M., Six views of embodied cognition. Psychonomic Bulletin & Review 9, 625–636 (2002)

(c) Wilson, A. & Golonka, S.; Embodied cognition is not what you think it is. Front. in Psychol, 4 (2013)

(d) Farina, M., Embodied cognition: dimensions, domains and applications. Adap Behav 29:1,73-88 (2021)

742. (a) ibid, 716a

(b) ibid, 716c

743. (a) Pribram, Karl H., Recollections. NeuroQuantology 9:3, 370-374 (2011)

(b) Pribram, Karl H. (1975), "12. Toward a holonomic theory of perception". In: Ertel, S., Kemmler, L., Stadler, M. (eds) Gestalttheorie in der modernen Psychologie, 161-184 (Steinkopff).

(c) ibid. Full paper and pdf download available online.

744. (a) ibid, 177b

(b) Gabor, D., Holographic Model of Temporal Recall. Nature 217, 584 (1968)

745. (a) Pribram, K.H. (1990). "Prolegomenon for a Holonomic Brain Theory". In: Haken, H., Stadler, M. (eds) Synergetics of Cognition. Springer Series in Synergetics, vol 45. Springer, Berlin, Heidelberg

(b) ibid. Full paper and pdf download available online

(c) ibid. 148a

746. (a) Neumann, Jane, Learning the systematic transformation of holographic reduced representations. Cognitive Systems Research 3:2, 227-235 (2002)

(b) Kelly, M.A., Blostein, D. & Mewhort, D.J.K.; Encoding structure in holographic reduced representations. Canadian Journal of Experimental Psychology 67:2, 79–93 (2013)

(c) ibid, 723a

(d) ibid, 723b

747. (a) Jäkel, S. & Dimou, L.; Glial Cells and Their Function in the Adult Brain: A Journey through the History of Their Ablation. Frontiers in Cellular Neuroscience, 11 (2017)

(b) Azevedo, F.A., Carvalho, L.R., Grinberg, L.T. et al.; Equal numbers of neuronal and nonneuronal cells make the human brain an isometrically scaled-up primate brain. J. Comp. Neurol., 513:5, 532-541 (2009)

748. (a) Micheva, K.D., Busse, B., Weiler, N.C. et al; Single-Synapse Analysis of a Diverse Synapse Population: Proteomic Imaging Methods and Markers. Neuron 68:4, 639 - 653 (2010)

(b) Blow, N., Following the wires. Nature Methods 4, 975–981 (2007)

(c) Elizabeth Armstrong Moore, Human brain has more switches than all computers on Earth. CNET, Nov 17, 2010

749. (a) Zingg, B., Hintiryan, H., Gou, L. et al.; Neural Networks of the Mouse Neocortex. Cell 156:5, 1096-1111 (2014)

(b) University of Southern California, "Internal logic: Eight distinct subnetworks in mouse cerebral cortex." ScienceDaily, 27 Feb 2014

750. (a) He, H., Kise, Y., Izadifar, A. et al.; Cell-intrinsic requirement of Dscam1 isoform diversity for axon collateral formation. Science 344:6188, 1182-1186 (2014)

(b) VIB - Flanders Interuniversity Institute for Biotechnology, "Mechanism explains complex brain wiring." ScienceDaily, 11 Jun 2014

(c) Paul, A., Crow, M., Raudales, R. et al.; Transcriptional Architecture of Synaptic Communication Delineates GABAergic Neuron Identity. Cell 171:3, 522-539.e20 (2017)

(d) Cold Spring Harbor Laboratory. "Neuron types in brain are defined by gene activity shaping their communication patterns." ScienceDaily, 21 Sep 2017

751. (a) Tsien, Joe Z., A Postulate on the Brain's Basic Wiring Logic. Trends in Neurosci. 38:11, 669-671 (2015)

(b) Medical College of Georgia at Georgia Regents University, "The power of two may help explain brain design." ScienceDaily, 22 Oct 2015

(c) Li, M., Liu, J. & Tsien, J.Z.; Theory of Connectivity: Nature and Nurture of Cell Assemblies and Cognitive Computation. Frontiers in Neural Circuits, 10 (2016)

752. (a) Xie, K., Fox, G.E., Liu, J. et al.; Brain Computation Is Organized via Power-of-Two-Based Permutation Logic. Frontiers in Systems Neuroscience, 15 (2016)

(b) Medical College of Georgia at Augusta University, "Our brains have a basic algorithm that enables our intelligence." ScienceDaily, 21 Nov 2016

753. (a) ibid, 696a

(b) ibid, 234

(c) Andrew, A.M., The decade of the brain - further thoughts. Kybernetes 26:3, 255-264 (1997)

754. (a) Johnstone, Henry W., "Sleep And Death". The Monist, 59:2, 218–233 (1976)

(b) ibid. Full paper and pdf download available online.

(c) Farhana Ayushi, Are sleep, dream and death related to each other? Medium, Jul 4, 2020

755. (a) Yuan, David & Raju, Hariharan; Spotlight on sudden arrhythmic death syndrome. Research Reports in Clinical Cardiology 10, 57–66 (2019)

(b) Zheng, J., Zheng, D., Su, T. & Cheng, J.; Sudden Unexplained Nocturnal Death Syndrome: The Hundred Years' Enigma. Journal of the American Heart Association 7:5, e007837 (2018)

(c) Behr, E.R., Dalageorgou, C. et al.; Sudden arrhythmic death syndrome: familial evaluation identifies inheritable heart disease in the majority of families. European Heart Journal 29:13, 1670–1680 (2008)

(d) Eckart, R.E., Shry, E.A., Burke, A.P. et al.; Sudden Death in Young Adults: An Autopsy-Based Series of a Population Undergoing Active Surveillance. J. American College of Cardiol 58:12, 1254-1261 (2011)

756. (a) Alexis C. Madrigal, The Dark Side of the Placebo Effect: When Intense Belief Kills. The Atlantic, Sep 14, 2011

(b) Rosen, Dennis, Sleep Paralysis: Night-mares, Nocebos, and the Mind-Body Connection. Review of book by Shelley R. Adler. Journal of Clinical Sleep Medicine 7:4, 418–419 (2011)

757. (a) Çaliyurt, O, Role of Chronobiology as a Transdisciplinary Field of Research: Its Applications in Treating Mood Disorders. The Balkan Medical Journal 34:6, 514–521 (2017)

(b) ibid. Full paper and pdf download also available at PMC5785655

(c) Forty-Third Annual Meeting of the British Medical Association. British Medical J, 2:25 (1875)

758. (a) Rattenborg, N.C., de la Iglesia, H.O. et al.; Sleep research goes wild: new methods and approaches to investigate the ecology, evolution and functions of sleep. Phil Trans. R.Soc. B, 372:1734, 20160251 (2017)

(b) Campbell, S.S. & Tobler, I.; Animal sleep: A review of sleep duration across phylogeny. Neuroscience & Biobehavioral Reviews 8:3, 269-300 (1984)

(c) Eric Suni, How Do Animals Sleep? Sleep Foundation, Mar 11, 2022

759. (a) Mascetti, G.G., Unihemispheric sleep and asymmetrical sleep: behavioral, neurophysiological, and functional perspectives. Nature and Science of Sleep 8, 221-238 (2016)

(b) Tamaki, M., Won Bang, J., Watanabe, T. & Sasaki, Y.; Night Watch in One Brain Hemisphere during Sleep Associated with the First-Night Effect in Humans. Current Biology 26:9, 1190-1194 (2016)

760. (a) Puttonen, E., Briese, C. et al.; Quantification of Overnight Movement of Birch (Betula pendula) Branches and Foliage with Short Interval Terrestrial Laser Scanning. Front. Plant Sci. 7 (2016)

(b) Vienna University of Technology, TU Vienna. "How do trees go to sleep?." ScienceDaily, 17 May 2016

761. (a) Brown, R.E., Basheer, R., McKenna, J.T. et al.; Control of Sleep and Wakefulness. Physiological Reviews 92:3, 1087-1187 (2012)

(b) Eban-Rothschild, A., Appelbaum, L. & de Lecea, L.; Neuronal Mechanisms for Sleep/Wake Regulation and Modulatory Drive. Neuropsychopharmacology 43, 937–952 (2018)

(c) Fuller, P.M., Gooley, J.J. & Saper, C.B.; Neurobiology of the Sleep-Wake Cycle: Sleep Architecture, Circadian Regulation, and Regulatory Feedback. Journal of Biological Rhythms 21:6, 482-493 (2006)

762. (a) Schwartz, J.R.L. & Roth, T.; Neurophysiology of Sleep and Wakefulness: Basic Science and Clinical Implications. Current Neuropharmacology 6:4, 367–378 (2008)

(b) ibid. Full paper and pdf download available at PMC2701283

(c) Krueger, J.M., Taishi, P., De, A. et al.; ATP and the purine type 2 X7 receptor affect sleep. Journal of Applied Physiology 109:5, 1318-1327 (2010)

(d) Washington State University. "Key mechanism behind sleep discovered: Finding holds promise for treatment of fatigue and sleep disorders." ScienceDaily, 15 Sep 2010

(e) Prerau, M.J., Hartnack, K.E., Obregon-Henao, G. et al.; Tracking the Sleep Onset Process: An Empirical Model of Behavioral and Physiological Dynamics. PLOS Comp. Biology 10:10, e1003866 (2014)

(f) PLOS. "Falling asleep: Revealing the point of transition." ScienceDaily, 2 Oct 2014

763. (a) Two-Process Model of Sleep Regulation (2009). In: Binder M.D., Hirokawa N., Windhorst U. (eds) Encyclopedia of Neuroscience. Springer, Berlin, Heidelberg.

(b) Borbély, A.A., Daan, S., Wirz-Justice, A. & Deboer, T.; The two-process model of sleep regulation: a reappraisal. Journal of Sleep Research 25, 131-143 (2016)

(c) Edgar, D.M., Dement, W.C. & Fuller, C.A.; Effect of SCN lesions on sleep in squirrel monkeys: evidence for opponent processes in sleep-wake regulation. J. of Neuroscience 13:3, 1065-1079 (1993)

764. (a) Saper, C.B., Cano, G. & Scammell, T.E.; Homeostatic, circadian, and emotional regulation of sleep. Journal of Comparative Neurology 493:1, 92-98 (2005)

(b) Donlea, J.M., Pimentel, D. & Miesenböck, G.; Neuronal Machinery of Sleep Homeostasis in Drosophila. Neuron 81:4, 860-872 (2014)

(c) University of Oxford, "Switch that says it's time to sleep identified." ScienceDaily, 19 Feb 2014

765. (a) Liu, S., Liu, Q., Tabuchi, M. & Wu. N.M.; Sleep Drive Is Encoded by Neural Plastic Changes in a Dedicated Circuit. Cell 165:6, 1347-1360 (2016)

(b) Johns Hopkins Medicine. "Fruit fly brains shed light on why we get tired when we stay up too late." ScienceDaily, 19 May 2016

(c) Ding, F., O'Donnell, J., Xu. Q. et al.; Changes in the composition of brain interstitial ions control the sleep-wake cycle. Science 352:6285, 550-555 (2016)

(d) University of Copenhagen The Faculty of Health and Medical Sciences. "Salts in the brain control our sleep-wake cycle." ScienceDaily, 29 Apr 2016

766. Mohawk, J.A., Green, C.B. & Takahashi, J.S.; Central and Peripheral Circadian Clocks in Mammals. Annual Review of Neuroscience 35:1, 445-462 (2012)

767. (a) Husse, J., Leliavski, A. et al; The light-dark cycle controls peripheral rhythmicity in mice with a genetically ablated suprachiasmatic nucleus clock. The FASEB Journal 28:11, 4950-4960 (2014)

(b) Federation of American Societies for Experimental Biology. "Peripheral clocks don't need the brain's master clock to function correctly." ScienceDaily, 30 Oct 2014

(c) University of California - Irvine. "Circadian clocks: Body parts respond to day and night independently from brain, studies show." ScienceDaily, 30 May 2019

(d) Welz, P-S., Zinna, V.M., Symeonidi, A. et al.; BMAL1-Driven Tissue Clocks Respond Independently to Light to Maintain Homeostasis. Cell 177:6, 1436-1447.e12 (2019)

(e) Koronowski, K.B., Kinouchi, K., Welz, P-S. et al.; Defining the Independence of the Liver Circadian Clock. Cell 177:6, 1448 1462.e14 (2019)

768. (a) Welsh, D.K., Takahashi, J.S. & Kay, S.A.; Suprachiasmatic Nucleus: Cell Autonomy and Network Properties. Annual Review of Physiology 72:1, 551-577 (2010)

(b) ibid. Full paper and pdf download available at PMC3758475

(c) Yao, Z. & Shafer, O.T.; The Drosophila Circadian Clock Is a Variably Coupled Network of Multiple Peptidergic Units. Science 343:6178, 1516-1520 (2014)

(d) University of Michigan. "Circadian clock like an orchestra with many conductors." ScienceDaily, 27 Mar 2014

769. (a) Cajochen, C., Kräuchi, K. & Wirz-Justice, A.; Role of Melatonin in the Regulation of Human Circadian Rhythms and Sleep. Journal of Neuroendocrinology 15:4, 432-437 (2003)

(b) Ardura, J., Gutierrez, R., Andres, J. & Agapito, T.; Emergence and Evolution of the Circadian Rhythm of Melatonin in Children. Hormone Research in Paediatrics 59:2, 66-72 (2003)

(c) Crowley, S.J., Van Reen, E. et al.; A Longitudinal Assessment of Sleep Timing, Circadian Phase, and Phase Angle of Entrainment across Human Adolescence. PLOS ONE 9:11, e112199 (2014)

(d) Sack, R.L., Lewy, A.J., Erb, D.L. et al.; Human Melatonin Production Decreases With Age. Journal of Pineal Research, 3:4, 379-388 (1986)

(e) Zeitzer, J.M., Duffy, J.F., Lockley, S.W. et al.; Plasma Melatonin Rhythms In Young and Older Humans During Sleep, Sleep Deprivation, and Wake. Sleep 30:11, 1437–1443 (2007)

(f) ibid. Full paper and pdf download available at PMC2082092

770. Roenneberg, T., Daan, S. & Merrow, M.; The Art of Entrainment. J. Biol. Rhythms 18:3, 183-194 (2003)

771. (a) Rebecca Boylei, The end of night. Aeon, 01 Apr 2014

(b) Fonken, L.K. & Nelson, R.J.; The Effects of Light at Night on Circadian Clocks and Metabolism. Endocrine Reviews 35:4, 648–670 (2014)

(c) Stiglic, N. & Viner, R.M.; Effects of screentime on the health and well-being of children and adolescents: a systematic review of reviews. BMJ Open 9:1 ,e023191 (2019)

772. (a) Cuesta, M., Cermakian, N. & Boivin, D.B.; Glucocorticoids entrain molecular clock components in human peripheral cells. The FASEB Journal 29:4, 1360-1370 (2015)

(b) Douglas Mental Health University Institute. "Is it possible to reset our biological clocks?" ScienceDaily, 16 Jan 2015

773. (a) Schulz, Hartmut, Rethinking Sleep Analysis. Journal of Clinical Sleep Medicine 4:2, 99–103 (2008)

(b) Aserinsky, E. & Kleitman, N.; Regularly Occurring Periods of Eye Motility, and Concomitant Phenomena, During Sleep. Science 118:3062, 273-274 (1953)

(c) Dement, W. & Kleitman, N.; Cyclic variations in EEG during sleep and their relation to eye movements, body motility, and dreaming. Electroencepha. and Clinical Neurophysio. 9:4, 673-690 (1957)

774. (a) Kleitman, Nathaniel, Basic Rest-Activity Cycle—22 Years Later. Sleep 5:4, 311–317 (1982)

(b) McCarley, R.W., Neurobiology of REM and NREM sleep. Sleep Medicine 8:4, 302-330 (2007)

(c) McCarley, R.W. & Hobson, J.A.; Neuronal excitability modulation over the sleep cycle: a structural and mathematical model. Science 189:4196, 58-60 (1975)

(d) Fuller, P.M., Saper, C.B. & Lu, J.; The pontine REM switch: past and present. The Journal of Physiology 584:3, 735-741 (2007)

775. (a) Eric Suni, Stages of Sleep. Sleep Foundation, Mar 11, 2022

(b) Steph Coelho, Sleep cycle stages and their effect on the body. Medical News Today, Nov 29, 2020

(c) ibid, 773a

(d) ibid, 774b

776. (a) Jay Summer, Sleep Spindles. Sleep Foundation, Mar 11, 2022

(b) Ioannides, A.A., Liu, L. & Kostopoulos, G.K.; The Emergence of Spindles and K-Complexes and the Role of the Dorsal Caudal Part of the Anterior Cingulate as the Generator of K-Complexes. Frontiers in Neuroscience 13 (2019)

777. (a) Jon Johnson, What to know about deep sleep. Medical News Today, Jun 3, 2019

(b) Singh, S., Kaur, H., Singh, S. & Khawaja, I.; Parasomnias: A Comprehensive Review. Cureus 10:12, e3807 (2018)

(c) Danielle Pacheco, Parasomnias. Sleep Foundation, Mar 11, 2022

778. (a) Siegel, Jerome M., The Neurobiology of Sleep. Seminars in Neurology 29(4): 277-296 (2009)

(b) Jayne Leonard, What is REM sleep? Medical News Today, Nov 24, 2021

(c) Brooks, P.L. & Peever, J.H.; Glycinergic and GABAA-Mediated Inhibition of Somatic Motoneurons Does Not Mediate Rapid Eye Movement Sleep Motor Atonia. J. of Neuroscience 28:14, 3535-3545 (2008)

(d) Berger, Albert J., What Causes Muscle Atonia in REM? Sleep 31:11, 1477–1478 (2008)

779. (a) Stevner, A.B.A., Vidaurre, D., Cabral, J. et al.; Discovery of key whole-brain transitions and dynamics during human wakefulness and non-REM sleep. Nature Communications 10, 1035 (2019)

(b) Aarhus Univ., New brain research challenges our understanding of sleep. ScienceDaily, 21 Mar 2019

780. (a) Aminoff, M.J., Boller, F. & Swaab, D.F. (2011), Foreword: Handbook of Clinical Neurology, Elsevier, vol. 98, vii. eds. Montagna, P. & Chokroverty, S.

(b) Jerome Siegel, Who Sleeps? The Scientist, Mar 1, 2016

(c) French, Christopher, Why did sleep evolve? Scientific American, Mind 23:6, 70 (2013)

(d) Frank, Marcos G., The Mystery of Sleep Function: Current Perspectives and Future Directions. Reviews in the Neurosciences 17:4, 375-392 (2006)

781. (a) Yamazaki, R., Toda, H., Libourel, P-A et al.; Evolutionary Origin of Distinct NREM and REM Sleep. Frontiers in Psychology, 11 (2020)

(b) Pallab Ghosh, Why do we sleep? BBC News, 15 May 2015

782. (a) Eric Suni, Sleep Deprivation. Sleep Foundation, Mar 18, 2022

(b) Medic, G., Wille, M. & Hemels, M.E.; Short- and long-term health consequences of sleep disruption. Nature and Science of Sleep 9, 151-161 (2017)

(c) Sehgal, A. & Mignot, E.; Genetics of Sleep and Sleep Disorders. Cell 146:2, 194-207 (2011)

(d) Shi, G., Xing, L., Wu, D. et al.; A Rare Mutation of ß1-Adrenergic Receptor Affects Sleep/Wake Behaviors. Neuron 103:6, 1044-1055.e7 (2019)

(e) Hillman, D., Mitchell, S., Streatfeild, J. et al.; The economic cost of inadequate sleep. Sleep 41:8, zsy083 (2018)

(f) Oxford University Press. "Inadequate sleep could cost countries billions." ScienceDaily, 4 Jun 2018

783. (a) Rachael Rettner, Lost Sleep Can't Be Made Up, Study Suggests. Live Science, Jan 13, 2010

(b) McCarthy, A., Wafford, K., Shanks, E. et al.; REM sleep homeostasis in the absence of REM sleep: Effects of antidepressants. Neuropharmacology 108, 415–425 (2016)

784. (a) Siegel, Jerome M., Sleep viewed as a state of adaptive inactivity. Nat Rev Neurosci 10, 747–753 (2009)

(b) Charles Q. Choi, New Theory Questions Why We Sleep. Live Science, Aug 25, 2009

(c) Siegel, Jerome M., Do all animals sleep? Trends in Neurosciences 31:4, 208–213 (2008)

(d) Horne, Jim, Why REM sleep? Clues beyond the laboratory in a more challenging world. Biological Psychology 92:2, 152-168 (2013)

785. (a) Dworak, M., McCarley, R.W., Kim, T. et al.; Sleep and Brain Energy Levels: ATP Changes during Sleep. Journal of Neuroscience 30:26, 9007-9016 (2010)

(b) Society for Neuroscience, "Brain's energy restored during sleep, suggests animal study." ScienceDaily, 7 Jul 2010

(c) Gonnissen, H.K.J., Drummen, M., Esteban, N.R. et al.; Overnight energy expenditure determined by whole-body indirect calorimetry does not differ during different sleep stages. The American Journal of Clinical Nutrition 98:4, 867–871 (2013)

786. (a) ibid, 764b

(b) ibid, 765a

(c) Martinez-Gonzalez, D., Lesku, J.A. & Rattenborg, N.C.; Increased EEG spectral power density during sleep following short-term sleep deprivation in pigeons (Columba livia): evidence for avian sleep homeostasis. Journal of Sleep Research 17:2, 140-153 (2008)

(d) ibid, 783b

787. (a) Cirelli, C. & Tononi, G.; Is Sleep Essential? PLoS Biol 6:8, e216 (2008)

(b) Krueger, J.M., Frank, M.G., Wisor, J.P. & Roy, S.; Sleep function: Toward elucidating an enigma. Sleep Medicine Reviews 28, 46–54 (2016)

788. (a) Van Cauter, E. & Plat, L.; Physiology of growth hormone secretion during sleep. The Journal of Pediatrics 128:5, S32-S37 (1996)

(b) Spiegel, K., Follenius, M., Simon, C. et al.; Prolactin Secretion and Sleep. Sleep 17:1, 20–27 (1994)

(c) ibid, 778c

(d) Cai, Zi-Jian, A new function of rapid eye movement sleep: Improvement of muscular efficiency. Physiology & Behavior 144, 110-115 (2015)

789. (a) Knutson, K.L., Spiegel, K., Penev, P. & Van Cauter, E.; The metabolic consequences of sleep deprivation. Sleep Medicine Reviews 11:3, 163-178 (2007)

(b) ibid. Full paper and pdf download available at PMC1991337

(c) Besedovsky, L., Lange, T. & Born, J.; Sleep and immune function. Pflügers Archiv - European Journal of Physiology 463, 121–137 (2012)

790. (a) Toda, H., Williams, J.A., Gulledge, M. & Sehgal, A.; A sleep-inducing gene, nemuri, links sleep and immune function in Drosophila. Science 363:6426, 509-515 (2019)

(b) Oikonomou, G. & Prober, D.A.; Linking immunity and sickness-induced sleep. Science 363:6426, 455-456 (2019)

(c) University of Pennsylvania School of Medicine, "To sleep, perchance to heal: Newly discovered gene governs need for slumber when sick: Direct link between illness and the need for more sleep." ScienceDaily, 31 Jan 2019

791. (a) Xie, L., Kang, H., Xu, Q. et al.; Sleep Drives Metabolite Clearance from the Adult Brain. Science 342:6156, 373-377 (2013)

(b) NIH/Nat. Institute of Neurological Disorders and Stroke, "Brain may flush out toxins during sleep; Sleep clears brain of molecules associated with neurodegeneration: Study." ScienceDaily, 17 Oct 2013

(c) Zada, D., Bronshtein, I., Lerer-Goldshtein, T. et al. Sleep increases chromosome dynamics to enable reduction of accumulating DNA damage in single neurons. Nature Communications 10, 895 (2019)

(d) Bar-Ilan University, "Sleep tight! Researchers identify the beneficial role of sleep: Sleep increases chromosome dynamics that clear out DNA damage accumulated during waking hours." ScienceDaily, 5 Mar 2019

792. (a) ibid, 787a

(b) Jenkins, John G. & Dallenbach, Karl M.; Obliviscence during Sleep and Waking. The American Journal of Psychology 35:4, 605–12 (1924)

(c) Vorster, A.P. & Born, J.; Sleep and memory in mammals, birds and invertebrates. Neuroscience & Biobehavioral Reviews 50, 103-119 (2015)

(d) Cairney, S.A., Durrant, S.J., Musgrove, H. & Lewis, P.A.; Sleep and environmental context: interactive effects for memory. Experimental Brain Research 214, 83 (2011)

(e) Inostroza, M. & Born, J.; Sleep for Preserving and Transforming Episodic Memory. Annual Review of Neuroscience 36:1, 79-102 (2013)

793. (a) Tarullo, A.R., Balsam, P.D. & Fifer, W.P.; Sleep and infant learning. Infant and Child Development 20:1, 35-46 (2011)

(b) ibid. Full paper and pdf download available at PMC3034475

(c) Allen, K.A., Promoting and Protecting Infant Sleep. Advances in Neonatal Care 12:5, 288-291 (2012)

(d) ibid. Full paper and pdf download available at PMC3439810

794. (a) Stickgold, R. & Walker, M.P.; Sleep-dependent memory consolidation and reconsolidation. Sleep Medicine 8:4, 331-343 (2007)

(b) ibid. Full paper and pdf download available at PMC2680680

795. (a) Winson, J., The biology and function of rapid eye movement sleep. Current Opinion in Neurobiology 3:2, 243-248 (1993)

(b) Katayose, Y., Tasaki, M., Ogata, H. et al.; Metabolic rate and fuel utilization during sleep assessed by whole-body indirect calorimetry. Metabolism - Clinical and Experimental 58:7, 920-926 (2009)

(c) Rasch, Björn & Born, Jan; About Sleep's Role in Memory. Physiological Reviews 93:2, 681-766 (2013)

796. (a) Lipinska, M., Timol, R., Kaminer, D. & Thomas, K.G.F.; Disrupted rapid eye movement sleep predicts poor declarative memory performance in post-traumatic stress disorder. J Sleep Res, 23:3, 311-319 (2014)

(b) Boyce, R., Glasgow, S.D., Williams, S. & Adamantidis, A.; Causal evidence for the role of REM sleep theta rhythm in contextual memory consolidation. Science 352:6287, 812-816 (2016)

(c) McGill University, "Rapid eye movement sleep: Keystone of memory formation." ScienceDaily, 13 May 2016

797. (a) Barnes, D.C. & Wilson, D.A.; Slow-Wave Sleep-Imposed Replay Modulates Both Strength and Precision of Memory. Journal of Neuroscience 34:15, 5134-5142 (2014)

(b) Society for Neuroscience (SfN), "Processing new information during sleep compromises memory." ScienceDaily, 8 Apr 2014

(c) Cairney, S.A., á Váli Guttesen, A., El Marj, N. et al.; Memory Consolidation Is Linked to Spindle-Mediated Information Processing during Sleep. Current Biology 28:6, 948-954.e4 (2018)

(d) Latchoumane, C-F.V., Ngo, H-V.V., Born, J. et al.; Thalamic Spindles Promote Memory Formation during Sleep through Triple Phase-Locking of Cortical, Thalamic, and Hippocampal Rhythms. Neuron 95:2, 424-435.e6 (2017)

798. (a) Lewis, P.A. & Durrant, S.J.; Overlapping memory replay during sleep builds cognitive schemata. Trends in Cognitive Sciences 15:8, 343-351 (2011)

(b) Fang, Z., Ray, L.B., Owen, A.M. & Fogel, S.M. (2017); Neural Correlates of human cognitive abilities during sleep. bioRxiv 130500

799. (a) Payne, J.D., Tucker, M.A., Ellenbogen, J.M. et al.; Memory for Semantically Related and Unrelated Declarative Information: The Benefit of Sleep, the Cost of Wake. PLoS ONE 7:3, e33079 (2012)

(b) Wilhelm, I., Diekelmann, S. & Born, J.; Sleep in children improves memory performance on declarative but not procedural tasks. Learning & Memory 15: 373-377 (2008)

(c) Wilhelm, I., Rose, M., Imhof, K. et al. The sleeping child outplays the adult's capacity to convert implicit into explicit knowledge. Nature Neuroscience 16, 391–393 (2013)

(d) Universitaet Tübingen, "Sleep reinforces learning: Children's brains transform subconsciously learned material into active knowledge." ScienceDaily, 26 Feb 2013

800. (a) Rauchs, G., Piolino, P., Bertran, F. et al.; Retrieval of Recent Autobiographical Memories is Associated with Slow-Wave Sleep in Early AD. Frontiers in Behavioral Neuroscience, 7 (2013)

(b) Scullin, M.K., Sleep, memory, and aging: The link between slow-wave sleep and episodic memory changes from younger to older adults. Psychology and Aging 28:1, 105–114 (2013)

(c) ibid. Full paper and pdf download available at PMC3532961

801. (a) Vertes, R. & Eastman, K.; The case against memory consolidation in REM sleep.
Behavioral and Brain Sciences 23:6, 867-876 (2000)

(b) Vertes, R. & Eastman, K.; REM sleep is not committed to memory.
Behavioral and Brain Sciences 23:6, 1057-1063 (2000)

(c) Vertes, Robert P., Memory Consolidation in Sleep. Neuron 44:1, 135-148 (2004)

(d) Siegel, J.M., The REM Sleep-Memory Consolidation Hypothesis. Science 294:5544, 1058-1063 (2001)

802. (a) Berry, J.A., Cervantes-Sandoval, I., Chakraborty, M. et al.; Sleep Facilitates Memory by Blocking
Dopamine Neuron-Mediated Forgetting. Cell 161:7, 1656-1667 (2015)

(b) Berry, J.A., Phan, A. & Davis, R.L.; Dopamine Neurons Mediate Learning and Forgetting through
Bidirectional Modulation of a Memory Trace. Cell Reports 25:3, 651-662.e5 (2018)

(c) Scripps Research Institute. "Scientists decode mechanism of remembering -- and forgetting -- in fruit
flies." ScienceDaily, 27 Nov 2018

(d) Danielle Pacheco, Memory and Sleep. Sleep Foundation, Mar 11, 2022

(e) Dudai, Y., Karni, A. & Born, J.; The Consolidation and Transformation of Memory.
Neuron 88:1, 20-32 (2015)

803. (a) ibid, 787a

(b) Dworak, M., McCarley, R.W., Kim, T. et al.; Sleep and Brain Energy Levels: ATP Changes during
Sleep. Journal of Neuroscience 30:26, 9007-9016 (2010)

(c) Public Library of Science, "Exploring The Function Of Sleep." ScienceDaily, 27 Aug 2008

804. (a) Tononi, G. & Cirelli, C.; Sleep and the Price of Plasticity: From Synaptic and Cellular Homeostasis to
Memory Consolidation and Integration. Neuron 81:1, 12-34 (2014)

(b) University of Wisconsin-Madison. "SHY hypothesis explains that sleep is the price we pay for
learning." ScienceDaily, 9 Jan 2014

(c) Hengen, K.B., Pacheco, A.T., McGregor, J.N. et al.; Neuronal Firing Rate Homeostasis Is Inhibited by
Sleep and Promoted by Wake. Cell 165:1, 180-191 (2016)

(d) Brandeis University. "Towards a new theory of sleep." ScienceDaily, 30 Mar 2016

(e) Brandeis University. "Sleep suppresses brain rebalancing." ScienceDaily, 21 Mar 2016

805. (a) Diering, G.H., Nirujogi, R.S., Roth, R.H. et al.; Homer1a drives homeostatic scaling-down of excitatory
synapses during sleep. Science 355:6324, 511-515 (2017)

(b) Johns Hopkins Medicine. "Sleep deprivation handicaps the brain's ability to form new memories,
mouse study shows." ScienceDaily, 2 Feb 2017

(c) Meyer, D., Bonhoeffer, T. & Scheuss, V.; Balance and Stability of Synaptic Structures during Synaptic
Plasticity. Neuron 82:2, 430-443 (2014)

806. (a) Kurth, S., Achermann, P., Rusterholz, T. & LeBourgeois, M.K.; Development of Brain EEG
Connectivity across Early Childhood: Does Sleep Play a Role? Brain Sciences 3:4, 1445-1460 (2013)

(b) University of Colorado at Boulder. "Connections in children's brains strengthen during sleep."
ScienceDaily, 20 Nov 2013

807. Schmidt, Markus H., The energy allocation function of sleep: A unifying theory of sleep, torpor, and
continuous wakefulness. Neuroscience & Biobehavioral Reviews 47, 122-153 (2014)

808. (a) Fultz, N.E., Bonmassar, G., Setsompop, K. et al.; Coupled electrophysiological, hemodynamic, and
cerebrospinal fluid oscillations in human sleep. Science 366:6465, 628-631 (2019)

(b) Xie, L., Kang, H., Xu, Q. et al.; Sleep Drives Metabolite Clearance from the Adult Brain.
Science 342:6156, 373-377 (2013)

(c) Grubb, Søren & Lauritzen, Martin; Deep sleep drives brain fluid oscillations.
Science 366:6465, 572-573 (2019)

(d) ibid, 795c

(e) A.Olena, Waves of Fluid Bathe the Sleeping Brain, Perhaps to Clear Waste. The Scientist, Oct31, 2019

809. (a) Franken, P., Kopp, C., Landolt, H-P. & Lüthi, A.; The functions of sleep.
European Journal of Neuroscience 29:9, 1739-1740 (2009)

(b) Chattu, V.K., Manzar, Md.D., Kumary, S. et al.; The Global Problem of Insufficient Sleep and Its
Serious Public Health Implications. Healthcare 7:1, 1 (2019)

810. (a) Cao, J., Herman, A.B., West, G.B. et al.; Unraveling why we sleep: Quantitative analysis reveals abrupt
transition from neural reorganization to repair in early development. Science Adv. 6:38, eaba0398 (2020)

(b) Van Savage, Geoffrey West; Why do we sleep? Aeon, 17 Sep 2021

811. Perälä, M. (2014), Ancient Theories. In: Knuuttila, S., Sihvola, J. (eds) Sourcebook for the History of the
Philosophy of Mind. Studies in the History of Philosophy of Mind, vol 12. Springer, Dordrecht.

812. (a) ibid, 773b

(b) Dement, W., & Kleitman, N.; The relation of eye movements during sleep to dream activity: An objective method for the study of dreaming. Journal of Experimental Psychology 53:5, 339–346 (1957)

(c) Hodoba, D., Hrabric, K., Krmpotic, P. et al.; Dream recall after night awakenings from tonic/phasic REM sleep. Coll Antropol. 32:Suppl, 69-73 (2008). PMID: 18405061.

813. (a) Baylor, G.W. & Cavallero, C.; Memory sources associated with REM and NREM dream reports throughout the night: a new look at the data. Sleep 24:2, 165-170 (2001). PMID: 11247052.

(b) ibid. Full paper and pdf download available online.

(c) Cavallero, C., Foulkes, D., Hollifield, M. & Terry, R.; Memory sources of REM and NREM dreams. Sleep 13:5, 449-455 (1990). PMID: 2287856.

(d) Foulkes, D., Dreaming and REM sleep. Journal of Sleep Research 2:4, 199-202 (1993)

814. (a) Leu-Semenescu, S., Uguccioni, G., Golmard, J-L. et al.; Can we still dream when the mind is blank? Sleep and dream mentations in auto-activation deficit. Brain 136:10, 3076–3084 (2013)

(b) Oxford University Press (OUP). "Dreaming still possible even when the mind is blank." ScienceDaily, 11 Sep 2013

(c) Nieminen, J., Gosseries, O., Massimini, M. et al.; Consciousness and cortical responsiveness: a within-state study during non-rapid eye movement sleep. Scientific Reports 6, 30932 (2016)

(d) Aalto Univ. "Dreaming also occurs during non rapid eye movement sleep." ScienceDaily, 9 Aug 2016

815. (a) Takeuchi, T., Miyasita, A. et al.; Intrinsic dreams are not produced without REM sleep mechanisms: evidence through elicitation of sleep onset REM periods. Journal of Sleep Research 10:43-52 (2001)

(b) ibid, 774b

816. (a) Solms, M., Dreaming and REM sleep are controlled by different brain mechanisms. Behavioral and Brain Sciences 23:6, 843-850 (2000)

(b) ibid. Full paper and pdf download available online.

(c) Eichenlaub, JB., Nicolas, A., Daltrozzo, J. et al.; Resting Brain Activity Varies with Dream Recall Frequency Between Subjects. Neuropsychopharmacology 39, 1594–1602 (2014)

(d) INSERM (Institut national de la santé et de la recherche médicale). "Why does the brain remember dreams?." ScienceDaily, 17 Feb 2014

817. (a) Siclari, F., Baird, B., Perogamvros, L. et al.; The neural correlates of dreaming. Nature Neuroscience 20, 872–878 (2017)

(b) Ashley P. Taylor, Scientists Identify More-Precise Neural Correlates of Dreaming. The Scientist, Apr 10, 2017

818. (a) Freud Museum London. Online site: https://www.freud.org.uk/

(b) McLeod, S.A., What are the most interesting ideas of Sigmund Freud? Simply Psychol, Apr 05, 2018

819. (a) Kramer, M., Does dream interpretation have any limits? An evaluation of interpretations of the dream of "Irma's Injection." Dreaming 10:3, 161–178 (2000)

(b) Palombo, S.R., Day Residue and Screen Memory in Freud's Dream of the Botanical Monograph. Journal of the American Psychoanalytic Association 36:4, 881-904 (1988)

(c) Zhang, W. & Guo, B., Freud's Dream Interpretation: A Different Perspective Based on the Self-Organization Theory of Dreaming. Frontiers in Psychology, 9 (2018)

(d) Birken, L., From Seduction Theory to Oedipus Complex: A Historical Analysis. New German Critique 43, 83–96 (1988)

(e) McLeod, Saul A., Oedipal complex. Simply Psychology, Sep 03, 2018

820. (a) McLeod, Saul A., Carl Jung. Simply Psychology, May 21, 2018

(b) Ann Hopwood, Jung's model of the psyche. Society of Analytical Psychology.

821. (a) Josie Malinowski, Was Freud right about dreams after all? Here's the research that helps explain it. The Conversation, Jul 14, 2016

(b) Patrick McNamara, The dream lag effect. Dreams participate in memory consolidation. Psychology Today, May 15, 2011

(c) Blagrove, M., Henley-Einion, J., Barnett, A. et al.; A replication of the 5–7 day dream-lag effect with comparison of dreams to future events as control for baseline matching. Consciousness and Cognition 20:2, 384-391 (2011)

(d) Tamsin Saxton, Why we are secretly attracted to people who look like our parents. The Conversation, Feb 25, 2016

822. (a) Hartmann, E., Outline for a theory on the nature and functions of dreaming. Dreaming 6:2,147–170 (1996)

(b) ibid. Full text available online

(c) Hartmann, E., Nightmare after Trauma as Paradigm for All Dreams: A New Approach to the Nature and Functions of Dreaming. Psychiatry 61:3, 223-238 (1998)

(d) Hartmann, E., The Underlying Emotion and The Dream: Relating Dream Imagery To The Dreamer'S Underlying Emotion Can Help Elucidate The Nature Of Dreaming.
International Review of Neurobiology 92, 197-214 (2010)

(e) Domhoff, G. W. (1999). Using Hall/Van De Castle Dream Content Analysis to Test New Theories: An Example Using a Theory Proposed by Ernest Hartmann. Presented at ASD annual meeting, CA.

(f) Desseilles, M., Dang-Vu, T.T, Sterpenich, V. & Schwartz, S.; Cognitive and emotional processes during dreaming: A neuroimaging view. Consciousness and Cognition 20:4, 998-1008 (2011)

823. (a) Coutts, R., Dreams as Modifiers and Tests of Mental Schemas: An Emotional Selection Hypothesis. Psychological Reports 102:2, 561-574 (2008)

(b) Coutts, R., A Pilot Study for the Analysis of Dream Reports Using Maslow's Need Categories: An Extension to the Emotional Selection Hypothesis. Psychological Reports 107:2, 659-673 (2010)

(c) Maslow, A.H., A theory of human motivation. Psychological Review 50:4, 370–396 (1943)

(d) McLeod, Saul A., Maslow's hierarchy of needs. Simply Psychology, Dec 29, 2020

(e) Coutts, R., Variation in the Frequency of Relationship Characters in the Dream Reports of Singles: A Survey of 15,657 Visitors to an Online Dating Website. Comprehensive Psychology, 1 (2015)

824. (a) Revonsuo, A., The reinterpretation of dreams: An evolutionary hypothesis of the function of dreaming. Behavioral and Brain Sciences, 23:6, 877-901 (2000)

(b) Valli, K., Revonsuo, A., Pälkäs, O. et al.; The threat simulation theory of the evolutionary function of dreaming: Evidence from dreams of traumatized children. Consciousness and Cogn. 14:1, 188-218 (2005)

(c) Valli, K. & Revonsuo, A.; The threat simulation theory in light of recent empirical evidence: A review. The American Journal of Psychology 122:1, 17–38 (2009)

(d) ibid. Full paper and pdf download available online.

(e) Jay Dixit, Dreams: Night School. Psychology Today, Nov 1, 2007

825. (a) Stickgold, R., Hobson, J.A., Fosse, R. & Fosse, M.; Sleep, Learning, and Dreams: Off-line Memory Reprocessing. Science 294:5544, 1052-1057 (2001)

(b) ibid. Full paper and pdf download available online.

(c) Hobson, J., REM sleep and dreaming: towards a theory of protoconsciousness.
Nature Reviews Neuroscience 10, 803–813 (2009)

(d) Lin Edwards, Dreams may have an important physiological function. Medical Xpress, Nov 12, 2009

826. (a) Domhoff, G.W., The neural substrate for dreaming: Is it a subsystem of the default network? Consciousness and Cognition 20:4, 1163-1174 (2011)

(b) ibid. Full text available online.

(c) Domhoff, G.W., The neurocognitive theory of dreams at age 20: An assessment and a comparison with four other theories of dreaming. Dreaming 29:4, 265–302 (2019)

(d) Zhang, Jie (2016), Towards a comprehensive model of human memory. ResearchGate 304604880.

827. Aristotle (350 BCE), Historia animalium (History of Animals), Book IV, 10. IntraText Digital Library.

828. (a) Lesku, J.A., Meyer, L.C.R. et al.; Ostriches Sleep like Platypuses. PLoS ONE 6:8, e23203 (2011)

(b) Shein-Idelson, M., Ondracek, J.M., Liaw, H-P et al.; Slow waves, sharp waves, ripples, and REM in sleeping dragons. Science 352:6285, 590-595 (2016)

(c) Max-Planck-Gesellschaft. "Do bearded dragons dream? Reptiles share sleep patterns with mammals and birds." ScienceDaily, 28 Apr 2016

(d) Leung, L.C., Wang, G.X. et al.; Neural signatures of sleep in zebrafish. Nature 571, 198–204 (2019)

(e) Katherine J. Wu, Like us, fish experience the 'dreaming' stage of sleep. PBS Nova, Jul 10, 2019

829. (a) Louie, K. & Wilson, M.A.; Temporally Structured Replay of Awake Hippocampal Ensemble Activity during Rapid Eye Movement Sleep Neuron 29:1, 145-156 (2001)

(b) Animals have complex dreams, MIT researcher proves. MIT News, Jan 24, 2001

(c) D. Halber, Memory experts show sleeping rats may have visual dreams. MIT News, Dec 18, 2006

(d) Jeanna Bryner, Animals Dream in Pictures, Too. Live Science, Dec 18, 2006

(e) Deborah Halber, Picower researcher explains how rats think. MIT News, Feb 12, 2006

830. (a) Do animals dream? Earthsky, Feb 7, 2019

(b) Dave, A.S. & Margoliash, D.; Song Replay During Sleep and Computational Rules for Sensorimotor Vocal Learning. Science 290:5492, 812-816 (2000)

(c) Ólafsdóttir, H.F., Barry, C., Saleem, A.B. et al; Hippocampal place cells construct reward related sequences through unexplored space. eLife 4, e06063 (2015)

831. (a) Naiman, R., Dreamless: the silent epidemic of REM sleep loss. Ann. NY Acad Sci, 1406:1,77-85 (2017)

(b) University of Arizona Health Sciences. "An epidemic of dream deprivation: Unrecognized health hazard of sleep loss." ScienceDaily, 29 Sep 2017

(c) Hannah Nichols, What does it mean when we dream? Medical News Today, Jun 28, 2018

832. (a) Bendor, D. & Wilson, M.; Biasing the content of hippocampal replay during sleep.
Nature Neuroscience 15, 1439–1444 (2012)
(b) ibid. Full paper and pdf download available at PMC4354843.
(c) Jeanna Bryner, Scientists 'Engineer' Dreams in Rats. Live Science, Sep 5, 2012

833. (a) van Eeden, F. (1913), A Study of Dreams. Proceedings of the Society for Psychical Research vol. 26
(copied & proofread by Blake Wilfong)
(b) Gackenbach, Jayne, Interview with Celia Green, Author of the 1968 Classic, "Lucid Dreams".
Lucidity Letter Vol.10, No.1&2 (1991)
(c) Celia Green's Oxford Forum. Opposing Orthodoxy
(d) Gackenbach, J. (1988). The Psychological Content of Lucid versus Nonlucid Dreams. In: Gackenbach,
J., LaBerge, S. (eds) Conscious Mind, Sleeping Brain. Springer, Boston, MA..

834. (a) Green, C. & Green, M. (1994), Lucid Dreaming: The Paradox of Consciousness During Sleep.
Routledge, ISBN 9780415112390
(b) Hearne, K., Keith Hearne's Work on Lucid Dreaming. Lucidity Letter Vol.10, No. 1&2 (1991)
(c) LaBerge, S., Physiological Mechanisms of Lucid Dreaming. Lucidity Letter Vol.10, No. 1&2 (1991)
(d) LaBerge, S., Lucid dreaming: Evidence and methodology. Behav.and Brain Sci. 23:6, 962-964 (2000)

835. (a) Holzinger, B., LaBerge, S. & Levitan, L.; Psychophysiological correlates of lucid dreaming.
Dreaming 16:2, 88–95 (2006)
(b) Baird, B., Castelnovo, A., Gosseries, O. & Tononi, G.; Frequent lucid dreaming associated with
increased functional connectivity between frontopolar cortex and temporoparietal association areas.
Scientific Reports 8, 17798 (2018)

836. (a) Ruhl, C., How to lucid dream: 6 techniques, benefits, and cautions. Simply Psychology, July 07, 2021
(b) Tart, C. T., & Dick, L.; Conscious control of dreaming: The posthypnotic dream.
Journal of Abnormal Psychology, 76(2), 304–315 (1970)
(c) Vaughan Bell, The mysteries of 'lucid' dreaming. The Guardian, 27 Apr 2014
(d) Michael Schulson, These Lucid-Dreaming Companies Want to Help You Control Your Dreams.
The Cut, Oct. 12, 2016
(e) Stumbrys, T., Erlacher, D., Schädlich, M. & Schredl, M.; Induction of lucid dreams: A systematic
review of evidence. Consciousness and Cognition 21:3, 1456-1475 (2012)

837. (a) Daisy Schofield, Lucid dreamers are using unproven tech to hack their sleep. Wired, 05 Jan 2021
(b) Blackmore, Susan (1991), Lucid Dreaming: Awake in Your Sleep? From: Skeptical Inquirer 15, 362-370

838. (a) Hurd, R. & Bulkeley, K., eds.; Lucid dreaming: New perspectives on consciousness in sleep: Science,
psychology, and education. Religion, Creativity, and Culture, vol 1-2 (2014). Praeger/ABC-CLIO.
(b) Voss, U., Holzmann, R., Tuin, I. & Hobson, J.A.; Lucid Dreaming: a State of Consciousness with
Features of Both Waking and Non-Lucid Dreaming. Sleep 32:9, 1191–1200 (2009)
(c) Dresler, M., Wehrle, R., Spoormaker, V.I. et al.; Neural Correlates of Dream Lucidity Obtained from
Contrasting Lucid versus Non-Lucid REM Sleep: A Combined EEG/fMRI Case Study.
Sleep 35:7, 1017–1020 (2012)
(d) Max-Planck-Gesellschaft. "Lucid dreamers help scientists locate the seat of meta-consciousness in the
brain." ScienceDaily, 27 Jul 2012

839. (a) Vaughan Bell, The Trippy State Between Wakefulness and Sleep. The Atlantic, Apr 20, 2016
(b) da Mota Gomes, Marleide & Nardi, Antonio E.; Charles Dickens' Hypnagogia, Dreams, and Creativity.
Frontiers in Psychology, 12 (2021)
(c) D. McLeester, Book Review: The Committee of Sleep by Deirdre Barrett. Dream Network, Oct 2001

840. (a) MIT Project Dormio: Interfacing with Dreams.
(b) T. Love, An MIT Lab Is Building Devices to Hack Your Dreams. One Zero, Medium, Apr 13, 2020
(c) Horowitz, A.H., Cunningham, T.J., Maes, P. & Stickgold, R.; Dormio: A targeted dream incubation
device. Consciousness and Cognition 83, 102938 (2020)
(d) ibid. Full paper and pdf download available at PMC7590944.

841. (a) Mazzoni, G.A.L. & Loftus, E.F.; When Dreams Become Reality.
Consciousness and Cognition 5:4, 442-462 (1996)
(b) Suter, Ronald, The Dream Argument. American Philosophical Quarterly 13:3, 185–94 (1976)
(c) Chappell, Sophie-Grace, "Plato on Knowledge in the Theaetetus", Stanford Encyclopedia of
Philosophy (Spring 2021 Edition), Edward N. Zalta (ed.)
(d) Möller, Hans-Georg, Zhuangzi's 'Dream of the Butterfly': A Daoist Interpretation.
Philosophy East and West 49:4, 439–50 (1999)

842. (a) Wilson, C. (2003), Meditation One: The possibility of a malevolent Demon is raised and the Meditator
resolves to doubt everything he can possibly doubt. In Descartes's Meditations: An Introduction (CUP).

(b) Odegard, D., Descartes and the Dream Argument. History of Philosophy Qtrly 12:2, 155–64 (1995)

(c) Windt, J.M., "Dreams and Dreaming", Stanford Encyclopedia of Philosophy (Summer 2021 Ed.)

(d) Stapleford, Scott, What's the point of a Dreaming Argument? Think, 18:52, 31-34 (2019)

843. Smith, Scott D., Coping with the mystery of death. CMAJ 181:8, 504-505 (2009)

844. Susana Monsó, What animals think of death. Aeon, 14 Sep 2021

845. (a) Jennett, Bryan & Plum, Fred; Persistent Vegetative State After Brain Damage. The Lancet 299:7753, 734-737 (1972)

(b) Halliday, S., Formby, A. & Cookson, R.; An Assessment Of The Court's Role In The Withdrawal Of Clinically Assisted Nutrition And Hydration From Patients In The Permanent Vegetative State. Medical Law Review 23:4, 556–587 (2015)

(c) Huxtable, R. Dying too soon or living too long? Withdrawing treatment from patients with prolonged disorders of consciousness after Re Y. BMC Med Ethics 20, 91 (2019)

846. (a) Andrews, Keith, Recovery of patients after four months or more in the persistent vegetative state. British Medical Journal 306, 1597 (1993)

(b) ibid. Full paper and pdf download available at PMC1678008.

(c) Faran, S., Vatine, J.J., Lazary, A. et al.; Late recovery from permanent traumatic vegetative state heralded by event-related potentials. J Neurol Neurosurg Psychiatry 77:8, 998–1000 (2006)

(d) ibid. Full paper and pdf download available at PMC2077634.

847. (a) Mackenzie Graham, The Ethics of Consciousness Hunting. Adrian Owen explains why fMRI has become an ethical obligation. Nautilus, Sep 5, 2018

(b) Mo Costandi, Detecting covert consciousness in the vegetative state. The Guardian, 02 Sep 2011

(c) Edlow, B.L., Claassen, J., Schiff, N.D. et al.; Recovery from disorders of consciousness: mechanisms, prognosis and emerging therapies. Nature Reviews Neurology 17, 135–156 (2021)

848. (a) K. Lunau, Light in the dark: What if vegetative patients are actually conscious? Maclean's, Sep 15, 2014

(b) Kate Lunau, The story behind a vegetative patient's shocking recovery. Maclean's, Dec 31, 2015

(c) Peterson, A.,; Owen, A.M. & Karlawish, J.; Alive inside. Bioethics 34:3, 295–305 (2020)

(d) Graham, M.; Residual Cognitive Capacities in Patients With Cognitive Motor Dissociation, and Their Implications for Well-Being, The Journal of Medicine and Philosophy, 46:6, 729–757 (2021)

849. (a) Pincherle, A., Rossi, F., Jöhr, J. et al.; Early discrimination of cognitive motor dissociation from disorders of consciousness: pitfalls and clues. Journal of Neurology 268, 178–188 (2021)

(b) Pozeg, P. & Jöhr, J. & Pincherle, A. et al.; Discriminating cognitive motor dissociation from disorders of consciousness using structural MRI. NeuroImage: Clinical 30, 102651 (2021)

(c) Jöhr, J., Halimi, F., Pasquier, J., Pincherle, A. et al.; Recovery in cognitive motor dissociation after severe brain injury: A cohort study. PLoS ONE 15:2, e0228474 (2020)

(d) Pincherle, A., Rosanova, M. & Diserens, K.; Editorial: New Advances in Diagnostic Tools and Rehabilitation of Disorders of Consciousness in the Acute Phase. Frontiers in Neurology, 12 (2021)

(e) Pan, J., Xie, Q., Qin, P. et al.; Prognosis for patients with cognitive motor dissociation identified by brain-computer interface. Brain 143:4, 1177–1189 (2020)

(f) Belkin, V.A., Belkina, A.Y., Pozdnyakov, D.G. & Belkin, A.A.; Case of cognitive motor dissociation diagnosed in patient with traumatic brain injury and hypoxia. J Neurol Stroke 12:1, 1-3 (2022)

(g) Jöhr, J.; Aureli, V.; Meyer, I. et al.; Clinical Cognitive Motor Dissociation: A Case Report Showing How Pitfalls Can Hinder Early Clinical Detection of Awareness. Brain Sciences 12:2, 157 (2022)

850. (a) Corazzol, M., Lio, G., Lefevre, A. et al.; Restoring consciousness with vagus nerve stimulation. Current Biology 27:18, R994–R996 (2017)

(b) Shawna Williams, Nerve Stimulation Revives Consciousness from Vegetative State. The Scientist, Sep 25, 2017

(c) Michael Price, Experimental nerve-stimulation therapy partially revives man in long-term vegetative state—but experts urge caution. Science, Brain & Behavior, 25 Sep 2017

851. (a) Have People Been Buried Alive? And could it still happen? Snopes, 09 Jun 1999

(b) Sara Malm, Back from the dead: Man declared deceased by doctors is found to be alive as he is lowered into a coffin in Peru. Mail Online, 25 Oct 2017

(c) Sara C. Nelson, 'Dead' Teenager Wakes Up On The Way To His Own Funeral. HuffPost, 21 Feb 2017

(d) "Dead" man wakes up under autopsy knife. Reuters, Sep 17, 2007

(e) Milwaukee man pronounced dead, then moves and breathes –authorities. Reuters, May 22, 2015

(f) NBC, Undertaker finds 'dead' woman really alive. The Associated Press, Feb 17, 2010

(g) Emily Fox, Woman dies of shock at own funeral. Daily Express, Jun 23, 2011

852. (a) Adam Hoffman, The Lazarus Phenomenon, Explained: Why Sometimes, the Deceased Are Not Dead, Yet. Smithsonian Magazine, Mar 31, 2016

(b) Honor Whiteman, The Lazarus phenomenon: When the 'dead' come back to life.
Medical News Today, May 26, 2017

(c) Alves, S., Campos, M. & Reis, G.; Lazarus syndrome in the emergency room: A case report.
Resuscitation 81:2, S25 (2010)

(d) Adhiyaman, V., Adhiyaman, S. & Sundaram, R.; The Lazarus phenomenon.
Journal of the Royal Society of Medicine 100:12, 552-557 (2007)

(e) Hornby, K., Hornby, L. & Shemie, S.D.; A systematic review of autoresuscitation after cardiac arrest*.
Critical Care Medicine 38:5, 1246-1253 (2010)

853. (a) Mxolisi Mngadi, 'Dead Man' Died Twice. Daily Sun (South Africa), Dec 08, 2016

(b) Sara C. Nelson, 'Dead' South African Car Crash Victim Found Alive In Mortuary Fridge.
HuffPost, Dec 12, 2016

854. (a) Helena Smith, Greek grave dug up after 'cries for help'. The Guardian, 26 Sep 2014

(b) Buried Alive: Family smash into coffin after hearing 'Dead' teenager screaming from inside.
Daily Express, Aug 26, 2015

(c) Matt Roper, Woman who was mistakenly 'buried alive' tried to 'fight her way out of sealed coffin' after being laid to rest 11 days before. Mail Online, 16 Feb 2018

(d) Carla Valentine, Why waking up in a morgue isn't quite as unusual as you'd think.
The Guardian, 14 Nov 2014

(e) Tia Ghose, Clinically Dead? The Blurred Line Between Life and Death. Live Science, Jun 19, 2014

855. (a) A Definition of Irreversible Coma: Report of the Ad Hoc Committee of the Harvard Medical School to Examine the Definition of Brain Death. JAMA 205:6, 337–340 (1968)

(b) Goila, A.K. & Pawar, M.; The diagnosis of brain death. Indian J Crit Care Med. 13:1, 7–11 (2009)

(c) ibid. Full paper and pdf download also available at PMC2772257.

(d) Burkle, C.M., Sharp, R.R. & Wijdicks, E.F.; Why brain death is considered death and why there should be no confusion. Neurology 83:16, 1464-1469 (2014)

(e) ibid. Full paper and pdf download available at PMC4206160.

856. (a) Spears, W., Mian, A. & Greer, D.; Brain death: a clinical overview. J. of Intensive Care 10, 16 (2022)

(b) Bell, M.D.D., Moss, E. & Murphy P.G.; Brainstem death testing in the UK'time for reappraisal?†
British Journal of Anaesthesia 92:5, 633-640 (2004)

(c) Smith, M., Brain Death: The United Kingdom Perspective. Seminars in Neurol. 35:2, 145-151 (2015)

(d) Bernat, James L., A Defense of the Whole-Brain Concept of Death.
The Hastings Center Report, 28:2, 14–23 (1998)

(e) Bernat, James L., The concept and practice of brain death. Progress in Brain Res. 150, 369-379 (2005)

(f) Chua, H.C., Kwek, T.K., Morihara, H. & Gao, D.; Brain Death: The Asian Perspective.
Seminars in Neurology 35:2, 152-161 (2015)

857. (a) Doyle, D. John, Life, Death and Brain Death: A Critical Examination.
Ethics in Biology, Engineering and Medicine 2:1, 11-31 (2011)

(b) Johnson, L. Syd M., Death by neurological criteria: expert definitions and lay misgivings.
QJM: An International Journal of Medicine 110:5, 267–270 (2017)

858. (a) Khushf, G., A matter of respect: a defense of the dead donor rule and of a "whole-brain" criterion for determination of death. The Journal of Medicine and Philosophy 35:3, 330–64 (2010)

(b) Truog, R.D. & Miller, F.G.; The Dead Donor Rule and Organ Transplantation.
New England Journal of Medicine 359:7, 674-675 (2008)

(c) ibid. Full paper and pdf download available online.

(d) Miller, F.G., Death and organ donation: back to the future. J of Medical Ethics 35:10, 616-620 (2009)

(e) Verheijde, J.L., Rady, M.Y. & McGregor, J.L.; Brain death, states of impaired consciousness, and physician-assisted death for end-of-life organ donation and transplantation.
Medicine, Health Care and Philosophy 12, 409–421 (2009)

859. (a) Smith, M., Brain death:time for an international consensus. British J of Anaesthesia 108:1,16-19 (2012)

(b) Lazar, N.M., Shemie, S., Webster, G.C. & Dickens, B.M.; Bioethics for clinicians: 24. Brain death.
CMAJ 164:6, 833-836 (2001)

(c) Pavlovic, D., Lehmann, C. & Wendt, M.; For an indeterministic ethics. The emptiness of the rule in dubio pro vita and life cessation decisions. Philosophy, Ethics, and Humanities in Medicine 4, 6 (2009)

(d) May, Arnd T., Physician-Assisted Suicide, Euthanasia, and Christian Bioethics: Moral Controversy in Germany. Christian bioethics: Non-Ecumenical Studies in Medical Morality 9:2-3, 273–283 (2003)

860. (a) Nguyen, Doyen, Brain Death and True Patient Care. The Linacre Quarterly 83:3, 258-282 (2016)

(b) ibid. Full paper and pdf download available at PMC5102188.

(c) Sade, R.M., Consequences of the Dead Donor Rule. Annals of Thoracic Surg. 97:4, 1131-1132 (2014)

(d) Miller, Franklin G., Heart Donation Without the Dead Donor Rule.
Annals of Thoracic Surgery 97:4, 1133-1134 (2014)

861. (a) Greer, D.M., Shemie, S.D., Lewis, A. et al.; Determination of Brain Death/Death by Neurologic Criteria: The World Brain Death Project. JAMA 324:11, 1078–1097 (2020)

(b) Paul Smyth, World Brain Death Project Publishes Consensus Report. Physicians Weekly, Aug 5, 2020

(c) Judy George, Brain Death: What Does it Mean? MedPage Today, Aug 3, 2020

(d) James Santiago Grisolia, The World Brain Death Project: Answering the Wrong Questions. MedPage Today, Aug 30, 2020

862. (a) Sharon Kaufman, Neither person nor cadaver. The body is warm, but the brain has gone dark: why the notion of brain death provokes the thorniest of medical dilemmas. Aeon, 06 Feb 2020

(b) Robbins, N.M. & Bernat, J.L.; What Should We Do About the Mismatch Between Legal Criteria for Death and How Brain Death Is Diagnosed? AMA Journal of Ethics 22:12, E1038-1046 (2020)

863. (a) Somjen, G.G., Aristides Leão's discovery of cortical spreading depression.
Journal of Neurophysiology 94:1, 2-4 (2005)

(b) Maranhão-Filho, P. & Vincent, M.; Professor Aristides Leão. Much More Than Spreading Depression. Headache: The Journal of Head and Face Pain 49:1, 110-116 ((2009)

(c) Dreier, J.P., Major, S., Foreman, B. et al.; Terminal spreading depolarization and electrical silence in death of human cerebral cortex. Annals of Neurology 83:2, 295-310 (2018)

(d) Rafi Letzter, Dying Brains Silence Themselves in a Dark Wave of 'Spreading Depression'.
Live Science, Feb 27, 2018

864. (a) Becker, L.B., Ostrander, M.P.,Barrett, J. & Kondos, G.T.; Outcome of CPR in a large metropolitan area — where are the survivors? Annals of Emergency Medicine 20:4, 355-361 (1991)

(b) Back to Life: The Science of Reviving the Dead. Newsweek, 22 Jul 2007

(c) Lance B. Becker, MD, Improving Survival from Cardiac Arrest. Interview by Katlyn Nemani, MD, CardioSource, Aug 15, 2015

(d) Shinozaki, K., Nonogi, H., Nagao, K. & Becker, L.B.; Strategies to improve cardiac arrest survival: a time to act. Acute Medicine & Surgery 3:2, 61-64 (2016)

865. (a) Stub, D., Bernard, S., Pellegrino, V. et al.; Refractory cardiac arrest treated with mechanical CPR, hypothermia, ECMO and early reperfusion (the CHEER trial). Resuscitation 86, 88-94 (2015)

(b) European Society of Cardiology, "Refractory cardiac arrest patients brought to hospital with ongoing CPR can recover." ScienceDaily, 29 Aug 2015

866. (a) González-Rosa, J.M., Burns, C.E. & Burns, C.G.; Zebrafish heart regeneration: 15 years of discoveries. Regeneration 4:3, 105– 123 (2017)

(b) ibid. Full paper and pdf download also available at PMC5617908.

(c) Agrawal, V., Johnson, S.A, Rein, J. et al.; Epimorphic regeneration approach to tissue replacement in adult mammals. PNAS 107:8, 3351-3355 (2010)

(d) Mason, C. & Dunnill, P.; A brief definition of regenerative medicine. Regenerative Med 3:1, 1-5 (2008)

(e) Sampogna, G., Guraya, S.Y. & Forgione, A.; Regenerative medicine: Historical roots and potential strategies in modern medicine. Journal of Microscopy and Ultrastructure 3:3, 101-107 (2015)

(f) Shomrat, T. & Levin, M.; An automated training paradigm reveals long-term memory in planarians and its persistence through head regeneration. J Exp Biol. 216:20, 3799–3810 (2013)

867. (a) Dyllan Furness, Can stem cell injections revive a dead brain? Ambitious 'Reanima Project' aims to find out. Digital Trends, May 4, 2016

(b) Non-randomized, Open-labeled, Interventional, Single Group, Proof of Concept Study With Multi-modality Approach in Cases of Brain Death Due to Traumatic Brain Injury Having Diffuse Axonal Injury. April 19, 2016. US ClinicalTrials.gov Identifier: NCT02742857

(c) Bioquark Inc. and Revita Life Sciences Receive IRB Approval for First-In-Human Brain Death Study. Cision PRWeb, Apr 20, 2016

868. (a) Pulla, Priyanka, Experiment to raise the dead blocked in India. Science Insider, 14 Nov 2016

(b) Srinivasan, S. & Johari, V.; Response to proposed research to reverse brain death: more than regulatory failure. Indian Journal of Medical Ethics 1:3, 134-137 (2016)

(c) Lewis, A. & Caplan, A.; Response to a trial on reversal of Death by Neurologic Criteria.
Critical Care 20, 377 (2016)

(d) Pastor, Ira S., A response to "Response to a Trial on Reversal of Death by Neurologic Criteria".
Critical Care 21, 30 (2017)

869. (a) Priyanka Pulla, How a Controversial Medical Trial to Reverse Brain Death Slipped Through Regulatory Cracks. The Wire (India), 17 Jun 2016

(b) Wang, Y., Zhao, Z., Rege, S. et al.; 3K3A–activated protein C stimulates postischemic neuronal repair by human neural stem cells in mice. Nature Medicine 22, 1050–1055 (2016)

(c) University of Southern California, "Hope for reversing stroke-induced long-term disability." ScienceDaily, 22 Aug 2016

(d) Lei, J., Wang, L., Gao, G. et al.; Right Median Nerve Electrical Stimulation for Acute Traumatic Coma Patients. Journal of Neurotrauma 32:20, 1584-1589 (2015)

870. (a) Philip Perry, Scientists Attempt to Reanimate the Brain Dead — What Could Go Wrong? Big Think, 30 Apr 2017

(b) Wagner, D.E., Wang, I.E. & Reddien, P.W.; Clonogenic Neoblasts Are Pluripotent Adult Stem Cells That Underlie Planarian Regeneration. Science 332:6031, 811-816 (2011)

(c) King, R.S. & Newmark, P.A.; The cell biology of regeneration. J of Cell Biology 196:5, 553–562 (2012)

871. (a) Honor Whiteman, Reversing brain death: Far-fetched or feasible? Medical News Today, Aug 18, 2017

(b) Mia De Graaf, Could we soon REVERSE death? US company to start trials 'reawakening the dead' in Latin America 'in a few months' - and this is how they'll do it. Dailymail.com, 5 Jun 2017

(c) Queen Muse, Philly-Based Bioquark Wants a Shot at Bringing the Dead Back to Life. Philly Magazine, Jul 25, 2019

872. (a) Lancaster, M., Renner, M., Martin, CA. et al.; Cerebral organoids model human brain development and microcephaly. Nature 501, 373–379 (2013)

(b) ibid. Full paper and pdf download available at PMC3817409.

(c) A group of stem-cell biologists have grown an "organoid" that resembles a brain. Economist, Sep 18, 2013

(d) Urbán, N. & Guillemot, F.; Neurogenesis in the embryonic and adult brain: same regulators, different roles. Frontiers in Cellular Neuroscience, 8 (2014)

873. (a) Vogel, Gretchen, Lab Dishes Up Mini-Brains. Science 341:6149, 946-947 (2013)

(b) Chambers, S.M., Tchieu, J. & Studer, L.; Build-a-Brain. Cell Stem Cell 13:4, 377-378 (2013)

(c) Bershteyn, Marina & Kriegstein, Arnold R.; Cerebral Organoids in a Dish: Progress and Prospects. Cell 155:1, 19-20 (2013)

874. (a) Mansour, A., Gonçalves, J., Bloyd, C. et al.; An in vivo model of functional and vascularized human brain organoids. Nature Biotechnology 36, 432–441 (2018)

(b) Salk Institute, "Grafted brain organoids provide insight into neurological disorders." ScienceDaily, 16 Apr 2018

(c) Lancaster, Madeline, Brain organoids get vascularized. Nature Biotechnology 36, 407–408 (2018)

875. (a) Method of the Year 2017: Organoids. Nature Methods 15, 1 (2018)

(b) de Souza, Natalie, Organoids. Nature Methods 15, 23 (2018)

(c) Eisenstein, M., Organoids: the body builders. Nature Methods 15, 19–22 (2018)

(d) Rios, A., Clevers, H., Imaging organoids: a bright future ahead. Nature Methods 15, 24–26 (2018)

(e) Arlotta, P., Organoids required! A new path to understanding human brain development and disease. Nature Methods 15, 27–29 (2018)

876. (a) Antonio Regalado, Researchers are keeping pig brains alive outside the body. MIT Technology Review, Apr 25, 2018

(b) Kristin Hugo, Scientists Keep Pig Brains Alive Without Their Bodies, Are Humans Next? Newsweek, Apr 27, 2018

(c) Pallab Ghosh, Ethics debate as pig brains kept alive without a body. BBC News, 27 Apr 2018

(d) Nicola Davis, Scientists 'keep pigs brains alive without a body for up to 36 hours'. The Guardian, 27 Apr 2018

(e) Farahany, N.A., Greely, H.T., Hyman, S. et al.; The ethics of experimenting with human brain tissue. Nature 556, 429-432 (2018)

877. (a) Canavero, Sergio, HEAVEN: The head anastomosis venture Project outline for the first human head transplantation with spinal linkage (GEMINI). Surgical Neurology International, 4 (2013)

(b) Ian Sample, First full body transplant is two years away, surgeon claims. The Guardian, 25 Feb 2015

(c) Lamba, N., Holsgrove, D. & Broekman, M.L.; The history of head transplantation: a review. Acta Neurochir 158, 2239–2247 (2016)

(d) Manjila, S., Alambyan, V., Singh, G. et al.; From Hypothermia to Cephalosomatic Anastomoses: The Legacy of Robert White (1926–2010) at Case Western Reserve University of Cleveland. World Neurosurgery, 113, 14-25 (2018)

878. (a) Canavero, Sergio, The "Gemini" spinal cord fusion protocol: Reloaded. Surgical Neurology International 6, 18 (2015)

(b) Canavero, S., Ren, X.-P., Kim, C-Y. & Rosati, E.; Neurologic foundations of spinal cord fusion (GEMINI). Surgery 160:1, 11-19 (2016)

(c) Shi, R., Polyethylene glycol repairs membrane damage and enhances functional recovery: a tissue engineering approach to spinal cord injury. Neuroscience Bulletin 29, 460–466 (2013)

879. (a) Ren, X-P., Song, Y., Ye, Y-J. et al.; Allogeneic Head and Body Reconstruction: Mouse Model. CNS Neuroscience & Therapeutics 20:12, 1056-1060 (2014)

(b) Ren, X-P., Ye, Y-J., Li, P-W. et al.; Head Transplantation in Mouse Model. CNS Neuroscience & Therapeutics 21:8, 615-618 (2015)

(c) Estrada, V., Brazda, N., Schmitz, C. et al.; Long-lasting significant functional improvement in chronic severe spinal cord injury following scar resection and polyethylene glycol implantation. Neurobiology of Disease 67, 165-179 (2014)

880. (a) Tom Lamont, 'I'll do the first human head transplant'. Interview with Sergio Canavero. The Guardian, 3 Oct 2015

(b) Sam Kean, The Audacious Plan to Save This Man's Life by Transplanting His Head. What would happen if it actually works? The Atlantic, Sep 2016

(c) Honor Whiteman, 30-year-old Russian man volunteers for world's first human head transplant. Medical News Today, Oct 22, 2015

881. (a) Christopher Hooton, Man undergoing head transplant could experience something 'a lot worse than death', says neurological expert. Independent Online, 9 Apr 2015

(b) Arthur Caplan, Commentary: Promise of world's first head transplant is truly fake news. Chicago Tribune, 13 Dec 2017

(c) Manjila, S., Alambyan, V., Singh, G. et al.; From Hypothermia to Cephalosomatic Anastomoses: The Legacy of Robert White (1926–2010) at Case Western Reserve University of Cleveland. World Neurosurgery 113, 14-25 (2018)

(d) McCrone, John, Monkey business. The Lancet Neurology 2:12, 772 (2003)

(e) Danielle Elliot, Human head transplant is "bad science," says neuroscientist. CBS News, Jul 2, 2013

882. (a) Darren Ó hAilín, Why human head transplants are still a long way from becoming a reality. The Conversation, 14 Aug 2015

(b) Quassim Cassam, Will head transplants create an entirely new person? The Conversation, Jun 23, 2015

(c) Lamba, N., Holsgrove, D. & Broekman, M.L.; The history of head transplantation: a review. Acta Neurochir 158, 2239–2247 (2016)

883. (a) Ren, X-P. & Canavero, S.; Human head transplantation. Where do we stand and a call to arms. Surgical Neurology International 7, 11 (2016)

(b) Ren, X-P., Orlova, E.V., Maevsky, E.I. et al.; Brain protection during cephalosomatic anastomosis. Surgery 160:1, 5-10 (2016)

(c) Jason Daley, Head Transplant Patient Will Use Virtual Reality to Smooth Transition to New Body. Smithsonian Magazine, Nov 23, 2016

884. (a) Li, P-W., Zhao, X., Zhao, Y-L. et al.; A cross-circulated bicephalic model of head transplantation. CNS Neuroscience & Therapeutics 23:6, 535-541 (2017)

(b) Abigail Beall, Rat heads are one thing but don't expect a human head transplant any time soon. Wired, May 05, 2017

(c) Dean Burnett, No, there hasn't been a human 'head transplant', and there may never be. The Guardian, 17 Nov 2017

(d) Allen, J.S., Emmorey, K., Bruss, J. & Damasio, H.; Neuroanatomical differences in visual, motor, and language cortices between congenitally deaf signers, hearing signers, and hearing non-signers. Frontiers in Neuroanatomy 7, 26 (2013)

885. (a) Hannah Osborne, Head Transplants: Sergio Canavero Says First Patient Will Be Chinese National, Not Valery Spiridonov. Newsweek, Apr 28, 2017

(b) Will Stewart, Volunteer set to become the first person to undergo a HEAD TRANSPLANT admits he will NOT now undergo the surgery and says: 'That's a weight off my chest'. Mail Online, 21 Jun 2017

(c) Didi Kirsten Tatlow, Doctor's Plan for Full-Body Transplants Raises Doubts Even in Daring China. New York Times, Jun 11, 2016

886. (a) AJOB Neuroscience, Volume 8, Issue 4 (2017)

(b) Ren, Xiaoping & Canavero, Sergio; HEAVEN in the Making: Between the Rock (the Academe) and a Hard Case (a Head Transplant). AJOB Neuroscience 8:4, 200-205 (2017)

(c) Wolpe, Paul Root, Ahead of Our Time: Why Head Transplantation Is Ethically Unsupportable. AJOB Neuroscience, 8:4, 206-210 (2017)

(d) Illes, Judy & McDonald, Patrick J.; Head Transplants: Ghoulish Takes on New Definition. AJOB Neuroscience 8:4, 211-212 (2017)

887. (a) Paul Root Wolpe, A human head transplant would be reckless and ghastly. It's time to talk about it. Vox, Apr 2, 2018

(b) Suskin, Z.D. & Giordano, J.J.; Body–to-head transplant; a "caputal" crime? Examining the corpus of ethical and legal issues. Philosophy, Ethics, and Humanities in Medicine 13, 10 (2018)

(c) Amy-Clare Martin, World's first human head transplant 'to take place within a decade'. Daily Record, 23 Dec 2019

(d) Sean Martin, World's first human head transplant could take place in 10 YEARS - shock claim'. Daily Express, Jan 3, 2020

(e) Kai Krause (2016), Complete Head Transplants. Response to the 2016 Edge.org question.

888. (a) DeGrazia, David, The Definition of Death. Stanford Encyclopedia of Philosophy (Summer 2021 Ed.)

(b) Veatch, Robert M., The Whole-Brain-Oriented Concept of Death: An Outmoded Philosophical Formulation. Journal of Thanatology 3:1, 13-30 (1975)

(c) ibid. Full paper and pdf download available online.

(d) Veatch, Robert M., The Impending Collapse of the Whole-Brain Definition of Death. The Hastings Center Report 23:4, 18–24 (1993)

889. (a) McMahan, Jeff, The Metaphysics Of Brain Death. Bioethics 9:2, 91-126 (1995)

(b) ibid. Full paper and pdf download available online.

(c) McMahan, Jeff, An Alternative to Brain Death. J. of Law, Medicine & Ethics 34:1, 44-48 (2006)

(d) ibid. Full paper and pdf download available online.

(e) Steven Luper, "Philosophy of Life" and "Philosophy of Death". Cambridge University Press, 1584 blog, 17 Feb 2014

(f) McMahan, Jeff, "Brain Death: Metaphysics, Morality, and Law". Colloquium: Ethics –Foundations and Applications. Berlin 11–14 Sep 2006

890. (a) Parfit, Derek, We Are Not Human Beings. Philosophy 87:1, 5–28 (2012)

(b) McGee, Andrew, We Are Human Beings. The Journal of Medicine and Philosophy: A Forum for Bioethics and Philosophy of Medicine 41:2, 148–171 (2016)

(c) ibid. Full paper and pdf download available at PMC4886465.

(d) Shewmon, D.A., The Brain and Somatic Integration: Insights Into the Standard Biological Rationale for Equating "Brain Death" With Death, The Journal of Medicine and Philosophy, 26:5, 457–478 (2001)

(e) ibid, 859b

(f) Potts, Michael, Brain Death and Integrated Functioning of the Organism. Response to: CMAJ 164:6, 833-836 (2001)

891. (a) Gillian, T., Brain Death and the Philosophical Significance of the Process of Development of, and Cessation of, Consciousness in Arousal and Awareness in the Human Person. Linacre Quarterly 68:1, 32-48 (2001)

(b) ibid. Full paper and pdf download available online.

(c) Seifert, J. (2004), Consciousness, Mind, Brain, and Death. In: Machado, C., Shewmon, D.A. (eds) Brain Death and Disorders of Consciousness. Advances in Experimental Medicine and Biology, vol 550

892. (a) Sarbey, Ben, Definitions of death: brain death and what matters in a person. Journal of Law and the Biosciences 3:3, 743–752 (2016)

(b) Mo Costandi, When Does Consciousness Begin and End? NOVA, PBS, May 27, 2015

(c) Holland, Stephen, On the Ordinary Concept of Death. J of Applied Philosophy 27:2, 109-122 (2010)

(d) Holland, Stephen, "Treatment decision, death and the value of life". QJM: An International Journal of Medicine 110:3, 121–123 (2017)

(e) Persson, Ingmar (2017), The End of Life and of Consciousness. In: Inclusive Ethics, OUP

893. (a) Mike Walsh, Is death just a software problem? Blogpost, Sep 24, 2016

(b) Roncaglia, M., On the Conservation of Information in Quantum Physics. Foundations of Physics 49, 1278–1286 (2019)

(c) Merkle, Ralph C.; The technical feasibility of cryonics. Medical Hypotheses 39:1, 6-16 (1992)

(d) ibid. Full paper and pdf download available online.

(e) Whetstine, L., Streat, S., Darwin, M. & Crippen, D.; Pro/con ethics debate: When is dead really dead?. Critical Care 9, 538 (2005)

894. (a) ibid, 718a

(b) ibid, 718b

(c) ibid, 718c

(d) ibid, 718d

(e) ibid, 722c

(f) ibid, 722d

895. (a) ibid, 719c

(b) ibid, 719d

(c) ibid, 723a

(d) ibid, 723b

(e) Cerullo, M.A., The Ethics of Exponential Life Extension through Brain Preservation. Journal of Evolution and Technology 26:1, 94-105 (2016)

896. (a) Merkle, Ralph C. (2016), Information-Theoretic Death.

(b) ibid, 895e

(c) Merkle, Ralph C., The technical feasibility of cryonics. Medical Hypotheses 39:1, 6-16 (1992)

(d) Merkle, Ralph C., The Molecular Repair of the Brain. Cryonics 15:1-2 (1994)

897. (a) Robert A. Freitas Jr., Institute for Molecular Manufacturing.

(b) Robert A. Freitas Jr., Nanomedicine. Kurzweil, Nov 18, 2003

(c) Sander Olson, Interview with Robert A. Freitas Jr. Part 2. Kurzweil, Feb 2, 2006

(d) Jokanovic, Vukoman, The Deep Scientific and Philosophic Approach to the Future Nanomedicine, Given on the Base of Author Introduction in the Monograph "Nanomedicine, the Greatest Challenge of the 21st Century". Drug Designing 3:2, 113 ((2014)

(e) Halappanavar, S., Vogel, U., Wallin, H. & Yauk, C.L.; Promise and peril in nanomedicine: the challenges and needs for integrated systems biology approaches to define health risk. WIREs Nanomedicine and Nanobiotechnology 10:1, e1465 (2018)

898. (a) Capurro,Rafael, Reflections On Ethical Aspects Of Nanomedicine. Capurro Fiek Foundation.

(b) Scientists' Open Letter on Cryonics. Biostasis.

(c) Medical Biostasis Protocol. https://www.biostasis.com/protocol/

(d) Moen, Ole Martin, The case for cryonics. Journal of Medical Ethics 41:8, 677-681 (2015)

899. (a) McIntyre, R.L. & Fahy, G.M.; Aldehyde-stabilized cryopreservation. Cryobiology 71:3, 448-458 (2015)

(b) Fahy G.M., Wowk B. (2015, Principles of Cryopreservation by Vitrification. In: Wolkers W., Oldenhof H. (eds) Cryopreservation and Freeze-Drying Protocols. Methods in Molecular Biology (Methods and Protocols), vol 1257. Springer, New York, NY.

(c) George Dvorsky, Brain Preservation Breakthrough Could Usher in a New Era in Cryonics. Gizmodo, Sep 02, 2016

(d) Aaron Frank, A Mammal's Brain Has Been Cryonically Preserved and Recovered. Motherboard, Vice, Sep 02, 2016

(e) 21st Century Medicine. Special Announcement: 21CM in the News.

(f) Alexandre Erler, Brain Preservation and Personal Survival: The Importance of Promoting Cryonics-Specific Research. Cryonics magazine, Nov-Dec 2017

900. (a) Goertzel, B. & Iklé, M.; Introduction. Special Issue on Mind Uploading. International Journal of Machine Consciousness 4:1, 1-3 (2012)

(b) David Smith, 2050 - and immortality is within our grasp. The Guardian, 22 May 2005

(c) Cheyenne Macdonald, Humans could achieve 'electronic immortality' by 2050 and attend our own FUNERALS in a new body, futurist claims (but he warns our minds could be 'enslaved' if we aren't careful). Daily Mail, 24 Jul 2018

(d) Laakasuo, M., Drosinou, M., Koverola, M. et al.; What makes people approve or condemn mind upload technology? Untangling the effects of sexual disgust, purity and science fiction familiarity. Palgrave Communications 4, 84 (2018)

(e) University of Helsinki, "Science fiction enthusiasts have a positive attitude to the digitizing of the brain." ScienceDaily, 12 Jul 2018

901. (a) Martin, G.M., On Immortality: An Interim Solution. Perspectives Biol. and Med. 14:2, 339-340 (1971)

(b) Vinge, Vernor (1993), The Singularity. Within 30 years, we will be in a Post-Human era. From the VISION-21 Symposium sponsored by NASA Lewis Research Center and Ohio Aerospace Institute.

(c) Ray Kurzweil (2001), The Law of Accelerating Returns. Kurzweilai.net, Mar 7, 2001

(d) Lev Grossman, 2045: The Year Man Becomes Immortal. TIME, Feb 10, 2011

902. (a) Randal A. Koene, The History of SIM, Whole Brain Emulation and Mind Uploading. Carbon Copies.

(b) Sandberg, A. & Bostrom, N. (2008), Whole Brain Emulation: A Roadmap. Technical Report #2008-3, Future of Humanity Institute, Oxford University.

(c) Koene, R.A., Tijms, B., van Hees, P. et al.; NETMORPH: A Framework for the Stochastic Generation of Large Scale Neuronal Networks With Realistic Neuron Morphologies. Neuroinform 7, 195–210 (2009)

903. (a) Koene, R.A., Fundamentals Of Whole Brain Emulation: State, Transition And Update Representations. International Journal of Machine Consciousness 4:1, 5-21 (2012)

(b) Koene, R.A., Experimental Research In Whole Brain Emulation: The Need For Innovative In Vivo Measurement Techniques. International Journal of Machine Consciousness 4:1, 35-65 (2012)

(c) Luke Muehlhauser, Randal Koene on whole brain emulation.
Machine Intelligence Research Institute, Mar 20, 2014

(d) Koene, R.A. & Deca, D. (eds.), Brain Emulation and Connectomics, a convergence of Neuroscience and Artificial Intelligence. Journal of Artificial General Intelligence 4:3, (2013)

904. (a) Mark O'Connell, 'Your animal life is over. Machine life has begun.' The road to immortality.
The Guardian, 25 Mar 2017

(b) Piccinini, G. (2021), The Myth of Mind Uploading. In: Clowes, R.W., Gärtner, K., Hipólito, I. (eds) The Mind-Technology Problem. Studies in Brain and Mind, vol. 18. Springer, Cham.

(c) Levin, Janet, "Functionalism", The Stanford Encyclopedia of Philosophy (Winter 2021 Edition).

(d) Alvarez, J.A., Emory, E.; Executive Function and the Frontal Lobes: A Meta-Analytic Review. Neuropsychology Review 16, 17–42 (2006)

(e) Paul G. Allen & Mark Greaves,The Singularity Isn't Near. MIT Technology Review, Oct 12, 2011

905. (a) Turing, Alan M., I.—Computing Machinery And Intelligence. Mind LIX/59:236, 433–460 (1950)

(b) R.Kurzweil, Kurzweil Responds: Don't Underestimate the Singularity. MIT Tech Review, Oct 20, 2011

(c) Gary Marcus, Ray Kurzweil's Dubious New Theory of Mind. New Yorker, Nov 15, 2012

(d) Thomson, E., Carra, R. & Nicolelis, M.; Perceiving invisible light through a somatosensory cortical prosthesis. Nature Communications 4, 1482 (2013)

(e) Antonio Regalado, The Brain Is Not Computable. A leading neuroscientist says Kurzweil's Singularity isn't going to happen. MIT Technology Review, Feb 18, 2013

906. (a) Tristan Quinn, The immortalist: Uploading the mind to a computer. BBC Horizon, 14 Mar 2016

(b) Richard A.L. Jones (2016), Against Transhumanism: The delusion of technological transcendence.

(c) Richard A.L. Jones (2014), Your mind will not be uploaded.

(d) Richard Jones, Could we upload a brain to a computer – and should we even try?
The Conversation, Jul 4, 2016

(e) Kasthuri, N., Hayworth, K.J., Berger, D.R. et al.; Saturated Reconstruction of a Volume of Neocortex. Cell 162:3, 648-661 (2015)

(f) Kenneth D. Miller, Will You Ever Be Able to Upload Your Brain? New York Times, Oct 10, 2015

907. (a) John Horgan (2008), The Consciousness Conundrum. Part of IEEE Special on The Singularity.

(b) Rodney Brooks (2008), I, Rodney Brooks, Am a Robot. Part of IEEE Special on The Singularity.

(c) Richard A.L. Jones (2008), Rupturing The Nanotech Rapture. Part of IEEE Special on The Singularity.

(d) Richard A.L. Jones (2014), Transhumanism has never been modern.

(e) ibid, 906d

(f) Vernor Vinge (2008), Signs of the Singularity. Part of IEEE Special on The Singularity.

908. (a) Ray Kurzweil, Live forever. Psychology Today, Jan 1, 2000

(b) Ben Goertzel, Technological Transcendence: An Interview with Giulio Prisco.
Humanity+ Magazine, Feb 8, 2011

(c) Giulio Prisco, Transhumanist spirituality, again. Blog post, Oct 18, 2008

(d) Patrick Hopkins, Toward a Transhumanist Theology. Metanexus, Aug 9, 2011

(e) Jessica Roy, The Rapture of the Nerds. TIME, Apr 17, 2014

909. (a) Wesley J. Smith, Transhumanism: A Wail of Despair in the Night. National Review, May 14, 2018

(b) Lincoln Cannon, Wesley Smith Lies About Transhumanism. Blog, 14 May 2018

(c) M.O'Gieblyn, God in the machine: my strange journey into transhumanism. Guardian, 18 Apr 2017

(d) Beth Singler, Faith. The most avid believers in artificial intelligence are aggressively secular – yet their language is eerily religious. Why? Aeon, 3 Jun 2017

(e) Ben Goertzel, Liberating Minds from Brains. Blog, Feb 25, 2002

(f) Ben Goertzel, A Cosmist Manifesto. Blog, Jul 2009-10

910. (a) Hopkins, Patrick D., Why Uploading Will Not Work, Or, The Ghosts Haunting Transhumanism. International Journal of Machine Consciousness 4:1, 229-243 (2012)

(b) Patrick Hopkins, Uploading Won't Help You. IEET, Aug 14, 2012

(c) Cerullo, M.A., Uploading and Branching Identity. Minds & Machines 25, 17–36 (2015)

(d) Berit Brogaard, Split Brains. The brain's processing of information affected by hemispheric transfer. Psychology Today, Nov 6, 2012

(e) Pinto, Y., Neville, D.A., Otten, M. et al.; Split brain: divided perception but undivided consciousness. Brain 140:5, 1231–1237 (2017)

(f) Universiteit van Amsterdam (UVA). "Split brain does not lead to split consciousness."
ScienceDaily, 25 Jan 2017

911. (a) Amy Harmon, The Neuroscience of Immortality. New York Times, Sep 12, 2015

(b) Susan Schneider, The Philosophy of 'Her'. The Stone, New York Times, Mar 2, 2014

(c) Fletcher, Jack M., A computational mind cannot recognize itself. Technoetic Arts 13:3, 261-267 (2015)

(d) Ian Pearson, When you're electronically immortal, will you still own your own mind? Blog, Jul 15, 2018

(e) Michael Graziano, Endless fun. The question is not whether we can upload our brains onto a computer, but what will become of us when we do. Aeon, 18 Dec 2013

(f) Keith B. Wiley, Mind Uploading and The Question of Life, the Universe, and Everything. IEET, Jul 20, 2015

912. (a) Machado, Calixto, Diagnosis of brain death. Neurology International 2:1, e2 (2010)

(b) Raymond Moody, Life after Life resource website.

(c) Kevin Williams, Dr. Raymond Moody's Near-Death Experience Research. NDE, 21 Sep 2019

(d) Piet Levy, Raymond Moody, Man Behind 'Near-Death Experience' Ponders The Afterlife. HuffPost, Apr 12, 2012

913. (a) Greyson, Bruce, The Near-Death Experience Scale. J Nerv Mental Disease 171:6, 369-375 (1983)

(b) Tara MacIsaac, Next Steps in Near-Death Experiences Research: Scientists Discuss. The Epoch Times, Aug 30, 2014

(c) Belanti, J., Perera, M. & Jagadheesan, K.; Phenomenology of Near-death Experiences: A Cross-cultural Perspective. Transcultural Psychiatry 45:1, 121-133 (2008)

(d) Tara MacIsaac, Interview: Bruce Greyson on Researching Near-Death Experiences at the University of Virginia. The Epoch Times, May 25, 2015

914. (a) Sleutjes, A., Moreira-Almeida, A. & Greyson, B.; Almost 40 Years Investigating Near-Death Experiences, The Journal of Nervous and Mental Disease 202:11, 833-836 (2014)

(b) Farah, Martha J. & Murphy, Nancey; Neuroscience and the Soul. Science 323:5918, 1168 (2009)

(c) Greyson, Bruce, Near-death experiences and the physio-kundalini syndrome. Journal of Religion and Health 32, 277–290 (1993)

(d) Tia Ghose, Near-Death Experiences May Be Triggered by Surging Brain Activity. Live Science, Aug 12, 2013

(e) B.Gholipour, Oldest Medical Report of Near-Death Experience Discovered. Live Science, Jul 24, 2014

(f) Tara MacIsaac, The Neuroscience of Near-Death Experiences. The Epoch Times, Apr 29, 2022

915. (a) Martens, P.R., Near-death-experiences in out-of-hospital cardiac arrest survivors. Meaningful phenomena or just fantasy of death? Resuscitation 27:2, 171-175 (1994)

(b) van Lommel, P., van Wees, R., Meyers, V. & Elfferich, I.; Near-death experience in survivors of cardiac arrest: a prospective study in the Netherlands. The Lancet 358:9298, 2039-2045 (2001)

(c) ibid. Full paper and pdf download available online.

(d) Jody Long, Review of "Near Death Experience In Survivors of Cardiac Arrest: A Prospective Study in the Netherlands" by Pim van Lommel et al. (2001). NDERF, Jun 3, 2002.

(e) Greyson, B., Fountain, N., Derr, L. & Broshek, D.; Out-of-body experiences associated with seizures. Frontiers in Human Neuroscience, 8 (2014)

(f) Blanke, O., Ortigue, S., Landis, T. & Seeck, M.; Stimulating illusory own-body perceptions. Nature 419, 269–270 (2002)

916. (a) Braithwaite, Jason J., Towards a Cognitive Neuroscience of the Dying Brain. The Skeptic 21:2 (2008)

(b) Tim Adams, Sam Parnia – the man who could bring you back from the dead. Guardian, 06 Apr 2013

(c) Horizon Research Foundation. http://www.horizonresearch.org/

(d) Parnia, S., Waller, D.G., Yeates, R. & Fenwick, P.; A qualitative and quantitative study of the incidence, features and aetiology of near death experiences in cardiac arrest survivors. Resuscit. 48:2, 149-156 (2001)

917. (a) University of Southampton, "World's Largest-ever Study Of Near-Death Experiences." ScienceDaily, 10 Sep 2008

(b) Parnia, S., Spearpoint, K., de Vos, G. et al.; AWARE—AWAreness during REsuscitation—A prospective study. Resuscitation 85:12, 1799-1805 (2014)

(c) University of Southampton, "Near-death experiences? Results of the world's largest medical study of the human mind and consciousness at time of death." ScienceDaily, 07 Oct 2014

(d) Parnia, S., Keshavarz, T., McMullin, M. & Williams, T.; Abstract 387: Awareness and Cognitive Activity During Cardiac Arrest. Circulation 140:Suppl_2, A387-A387 (2019)

(e) Kate Anderton, Modern resuscitation science: Illuminating the complex processes of death. News-Medical.Net, Nov 15, 2019

(f) Parnia, S., Do reports of consciousness during cardiac arrest hold the key to discovering the nature of consciousness? Medical Hypotheses 69:4, 933-937 (2007)

(g) Philip Perry, After death, you're aware that you've died, say scientists. Big Think, Oct 24, 2017

918. (a) Sue Blackmore, Back from the grave. The Guardian, 19 Sep 2008

(b) Susan Blackmore (1993), Dying to Live: Near-Death Experiences (extract). Prometheus Books NY.

(c) O'Brien, Michael, The Day I Died. BMJ 326:7383, 288 (2003)

(d) Marsh, M.N. (2010), Out-of-Body and Near-Death Experiences: Brain-State Phenomena or Glimpses of Immortality? Oxford University Press, ISBN-13: 9780199571505

919. (a) Kevin Williams, George Ritchie's Near-Death Experience. NDE, Sep 26, 2019

(b) Mays, R.G. & Mays, S.B. (2008-2010); Investigation of George Ritchie's NDE OBE.

(c) Eben Alexander, The Science of Heaven. Newsweek, Nov 18, 2012

(d) Alexander III, Eben, My Experience in Coma. AANS Neurosurgeon: Features 21:2 (2012)

(e) Oliver Sacks, Altered States. Self-experiments in chemistry. New Yorker, Aug 27, 2012

(f) Oliver Sacks, Seeing God in the Third Millennium. How the brain creates out-of-body experiences and religious epiphanies. The Atlantic, Dec 12, 2012

920. (a) Clint Witchalls, Go towards the light. The Independent, 08 Mar 2004

(b) Grof, Stanislav (1979), Treating Death. In: The Coming Age of Psychosomatics. Pergamon, pg 385, M. Carruthers, P. Mellett (eds.)

(c) Grof, Stanislav, The Experience of Death and Dying: Psychological, Philosophical, and Spiritual Aspects. Stan Grof online resources.

(d) Review: Broca's Brain by Carl Sagan. Kirkus, May 1, 1979

921. (a) Blackmore, Susan, Birth and the OBE: An Unhelpful Analogy. Journal of the American Society for Psychical Research 77, 229-238 (1983)

(b) Blackmore, Susan, Near-Death Experiences: In or out of the body? Skeptical Inquirer 16, 34-45 (1991)

(c) Patihis, L., & Younes Burton, H.J.; False memories in therapy and hypnosis before 1980. Psychology of Consciousness: Theory, Research, and Practice 2:2, 153–169 ((2015)

(d) ibid. Full paper and pdf download available online.

(e) Bateman, L., Jones, C. & Jomeen, J.; A Narrative Synthesis of Women's Out-of-Body Experiences During Childbirth. Journal of Midwifery & Women's Health 62, 442-451 (2017)

922. (a) Smith, David W., "Phenomenology", Stanford Encyclopedia of Philosophy (Summer 2018 Edition).

(b) Thonnard, M., Charland-Verville, V., Brédart, S. et al.; Characteristics of Near-Death Experiences Memories as Compared to Real and Imagined Events Memories. PLoS ONE 8:3, e57620 (2013)

(c) University of Liège, "Memories of near death experiences: More real than reality?" ScienceDaily, 27 Mar 2013

(d) Charland-Verville, V., Martial, C., Cassol, H. & Laureys, S. (2018). Near-Death Experiences: Actual Considerations. In: Schnakers, C., Laureys, S. (eds) Coma and Disorders of Consciousness. Springer.

(e) ibid. Full paper and pdf download available online.

(f) Palmieri, A., Calvo, V., Kleinbub, J. et al.; "Reality" of near-death-experience memories: evidence from a psychodynamic and electrophysiological integrated study. Frontiers in Human Neuroscience 8, (2014)

923. (a) Facco, Enrico & Agrillo, Christian; Near-death experiences between science and prejudice. Frontiers in Human Neuroscience 6, (2012)

(b) Palmer, John. Editorial, Statistical Issues In Parapsychology: Hypothesis Testing—Plus An Addendum On Bierman et al. (2016). Journal of Parapsychology 80:2, 141–143 (2016)

924. (a) ibid, 148a

(b) ibid, 743a

(c) ibid. 723b

925. (a) Sno, H.N. & Linszen, D.H.; he déjà vu experience: remembrance of things past? American Journal of Psychiatry 147:12, 1587-1595 (1990)

(b) ibid. Full paper and pdf download available online.

(c) JZL CK, Déjà-Vu; Explained. Medium, May 30, 2020

(d) Naveed Saleh, 4 Possible Explanations for Déjà Vu. Psychology Today, Oct 26, 2016

926. (a) Michael D. Lemonick, Explaining Déjà Vu. Memory experts find the brain circuit that may be the cause of these eerie experiences. TIME, Aug. 09, 2007

(b) Illman, N.A., Butler, C.R., Souchay, C. & Moulin, C.J.A.; Déjà Experiences in Temporal Lobe Epilepsy. Epilepsy Research and Treatment, ID 539567 (2012)

(c) Vlasov, P.N., Chervyakov, A.V. & Gnezditskii, V.V.; Déjà vu phenomenon-related EEG pattern. Case report. Epilepsy & Behavior Case Reports 1, 136-141 (2013)

(d) Adachi, T., Adachi, N., Takekawa, Y. et al.; Déjà vu experiences in patients with schizophrenia. Comprehensive Psychiatry 47:5, 389-393 (2006)

(e) Adachi, N., Akanu, N., Adachi, T. et al.; Déjà Vu Experiences Are Rarely Associated With Pathological Dissociation. The Journal of Nervous and Mental Disease 196:5, 417-419 (2008)

927. (a) Melissa Dahl, A New Theory on Déjà Vu: It's How Your Memory Fact-checks Itself.
The Cut, New Yorker, Aug 17, 2016
(b) Jersakova, R., Moulin, C.J.A. & O'Connor, A.R.; Investigating the Role of Assessment Method on Reports of Déjà Vu and Tip-of-the-Tongue States during Standard Recognition Tests.
PLoS ONE 11:4, e0154334 (2016)
(c) O'Connor, A.R., Wells, C. & Moulin, C.J.A.; Déjà vu and other dissociative states in memory.
Memory 29:7, 835-842 (2021)

928. (a) Pégard, N.C., Mardinly, A.R., Oldenburg, I.A. et al.; Three-dimensional scanless holographic optogenetics with temporal focusing (3D-SHOT). Nature Communications 8, 1228 (2017)
(b) Philip Perry, Scientists create holographic projections in the brain that can create false memories.
Big Think, May 13, 2018
(c) The Psychology of Déjà vu. Association for Psychological Science, Nov 18, 2008
(d) Cleary, A.M. & Claxton, A.B.; Déjà Vu: An Illusion of Prediction. Psychol. Sci. 29:4, 635-644 (2018)
(e) Colorado State University, "Déjà vu and feelings of prediction: They're just feelings: Researchers recreated deja vu in human subjects." ScienceDaily, 1 Mar 2018

929. (a) Smith, Andra & Messier, Claude; Voluntary out-of-body experience: an fMRI study.
Frontiers in Human Neuroscience, 8 (2014)
(b) Guterstam, A. & Ehrsson, H.H.; Disowning one's seen real body during an out-of-body illusion.
Consciousness and Cognition 21:2, 1037-1042 (2012)
(c) Guterstam, A., Björnsdotter, M., Gentile, G. & Ehrsson, H.H.; Posterior Cingulate Cortex Integrates the Senses of Self-Location and Body Ownership. Current Biology 25:11, 1416–1425 (2015)
(d) Karolinska Institutet, "Brain scan reveals out-of-body illusion." ScienceDaily, 30 Apr 2015
(e) Tanya Lewis, Out-of-Body Experience Is Traced in the Brain. Live Science, Apr 30, 2015

930. (a) Bourdin, P., Barberia, I., Oliva, R. & Slater, M.; A Virtual Out-of-Body Experience Reduces Fear of Death. PLoS ONE 12:1, e0169343 (2017)
(b) Shayla Love, The VR Experience That Might Make You Less Afraid to Die Virtual reality can create an out-of-body experience, but can it also reduce the fear of death? VICE, 31 Jan 2018

931. (a) Aaron Frank, NBA Courtside at Home? Live Action Virtual Reality is Here and Better than Expected.
Singularity Hub, Jul 22, 2014
(b) Aaron Frank, Neurogames are Ready to Take Flight — Expect a Breakout Year Ahead.
Singularity Hub, May 18, 2014
(c) Michio Kaku, Advances in Holographic Technology Could Have Far-Reaching Implications.
Big Think, Nov 9, 2010
(d) Jason Dorrier, How to Virtually 'Possess' Another Person's Body Using Oculus Rift and Kinect.
Singularity Hub, Jul 30, 2014
(e) Age simulation suit GERT. https://www.age-simulation-suit.com/

932. (a) ibid, 922d
(b) Griffith, Linda J., Near-death experiences and psychotherapy.
Psychiatry (Edgmont (Pa.: Township)) 6:10, 35-42 (2009)
(c) Laureys, Steven, Preface. In: The Boundaries of Consciousness: Neurobiology and Neuropathology, S. Laureys (ed). Progress in Brain Research 150:xiii-xiv (2005)
(d) Zeman, Adam, What in the world is consciousness? In: The Boundaries of Consciousness: Neurobiology and Neuropathology, S. Laureys (ed). Progress in Brain Research 150, 1-10 (2005)
(e) Greenfield, S.A. & Collins, T.F.T.; A neuroscientific approach to consciousness. In: The Boundaries of Consciousness: Neurobiology and Neuropathology, S. Laureys (ed).
Progress in Brain Research 150, 11-23, 586-587 (2005)
(f) French, C.C., Near-death experiences in cardiac arrest survivors. In: The Boundaries of Consciousness: Neurobiology and Neuropathology, S. Laureys (ed). Progress in Brain Research 150, 351-367 (2005)

933. (a) Rass, R. (2014), Foreword, Rethinking Mortality: Exploring the Boundaries between Life and Death.
Ann. N.Y. Acad. Sci., 1330: v-vi.
(b) Paulson, S. (2014), Introduction, Rethinking mortality: exploring the boundaries between life and death. Ann. N.Y. Acad. Sci., 1330: 1-3.
(c) Paulson, S., Becker, L.B., Parnia, S. & Mayer, S.A. (2014); Reversing death: the miracle of modern medicine. Ann. N.Y. Acad. Sci., 1330: 4-18.
(d) Paulson, S., Fenwick, P., Neal, M., Nelson, K. & Parnia, S. (2014); Experiencing death: an insider's perspective. Ann. N.Y. Acad. Sci., 1330: 40-57.
(e) Paulson, S., Comfort, C.P., Lee, B.C., Shemie, S. & Solomon, M.Z. (2014); Prolonging life: legal, ethical, and social dilemmas. Ann. N.Y. Acad. Sci., 1330: 19-39.

(f) Paulson, S., Kellehear, A., Kripal, J.J. & Leary, L. (2014); Confronting mortality: faith and meaning across cultures. Ann. N.Y. Acad. Sci., 1330: 58-74.

(g) Parnia, Sam (2014), Death and consciousness—an overview of the mental and cognitive experience of death. Ann. N.Y. Acad. Sci., 1330: 75-93.

(h) Natalie Wolchover, Near-Death Experiences are Lucid Dreams, Experiment Finds. Live Science, Mar 16, 2012

(i) Nelson, K.R. (2014), Near-death experience: arising from the borderlands of consciousness in crisis. Ann. N.Y. Acad. Sci., 1330: 111-119.

934. (a) The Manifesto for a Post-Materialist Science (2014), OpenSciences.org

(b) Pim van Lommel (2015), Introduction: Nonlocal Consciousness.

(c) Cardeña, Etzel, A call for an open, informed study of all aspects of consciousness. Frontiers in Human Neuroscience, 8 (2014)

(d) Beyond the Brain. Further reaches of consciousness research. https://beyondthebrain.org/

(e) Stephanie Pappas, Can science 'prove' there's an afterlife? Netflix documentary says yes. Live Science, Jan 17, 2021

935. (a) Ulf Wolf, Pim van Lommel — Review of "Consciousness Beyond Life: The Science of the Near-Death Experience". Medium, Nov 23, 2021

(b) van Lommel, P., Getting Comfortable With Near-Death Experiences: Dutch Prospective Research on Near-Death Experiences During Cardiac Arrest. Missouri Medicine, 111:2, 126–131 (2014)

936. (a) Dolgin, Elie, How to defeat dementia. Nature 539, 156–158 (2016)

(b) University of Rochester Medical Center, "Parkinson's disease: A looming pandemic." ScienceDaily, 13 Nov 2017

(c) Nahm, M., Terminal Lucidity in People with Mental Illness and Other Mental Disability: An Overview and Implications for Possible Explanatory Models. Journal of Near-Death Studies 28:2, 87-106 (2009)

(d) Nahm, M., Greyson, B., Williams Kelly, E. & Haraldsson, E.; Terminal lucidity: A review and a case collection. Archives of Gerontology and Geriatrics 55:1, 138-142 (2012)

(e) Nahm, M. & Greyson, B.; The Death of Anna Katharina Ehmer: A Case Study in Terminal Lucidity. OMEGA - Journal of Death and Dying 68:1, 77-87 (2014)

(f) Jesse Bering, One Last Goodbye: The Strange Case of Terminal Lucidity. Sci. Amercan, Nov 25, 2014

937. (a) Lydia Denworth, "Awakenings" in Advanced Dementia Patients Hint at Untapped Brain Reserves. Scientific American, Aug 1, 2019

(b) Mashour, G.A., Frank, L., Batthyany, A. et al.; Paradoxical lucidity: A potential paradigm shift for the neurobiology and treatment of severe dementias. Alzheimer's & Dementia 15:8, 1107-1114 (2019)

(c) Michigan Medicine - University of Michigan, "Moments of clarity in dementia patients at end of life: Glimmers of hope?" ScienceDaily, 28 Jun 2019

(d) Eldadah, B.A., Fazio, E.M. & McLinden, K.A.; Lucidity in dementia: A perspective from the NIA. Alzheimer's & Dementia 15:8, 1104-1106 (2019)

938. (a) M. Heidegger (1959), An Introduction to Metaphysics. Yale University Press, New Haven and London

(b) Mei, T.S., Heidegger And The Appropriation Of Metaphysics. Heythrop Journal 50:2, 257-270 (2009)

(c) Witherall, Arthur, The Fundamental Question. Journal of Philosophical Research 26, 53-87 (2001)

(d) ibid. Full paper and pdf download available online.

(e) ibid, 283a

(f) ibid, 283c

939. (a) Richard Webb, Metaphysics special: Why is there something rather than nothing? The Scientist, 31 Aug 2016

(b) Carroll, Sean M. (2018), Why Is There Something, Rather Than Nothing? arXiv:1802.02231

(c) Pearce, D. (2014), Why does the universe exist? Why is there something rather than nothing? Quora

(d) Witherall, Arthur (2014), The Zero Ontology - David Pearce on Why Anything Exists. Hedweb.

(e) Joronen, M., The Technological Metaphysics of Planetary Space: Being in the Age of Globalization. Environment and Planning D: Society and Space 26:4, 596-610 (2008)

940. (a) David Brooks, What Is Your Purpose? New York Times, May 05, 2015

(b) CCCB, The Human Condition. The Barcelona Debate 2008. 21 Jan – 10 Mar 2008

(c) Harry Wallop, Gen Z, Gen Y, baby boomers – a guide to the generations. The Telegraph, 31 Jul 2014

941. (a) Andy Beckett, Post-work: the radical idea of a world without jobs. The Guardian, 19 Jan 2018

(b) Samuel Alexander, Life in a 'degrowth' economy, and why you might actually enjoy it. The Conversation, Oct 1, 2014

(c) Decker, J.M. (2004), The 'Post-Ideological' Era?. In: Ideology. Transitions. Palgrave, London.

(d) Scotty Hendricks, Young Americans are ditching democracy, say Harvard researchers. Big Think, Dec 08, 2016

(e) "Nones" on the Rise. Pew Research Center. Oct 9, 2012

(f) Kyrlezhev, A., The Postsecular Age: Religion and Culture Today. Relig, State, Soc 36:1, 21-31 (2008)

(g) ibid, 934a

(h) Yuval Noah Harari, Are we living in a post-truth era? Yes, but that's because we're a post-truth species. TED.com, Sep 7, 2018

(i) Ben McGrath, The Dystopians. Bad times are boom times for some. The New Yorker, Jan 18, 2009

(j) William Hawes, The Great Unraveling: Using Science and Philosophy to Decode Modernity. Counterpunch, Dec 22, 2017

942. (a) Neel Burton, What Is Eudaimonia? Psychology Today, Jun 28, 2020

(b) Huta, V. & Waterman, A.S.; Eudaimonia and Its Distinction from Hedonia: Developing a Classification and Terminology for Understanding Conceptual and Operational Definitions. Journal of Happiness Studies 15, 1425–1456 (2014)

(c) Positive Psychology (basics). Psychology Today.

(d) Aristotle (350 BCE), Nicomachean Ethics. Internet Classics Archive.

(e) Kraut, Richard, "Aristotle's Ethics", Stanford Encyclopedia of Philosophy (Summer 2022 Ed.)

943. (a) Jun Shan, The Meaning of Yin and Yang. ThoughtCo, Feb 03, 2020.

(b) Wang, Robin R., "Yinyang (Yin-yang)". In: Internet Encyclopedia of Philosophy.

(c) Fraser, Chris, "Mohism", The Stanford Encyclopedia of Philosophy (Spring 2022 Edition).

(d) Ivanhoe, P.J. (1998), Mohist philosophy. In: Routledge Encyclopedia of Philosophy.

944. (a) Gosling, Justin (1998), Hedonism. In: Routledge Encyclopedia of Philosophy.

(b) Weijers, Dan, Hedonism. In: Internet Encyclopedia of Philosophy.

(c) Moore, Andrew, "Hedonism", Stanford Encyclopedia of Philosophy (Winter 2019 Edition).

(d) John Stuart Mill (1863), Utilitarianism. HedWeb

(e) Schefczyk, Michael, John Stuart Mill: Ethics. In: Internet Encyclopedia of Philosophy.

945. (a) Moccia, L., Mazza, M., Di Nicola, M. & Janiri, L.; The Experience of Pleasure: A Perspective Between Neuroscience and Psychoanalysis. Frontiers in Human Neuroscience 12, 359 (2018)

(b) Barnhart, J.E., Freud's Pleasure Principle and the Death Urge. The Southwestern Journal of Philosophy 3:1, 113–20 (1972)

(c) Van de Vijver, G., Bazan, A. & Detandt, S.; The Mark, the Thing, and the Object: On What Commands Repetition in Freud and Lacan. Frontiers in Psychology, 8 (2017)

(d) Hindriks, Frank & Douven, Igor; Nozick's experience machine: An empirical study. Philosophical Psychology 31:2, 278-298 (2018)

(e) Buscicchi, Lorenzo, The Experience Machine. In: Internet Encyclopedia of Philosophy.

946. (a) Baltzly, Dirk, "Stoicism", Stanford Encyclopedia of Philosophy (Spring 2019 Edition).

(b) Lary Wallace, Indifference is a power. Aeon, 24 Dec 2014

(c) Pigliucci, Massimo, Stoicism. In: Internet Encyclopedia of Philosophy.

(d) Leira, H., "Justus Lipsius, political humanism and the disciplining of 17th century statecraft". Review of International Studies 34:4, 669-692 (2008)

947. (a) Matthew Sharpe, Stoicism 5.0: The unlikely 21st century reboot of an ancient philosophy. The Conversation, Jul 13, 2017

(b) Rowland Manthorpe, All that's good and bad about Silicon Valley's Stoicism fad. Wired, 26 Oct 2017

(c) Massimo Pigliucci, Anger is temporary madness: the Stoics knew how to curb it. Aeon, 13 Oct 2017

(d) Jules Evans, Anxious? Depressed? Try Greek philosophy. The Telegraph, 29 Jun 2013

(e) Massimo Pigliucci, How to Be a Stoic. The Stone, New York Times, Feb 2, 2015

948. (a) Scotty Hendricks, God's Answer to Nietzsche, the Philosophy of Søren Kierkegaard. Big Think, Dec 17, 2017

(b) Scotty Hendricks, "God is dead": What Nietzsche really meant. Big Think, Aug 2016 (updated Jan 29, 2022)

(c) Davenport, Manuel M., The Post-Existential Blues. Cross Currents 30:1, 1–11 (1980)

(d) Crowell, Steven, "Existentialism", Stanford Encyclopedia of Philosophy (Summer 2020 Edition).

(e) Guignon, Charles B. & Aho, Kevin (2004); Existentialism. In: Routledge Encyclopedia of Philosophy.

(f) Ayesh Perera, An Overview of Viktor Frankl's Logotherapy. Simply Psychology, Jun 26, 2020

(g) Ed Simon, What Viktor Frankl's logotherapy can offer in the Anthropocene. Aeon, 11 Feb 2020

(h) McCann, H.J. & D.M. Johnson, "Divine Providence", Stanford Encyclopedia of Philosophy (Spring 2017 Edition), Edward N. Zalta (ed.)

949. (a) Anthony Draper, Existentialism is a Christianism. Notes on Sartre's Existentialism is a Humanism. Aletheia, Medium, Apr 5 2022

(b) Existentialism vs Absurdism — Explanations and Key Differences of Each. Thinking Deeply with Ben, Medium, Sep 14, 2020

(c) Aronson, Ronald, "Albert Camus", Stanford Encyclopedia of Philosophy (Spring 2022 Edition).

(d) Panumas King, Albert Camus and the problem of absurdity. OUP blog, May 25th 2019

(e) Mark Byron, Guide to the Classics: Samuel Beckett's Waiting for Godot, a tragicomedy for our times. The Conversation, Jun 2, 2021

(f) Esther Lombardi, Themes and Related Quotes From "Waiting for Godot". ThoughtCo, July 09, 2019

950. (a) Stone, A. (2013), Existentialism. In: The Oxford Handbook of Atheism, S.Bullivant & M.Ruse (eds).

(b) Definition of Humanism. American Humanist Association.

(c) Leiter, Brian, "Nietzsche's Moral and Political Philosophy", Stanford Encyclopedia of Philosophy (Summer 2021 Edition), Edward N. Zalta (ed.)

(d) Migotti, Mark, Slave Morality, Socrates, and the Bushmen: A Reading of the First Essay of On the Genealogy of Morals. Philosophy and Phenomenological Research 58:4, 745–779 (1998)

(e) ibid, 638a

951. (a) Newberg, Andrew, Ask the Brains. Is there a difference between the brain of an atheist and the brain of a religious person? Scientific American, Mind 22, 6, 70 (2012)

(b) Schellenberg, J., The hiddenness argument revisited (I). Religious Studies 41:2, 201-215 (2005)

(c) ibid. Full paper and pdf download available online

(d) J.L. Schellenberg, Does 'divine hiddenness' belong to theists or to atheists? The Hiddenness Argument. OUP blog, Aug 15th 2015.

952. (a) McKim, Robert, Review: J.L. Schellenberg, Divine Hiddenness And Human Reason. Faith and Phil.: J of Soc of Christian Psers. 12:2, 8 (1995)

(b) Howard-Snyder, D., Review of Divine Hiddenness and Human Reason by J. L. Schellenberg. Mind 104:414, 430–435 (1995)

(c) Vandergriff, K. Re-evaluating the hiddenness argument from above. International Journal for Philosophy of Religion 85, 193–211 (2019)

(d) Teeninga, L., Divine Hiddenness, Greater Goods, and Accommodation. SOPHIA 56, 589–603 (2017)

953. (a) Beebe, James R., Logical Problem of Evil. In: Internet Encyclopedia of Philosophy.

(b) Trakakis, Nick, The Evidential Problem of Evil. In: Internet Encyclopedia of Philosophy.

(c) Tooley, Michael, "The Problem of Evil", Stanford Encyclopedia of Philosophy (Winter 2021 Ed.)

(d) Tooley, Michael (2019), The Problem of Evil (Elements in the Philosophy of Religion). CUP.

954. (a) Garrard, Eve, Evil as an Explanatory Concept. The Monist 85:2, 320–336 (2002)

(b) Singer, Marcus, The Concept of Evil. Philosophy 79:2, 185-214 (2004)

(c) McFarland, Ian A., The Problem with Evil. Theology Today 74:4, 321-339 (2018)

955. (a) Rowe, William L., The Problem of Evil and Some Varieties of Atheism. American Philosophical Quarterly 16:4, 335–341 (1979)

(b) Oppy, Graham (2006), Arguments from Evil. In: Arguing about Gods (pp. 259-330). CUP.

(c) McCloskey, H.J., The Problem of Evil, J. of the American Acad. of Religion XXX:3, 187–197 (1962)

(d) Newman, Lex, "Descartes' Epistemology", Stanford Encyclopedia of Philosophy (Winter 2016 Ed.)

(e) Law, Stephen, The evil-god challenge. Religious Studies 46:3, 353-373 (2010)

(f) Stephen Law, A New Problem of Evil. LSE blog, Feb 29, 2016

(g) Collins, John M., The evil-god challenge: Extended and defended. Religious Studies 55:1, 85-109 (2019)

(h) Russell, P. & A.Kraal, "Hume on Religion", Stanford Encyclopedia of Philosophy (Winter 2021 Ed.)

956. (a) Swinburne, Richard (1998), Theodicy in Christian Tradition. In: Providence and the Problem of Evil, Oxford University Press.

(b) Tornau, Christian, "Saint Augustine", Stanford Encyclopedia of Philosophy (Summer 2020 Ed.)

(c) Natoli, Charles (2009), Augustine's Choice: The Lord of Light or the Light of the Lord? Philosophy Now, Issue 71, Jan/Feb 2009

(d) Saint Augustine, Bishop of Hippo, The Confessions of Saint Augustine, Book V (401 CE). Trans. by Edward Bouverie Pusey [1909-14]. Project Gutenberg online library.

(e) Coombes, Michael J. (2014), Augustine's Contra Fortunatum: Perspectives from critical discourse analysis and argumentation theory. SUNScholar, Stellenbosch University.

(f) Smith, Kerri, Neuroscience vs philosophy: Taking aim at free will. Nature 477, 23–25 (2011)

957. (a) Marcar, G.P., Aquinas' Quinque Viae: Fools, Evil, and the Hiddenness of God. Heythrop Journal 56:1, 67-75 (2015)

(b) Ziegler, P.G., "Bound Over to Satan's Tyranny": Sin and Satan in Contemporary Reformed Hamartiology. Theology Today 75:1, 89-100 (2018)

(c) David B. McCalmont, Question of Evil Remains Unanswered. American Humanist Association.

(d) Dostoyevsky, Fyodor M., The Brothers Karamazov, Book 5, Ch. 4. Trans. by Constance Garnett. Project Gutenberg online library.

958. (a) Hick, John (1966), Evil and the God of Love. Palgrave Macmillan, London (1985 - 2010 ed.)

(b) ibid. Full paper and pdf download available online.

(c) Badham, P. (1990), An Irenaean Theodicy. In: Badham, P. (eds), A John Hick Reader.

(d) Edwards, Mark J., "Origen", The Stanford Encyclopedia of Philosophy (Summer 2022 Edition).

(e) Scott, Mark S.M., Suffering and Soul-Making: Rethinking John Hick's Theodicy.
The Journal of Religion 90:3, 313-334 (2010)

(f) Cramer, David C., "John Hick (1922—2012)". In: Internet Encyclopedia of Philosophy.

(g) Walls, Jerry L., Swinburne's Hell and Hick's Universalism. Ars Disputandi 4:1, 11-14 (2004)

959. (a) Keith Ward, Freedom And The Irenaean Theodicy. J. of Theological Studies XX:1, 249–254 (1969)

(b) Davies, B.A., A Modern Irenaean Theodicy — Professor Hick On Evil.
New Blackfriars 57:678, 512–519 (1976)

(c) Trakakis, N., Theodicy: The Solution to the Problem of Evil, or Part of the Problem?
SOPHIA 47, 161 (2008)

960. (a) Lennon, T.M. & M. Hickson, "Pierre Bayle", Stanford Encyclopedia of Philosophy (Winter 2017 Ed.)

(b) Irwin, Kristen, "Pierre Bayle (1647–1706)". In: Internet Encyclopedia of Philosophy.

(c) Melamed, Yitzhak Y. & Martin Lin, "Principle of Sufficient Reason", Stanford Encyclopedia of Philosophy (Summer 2021 Edition), Edward N. Zalta (ed.)

(d) Murray, Michael J. & Sean Greenberg, "Leibniz on the Problem of Evil", Stanford Encyclopedia of Philosophy (Winter 2016 Edition), Edward N. Zalta (ed.)

961. (a) Voltaire (1755), Poem on the Lisbon Disaster; or an Examination of the Axiom "All is Well". In: Toleration and Other Essays, trans. Joseph McCabe (New York: G.P. Putnam's Sons, 1912), pp. 255–263. Chap. 39 in Emotions in Europe 1517–1914 by K. Barclay & F. Soyer (2021).

(b) Voltaire (1759), Candide, ou l'Optimisme (Candide, or All for the Best). Introduced by Philip Littell. Project Gutenberg online library.

(c) Murray, Michael J. & Sean Greenberg, "Leibniz on the Problem of Evil", Stanford Encyclopedia of Philosophy (Winter 2016 Edition), Edward N. Zalta (ed.)

962. (a) Mackie, J.L., IV.—Evil And Omnipotence. Mind LXIV:254, 200–212 (1955)

(b) Mackie, J.L., Theism and Utopia. Philosophy 37:140, 153-158 (1962)

(c) LaFollette, H., Plantinga on the Free Will Defense. Intl. J. for Phil. of Religion 11, 123–132 (1980)

(d) Bergmann, M., Might-Counterfactuals, Transworld Untrustworthiness and Plantinga's Free Will Defence. Faith and Philosophy: Journal of the Society of Christian Philosophers 16:3, 336-351 (1999)

(e) Dore, C. (1984). Does Suffering Serve Valuable Ends?. In: Theism. Philosophical Studies Series in Philosophy vol 30. Springer, Dordrecht

963. (a) Adams, R.M., Review of The Miracle of Theism: Arguments for and Against the Existence of God by J.L. Mackie. The Philosophical Review 95:2, 309–316 (1986)

(b) Montgomery, R.P., The Miracle of Theism: Arguments For and Against the Existence of God by J.L. Mackie. Theology Today 41:1, 91-94 (1984)

(c) ibid, 953b

(d) McBrayer, Justin (2015), Sceptical theism. In: Routledge Encyclopedia of Philosophy.

964. (a) ibid, 604a

(b) Persson, I. & Savulescu, J., The Perils of Cognitive Enhancement and the Urgent Imperative to Enhance the Moral Character of Humanity. Journal of Applied Philosophy 25:3, 162-177 (2008)

(c) Julian Savulescu and Ingmar Persson, Unfit for the future: The urgent need for moral enhancement. OUP blog, Aug 30, 2012

(d) Hughes, James (2014), Enhancing Virtues: Building the Virtues Control Panel. IEET.

(e) FTP025: James Hughes – Cyborg Buddha, Transhuman Enlightenment and Basic Income.
Future Thinkers Podcast, episode #025

965. (a) Harris, J., Is Gene Therapy A Form Of Eugenics? Bioethics 7:2-3, 178-187 (1993)

(b) Harris, J., Moral Enhancement And Freedom. Bioethics, 25:2, 102-111 (2011)

(c) Savulescu, J. & Persson, I.; Moral Enhancement, Freedom, And The God Machine.
The Monist 95:3, 399–421 (2012)

(d) ibid. Full paper and pdf download available at PMC3431130.

(e) Richard Weikart, Can We Make Ourselves More Moral? Designer Babies, Hormone Therapy, and the New Eugenics of Transhumanism. Public Discourse, Jun 6, 2016

966. (a) Brown, F.L., Keefer, L.A. Anti-Natalism from an Evolutionary Psychological Perspective. Evolutionary Psychological Science 6, 283–291 (2020)

(b) Joshua Rothman, The Case for Not Being Born. The New Yorker, Nov 27, 2017

(c) Woolfe, Sam, On Antinatalism and Depression. Epoché Philosophy Monthly, 30 (2020)

(d) Troxell, Mary, "Arthur Schopenhauer (1788—1860)". In: Internet Encyclopedia of Philosophy.

(e) Derek Beres, Is living really better than never being born at all? Big Think, Dec 14, 2017

967. (a) Zapffe, Peter W. (1933), The Last Messiah. Trans. from the Norwegian by G.R. Tangenes. Philosophy Now, Issue 45: Mar/Apr 2004

(b) Tangenes, Gisle R.(2004), The View from Mount Zapffe. Philosophy Now, 45: Mar/Apr 2004

(c) R.Tuhus-Dubrow, I wish I'd never been born: the rise of the anti-natalists. The Guardian, 14Nov 2019

(d) Schönegger, P., What's up with anti-natalists? An observational study on the relationship between dark triad personality traits and anti-natalist views. Philosophical Psychology 35:1, 66-94 (2022)

(e) Declan Leary, Against Anti-natalism. National Review, May 29, 2019

968. (a) Kahane, Guy, Our Cosmic Insignificance. Noûs 48:4, 745-772 (2014)

(b) Kahane, Guy, If Nothing Matters. Noûs 51:2, 327-353 (2017)

(c) Nick Hughes, Do we matter in the cosmos? Aeon, 29 Jun 2017

(d) Galen Guengerich, You Are the Center of the Universe. Psychology Today, Aug 24, 2014

(e) Emily Fox Gordon, The Meaning of Fulfillment. New York Times, Oct 25, 2014

969. (a) Roser, Max & Ortiz-Ospina, Esteban (2013-2019), Global Extreme Poverty. Our World In Data.

(b) Kushlev, K., Dunn, E.W. & Lucas, R.E.; Higher Income Is Associated With Less Daily Sadness but not More Daily Happiness. Social Psychological and Personality Science 6:5, 483-489 (2015)

(c) Dolan, P., Kudrna, L. & Stone, A.; The Measure Matters: An Investigation of Evaluative and Experience-Based Measures of Wellbeing in Time Use Data. Soc Indic Res 134, 57–73 (2017)

(d) Roser, Max & Ortiz-Ospina, Esteban (2013-2017), Happiness and Life Satisfaction. OWD.

(e) Stéphanie Thomson, How to Deal With the Anxiety of Uncertainty. Wired, 02 Sep 2020

(f) David Bather Woods, The Semi-satisfied Life. Aeon, 18 Aug 2020

970. (a) UN Sustainable Development Goals Report 2020. https://unstats.un.org/sdgs/report/2020/

(b) Fikslin, R.A., Toward an Intersectional Psychological Science of Reproductive Norms: Generating Research Across the Natalism Spectrum. Psychology of Women Quarterly 45:3, 308-324 (2021)

(c) Coronavirus: Kenyans moved by widow cooking stones for children. BBC News, 30 Apr 2020

(d) Mombasa woman who boiled stones for her children moves into her new house (video). NTV Kenya, YouTube, 8 Dec 2020

971. (a) Ritchie, Hannah, Roser, Max & Ortiz-Ospina, Esteban (2015); "Suicide". Our World In Data.

(b) World Health Organization. Suicide Fact Sheet, 17 June 2021

(c) J. Wildfire, A Definitive Guide to Why Life Is So Terrible for Most Millennials. Medium, Feb 1, 2021

(d) Raymond Tallis, A Defence of Progress. How to avoid the self-fulfilling prophecy of pessimism. IAI News, Issue 84, 8 Jan 2020

972. (a) Freud, Sigmund (1918). Reflections on War and Death; II. Our Attitude Towards Death. Bartleby.com

(b) Mysteries of Egypt, Life after Death. Canadian Museum of History.

(c) Becker, Ernest (1973), The Denial Of Death. Open Library ID OL5411118M.

(d) Kirill Khrestinin, Commentary on The Denial of Death. Ernest Becker Foundation, Mar 11, 2021

(e) Antal Polony, Book Review: "The Denial of Death" by Ernest Becker. SevenPonds, Jul 6, 2012

973. (a) Jeff Greenberg, This Mortal Coil. Aeon, 12 Feb 2020

(b) Tim Lott, The Worm at the Core: On the Role of Death in Life – review. The Guardian, 31 Jul 2015

(c) Pyszczynski, T., Lockett, M., Greenberg, J., & Solomon, S.; Terror Management Theory and the COVID-19 Pandemic. Journal of Humanistic Psychology 61:2, 173–189 (2021)

(d) This Mortal Life. Impact of COVID-19. Ernest Becker Foundation, May 2020.

974. (a) Stannard, D.E., Book Review - Western Attitudes toward Death: From the Middle Ages to the Present by Philippe Ariès. Trans. by P.M. Ranum. The American Historical Review 80:5, 1297–1298 (1975)

(b) Drummond, Jaye (2014), Review of Aries Western Attitudes Toward Death. Wright State University, HST 7220-01. Response Paper #102.

(c) Aramesh, K., History of attitudes toward death: a comparative study between Persian and western cultures. J Med Ethics Hist Med. 9: 20 (2016)

975. (a) Neimeyer, R.A., Wittkowski, J. & Moser, R.P.; Psychological research on death attitudes: an overview and evaluation. Journal of Death Studies 28:4, 309-340 (2004)

(b) Book review. The Empire of Death: A Cultural History of Ossuaries and Charnel Houses by Paul Koudounaris. Publishers Weekly, 30 Jan 2012

(c) Book review. Heavenly Bodies: Cult Treasures & Spectacular Saints from the Catacombs by Paul Koudounaris. Publishers Weekly, 09 Dec 2013

(d) Melanie McDonagh, Book review - The Empire of Death: A Cultural History of Ossuaries and Charnel Houses by Paul Koudounaris. The Spectator, 5 Nov 2011

(e) Sarah Gilbert, Heavenly Bodies: Relics of Catholic Saints - in pictures. The Guardian, 19 Nov 2013

976. (a) Sophie Elmhirst, Take me to the death cafe. Prospect Magazine, Jan 22, 2015

(b) Death Cafes. A global franchise. https://deathcafe.com/

(c) The Order of the Good Death. https://www.orderofthegooddeath.com/

(d) SevenPonds. Embracing end-of-life experiemce. https://www.sevenponds.com/

977. (a) Öhman, C.J. & Watson, D.; Are the dead taking over Facebook? A Big Data approach to the future of death online. Big Data & Society (2019)

(b) University of Oxford, "The dead may outnumber the living on Facebook within 50 years." ScienceDaily, 27 Apr 2019

978. (a) Tony Walter. End Of Life Studies & Publications.

(b) Centre for Death & Society, University of Bath, England. Projects Archive.

(c) Centre for Death & Society, University of Bath, England. Future Cemetery collaboration.

(d) Jonsson, Annika & Walter, Tony; Continuing bonds and place. Death Studies 41:7, 406-415 (2017)

979. (a) DeathTech Research Team, University of Melbourne, Australia.Projects summary.

(b) REACT Heritage, Arnos Vale Cemetery Trust, England. Future Cemetery update.

(c) Meese, J, Nansen, B., Kohn, T. et al.; Posthumous personhood and the affordances of digital media, Mortality 20:4, 408-420 (2015)

(d) Arnold, M., Gibbs, M., Kohn, T. et al. (2017); Death and Digital Media. Routledge, 1st Ed., eBook ISBN 9781315688749

(e) Nansen, B., Gould, H., Arnold, M. & Gibbs, M.; Media, mortality and necro-technologies: Eulogies for dead media. New Media & Society (2021)

980. (a) Andres Jauregui, Tupac Hologram: AV Concepts Brings Late Rapper To Life At Coachella (VIDEO) 4.2k. Huffington Post, 16 Apr 2012

(b) Tupac at Coachella -- Rises from the Dead ... Performs as Hologram. TMZ, Apr 16, 2012

(c) Tupac Hologram at Coachella. Late rapper 'performs' with Snoop Dogg. Rolling Stone, Apr 16, 2012

(d) Roxanne Palmer, How Does The Coachella Tupac 'Hologram' Work? International Business Times, 17 Apr 2012

(e) How did they do it? Elvis and Celine duet on Idol. WMC, Apr 26, 2007

981. (a) Laura Snapes, Hologram of Amy Winehouse set for 2019 worldwide tour. The Guardian, 12 Oct 2018

(b) Laura Snapes, Amy Winehouse hologram tour postponed due to 'unique sensitivities'. The Guardian, 22 Feb 2019

(c) Laura Barton, Back from the black: should Amy Winehouse and other stars be turned into holograms? The Guardian, 19 Oct 2018

982. (a) An Evening With Whitney: The Whitney Houston Hologram Tour 2020. Base Hologram.

(b) Ethan Millman, 'The Only Thing Missing Was Her, Physically.' Inside the Whitney Houston Hologram Tour. Rolling Stone, Feb 19, 2020

(c) Dave Simpson, An Evening With Whitney review – Houston hologram is ghoulish cash-in. The Guardian, 28 Feb 2020

(d) Will Gompertz, "Whitney Houston: Will Gompertz reviews hologram show in Sheffield". BBC News, 29 Feb 2020

(e) Sateena K. Dosanjh, I went to the Whitney Houston hologram tour last night – and what I saw blew my mind. Independent, 11 Mar 2020

983. (a) Tired of Zoom calls? Company offers at-home hologram machines. Fox News, Aug 7, 2020

(b) Robert Kardashian Digital Recreation. Kaleida, Oct 2020

(c) Alyx Gorman, Kim Kardashian's father resurrected as hologram in birthday present from Kanye West. The Guardian, 30 Oct 2020

984. (a) Robin Hanson, "The Age of Em". First, we will upload brains to computers. Then, those computers will take over the world. Business Insider, Apr 30, 2016

(b) Ariel Conn, The Age of Em: Review and Podcast. The Future of Life Institute, Sep 28, 2016

(c) Steven Poole, The Age of Em review – the horrific future when robots rule the Earth. The Guardian, 15 Jun 2016

(d) Baum, Seth D., The Social Science of Computerized Brains – Review of The Age of Em: Work, Love, and Life When Robots Rule the Earth by Robin Hanson (2016). Futures 90, 61-63 (2017)

985. (a) Jason Heller, 'To Be A Machine' Digs Into The Meaning Of Humanity. NPR, Feb 28, 2017

(b) Paul Laity, To Be a Machine by Mark O'Connell review – solving the problem of death. The Guardian, 23 Mar 2017

(c) Francesca Minerva & Adrian Rorheim, What are the ethical consequences of immortality technology? Aeon, 8 Aug 2017

(d) Terry Bisson (1990), They're Made Out of Meat.

986. (a) Ian Sample, Doubting death: how our brains shield us from mortal truth. The Guardian, 19 Oct 2019

(b) Breitbart, William, On the inevitability of death. Palliative and Supportive Care 15:3, 276-278 (2017)

(c) James Baillie, We all know that we will die, so why do we struggle to believe it? Aeon, 4 Nov 2019

(d) Ruíz-Fernández, M.D., Fernández-Medina, I.M., Granero-Molina, J. et al.; Social acceptance of death and its implication for end-of-life care. Journal of Advanced Nursing 77:7, 3132-3141 (2021)

987. (a) Rice, Hugh, "Fatalism", Stanford Encyclopedia of Philosophy (Winter 2018 Ed), E.N. Zalta (ed.)

(b) Alex Broom, Before you go … are you in denial about death? The Conversation, Nov 26, 2014

(c) Solomon, Robert C., On Fate and Fatalism. Philosophy East and West 53:4, 435–454 (2003)

(d) Antonia Macaro, Is meditating on death like putting on a fur coat in summer? Aeon, 30 Mar 2018

(e) de Montaigne, Michel, "Of Physiognomy". Book 3, Ch. XII in Essays (1580). Trans. by C. Cotton, ed. by W.C. Hazlitt Project Gutenberg online library.

988. (a) Bradshaw, C.J.A., Ehrlich, P.R., Beattie, A. et al.; Underestimating the Challenges of Avoiding a Ghastly Future. Frontiers in Conservation Science, 1 (2021)

(b) Goldin, Ian, The second Renaissance. Nature 550, 327–329 (2017)

(c) Ortiz-Ospina, Esteban (2019, The rise of social media. Our World In Data.

(d) Moshe Y Vardi, Are robots going to steal your job? Probably. The Conversation, Apr 6, 2016

(e) Emily Reynolds, The household robots who will do your chores. Wired, 27 Feb 2016

(f) Report: What Does it Mean to be Human in the Digital Age? The Oxford Research Centre in the Humanities (TORCH), 25 Jan 2016.

989. (a) Guy Standing, Who will be a voice for the emerging precariat? The Guardian, 01 Jun 2011

(b) Wood, A.J., Graham, M., Lehdonvirta, V. & Hjorth, I.; Good Gig, Bad Gig: Autonomy and Algorithmic Control in the Global Gig Economy. Work, Employment and Society 33:1, 56-75 (2019)

(c) Arnold, C., Money for nothing: the truth about universal basic income. Nature 557, 626-628 (2018)

(d) Kenan Malik, These radical ideas might seem utopian but at least they fire the imagination. Labour's proposal of basic services for all takes a once fringe idea mainstream. The Guardian, 29 Sep 2019

(e) Dylan Matthews, Modern Monetary Theory, explained. Vox, Apr 16, 2019

(f) Natalie Shoemaker, Rutger Bregman's 'Utopia for Realists' Shows Us Why We Deserve Universal Basic Income. Big Think, 19 Apr 2016

990. (a) Milton Ezrati, Universal Basic Income: A Thoroughly Wrongheaded Idea. Forbes, Jan 15, 2019

(b) Mair, Simon, Druckman, Angela & Jackson, Tim; A tale of two utopias: Work in a post-growth world. Ecological Economics 173, 106653 (2020)

(c) Kelsey Piper, The important questions about universal basic income haven't been answered yet. Vox, Feb 13, 2019

(d) Jeylan Mortimer, Mike Vuolo & Jeremy Staff; How Unemployment Affects Twentysomethings' Self-Worth. Harvard Business Review, Dec 22, 2016

(e) Richard V. Reeves, The respect deficit. Aeon, 08 Aug 2018

991. (a) Jonathan Coopersmith, Is technology making us dumber or smarter? Yes. The Conversation, Jun 17, 2016

(b) Chaos Monkey Guide for Engineers. Gremlin Inc.

(c) Richard Gray, What would happen in an apocalyptic blackout? BBC Future, 24 Oct 2019

(d) Steven Poole, The Knowledge: How to Rebuild Our World from Scratch – review. The Guardian, 03 Apr 2014

992. (a) David Krakauer & Geoffrey West, The Damage We're Not Attending To. Scientists who study complex systems offer solutions to the pandemic. Nautilus, Jul 8, 2020

(b) Jessica Flack & Melanie Mitchell, Uncertain times. Published in association with Santa Fe Institute. Aeon, 21 Aug 2020

(c) Philip Ball, How Life (and Death) Spring From Disorder. Quanta, Jan 26, 2017

(d) Sims, C.A., The Dangers of Individualism and the Human Relationship to Technology in Philip K. Dick's "Do Androids Dream of Electric Sheep?" Science Fiction Studies 36:1, 67–86 (2009)

Acknowledgments

This book would not be possible without the ready access to online research material I have been privileged to enjoy since the dawn of the Internet. I therefore wish to acknowledge and extend general thanks to contributors and editors at those academic journals that have long provided open access to content. Free peer-reviewed literature at sites like *PLOS, e-LIFE* and *PNAS* is now supplemented by advance uploads at platforms like *arXiv, bioRxiv* and the multidisciplinary *Preprints*.

News sites that carry related press statements, commentaries, interviews and feature articles have been equally invaluable. Editors, writers and technical staff at *Science Daily, SciTechDaily, The Scientist, Science X, Quanta, Philosophy Now, Psychology Today, Aeon, Nautilus, The Conversation, Big Think, The Edge* and many other publications work tirelessly to keep the public informed of new research and ideas that are rapidly reshaping human perceptions of life and the universe.

The above resources are significantly augmented by the large body of material available at collaborative encyclopaedias like *Scholarpedia* and *Wikipedia*, as well as numerous special interest blogs.

Due to the generosity, hard work and dedication of this rapidly-growing global information community, we can confidently declare that humanity has truly entered an era of democratised knowledge.

I salute you all.

About the author

Eugene Bell-Gam is a non-fiction writer whose focus is the 'big questions' of life. Based in Middlesex, England, he follows leading-edge research around the world and keenly explores new thinking on how to improve the human condition. Having spent his formative years in Sierra Leone (a country renowned for its great natural beauty and diversity), Bell-Gam has cultivated a life-long interest in existential explanations across all cultures and knowledge disciplines.